EARTH AND SPACE Science

Student Edition

Colorado Springs, Colorado

Development Team

Vice President for Purposeful Design Publications	Steven Babbitt
Directors for Textbook Development	Don Hulin Lisa Wood
Textbook Training and Development Coordinator	Cindi Banse
Editorial Team	Merrilee Berndt Lindsey Duncan Janice Giles Julie Holmquist Macki Jones Adelle Moxness Jessica Reid Ian Work
Design Team	Claire Coleman Steve Learned Christian Massey
Cover Design	Mike Riester
Art Illustrations	Aline Heiser

Purposeful Design Publications is grateful to Christian Schools International for the contributions they made to the original content of the Purposeful Design Earth and Space Science course.

EARTH AND SPACE Science

Student Edition

Purposeful Design

Printed in the United States of America
28 27 26 25 24 23 22   3 4 5 6 7 8

Earth and Space Science – Student Edition
Purposeful Design Science series
ISBN 978-1-58331-543-9, Catalog #20081

Purposeful Design Publications is the publishing division of the Association of Christian Schools International (ACSI) and is committed to the ministry of Christian school education, to enable Christian educators and schools worldwide to effectively prepare students for life. As the publisher of textbooks, trade books, and other educational resources within ACSI, Purposeful Design Publications strives to produce biblically sound materials that reflect Christian scholarship and stewardship and that address the identified needs of Christian schools around the world.

References to books, computer software, and other ancillary resources in this series are not endorsements by ACSI. These materials were selected to provide teachers with additional resources appropriate to the concepts being taught and to promote student understanding and enjoyment.

Purposeful Design Publications
A Division of ACSI
731 Chapel Hills Drive • Colorado Springs, CO 80920
800/367-0798
www.purposefuldesign.com

Table of Contents

Geology

UNIT 1

Geologic Changes

Chapter 1: *Weathering and Erosion*

Chapter 2: *Soil*

UNIT 3

The Dynamic Earth

Chapter 1: *Crust Movement*

Chapter 2: *Earthquakes*

Chapter 3: *Volcanoes*

UNIT 4

Water and Water Systems

Chapter 1: *Water*

Chapter 2: *Oceans*

Chapter 1: *Atmosphere*

Chapter 2: *Weather*

Chapter 3: *Climate*

Meteorology

UNIT 5

UNIT 6

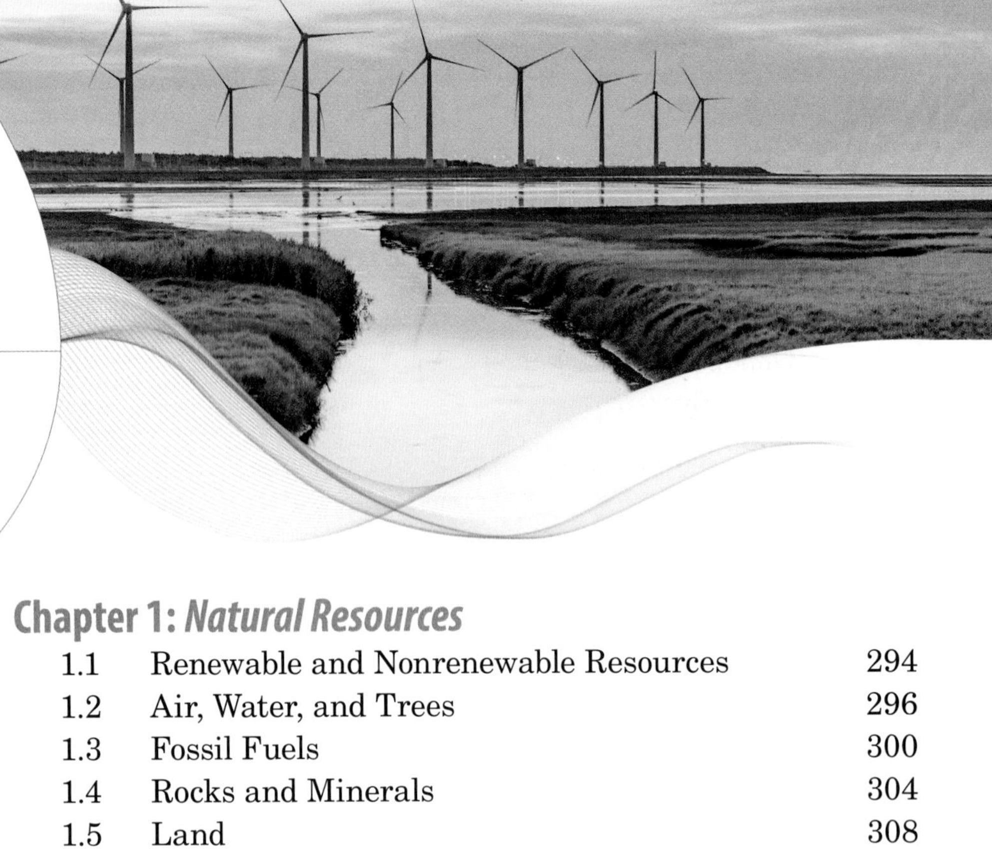

The Environment

Chapter 1: *Natural Resources*

Chapter 2: *Pollution Solutions*

Astronomy

UNIT 7

Chapter 1: *Solar System*

Chapter 2: *Planets*

Chapter 3: *Sun, Earth, and Moon*

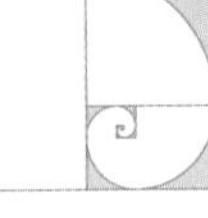

The Great Expanse

Chapter 1: *Stars and the Universe*

Chapter 2: *Space Exploration*

The Scientific Method

Background

The word *science* comes from the Latin word *scire*, which means "to know." A scientist is someone who does science—a person who wants to understand the natural world and all of its complexities.

Even after scientific experiments, many scientific hypotheses are disputed within the scientific community; all are subject to revisions and changes as new data and experimental evidence are collected. Theories and laws, however, are supported by a substantial number of experiments and observations. Ideally, scientists are open to constructive criticism about their hypotheses. When scientists communicate in scientific journals or at conventions, they work toward finding new evidence and creating solutions to resolve conflicting interpretations and viewpoints.

The scientific method is an orderly, systematic approach to solving a problem or answering a question. Although different scientific endeavors require different approaches and steps, the following terminology and steps are often used. You need to become familiar with the vocabulary of science as well as realize that scientists understand that the scientific method is not a rigid set of steps that is always followed. Various orders are possible, and sometimes steps are eliminated or repeated.

Vocabulary

control—the sample in an experiment in which the variables are kept at a base level
hypothesis—a prediction of what you think will happen and which can be tested to see if it is true
inference—an educated guess based on observation
observation—something noticed through the senses
scientific law—a generalization based on observations that describe the ways an object behaves under specific conditions
scientific method—the series of steps that scientists follow when they investigate problems or try to answer questions
theory—an explanation of the scientific laws
variable—a changeable factor that could influence an experiment's outcome

Scientific Method

1. **Identify or define the problem**.

2. **Make a hypothesis**. Not all predictions are hypotheses; they must be measurable. For example, "If the rate of fermentation

is related to temperature, then increasing the temperature will increase gas production" is a hypothesis. On the other hand, "If yeast is heated, then more gas will be produced" is not a hypothesis because it offers no proposition to test. It does not show a relationship or suggest variables. A hypothesis may also be a question ("Does temperature affect the fermentation of yeast?") or a conditional statement ("Temperature may affect the fermentation of yeast").

3. **Experiment, controlling the variables**. Scientists repeat and refine the experiment based on the findings. They will not allow a hypothesis to remain untested; it must be tested and shown valid.

4. **Make observations and record the results**. Most scientists accurately record their observations and measurements in a journal or on a computer.

5. **Make inferences and conclusions**. A conclusion is a statement about what a scientist has learned and whether or not the scientist's hypothesis was supported. Scientists often learn as much from an incorrect hypothesis as from a correct one. You may feel pressure to have your experiment show that your "guess" was correct, but you need to understand that sometimes scientists arrive at completely unexpected conclusions and that an incorrect hypothesis is never considered a failure. For example, sometimes an unexpected conclusion raises new questions that will lead to another experiment and conclusion. The purpose of science is not to prove what is already known; the purpose is to increase the understanding of God's world!

6. **Apply the findings**. Scientists add their conclusions to their understanding of the natural and technical universe. To do so with wisdom and stewardship benefits all creation.

Measurements

Background

The metric system is a universal system of measurements that serves as a standard for scientific research throughout the world and in many countries for everyday use. Since 1899, international conferences have been held to standardize the metric system. In 1960, the 11th International Conference of Weights and Measures substantially changed the system, renaming it the International System of Units (abbreviated SI). It is helpful to become more familiar with the metric system and have practice estimating measurements. Throughout this course, the metric system is used predominantly.

Using the SI system of measurement has several advantages. It is based on standards that have been recognized by the international science community for use in the sciences and commerce, making the system universally adopted. All of the unit conversions used in the metric system are based on the number 10, and only decimal multiples of the basic units of length, volume, and mass are employed.

The instrument frequently used to determine the mass of a small object is the triple-beam balance, which is normally capable of measuring masses to the hundredth of a gram. The volume of substances can be determined by using a variety of different methods, depending upon the phase and shape of the substance being measured. Graduated cylinders are used to accurately measure the volume of liquids to the nearest milliliter. Graduated cylinders can also be used to measure granular solids, but this method is inaccurate for substances with large granules. The volume of cubic or rectangular box shapes can be calculated by using the formula $V = l \times w \times h$. (Volume equals length times width times height). Water displacement is used to find the volume of irregularly shaped objects that will not dissolve in water. A certain amount of water is poured into a graduated cylinder, and the object is dropped into the cylinder. The volume that the water rises is the volume of the object.

Although students in the United States are more familiar with the Fahrenheit scale, the Celsius (Centigrade) scale is much more common around the world. Scientists use the Celsius scale or the Kelvin scale, which is an absolute scale. Absolute zero was given the value 0 Kelvin; thus the Kelvin scale has no negative numbers. Absolute zero corresponds to –273.15°C and –459.7°F. Celsius temperatures can be converted to the Kelvin scale by using the following formula: K = C + 273.15. Kelvin is an absolute scale and thus has no degrees. The Fahrenheit scale assigns a temperature of 32° for the freezing point of water and 212° for the boiling point of water. The Celsius scale standardized the temperature scale by assigning a value of 0° for the freezing point of water and 100° for the boiling point of water. The size of the divisions used in the Fahrenheit and Celsius scales are not equal. The formula used to convert Celsius to Fahrenheit is $F = 9/5C + 32$. The formula for converting Fahrenheit to Celsius is $C = 5/9(F - 32)$.

One way to record these measurements is on graphs. A graph is a pictorial representation of statistical data or of relationships between variables. While graphs can serve a predictive function because they show general tendencies in the quantitative behavior of data, as approximations they are sometimes inaccurate and misleading. Most graphs include two axes. The horizontal axis represents the independent variables, and the vertical axis represents the dependent variables. In line graphs (the most common type), the horizontal axis often represents time. Bar graphs can be used to depict the relationship between two nontemporal numerical values. Such information can also be expressed in a circular graph (pie graph) that illustrates the part-to-whole relationship. The size of each sector is directly proportional to the percentage of the whole it represents; this graph is often used to emphasize proportions.

Scientific measurements require specific words to be used in descriptions so the language of science is understood worldwide. You need to have a working knowledge of the following terms:

Vocabulary

astronomical unit—the average distance between Earth and the sun (about 149,600,000 km)
Celsius scale—a temperature scale in which 0° represents the freezing point of water and 100° represents the boiling point of water
density—the mass per unit of volume of a substance
gram—the standard unit for mass in the metric system
light-year—the distance light travels in a vacuum in one year, approximately 9.46×10^{12} km
liter—the standard unit for the volume of liquid in the metric system
meter—the standard unit for length in the metric system
metric system—a universal system of measurement based on the number 10 used by scientists around the world

Laboratory Safety

Background

Each lab has specific safety needs, and you must focus on the teacher's instructions. Take only your notebook, student text, and a pen or pencil to the laboratory area. Leave all other items at your desk. Read and review your teacher's procedures to be certain that you understand the instructions.

Safety Rules

Some standard safety rules include the following:

- Wash your hands before and after any hands-on activity or experiment. Wear protective gear appropriate to the activity. Some activities require goggles or gloves. Sanitize safety goggles after each use.
- Report any spills or breakage to your teacher immediately.
- Store equipment and materials in a safe location and make sure that you return them to their designated places after use. Always test and check the materials prior to use.
- Do not eat or handle supplies unless instructed to do so.
- Be aware of allergies that you may have to science activity materials and take any necessary precaution.
- Carry only one jar at a time.
- Never lean on aquarium glass.
- Never prop a meterstick over your shoulder.
- Carry microscopes with two hands.
- Never eat or drink during a science activity.
- Remove loose or bulky clothing to reduce the chance of spreading fire or knocking over equipment.
- Keep equipment (especially breakable or expensive items such as glassware or microscopes) away from the edge of work surfaces.
- Wear safety goggles, especially for activities involving potentially harmful chemicals, glassware, or heat. (When your teacher is wearing goggles, you must wear goggles.)
- Use plastic equipment if possible. However, if glassware is used and does break, back away from the accident and do not touch the shattered glass. Designate someone to retrieve a dustpan and broom and alert the teacher.
- Know basic chemical safety. Many chemicals are labeled with three hazards—health, flammability, and reactivity—rated on a scale of 0 to 4. A 0 rating indicates that the substance is not a threat for this hazard, and a 4 means it is a substantial threat.
- Be aware of two common safety symbols—flames (signifying flammability) and a test tube being poured on a hand (signifying a corrosive substance). These symbols are

primarily for storage purposes, but they also warn the user of these two dangers. Different chemicals have different disposal guidelines. Follow your teacher's directions regarding how to properly dispose of the chemicals and materials you use.

Safety Procedures

- Be a good example. Follow the safety rules at all times.
- Inspect the lab area to look for possible hazards before you start an experiment.
- Inspect your equipment.
- Report hazards to your teacher immediately.
- Know the location of your lab's fire bucket, fire blanket, fire extinguisher, and safety shower, if available.

UNIT 1

Geology

Chapter 1: *Introduction to Earth Science*
Chapter 2: *Minerals*
Chapter 3: *Rocks*
Chapter 4: *The Structure of the Earth*

Vocabulary

asthenosphere
astronomy
carbon-14 dating
clastic rock
cleavage
contact metamorphism
continental crust
contour line
convection current
core
crust
density
dynamic metamorphism
earth science
environmental science
extrusive rock
felsic rock
fluorescence
foliated structure
fracture
geology
hardness
igneous rock
inner core
intrusive rock
latitude
lava
lithification
lithosphere
lodestone
longitude
luster
mafic rock
magma
magnetosphere
mantle
metamorphic rock
metamorphism
meteorology
mineral
mineralogy
Moho
naturalism
nonfoliated structure
nonsilicate mineral
oceanic crust
oceanography
outer core
phosphorescence
prime meridian
projection
P wave
radioactivity
regional metamorphism
rock cycle
sedimentary rock
sediments
seismic wave
shale
silicate mineral
streak
S wave
theism
varves

Key Ideas

- Systems, order, and organization
- Evidence, models, and explanation
- Change, constancy, and measurement
- Form and function
- Abilities necessary to do scientific inquiry
- Structure of the earth system
- Earth's history
- Origin and evolution of the earth system
- Origin and evolution of the universe
- Understandings about science and technology
- Natural resources
- Science and technology in society
- Science as a human endeavor
- Nature of science
- History of science
- Nature of scientific knowledge

SCRIPTURE

Lord, our Lord, how majestic is Your name in all the earth! You have set Your glory in the heavens.

Psalm 8:1

1.1.1 *The Study of Earth Science*

OBJECTIVES

- Explain the purpose of earth science.
- Explain the difference between science and technology.
- Identify the major branches of earth science.
- Describe a practical application of earth science.

VOCABULARY

- **astronomy** the study of physical things beyond the earth's atmosphere
- **earth science** the study of the earth and the universe around it.
- **environmental science** the study of the relationship between organisms and the environment
- **geology** the study of the solid earth
- **meteorology** the study of the atmosphere
- **oceanography** the study of the earth's oceans

Earth is a marvelous planet. Romans 1:20 and Psalm 19 explain that God uses His creation to reveal truth about Himself. Science is the orderly study of creation using observations and experiments. Science helps people understand the truth about God's world and God Himself.

Closely related to science is technology. Technology is the practical application of science. For example, science reveals the properties of minerals and ocean tides. Technology puts this knowledge to use. Minerals can be used for many things, such as ink or concrete. People have converted the power of tides into electricity. Technology is neither good nor bad. God gave people the responsibility to develop technology that glorifies Him. God is glorified when people enhance the safety, beauty, diversity, and usefulness of the world around them.

Science has a long history. The Chinese kept written records of earthquakes as early as 780 BC. The ancient Greeks catalogued rocks and minerals. Nearly 2,000 years ago the Babylonians mapped the positions of stars and planets. Between 300 and 400 AD, the Maya measured the movements of the moon, sun, and planets. Their observations helped them create accurate calendars to aid in farming. The telescope and microscope were invented in the 17th century. These extended the study of the visible world to include both enormous planets and tiny particles and organisms. Over time, studies such as these gave birth to the field of earth science.

Science helps people understand God's amazing creation. From the tiniest cell to the largest galaxy, God's role as Creator is displayed through science.

Earth science is the study of the earth and the universe. You are affected by earth science and technology every day. For example, you may use weather forecasts to plan what you will wear the next day. The concrete in the roads and buildings you see is a careful mixture of various rocks and minerals. When you travel in an automobile, train, or airplane, you are likely using fossil fuels. Your home's lights use electricity generated by the sun, wind, water, or fossil fuels. When you work at a computer, you are benefiting from silicon, a mineral used in computer chips. Studying earth science can help you better appreciate the resources that enable the technology you use every day.

Mayan calendar

Because earth science covers a wide range of subjects, it is divided into separate branches. These branches are geology, oceanography, meteorology, astronomy, and environmental science.

The first branch of earth science, **geology**, is the study of the solid earth. Geology is divided into more specific fields of study, some of which include mineralogy, paleontology, seismology, and volcanology.

The study of rocks and minerals is called *mineralogy*. Mineralogists seek to understand the earth's structure and processes. This study has led to a variety of technologies, such as glass, soft drinks, and medicines.

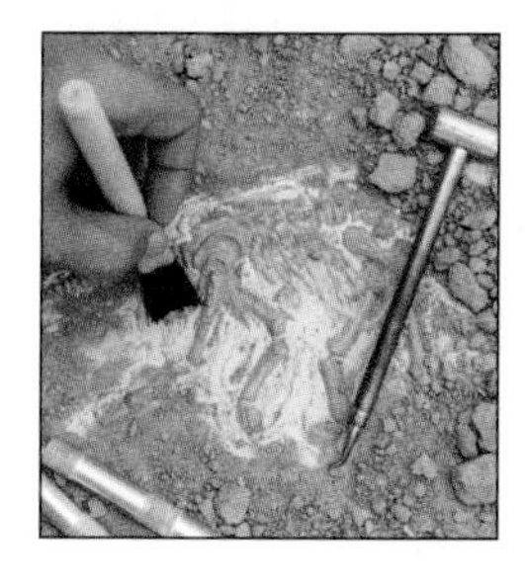

Paleontology, the study of artifacts and fossils, provides scientists with a glimpse into what the world was like earlier in its history. The data gathered by paleontologists is even used to help locate deposits of oil and natural gas, which some scientists say are linked to the remains of specific organisms.

Silicon is a mineral used to make computer chips.

Seismology is the study of earthquakes as well as Earth's layers and composition. Using technology, seismologists work to predict earthquakes and to assess earthquake risk in different regions. Their studies of the earth's layers have led to technologies that help locate petroleum and minerals and explore features of the ocean floor.

Volcanology is the study of volcanoes and the materials produced by volcanoes. Volcanologists examine the causes and effects of volcanoes. They also try to predict when the next eruption might occur. The technology used by volcanologists is also used to find the locations of ores.

Oceanography, the second branch of earth science, is the study of Earth's oceans, from the surface to the deepest ocean trenches. Oceanography, like geology, has many different specialized fields of study.

Physical oceanography is the study of waves and ocean currents. Physical oceanographers might develop technologies that help predict climate events such as El Niño that depend on ocean currents.

Chemical oceanography is the study of chemicals in the oceans, including those natural to the ocean, such as salt, as well

Chemical oceanographers study the chemical makeup of the earth's oceans.

Geologists

Geologists use their knowledge of science to help people stay safe, to care for creation, and to use responsibly the resources God has placed in the earth.

Some geologists create maps that help people study the earth or even just find their way around. Others study earthquakes or volcanoes—they keep track of the tremors in the earth or work with engineers to help design buildings that will withstand the shakes of an earthquake. Some geologists help design waste disposal sites so the garbage people throw away each day does not pollute the water or air. Still other geologists spend weeks at a time on boats, studying the ocean floor. God created a wide and wonderful world, and there are many methods of studying it—inside and outside!

as those that enter the ocean from outside sources. Chemical oceanographers might devise technologies to clean up an oil spill.

Meteorologists do more than predict the weather. They also study climate patterns to help people prepare for floods, severe winters, and droughts.

The third branch of earth science is **meteorology**, which is the study of the atmosphere. Meteorology is usually associated with weather forecasting, but it investigates climates too. Meteorologists do more than help people plan what to wear each day. Their predictions of severe weather have given people in affected areas the opportunity to find shelter before a storm occurs. Their studies of climate patterns have led to mapping and forecasting technologies that help people prepare for floods, harsh winters, and droughts.

Astronomy is the fourth branch of earth science; it is the study of physical things beyond the earth's atmosphere. These objects include other planets, stars, asteroids, and comets. Because most objects in space are too far away to study directly, astronomers rely on technology such as various kinds of telescopes and space probes. Astronomy gives a glimpse into the wonder of God's amazing handiwork beyond Earth. Studies linked to astronomy have led to better understandings of Earth's many systems and new technologies such as improved diabetes treatment and global positioning systems (GPS).

"Look up at the sky and count the stars—if indeed you can count them." Genesis 15:5

The final branch of earth science is environmental science. **Environmental science** is the study of humans' relationship to their environment. Therefore, it interacts with many other sciences. Environmental scientists may help geologists find methods to obtain natural resources without causing permanent damage to the land. They may work with oceanographers to develop a plan for maintaining a healthy environment for the ocean's creatures. Environmental scientists may work with meteorologists to draft laws governing technology that affects the earth's atmosphere. God wants people to be good stewards of the earth He gave them. Environmental scientists work to preserve Earth's resources for use by all the planet's organisms.

LESSON REVIEW

1. Why is earth science important?
2. What is the difference between science and technology?
3. Give an example of technology that might arise from each of the major branches of earth science.
4. List two ways environmental scientists may work with other scientists to promote good stewardship of the earth.

Environmental scientists look for the best ways to maintain Earth's resources for the sake of all the organisms that use them.

People have pondered the origins of Earth for centuries. The issue of Earth's age gives rise to many questions. What does science indicate about the age of Earth? Is Earth old? Is it young? What do Christians believe? People sometimes have differing views on the age of Earth, and the questions sparked by this topic can challenge followers of Christ as well.

There are two basic positions on the origin of the universe: naturalism and theism. **Naturalism** is the belief that matter and energy are all that exist and that the universe began as a result of a series of undirected natural processes. Naturalism does not support the idea of any supernatural force or significance to life. The theory of evolution arose from the naturalist philosophy that all life is random and that the existence of life in its various forms occurred though undirected natural processes. In contrast, **theism** is the belief that a supernatural being, whom Christians recognize as the God of the Bible, personally and purposefully created the universe. The order and intricate design of the universe was intentional—it was what God intended for His creation. Christians agree that the God of the Bible is the Creator of the universe even when they do not agree on when and how Creation occurred.

Scientists have tried to determine how old the earth and its various features are throughout history. In the last half of the 18th century, geologists discovered that sediments were deposited in layers that were eventually fused into sedimentary rock. They knew that the lower layers were older than the upper layers, but that did not tell them exactly how old the layers were any more

OBJECTIVES

- Compare naturalism and theism.
- Describe various views of the time of Creation.
- Explain carbon-14 dating

VOCABULARY

- **carbon-14 dating** the method used to determine the age of items of organic origin by measuring the radioactivity of their carbon 14 content
- **naturalism** the belief that matter and energy are all that exist and that undirected natural processes formed the universe
- **theism** the belief that the universe was created purposefully by a supernatural being
- **varves** the light and dark layers of sediments deposited in a yearly cycle

FYI

What is Uniformitarianism?

Before the 18th century, most people accepted that Earth had been created by supernatural means and that Earth's geology was shaped by catastrophic events such as the Flood. In the late 1700s, scientists proposed the theory that Earth's past and present geological processes are uniform, which means they act in the same way and at the same intensity today as they have throughout history. This theory was called *uniformitarianism* by William Whewell, a British scholar, in 1832. The principles of uniformitarianism were fundamental to the development of the science of geology. Most geologists rely on what they observe in the present to interpret past events, meaning the present is the key to the past.

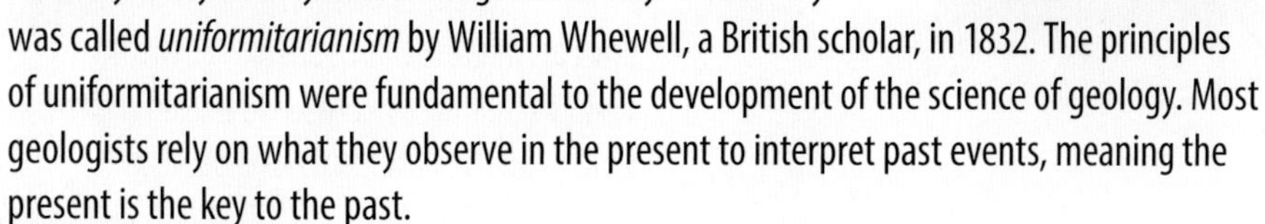

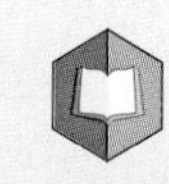

BIBLE CONNECTION

Creator God

Read Genesis 1, Genesis 2, and Psalm 90. What does each passage tell you about the Creation?

CHALLENGE

Future Technology
Have you ever thought about how the advances in technology during the past century have affected what is now known about the universe? Just consider: The Wright brothers flew the first airplane in 1903, and in 2011, the International Space Station was completed. How did the creation of the first electronic computer in 1945 affect science? What will future advances in technology tell people about Earth and the rest of the universe?

FYI

Half-Lives

Substance	Half-life
Carbon 14	5,730 years
Chlorine 36	400,000 years
Cobalt 60	5.26 years
Iodine 131	8.07 days
Phosphorus 32	14.3 days
Polonium 15	0.0018 seconds

Substance	Half-life
Radium 226	1,600 years
Radon 222	3.5 days
Sodium 24	15 hours
Thorium 232	14 billion years
Uranium 235	710 million years
Uranium 238	4.5 billion years

than knowing that the bottom layers of papers in a recycling bin were put in first indicates exactly when the papers were placed there. But as geology progressed as a science, geologists developed tools for dating the earth and portions of Earth's crust. The methods they use to date the earth's crust depend on the orderly manner in which the rocks and minerals were formed.

One method scientists use to date rocks and artifacts is called *radiometric dating*, which involves analyzing the radioactive elements they contain. A radioactive element is one that decays into another element. Scientists believe the decay of an element happens at a fixed rate called *the half-life*. An element's half-life is the time it takes for one half of the atoms of that element to decay into atoms of another element. A common type of radiometric dating is **carbon-14 dating**, which has been used to determine

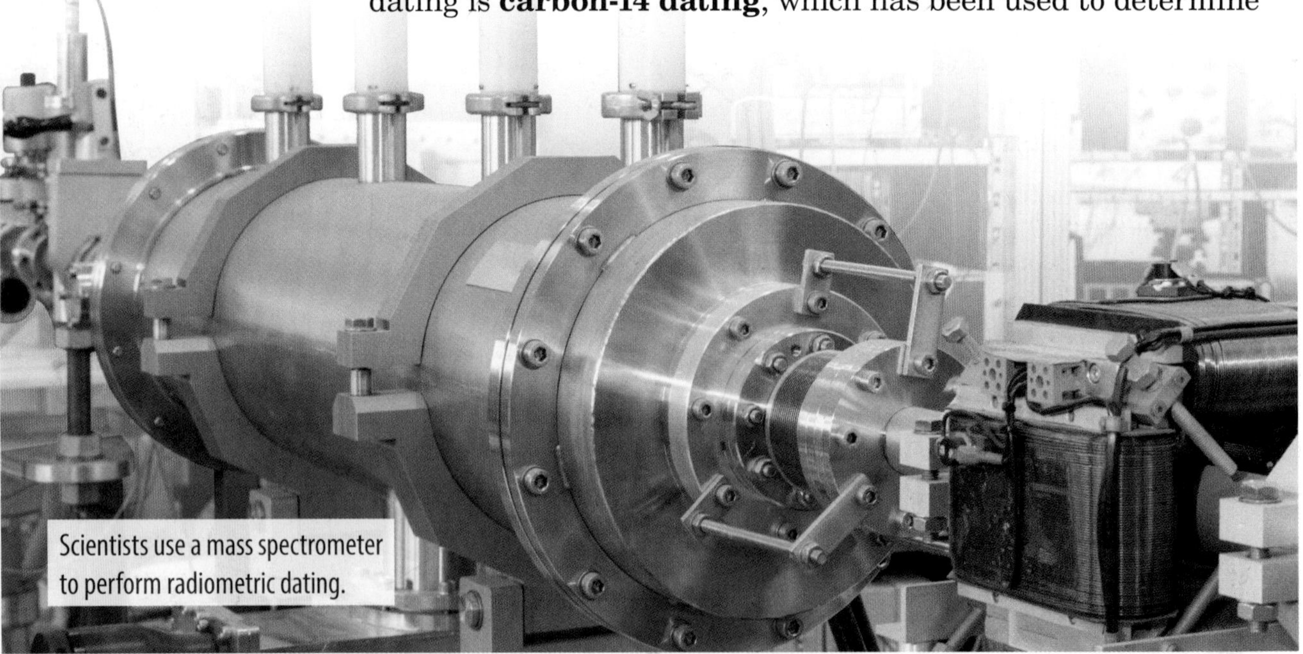

Scientists use a mass spectrometer to perform radiometric dating.

the age of items of organic origin by measuring the radioactivity of their carbon-14 content. The half-life of carbon 14 is the amount of time it takes for half of the carbon-14 atoms in a sample to decay into nitrogen-14 atoms, which is 5,730 years. If half of the carbon-14 atoms in a bone have decayed into nitrogen-14 atoms, scientists calculate that the bone is 5,730 years old. This method has become more accurate since it was first used in the 1940s as it now takes into account differing levels of carbon dioxide in the atmosphere over time. Carbon-14 dating can only be used to date organic materials, such as bones, shells, wooden objects, or papyrus scrolls, because all organic materials contain carbon. This method cannot be used to date minerals, which do not contain the remains of living things. By using carbon-14 dating, scientists can date materials up to 50,000 years old. Carbon 14 is one of more than 40 radioactive elements scientists use to date materials. Scientists use other radioactive elements with longer half-lives, such as uranium, to date rocks in the earth's crust. Tests using the radiometric dating method indicate the earth is 4.6 billion years old.

Varves

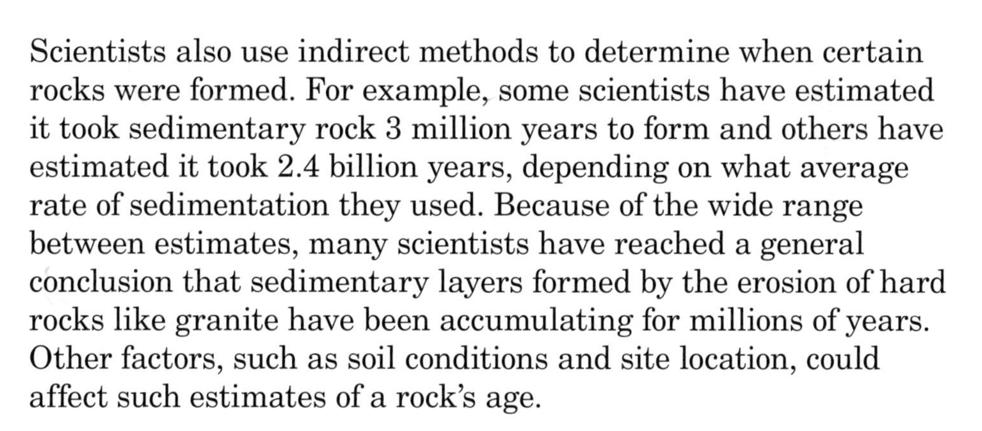

Scientists also use indirect methods to determine when certain rocks were formed. For example, some scientists have estimated it took sedimentary rock 3 million years to form and others have estimated it took 2.4 billion years, depending on what average rate of sedimentation they used. Because of the wide range between estimates, many scientists have reached a general conclusion that sedimentary layers formed by the erosion of hard rocks like granite have been accumulating for millions of years. Other factors, such as soil conditions and site location, could affect such estimates of a rock's age.

Varves, the light and dark layers of sediment deposited yearly in some lakes, are also used by geologists to estimate the age of rocks. Each year, the light layer of coarse rock in a varve collects during the summer, and the finer, dark particles are laid down during winter. Therefore, one varve represents one year. Just as a tree's age can be determined by counting its rings, geologists can estimate how long it took for the rock layers to be formed by counting a sedimentary rock's varves.

According to current scientific data, Earth may be as old as 4.6 billion years old. Not all people accept this scientific view on the age of the earth, however. Some people believe Earth is

FYI

Scientific Data

Why is scientific data generally considered trustworthy? Scientists repeat their experiments and studies over and over to make sure they get the same results. Sometimes they use multiple methods to check their work. For example, when dating an artifact or a rock, scientists double-check their results by using several different radioactive elements. They also repeat other scientists' experiments to verify data is correct. By using different independent methods and comparing their results, scientists are able to assure that their data is reliable.

BIBLE CONNECTION

God as Creator

Does Scripture say anything about microevolution or macroevolution? Read Genesis 1:24–25, 2:7. Could these Scriptures be used as support for different views on the origin of creatures? In considerations like these, it is wise to remember what unites Christians is their belief in God as Creator and Sustainer. As it says in 1 Samuel 2:8b, "For the foundations of the earth are the Lord's; on them He has set the world."

actually very young. Some Christians believe Genesis 1 implies God made everything in the universe in six literal 24-hour days. They believe that Earth as it was created was very different than it is today and that Earth's geologic features, such as rock layers and fossils, were caused by major events like the Flood. By using the genealogies and historical events in Scripture as well as some other scientific data to establish a time line, young-earth supporters believe that the planet is 6,000–12,000 years old.

Other Christians believe that the Earth is very old. Many old-earth supporters believe God made the stars and planets, including Earth, about 12–15 billion years ago, perhaps even through what is called *the big bang*. Some believe the big bang was the creation of energy and matter, described as *light* in Genesis 1:3, on the first day of Creation. Some old-earth believers think the unfolding evolutionary process resulted in the creation of life-forms. Others believe God used evolution, but intervened at times to suddenly create living things. In general, old-earth supporters use scientific discoveries from such fields as biology, astronomy, and geology as evidence that the earth is billions of years old and that the geologic features of the planet are the result of slow changes and natural processes.

Christians also have different views on how God created. One view is called *special creation*, which states that God miraculously created every basic living thing. Any variations evident in living things today, such as the different types of dogs, came about through natural processes. The producing of small changes in organisms is called *microevolution*. In microevolution, new varieties of animals within one species can emerge, but entirely new species of animals cannot be produced from one species.

FYI

Appearance of Age

As geological discoveries indicating that Earth was very old were made in the 18th century, many Christians wondered which to believe—the Bible or science. In 1857, British biologist and preacher Phillip Gosse introduced a new theory—the appearance of age theory. The appearance of age theory states that the Earth is only a few thousand years old, but God created it to appear old. Some Christians believe this today and use this theory to address scientific data from radiometric dating. Other believers disregard this theory because it implies the Creator was deceptive, which conflicts with verses such as Proverbs 14:5 and Leviticus 19:11 that underscore God's condemnation of deception.

Advocates of special creation believe God established limits on the amount of natural change that could occur in organisms. For example, there may be new varieties of dogs in the future, but they will still all be dogs and not new creatures.

Another view of how God created is called *theistic evolution.* According to this view, God used the process of evolution rather than sudden works of power to create major groups of living things. He then used natural processes to produce whole new species of creatures. In this view, God did not set limits on how much an organism can change. Therefore, given time, organisms can develop into different species of creatures. This production of entirely new creatures is called *macroevolution.* Theistic evolutionists believe that these changes happen as part of God's plan and that He uses evolution as a tool to create the creatures He wants. Christians are biblical theists who recognize the Creator as the God of the Bible.

No one knows precisely how Earth was created. The most important thing to know is that God is the one who decreed the world into existence. Part of loving God with all your mind includes learning more about His creation. As finite creatures, people will probably never be able to prove the exact time frame of Creation. However, as scientists study the work of an orderly God, they will continue to make amazing discoveries that may adjust what is considered scientific fact today. Such discoveries will continue to reveal the Creator's infinite power to all people.

FYI

Radiometric Dating and Young Earth

All scientific research begins with an assumption about what is fact. Young-earth scientists often disagree with some of the assumptions made in radiometric dating. For example, scientists cannot prove that conditions eons ago were the same as they are now or that a rock that contains a radioactive element was not once contaminated by rainfall or even lava. It is also assumed that radioactive elements like carbon 14 have always decayed at the same rate, an assumption that many young-earth scientists dispute.

LESSON REVIEW

1. Compare and contrast naturalism and theism.
2. Some Christians believe Earth is old and some believe it is young. Describe the old-earth and young-earth views of when Creation happened.
3. How do scientists use carbon-14 dating to determine a date for an artifact?
4. How can varves help scientists estimate the age of a rock?

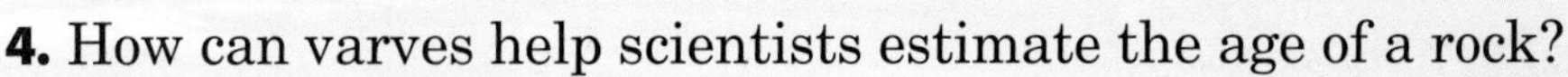

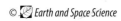

1.1.3 *Maps*

OBJECTIVES

- Identify lines of longitude and latitude and demonstrate their use in connection with determining location and time.
- Explain the challenges in creating an accurate map.
- Create a landscape model and craft a topographic map of the features of that model.
- Infer the purpose of a map based on its features.

VOCABULARY

- **contour line** a line on a map that joins points of equal elevation
- **latitude** the distance in degrees north or south of the equator
- **longitude** the distance in degrees east or west of the prime meridian
- **prime meridian** an imaginary line that divides the earth into the Western Hemisphere and the Eastern Hemisphere
- **projection** a system of lines drawn on a flat surface to represent curves

Maps are very important to earth scientists. Geologists use maps to search for oil deposits. Oceanographers use maps to travel across and down into the oceans. Meteorologists use maps when they travel to the South Pole to study the ozone hole over Antarctica. Astronomers use maps to recall the placement of each star. Environmental scientists use maps to keep track of the changes in regions of land.

The earth is most accurately represented by a globe. A globe helps people visualize the earth as a sphere. On the top of the globe is the North Pole, the northernmost point on Earth; at the bottom is the South Pole, the southernmost point on Earth.

The equator is an imaginary line that divides the earth into the Northern Hemisphere and the Southern Hemisphere. Parallels are imaginary lines around the earth that are parallel to the equator. Parallels show lines of **latitude**, the distance in degrees north or south of the equator. The equator is at 0° latitude.

Meridians are imaginary lines on Earth's surface that pass through the North Pole and the South Pole. The **prime meridian** is an imaginary line that divides the earth into the Western Hemisphere and the Eastern Hemisphere. Meridians show lines of **longitude**, the distance in degrees east or west of the prime meridian. The prime meridian is at 0° longitude.

The lines of latitude and longitude form an imaginary grid that is used to pinpoint a location on Earth. To provide greater accuracy, each degree is divided into 60 minutes [symbolized by a single prime mark(')], and each minute is divided into 60 seconds [symbolized by double prime marks (")]. For example, Sao Paulo, Brazil, is approximately located at 23°33'1" S 46°37'59" W, and

Lines of Latitude

Lines of Longitude

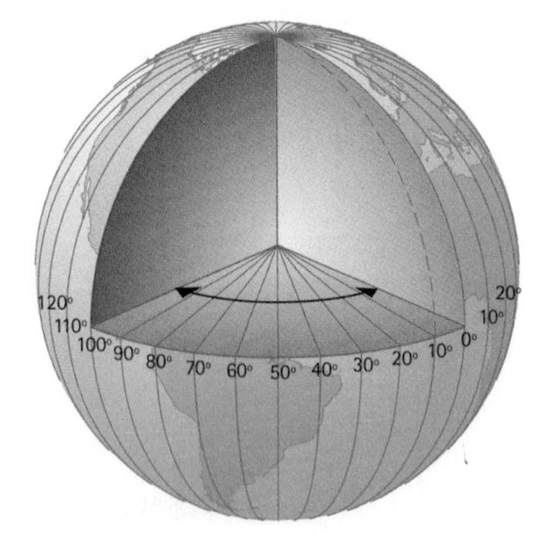

Lima, Peru, is approximately located at 12°2'47" S 77°2'34" W. These numbers show that Lima is northwest of Sao Paulo.

When you look at a globe or a map, you will notice that the hemispheres are divided into additional parts. The Tropic of Cancer (from the equator to 23°27' N) is roughly the northernmost boundary of the tropics. The tropic of Capricorn (from the equator to 23°27' S) is the southernmost boundary of the tropics. The Arctic Circle begins at 66°33' N, and the Antarctic Circle begins at 66°33' S.

Along with helping to determine location, lines of longitude are also used to help determine time. To compensate for the earth's rotation, time zones were established to make sure that daylight hours match daytime and night hours match nighttime. The world has 24 time zones. The prime meridian serves as hour 0, and lines of longitude divisible by 15 serve as the approximate midpoints for the different time zones. The international date line runs approximately along 180° longitude and indicates where one date ends and the next begins. Traveling east from the prime meridian, an hour is added to the time in each time zone until the international date line. Traveling west, hours are subtracted until the international date line is reached. Time zones are not uniform. Each nation may adjust the lines within its borders to accommodate its population or other needs.

FYI

International Date Line

The international date line, which is on the opposite side of the world from the prime meridian, is at 180° longitude. The international date line separates one calendar day from the next. If you travel east around the world and adjust your calendar watch whenever you enter a new time zone, by the time you get back to your starting point, you would be a day behind everyone else. If you travel west, by the time you get back to your starting point, you would be a day ahead of everyone else.

World Map

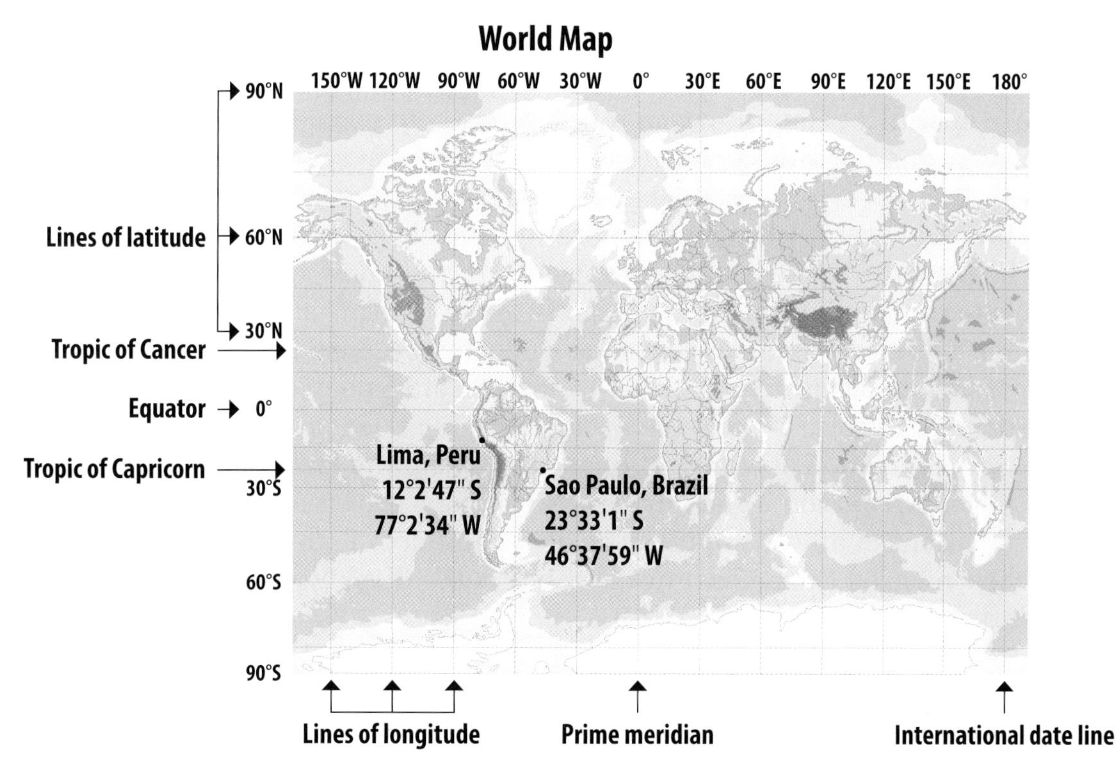

TRY THIS

Topographic Map

Look at a topographic map. Copy the map of a region onto graph paper. Then exchange maps with a partner and make a model of that map with modeling clay. (You can make your own modeling clay by mixing 750 mL of flour with 750 mL of salt and adding 300 mL of water.) Make your model according to the scale noted on the map.

Time Zone Map

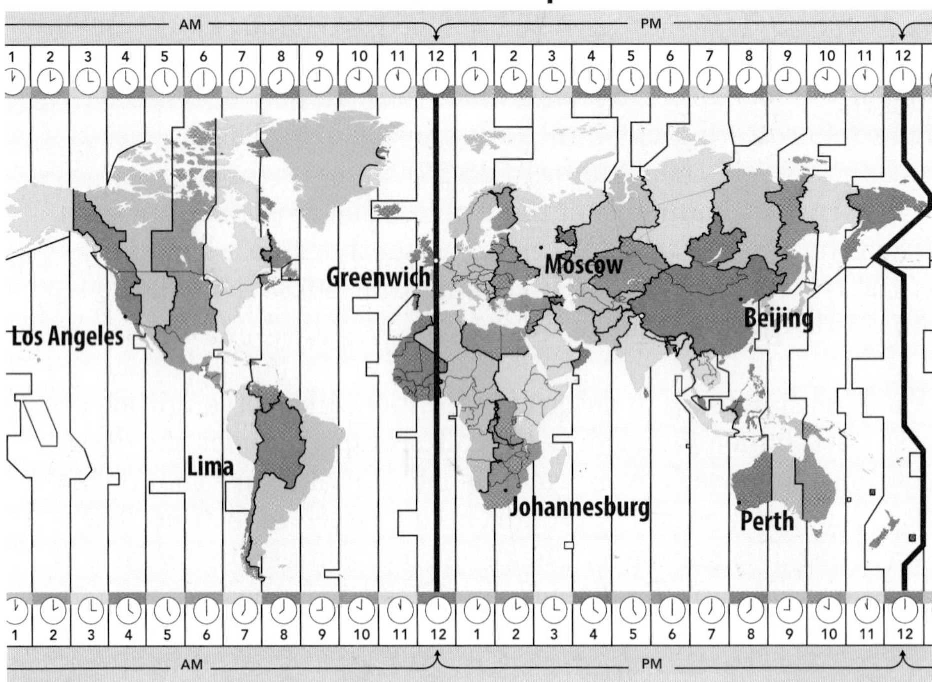

Maps and globes have four basic functions, but only a globe can accurately display all four at the same time. The four functions are to correctly show size, shape, distance, and direction. Even though globes are very useful in helping people understand the earth, maps are usually more useful to scientists. A map is a representation, usually on a flat surface, of a portion of land, water, or sky. Maps show various features and how those features are spatially related to each other. Maps help people find their way around or find an object for which they are searching.

Have you ever tried to peel an orange and then flatten out the pieces to make a whole orange? If so, you know what cartographers, or mapmakers, go through to draw a round Earth on a flat piece of paper. Maps are distorted because it is not possible to accurately show every feature of a sphere on a flat surface. To solve this problem, cartographers use projections. A **projection** is a system of lines portraying the features of a curved surface on a flat surface. Projections are created through variations of any one of three basic techniques. Techniques are chosen based on the part of the earth being displayed and the intended function of the map.

To understand the three main projection techniques, imagine that a piece of paper is placed on or around a globe and the image from the globe is projected onto the paper. On every projection map, the greatest accuracy will be where the paper touches the globe, but accuracy will decrease in areas farther from the touch points.

An azimuthal projection looks as if the paper was laid flat over a portion of the globe. In azimuthal projections, the size and shape of areas very near the map's center are fairly accurate, and the correct direction from the center to any area on the map is shown. Size and shape become increasingly distorted the farther

FYI

Parts of a Map

Knowing the parts of a map transforms it from an interesting picture of a region to a useful tool. All the symbols used on a map are explained in the map key, usually located at the bottom right corner of the map. The compass rose is a symbol serving as a direction marker, and it tells the reader where the cardinal directions—north, south, east, and west—are located. The compass rose may also indicate intermediate directions such as northeast or southwest, which fall between the cardinal directions. The scale is a measurement line explaining to the reader what distance of the earth is represented by the measurement on the scale bar. For example, a distance of one centimeter on the map may be drawn to represent 2,000 kilometers.

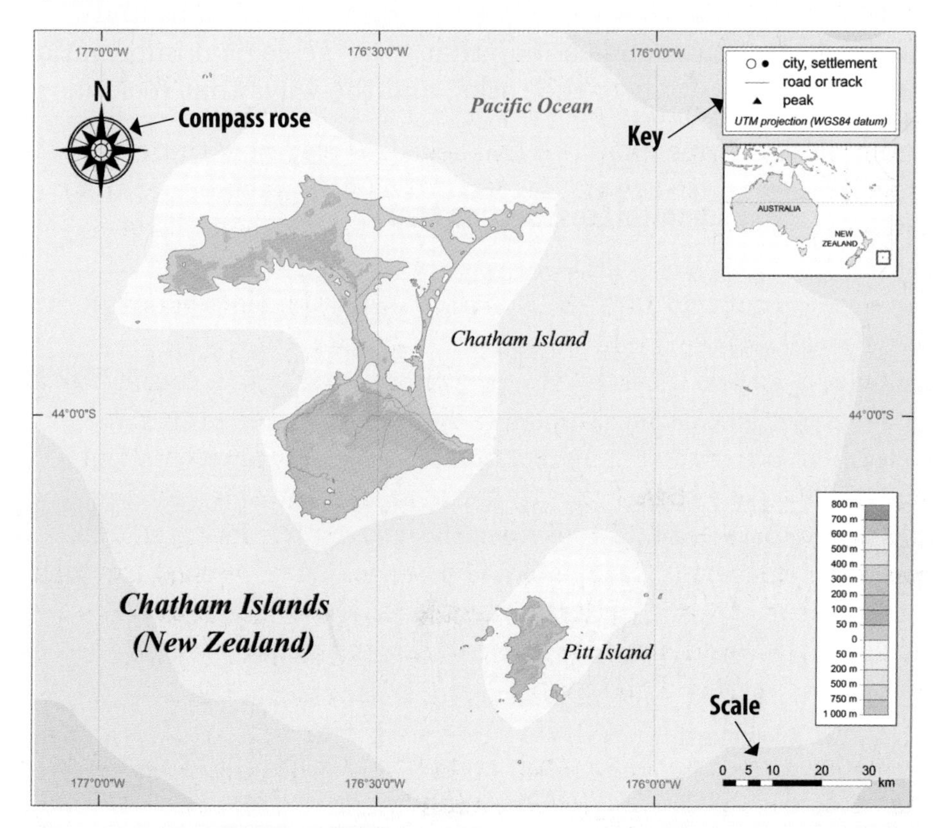

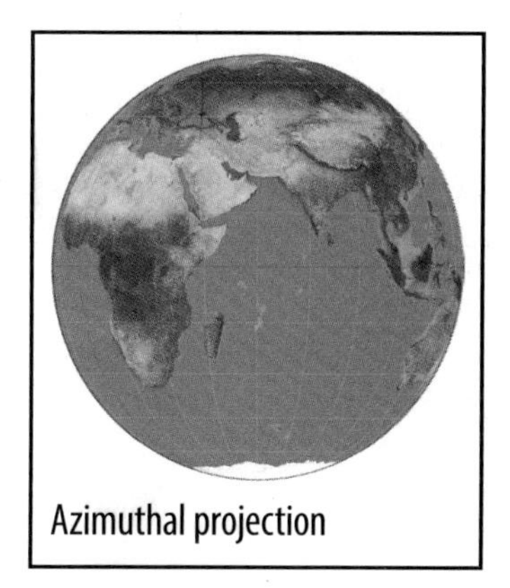

Azimuthal projection

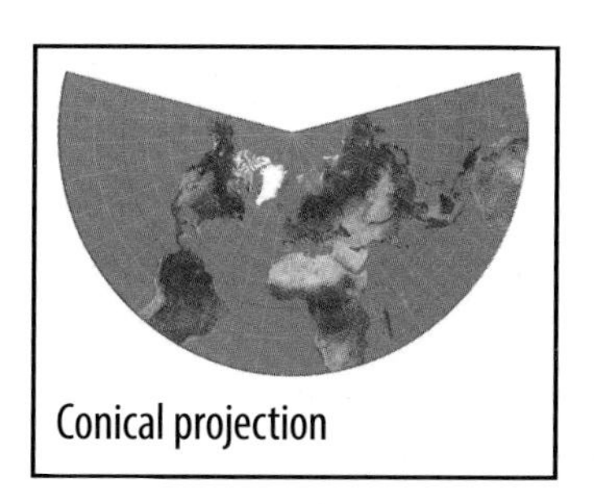

Conical projection

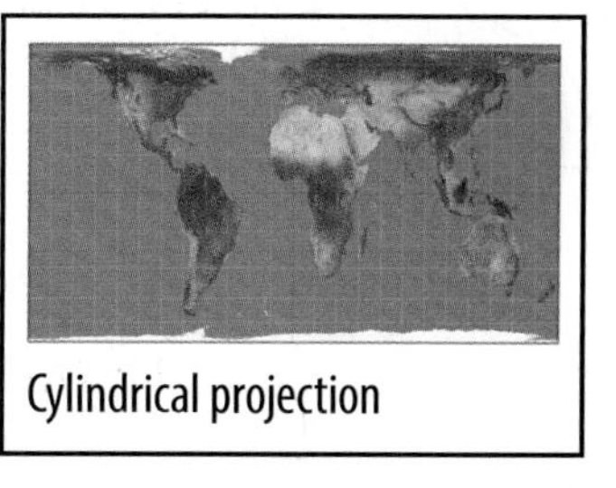

Cylindrical projection

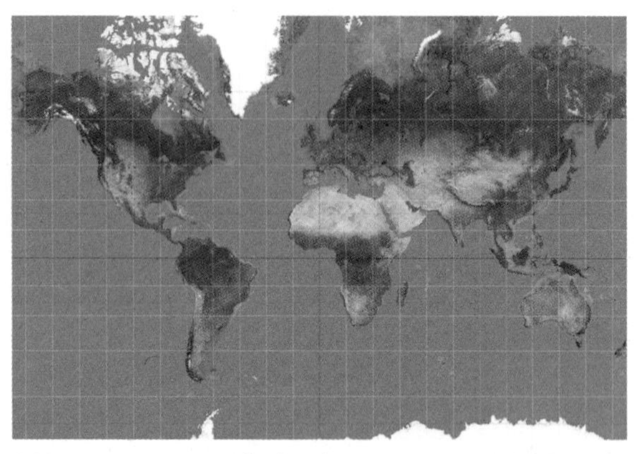
A Mercator map is a cylindrical projection.

an area is from the map's center. The accuracy of distances depends on how the projection was made. These maps are often used to show the earth's poles.

A conical projection looks as if the paper was rolled into a cone and then placed over the globe. Depending on how the projection was made, either the shapes or sizes of areas will be most accurate. Directions and distances between areas are fairly accurate, but they become distorted in areas farther from where the cone touches the globe. These maps are often used to show areas between the equator and a pole.

A cylindrical projection looks as if the paper was rolled into a cylinder or tube and then placed over the globe. Cylindrical projections usually show accurate shapes of areas. The size of areas and the distance between them become increasingly distorted the farther the area is from where the paper touches the globe. The accuracy of direction depends on how the projection was made. These maps are often used to show the whole world or areas along the equator.

Each branch of earth science has its own types of maps and charts. A geologic map is a map that gives geological information such as rock type, age of the rocks, and the ways that rock has

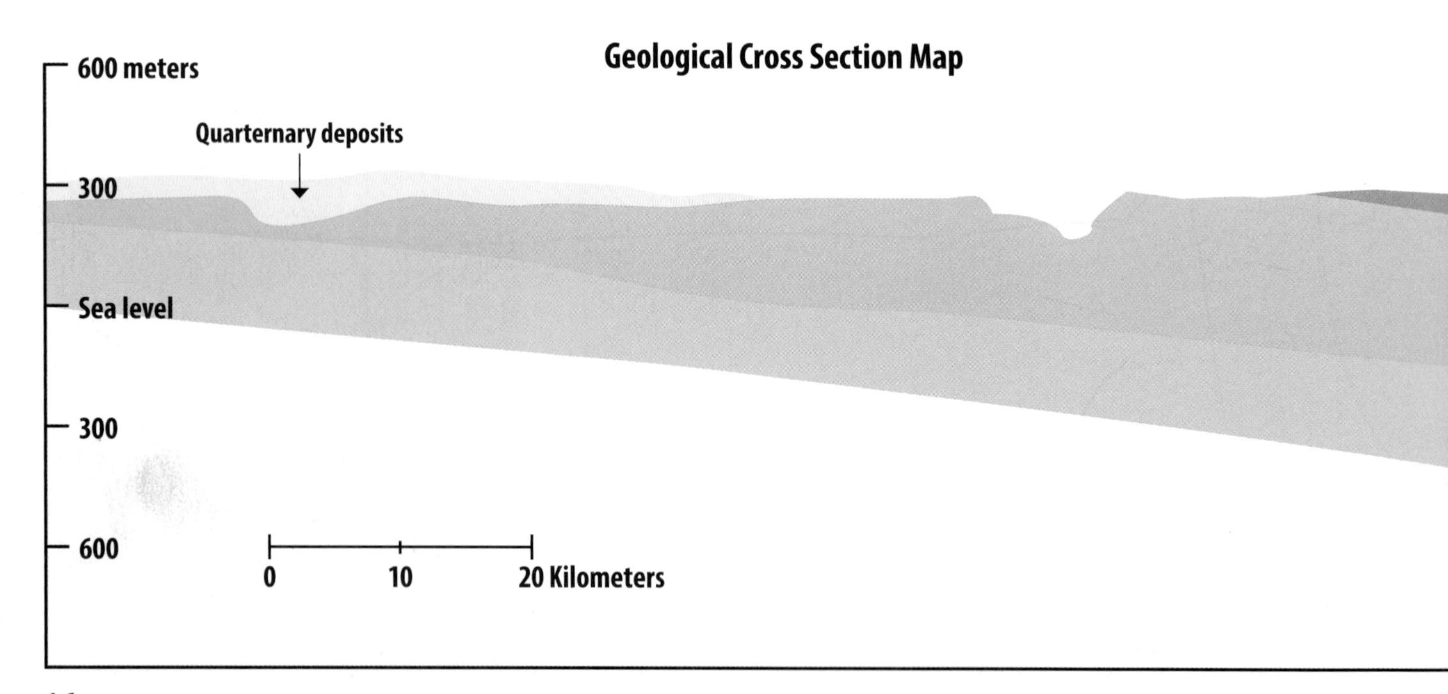

changed. Geologic maps may also show the locations of past volcanic eruptions and earthquakes. Geologic maps are helpful in pointing out dangerous conditions such as potential landslides. They also show information that is helpful for the construction of wells and sewage systems—for example, they may show the level of the water table.

Geologic maps can be of several different types. A tectonic plate map is a map that shows the positions of the earth's plates and may also show the locations of faults, earthquakes, and volcanoes. A bedrock formation map is a map that plots different rock types from a particular time period.

Another type of geologic map is a paleogeographic map, which shows what a region is believed to have looked like long ago. A paleogeographic map shows ancient seas, mountain ranges, and any other important geological features. Natural history museums often use paleogeographic maps to bring the past to life by showing what plants and animals may have lived in a region at a particular time. For example, part of a paleogeographic map might show swamp lands where dinosaurs flourished. Although these maps are interesting, nobody can prove that their details are accurate.

Some geologic maps include a cross-section diagram that shows what rock formations at different depths would look like if an imaginary trench were dug straight down from the surface of

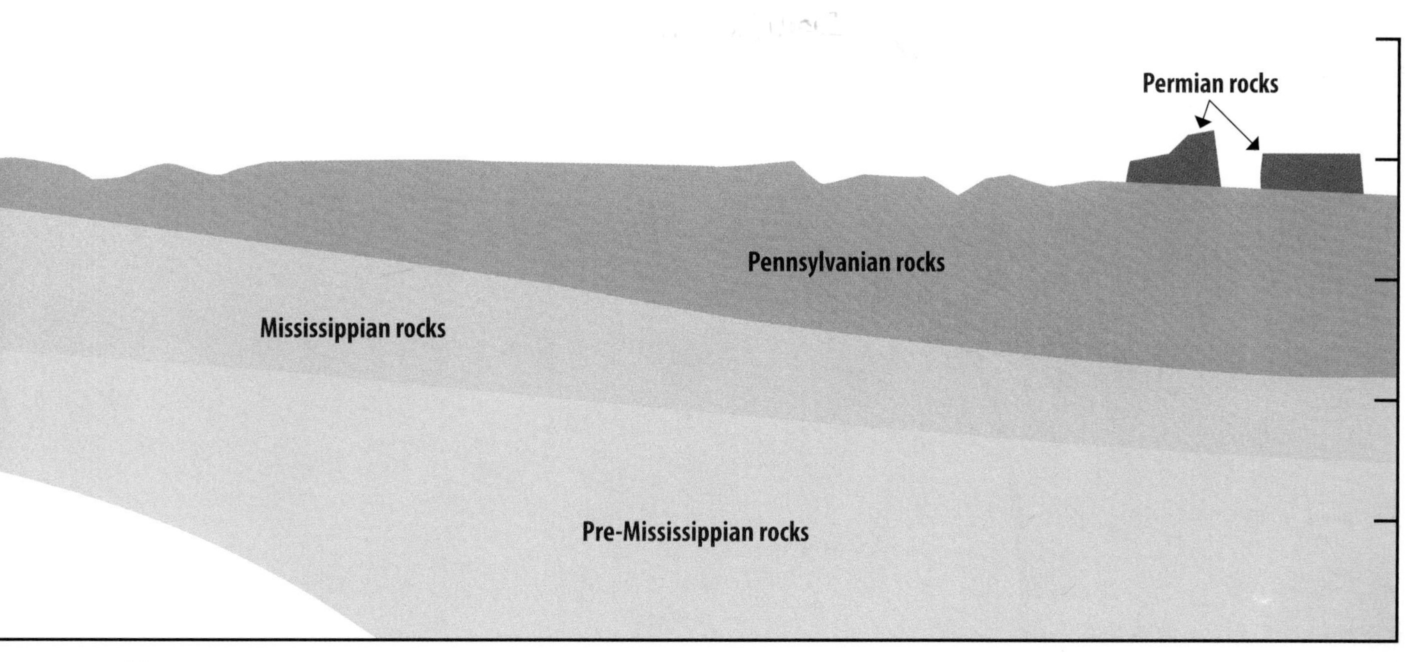

land. Using a cross-section diagram is like looking at an ant farm behind a pane of glass. When you look into an ant farm, you can see the tunnels dug by the ants and their activities below the surface of the soil; a cross-section diagram shows you how the different layers of rock formations appear. Sometimes you can see a real cross-section of rock layers along a highway road cut.

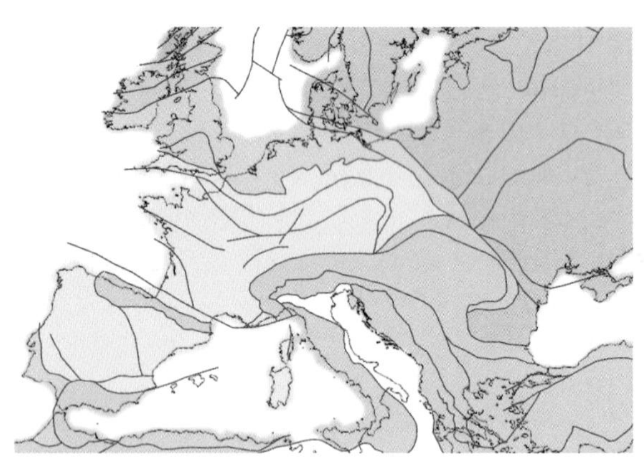
Tectonic map of Europe

Topographic maps, also called *contour maps*, are very useful to geologists. A topographic map is a map that shows the different heights and shapes of the land using contour lines. A **contour line** is a line on a map that joins points of equal elevation. Contour lines are usually drawn roughly parallel to one another. They form circles or ovals at the tops of hills or in depressions in the land. The spacing of the lines represents the slope of the land. You can tell how steep the terrain is by looking at the distance between each contour line. Contour lines drawn close together show a steep incline; lines drawn farther apart show a gentler slope. The contour lines are usually marked with numbers to signify an elevation in feet above sea level. Topographic maps are helpful in identifying hills on hiking trails or for builders who need to know where the ground is uneven. Topographical maps can also

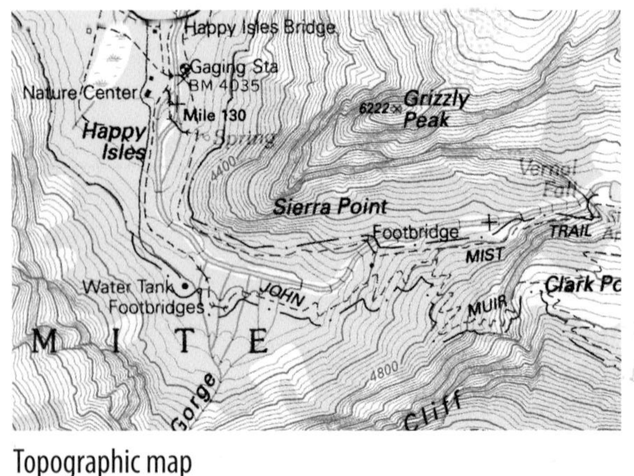

Topographic map

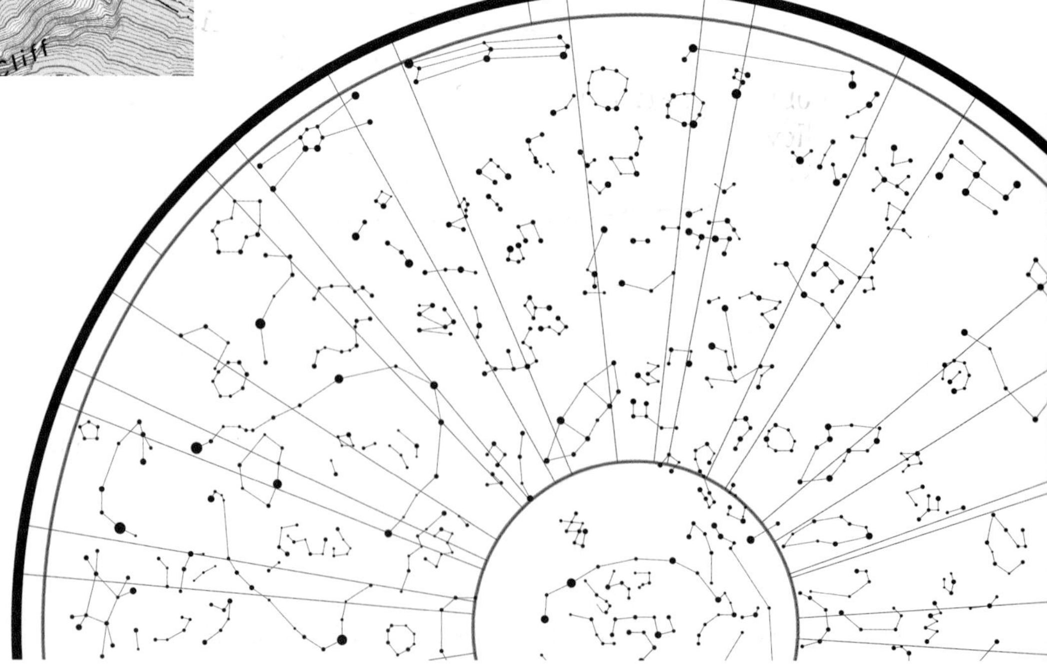
Star chart

HISTORY

Star Charts

Early stargazers saw shapes of people, animals, and objects among the stars. Today, astronomers still recognize these shapes and call them *constellations*. The International Astronomical Union recognizes 88 official constellations. All parts of the sky have been assigned to one constellation or another. Star charts show the borders of the constellations, and they may also connect the brighter stars with lines to show the figure that gives the constellation its name. However, stars within the same constellation may be connected in different ways by different cultures. The constellation with the largest area is Hydra. The smallest constellation is Crux, which helps sailors in the tropics and the Southern Hemisphere navigate their boats at night and reminds Christians of the cross of Jesus Christ.

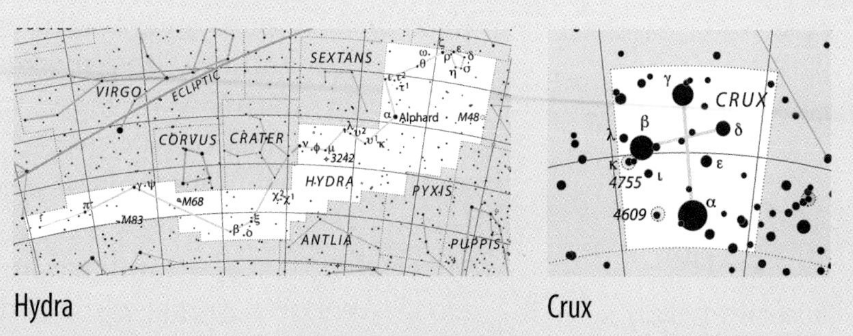

Hydra

Crux

show underwater features. These maps are called *bathymetric maps*.

Meteorologists also use maps. When you watch the weather report, you see a weather map, a map that uses symbols to track cloud cover, wind, and other weather conditions. To keep track of the long-term climactic conditions of a region, meteorologists use a climate map, which summarizes an area's annual rainfall, snowfall, and temperatures.

Astronomers use maps called *star charts*. Astronomers usually have their star charts bound together into a star atlas, which is a collection of maps or charts on a related subject. Astronomers also use a sphere called *a celestial globe* to help them locate celestial objects. Earth is pictured at the center of this sphere, and a hollow plastic shell around the Earth represents the night sky. Celestial bodies are imprinted on this shell. The sphere can rotate to show the movement of stars in the night sky.

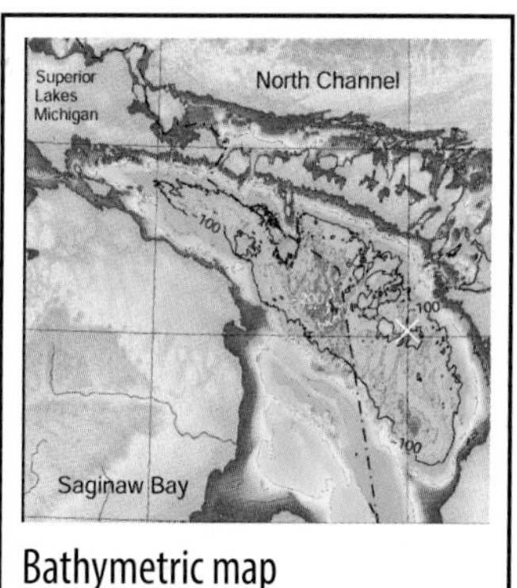

Bathymetric map

LESSON REVIEW

1. How are lines of latitude related to the equator?
2. What are the two functions of lines of longitude?
3. Why is making an accurate map challenging?
4. What are the three basic types of projection maps, and what are the strengths of each?
5. What kind of map would a seismologist use to study earthquake patterns?
6. If you were skiing and wanted to avoid steep hills, which of the maps discussed in this lesson would you use?

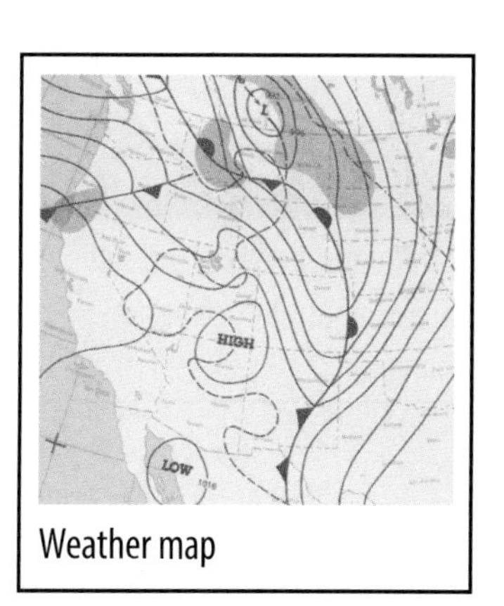

Weather map

1.2.1 *Introduction to Minerals*

OBJECTIVES

- Explain the basic characteristics of a mineral.
- Distinguish between minerals and nonminerals.

VOCABULARY

- **mineral** a naturally occurring, inorganic solid with a definite chemical composition and a crystalline structure
- **mineralogy** the study of minerals

Diamonds, iron ore, and salt are all naturally occurring minerals.

Throughout history, minerals have been among people's most prized material possessions. Hundreds of years ago North African caravans braved thousands of kilometers of harsh desert to trade salt, which at the time was nearly as valuable as gold. Europeans came to the Americas to search for gold and other precious minerals and waged war to take and keep them. For centuries, people have traveled great distances, fought battles, and taken great risks to get metals and gems.

Minerals are still valuable. Diamonds and gold are some of the most expensive items sold anywhere. Other minerals are valued for their usefulness. Iron is used in construction, aluminum is used in foil or airplane parts, salt seasons food, and uranium can help treat cancer.

A diamond, a lump of iron ore, and a grain of salt have different properties and are made of different elements. However, they have one thing in common: they are all minerals. A **mineral** is a naturally occurring, inorganic solid that has a definite chemical composition and a characteristic crystalline structure.

The study of minerals is called **mineralogy**. Around 4,000 minerals are already known, and scientists are discovering more all the time. To determine whether a substance is a mineral, scientists ask four basic questions. If the answer to all four questions is yes, then they classify the substance as a mineral.

Is the substance natural? All minerals occur naturally: they are formed by the processes of nature, not by humans. Scientists can produce some substances—such as ruby, quartz, and zirconia

Coal is formed by the remains of plants and animals and is not considered a mineral.

(which looks like a diamond)—in a laboratory. These substances look a lot like their natural counterparts and they have similar or identical chemical compositions, but they are not minerals because they were never a natural part of the earth's crust. Substances such as steel and bronze are alloys, which are combinations of two or more metals or a metal and another material. Alloys are not considered minerals because they are industrially manufactured.

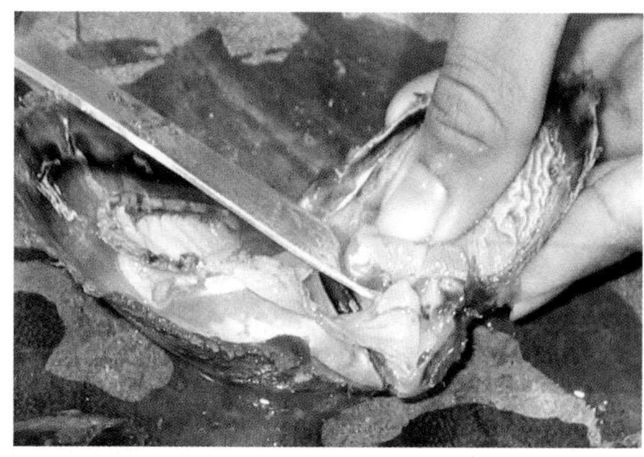

Removing a pearl from a pearl oyster

Is the substance inorganic? An inorganic substance is a substance that is not made up of living things or the remains of living things. Obviously, a worm living in the soil is not a mineral, but neither is coal. Like a worm, coal is an organic substance. It is made of the remains of ancient plants and animals. A few organic substances are classified as minerals because they share all the other properties of minerals. One such substance is aragonite, which is produced by oysters to create their shells and pearls.

Is the substance a uniform crystalline solid (crystal)? All substances on Earth normally exist as solids, liquids, or gases. Minerals always exist in solid form. Although mercury is inorganic and has a uniform composition, it is not a mineral because it is liquid in its natural state. A uniform crystalline solid is a solid that cannot be physically broken down into other components and whose particles are arranged in a regular,

BIBLE CONNECTION

Salty Facts

- Marco Polo reported seeing salt coins in Cathay (North China).
- *To salt away* means "to store or lay aside for later need." Before refrigeration was common, meat was salted to preserve it for later.
- Salt was once traded ounce for ounce for gold.
- Rome's major highway was the Via Salacia (salt road). Soldiers used this highway to carry salt up from the Tiber River, where barges brought salt from the salt pans of Ostia, the port city for Rome.
- Roman soldiers were once paid in salt—the word *salary* comes from the Latin word *sal*, which means "salt."
- When Jesus said, "You are the salt of the earth," (Matthew 5:13), He was not only telling people to be "flavorful" Christians and a preservative, He was also telling them that they were valuable.

Mercury is not a mineral because it is liquid in its natural state.

repeating, three-dimensional pattern. The crystalline structure is obvious in some minerals, such as quartz. In other minerals, it can be seen only with the help of a microscope. The different crystalline structures of minerals account for differences in their properties.

Does the substance have a definite chemical composition? Chemical composition is the relative abundance of the different types of atoms in a substance. All minerals have a chemical composition. Scientists use a formula, such as H_2O for water, to represent a substance's chemical composition. Minerals can be elements or compounds. Elements consist of only one kind of atom; compounds consist of multiple kinds of atoms. Gold is a mineral made of only one element; it is made of only gold atoms. The formula for gold is Au. Fluorite, another mineral, is a compound made of calcium and fluoride ions arranged in a specific pattern. The formula for fluorite is CaF_2. Rocks, like minerals, are naturally occurring, inorganic, and solid. However, they are not minerals because they do not have a uniform crystalline structure. In addition, they often include at least microscopic traces of multiple minerals or organic substances, which prevents them from having a definite chemical composition.

LESSON REVIEW

1. What is the study of minerals called?
2. Name five minerals and their uses.
3. What four basic characteristics do all minerals share?
4. Explain whether a rock is a mineral. Why?

The mineral fluorite is colorless when pure, but is colored by impurities.

God created an orderly world; people can study parts of it more efficiently by grouping similar things together. Just as plants and animals can be organized into related groups according to their common features, minerals can also be classified. Minerals are classified according to their chemical compositions and structures.

Minerals can first be divided into silicates and nonsilicates. Silicate minerals are the most plentiful of all the mineral classes. All **silicate minerals** have a silicon atom bonded with four oxygen atoms (SiO_4) as a foundation. These minerals make up more than 90% of the earth's crust. (Oxygen makes up 46.6% of the crust by weight, and silicon makes up 27.7%.) The basic combination of silicon and oxygen can bond with other elements (such as iron, aluminum, and potassium) to form different silicate minerals. Silicate minerals can be further subdivided into smaller groups, including feldspar, quartz, mica, and talc.

Feldspar minerals are the most common silicate mineral. They make up more than half of the crust and are a part of all types of rock. They all have a base of silicon, oxygen, and aluminum. Different feldspar minerals are distinguished by their other elements called *additives*. The most common feldspar additives include potassium ($KAlSi_3O_8$), sodium ($NaAlSi_3O_8$), and calcium ($CaAl_2Si_3O_8$). The combination of additives gives feldspar a wide range of colors. For example, the range of gray to pink grains visible in granite rock are a type of feldspar. Because feldspar minerals have such a beautiful range of colors, they are often used as decorative stone on buildings.

OBJECTIVES

- Identify the primary elements in each of several main mineral groups.
- Distinguish mineral groups from each other using their chemical composition and structure.

VOCABULARY

- **nonsilicate mineral** a mineral composed of elements or bonded groups of elements other than bonded silicon and oxygen
- **silicate mineral** a mineral formed by bonded silicon and oxygen atoms

Feldspar minerals are frequently used as decorative stone on buildings because they occur in many beautiful colors.

BIBLE CONNECTION

Precious Jewels

Revelation 21 paints an amazing picture of the new Holy City of Jerusalem with walls composed of minerals and gemstones. King David and the people of ancient Israel contributed minerals and gems for the first Temple. Throughout the Bible, gems are used to describe things God considers to be of great worth, such as wisdom and a wife of noble character.

Quartz is the second most common mineral in the earth's crust. It is mainly formed from silicon and oxygen. Pure quartz (SiO_2) is clear, but the addition of other elements can give it different colors. The most common colors are rose, violet, or smoky. Quartz is the hardest of the most common minerals. This quality makes it ideal for sandpaper and industrial cleaners. Quartz is the most common mineral in sand; the clear grains are quartz.

Mica is a soft, often shiny mineral. These minerals form extremely thin, shiny, flexible sheets called *books*, which can easily be separated with a knife. They primarily contain silicon, oxygen, hydrogen, aluminum, and potassium along with a variety of other elements including magnesium, iron, sodium, and lithium. A common form of mica is called *muscovite*. Mica can be found in granite along with feldspar and quartz. Mica is used in insulation, wallpaper, paint, and tile.

Talc is the softest known mineral. It primarily contains silicon, oxygen, hydrogen, magnesium, and usually impurities such as

Muscovite mica

iron, nickel, or aluminum. Talcum powder is made of talc; other uses of talc include roofing materials, paint, and paper.

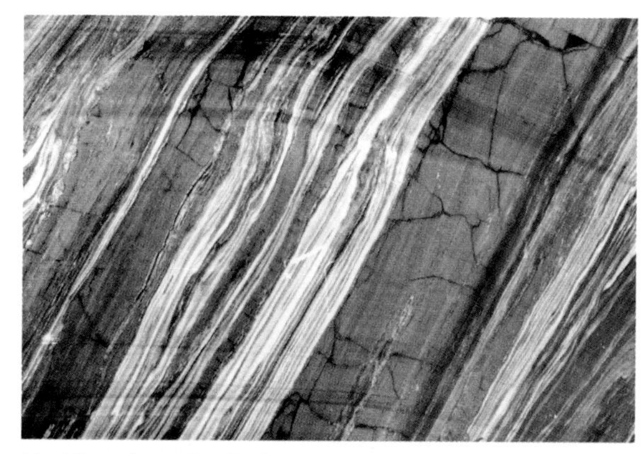
Marble rock made of calcium magnesium carbonate

Less than 10% of the earth's crust is made of nonsilicate minerals. **Nonsilicate minerals** are composed of elements or bonded groups of elements other than bonded silicon and oxygen. Categories of nonsilicate minerals include carbonates, oxides, sulfates, sulfides, halides, and native elements.

Carbonates are minerals that contain a carbon atom bonded to three oxygen atoms (CO_3); this combination then bonds with a metal. Carbonates such as calcite ($CaCO_3$) are the main components of limestone and marble. Other carbonates help form the shells of many shellfish such as oysters. Carbonate minerals are used in cement and building stones. Carbonates are easy to identify because they fizz and dissolve when they come in contact with acid.

Oxides are minerals in which oxygen is combined with one or two metals. The simple chemical formulas of oxides distinguish

What a Gem

Gemstones are minerals whose beauty, durability, and rarity make them valuable. A gem's value depends on its scarcity, color, clarity, cut, and carat weight. Gemstones are usually polished and cut into different shapes so that they shine and sparkle. Translucent and opaque gemstones are usually cut into oval shapes. Transparent gemstones, such as diamonds, are faceted so they reflect light in a dazzling display of sparkles. After being cut and polished, gems are typically set in precious metals, such as gold or silver, and made into jewelry.

Jewelers identify gems according to their chemical and physical properties. Each gem is made of specific elements and has a chemical formula. However, some gems have the same chemical formulas as minerals that are not gems. A common example is that of diamond (a gem) and graphite (a mineral used in pencils). Both minerals are made of silicon and oxygen (SiO_2). However, diamonds are formed under much greater temperature and pressure than graphite, which causes them to become much harder. Jewelers, therefore, also use various physical properties to help them identify gems.

The oxide hematite (Fe_2O_3) is often mined for iron.

Pyrite, also known as *fool's gold*, is a sulfide.

them from other mineral categories that include oxygen, such as silicates. In other mineral classes, oxygen bonds to one or more other elements and the bonded group acts as a unit. In oxides, however, the oxygen is a unit all by itself. For example, naturally occurring ice (H_2 + O) is considered an oxide; oxygen acts on its own and bonds with hydrogen. In contrast, the oxygen in sodium feldspar is part of the aluminum silicate group that combines with sodium (Na + $AlSi_3O_8$). Quartz is an exception to this principle. Although quartz has a simple formula containing only silicon and oxygen (SiO_2), it is classified as a silicate because the structure of its atoms is closer to other silicates than to oxides. Oxides are often mined for their metals, such as hematite (Fe_2O_3) for iron and cassiterite (SnO_2) for tin.

Sulfate minerals are primarily composed of a sulfur atom bonded with four oxygen atoms (SO_4). The bonded oxygen and sulfur then attaches to a metal element. One of the most common sulfates is gypsum. Gypsum has a wide variety of uses, including plaster of paris, fertilizer, paper, and jewelry.

The sulfide mineral class is distinguished from other categories containing sulfur in much the same way that oxides are separated from other minerals containing oxygen. Just as oxides are distinguished by oxygen bonding directly to metals, sulfides are characterized by sulfur bonding directly to metals. Pyrite, also known as *fool's gold*, is a sulfide in which iron bonds to sulfur (Fe + S_2). Similar to oxide minerals, sulfide minerals are mined for their metals, such as iron, copper, or lead.

Halide minerals contain combinations of a halogen (fluorine, chlorine, bromine, or iodine) with one or more metals. Halite (NaCl), which is called *rock salt* when found in rock form, is often used for melting ice on roads or as table salt. Other halide uses include fertilizers and the making of steel and aluminum.

Native elements are minerals that are made of only one element. At least 19 minerals are native elements. They are divided into three groups: metals, semimetals, and nonmetals. Metals conduct electricity and heat, and they can be bent without breaking.

Commonly known metal native elements include gold, silver, platinum, iron, zinc, tin, mercury, lead, and copper. Semimetals are poor conductors of electricity and heat, and they break easily when bent. The more common semimetal native elements include arsenic and bismuth. Nonmetals do not conduct electricity or heat. Nonmetal native elements include carbon, graphite, and sulfur.

Natural copper

LESSON REVIEW

1. What is the main difference between the elemental components of feldspar and quartz?
2. How are oxides distinguished from other minerals containing oxygen?
3. Why is quartz classified as a silicate instead of an oxide?
4. How are sulfates distinguished from sulfides?
5. Which mineral classifications have a single element to which other elements are bonded? For each class, what is the primary element to which other elements are added?
6. Which mineral classifications have a bonded core group of elements to which other elements may bond? What is the core group of elements for each class?

Halite is used for melting ice on roads or as table salt.

1.2.3 *General Mineral Properties*

OBJECTIVES

- Describe the general properties of minerals.
- Classify minerals using mineral properties.

VOCABULARY

- **cleavage** a mineral's tendency to split along definite, flat surfaces
- **density** the mass per unit of volume of a substance
- **fracture** a mineral's tendency to break along irregular lines
- **hardness** a mineral's resistance to being scratched
- **luster** the way a mineral's surface reflects light
- **streak** the color of the powder left by a mineral when it is rubbed against a hard, rough surface

Some minerals have identical or nearly identical chemical formulas. Not only this, but some minerals look so much alike that just looking at them is not enough to distinguish between them. Fortunately, minerals possess general physical properties that enable people to distinguish between them. These properties are based not only on the elements that compose each mineral but also on the way that the atoms in the mineral are bonded together. These physical properties include color, luster, hardness, streak, cleavage, fracture, and density. One property is usually not enough to identify a mineral; two minerals might have the same color or hardness, for example. Identifying a mineral requires at least two physical properties.

Many minerals are colored. However, color alone cannot identify a mineral because many minerals are the same color. For example, hornblende, magnetite, and sphalerite can all be black. Even the color of one mineral can vary, depending on the additives or impurities present. Corundum, for example, is a clear mineral made of oxygen and aluminum, but the addition of tiny amounts of chromium results in a ruby, which has a deep red color. Blue sapphire is corundum that contains traces of iron and titanium that give it a blue color. Quartz is often clear, but the addition of manganese makes it a purple amethyst.

Luster is another property of minerals. Luster describes the way that a mineral's surface reflects light. Minerals that contain metals reflect a lot of light, so they are said to have a metallic (shiny) luster. Other minerals, which do not reflect as much light, have a nonmetallic luster. Nonmetallic luster has several categories, including glassy, waxy, earthy, dull, and resinous. Most quartz, for example, has a glassy luster. Turquoise has a waxy luster, as if it were covered with wax. Some minerals, such as kaolinite, have an earthy luster. Diamonds have a luster that sparkles, called *adamantine*.

Rock showing black hornblende with a dull luster

Black sphalerite with a resinous luster

Red corundum (ruby) with a glassy luster

Blue corundum (sapphire) with a glassy luster

FYI

Field Hardness Scale

Hardness	Common Tests
1	Easily scratched with a fingernail.
2	Scratched with a fingernail.
3	Scratched with a penny.
4	Easily scratched with a knife.
5	Scratched with a knife; barely scratches glass.
6	Scratched with a steel file; easily scratches glass.
7	Scratches a steel file and glass.

Mohs Hardness Scale

Hardness	Mineral
1	Talc
2	Gypsum
3	Calcite
4	Fluorite
5	Apatite
6	Feldspar
7	Quartz
8	Topaz
9	Corundum
10	Diamond

Turquoise has a waxy luster.

Kaolinite has an earthy luster.

Hardness, a mineral's resistance to being scratched, is another way of identifying a mineral sample. Not all minerals are equally hard. A mineral's hardness depends on the strength of the bonds between the ions or atoms and the internal arrangement of the mineral's atoms. Harder minerals have stronger elemental bonds. Diamond, the strongest mineral, has carbon atoms that are each strongly bonded to four other carbon atoms. Graphite, a relatively soft mineral, has sheets of thin carbon atoms weakly bonded together. Although graphite and diamond are both composed entirely of carbon, the way the carbon atoms are arranged and bonded produces minerals of different hardness.

Diamond (left, showing adamantine luster) and graphite (above) are both pure carbon, but diamond is significantly harder.

FYI

Mineral Properties Chart						
	Mineral	Color**	Luster	Hardness*	Streak	Density*
	calcite	many colors	glassy	3.0	white	2.7
	feldspar	white, pink, gray, brown	glassy	6.0	white	2.6
	fluorite	many colors	glassy	4.0	white	3.2
	galena	lead-gray	metallic	2.5	lead-gray	7.4–7.6
	halite	colorless, white, yellow, red, blue	glassy	2.5	white	2.2
	hematite	gray, black, red	metallic	5.5–6.5	red to reddish-brown	4.9–5.3
	hornblende	green to black	glassy, pearly, dull	5.0–6.0	green-gray to gray	3.0–3.5
	magnetite	black	metallic	5.5–6.0	black	5.2
	malachite	green	glassy, silky	3.5–4.0	green	3.6–4.0
	muscovite	white, gray, colorless	glassy, silky, pearly	2.0–2.5	white	2.8–3.0
	olivine	olive green	glassy	6.5–7.0	white, gray	3.2–3.4
	quartz	colorless, white	glassy	7.0	white	2.7
	sphalerite	yellow, brown, black, red, green, white, colorless	waxy, resinous	3.0–4.0	white, light brown	4.0

**All values are g/cm^3 rounded to two significant digits. **Most common colors are listed; other colors may exist.*

A commonly used scale of hardness is the Mohs hardness scale, which is a list of ten minerals that represent different degrees of hardness. However, a field hardness scale, which uses materials with known Mohs scale hardness ratings, can be used when the minerals from the Mohs scale are not available. To determine the hardness of an unknown mineral, scratch the mineral with each item on the field hardness scale in turn, starting with the least hard. The test stops once the mineral sample has been scratched.

Streak plates with pyrite (left) and rhodochrosite (right) and their streak colors

The Mohs scale starts with talc (the softest known mineral) and ends with diamond (the hardest known mineral). Minerals with large numbers on the Mohs and field scales can scratch those with smaller numbers; any mineral can scratch talc. The difference in hardness between any two consecutive minerals on the Mohs scale is not the same. For example, there is only about a 25% difference in hardness between calcite and fluorite, but there is a difference of more than 300% between corundum and diamond.

A mineral with a hardness rating of 6 or less can also be identified by its streak. **Streak** is the color of the powder left by a mineral when it is rubbed against a hard, rough surface, such as a streak plate, which is a ceramic tile with a dull, unglazed surface. A streak plate has a hardness of about 7. A mineral's streak may be a different color than the mineral itself. For example, pyrite is yellow in color, but it has a green-black to brown-black streak. Hematite, which may vary in color from red to brown to black, always produces a rust-red streak. Not all minerals leave colorful streaks. Fluorite, for example, can appear in many different colors, but it always leaves a white streak, just like calcite.

Labradorite showing perfect cleavage and pearly luster

Another identifying property of minerals is **cleavage**, a mineral's tendency to split along definite, flat surfaces. Cleavage occurs along surfaces parallel to the plane of the crystal where the bonds between the atoms of the crystal are weak. Different minerals have different cleavages. For example, halite breaks into small cubes. The cleavage of topaz occurs along a single plane parallel to its base. A mineral that breaks easily and cleanly in one or more directions is said to have *perfect cleavage*.

Gypsum showing perfect cleavage and silky luster

BIOGRAPHY

Friedrich Mohs

Born the son of a merchant in 1773, German scientist Friedrich Mohs is best known for his contribution to minerology. Mohs studied mathematics, physics, chemistry, and mechanics. After graduating from the University of Halle, Mohs worked in mining. In 1802, Mohs went to Vienna to classify an important private mineral collection. His system of mineral classification stressed the physical properties of minerals, which conflicted with the accepted classification by chemical composition. Mohs went on to become a professor of mineralogy and developed the Mohs scale of hardness that is still used today. He spent much of his later career in Vienna, where he organized the imperial mineral collection and oversaw mining for the government. Mohs died in 1839 during a trip to Italy to inspect volcanic activity.

For example, calcite breaks perfectly along three planes. Some minerals break perfectly in one direction yet not so well in others. Gypsum and labradorite, for example, break perfectly on only one plane, but each cleaves with lesser success along at least one other plane.

Many minerals fracture instead of cleave. Cleavage results in a smooth surface, but **fracture** is the term used to describe a mineral's tendency to break along irregular lines. Various minerals fracture in different ways. An uneven fracture is a break along a flat surface with an irregular pattern; pyromorphite has an uneven fracture. A mineral with a splintery or fibrous fracture breaks into pieces that look like wood; chrysotile serpentine fractures this way. A conchoidal or shell-like fracture of a mineral is smooth and curved, like the inside of a clam shell or broken glass; quartz has a conchoidal fracture.

Pyromorphite displays an irregular fracture.

Finally, density is also useful in identifying minerals. **Density** is the mass per unit of volume of a substance. A mineral's density can be determined by dividing its mass in grams by its volume in cubic centimeters. The formula is $D = m/V$. One quick way to judge mineral density is by heft, which is how heavy samples of equal sizes feel. If

Chrysotile serpentine (top left) displays a fibrous fracture.

Rutile quartz (top right) has a conchoidal fracture.

you pick up two minerals that are the same size and notice that one is heavier than the other, the heavier mineral is the more dense. For example, a piece of galena feels heavier than a piece of muscovite the same size, which means that the galena is more dense than the muscovite.

LESSON REVIEW

1. List and define seven physical properties of minerals.
2. Identify one mineral that has a waxy luster.
3. What determines a mineral's hardness?
4. What is the formula for density?
5. Which mineral is often black, has a metallic luster, produces a reddish streak, has a density of approximately 4.9 g/cm^3, and has a hardness of about 5.5?

Galena (bottom left, showing a metallic luster) has a higher density than muscovite (bottom right, showing both pearly and glassy luster).

1.2.4 *Special Mineral Properties*

OBJECTIVES

- Describe several special mineral properties.
- Assess the usefulness of special mineral properties in producing a definitive identification of a mineral sample.

VOCABULARY

- **fluorescence** the ability of a mineral to glow and change color under ultraviolet light
- **lodestone** a piece of magnetite that naturally acts as a magnet
- **phosphorescence** the ability of some fluorescent minerals to continue to glow after an ultraviolet light is no longer focused on them
- **radioactivity** the ability of an element to give off nuclear radiation as a result of a change in the atom's nucleus

All minerals have color, luster, streak, hardness, cleavage or fracture, and density. Some minerals have other special identifying properties as well.

Taste is one such property. Only minerals that dissolve in water have taste. Some taste salty or bitter; others do not have a taste that is easily described. Halite, common table salt ($NaCl$), and sylvite (KCl) are alike in most of their physical properties, but they have distinctly different tastes. Some minerals are toxic, so it is unsafe to routinely taste minerals.

A few minerals have a distinctive smell. Usually the odor is strongest in a mineral that has been struck or recently dug up. Sulfides such as pyrite have a rotten egg smell. Arsenopyrite smells like garlic. Clay minerals have an "earthy" smell.

Some minerals react with other substances. For example, calcite will fizz if weak hydrochloric acid is dropped on it. This test helps identify limestone and marble rock because they are composed mainly of calcite.

Flexibility is a property of some minerals. The chlorites, for example, are so flexible that thin layers can be bent without breaking. Biotite, a type of mica, is both flexible and elastic.

Some minerals contain enough iron to make them magnetic. *Ferromagnetism* describes a mineral's strong attraction to magnetic fields. In contrast, *paramagnetism* describes a mineral's weak, indistinct, attraction to magnetic fields. *Diamagnetism* is the property of being repelled from magnetic fields; bismuth, a metal, is an example of a diamagnetic mineral.

Magnetite is a naturally occurring mineral that is naturally magnetic. A **lodestone** is a piece of magnetite that is strongly

Halite (left) and sylvite (middle) are minerals that can be safely identified through taste. Sulfur (right) has a distinctive smell.

Biotite mica (left) has thin, flexible layers. Lodestone (middle) and bismuth (right) both have a magnetic field.

magnetic. Early sailors created compasses using lodestones, or needles magnetized by lodestones, to help them navigate. When allowed to turn freely, one end of the lodestone or magnetized needle always points to the magnetic North Pole.

Fluorescence is the ability of a mineral to glow and change color under ultraviolet light. Fluorescent minerals contain particles known as *activators*, which respond to ultraviolet light by visibly glowing in darkness. Fluorescence is an unreliable method for mineral identification because two different samples of the same type of mineral from the same general area may fluoresce in different colors or not at all. Once a mineral has been identified, however, its fluorescent color can sometimes be used to identify its place of origin. **Phosphorescence** is the ability of a few fluorescent minerals to continue glowing for a short time after an ultraviolet light is no longer focused on them. For example, calcite is sometimes phosphorescent. Like fluorescence, phosphorescence is rarely used to identify a mineral.

Wernerite in daylight

Some minerals can be identified by the way light interacts with them. Refraction is the bending of a light wave caused by a change in the wave's speed as it passes from one medium to another. Light rays refract, or bend, when they pass through two substances of different densities, such as moving through air and a transparent crystal. The ability of a mineral to produce two images is called *double refraction*. Double refraction occurs when a transparent substance divides light rays into two parts, creating a

The same wernerite sample under ultraviolet light

Iceland Spar calcite

double image of any object viewed through it. Calcite crystals have this property.

Another special property of some minerals is texture. Some metallic minerals have a jagged texture. Other minerals, such as talc and graphite, have a greasy or oily feel. Copper feels rough. Because diamonds absorb heat so well, they feel cold at room temperature; similarly, graphite, which is a good conductor of both electricity and heat, also feels cold at room temperature. Fibrous minerals, such as chrysotile (a type of asbestos), have a distinct, silky feel. Texture alone is not a reliable characteristic for distinguishing minerals because different people may use different descriptions to explain how something feels.

A few minerals are radioactive. The ability of an element to give off nuclear radiation as a result of a change in the atom's nucleus is called **radioactivity**. Nuclear radiation occurs when an atom's nucleus decays, emitting energy in the form of alpha or beta particles, gamma rays, or X-rays. A radioactive mineral is unstable; its elements continually break down, very slowly destroying the mineral's crystal structure. Radioactive minerals can be detected with an instrument called *a Geiger counter*. Radioactive elements include uranium and radium. The mineral uraninite is the chief source of uranium.

Natural copper has a rough texture.

CAREER

Gemologist

Gemology is the science of gems, both natural and artificial gemstone materials. It is a rewarding and challenging career with many job opportunities. People who choose gemology as a career use their science and math skills to work in the field or in a lab. Gemologists may do a variety of things, such as traveling to find gems, identifying gems' physical properties, giving gems a grade value to indicate their worth, and turning gems into beautiful jewelry or art. In order to become a certified gemologist, people must take classes to learn how gems are created, how to treat and care for gems, how to tell if gems are natural or synthetic, and how to collect or sell gems. There is so much to know about gems that some gemologists specialize in one type of gem! Many gemologists join organizations, such as the International Gem Society, to share their knowledge and learn from others in their field. Gemology would be an interesting career to consider.

When you work at a computer, you are benefiting from silicon, a mineral used in computer chips.

LESSON REVIEW

1. Why is taste not a good property to use when determining the identity of an unknown mineral?
2. What element causes some minerals to be magnetic?
3. Explain the difference between fluorescence and phosphorescence in minerals.
4. Why is fluorescence an unreliable property for determining a mineral's identity?
5. What is refraction?
6. What causes nuclear radiation?

Zircon gives off nuclear radiation.

1.3.1 *Igneous Rock*

OBJECTIVES

- Define and identify igneous rock.
- Describe how the cooling rate of magma affects the texture of igneous rock.
- Classify igneous rock according to mineral composition and texture.
- Simulate the formation of igneous rock in order to understand how formation affects the crystal size.

VOCABULARY

- **extrusive rock** an igneous rock formed when lava cools on the earth's surface
- **felsic rock** a light-colored, lightweight igneous rock that is rich in silicon, aluminum, sodium, and potassium
- **igneous rock** a rock formed from cooled and hardened magma
- **intrusive rock** an igneous rock formed when magma cools beneath the earth's surface
- **lava** the magma that has reached the earth's surface
- **mafic rock** the dark-colored, heavy igneous rock that is rich in iron, magnesium, and calcium
- **magma** the melted rock beneath the earth's surface

Rocks have always played an important role in society. Throughout the Bible, there are countless examples of God's people harvesting and fashioning rocks to create useful items and structures that would better serve their needs. Some examples include the creation of great cities using the rocks that were quarried and the use of rocks such as flint to fashion weapons and tools. Today, individuals still build cities from rocks—usually in combination with cement, which is made from a type of rock known as *limestone*. A rock is a hard substance composed of one or more minerals. Many of the substances used in the modern world are found in the earth's crust. Fossil fuels derived from coal provide energy. Ores provide useful metals. The silicon used to make computer chips is taken from rocks.

Not only do rocks play an important role in society, they also show God's creativity and love of variety. He fashioned rocks to have a wide array of shapes, textures, and colors. Some rock was formed when magma from deep inside the earth cooled and hardened. Other rock formed gradually over many years as grains of sand and various sediments were compressed together and eventually turned to stone. Still other rock was formed when extreme heat and pressure deep inside the earth caused some rocks to change into completely different rocks.

Rocks are all around even though they may not be obvious at first glance. As Moses mentioned in Deuteronomy 33:19, there are "treasures hidden in the sand." Rock is classified in an orderly way according to how it was formed. The three main types of rock are igneous, sedimentary, and metamorphic. Look around at the many products and materials at home and school. How many of these things can be traced to substances obtained from rock? Imagine trying to melt a rock. How much heat would

Cliffs on Svalbard, a Norwegian archipelago

BIOGRAPHY

Florence Bascom

Florence Bascom (1862–1945) was an American educator and geological survey scientist. She received the first PhD awarded to a woman at Johns Hopkins University, Baltimore, and she was the first woman hired by the United States Geological Survey. Florence founded the department of geology at Bryn Mawr College and is best known for her innovative use of petrography, which is the description and systematic classification of rocks.

be required to do that, and what kind of result would you expect? The inside of the earth is so hot that some of the rocks found there are slightly flexible. Below the earth's crust, pockets of flexible rocks rise toward areas of lower pressure that are close to the surface. The reduction of pressure allows the rocks to melt. These rocks are referred to as *magma*. **Magma** is melted rock beneath the earth's surface. Magma, which is very hot, is composed not only of melted rock but also water vapor, carbon dioxide, and rock crystals. **Lava** is magma that has reached the earth's surface. **Igneous rock** are rocks formed from cooled and hardened magma. The name *igneous* comes from the Latin word *ignis*, which means "fire."

Lava cooling to form igneous rock

One way igneous rocks are classified is by their mineral content. **Felsic rock** is light-colored, lightweight igneous rock that is rich in silicon, aluminum, sodium, and potassium. These rocks form from minerals that are acidic and have low melting points (600°C–750°C). Rhyolite and granite are examples of felsic rock. **Mafic rock** is dark-colored, heavy igneous rock that is rich in iron, magnesium, and calcium. These rocks form from minerals that are alkaline (basic) and have higher melting points (1,000°C–1,200°C). Gabbro and basalt are examples of mafic rock. Some rocks are classified somewhere in between felsic and mafic rock depending on their composition. These rocks are called *intermediate rock*.

Although igneous rock forms from magma, it does not all have the same texture. Therefore, igneous rock is also classified by texture—the size, shape, arrangement, and distribution of the minerals that make up the rock. Igneous rock has four basic textures: fine-grained, coarse-grained, glassy, or porphyritic. Fine-grained igneous rock, such as basalt, has interlocking mineral crystals that can be seen only under a microscope. Coarse-grained igneous rock, such as granite, has interlocking mineral crystals of roughly the same size that can be seen

Rhyolite is an example of a felsic rock.

Gabbro is an intrusive igneous rock.

without a microscope. Glassy igneous rock, such as obsidian, contains no crystals. Porphyritic igneous rock, such as trachyte, has large crystals scattered on a background of much smaller crystals.

The crystal size of an igneous rock is determined by how quickly it cooled, which depends partly on whether the rock cooled on or below the earth's surface. **Intrusive rock** is igneous rock formed when magma cools beneath the earth's surface. Intrusive rock forms as magma oozes up through rocks and squeezes between them to cool before reaching the earth's surface. When these rocks cool slowly, they have large, coarse-grained mineral crystals that are easily seen with the naked eye. However, if the rocks cool quickly, they contain fine-grained crystals that cannot be identified without a magnifying glass or a microscope. Most intrusive rock is coarse-grained. Gabbro is a coarse-grained intrusive igneous rock.

Giant's Causeway in northern Ireland is composed of basalt columns.

Obsidian

Prior to the Spanish conquest, the Aztec people were fascinated with obsidian and its many uses, primarily in the areas of hunting and warfare. They found that swords (which they called *macuahuitl*) made with obsidian were sharper than steel. However, this material is brittle and cannot be resharpened, which led to the eventual takeover of steel with the introduction of metallurgy. The Aztec people also used obsidian to shape the shafts of spears, arrows, and swords, to cut feathers and cotton thread used to make ornamental head mantles, and to decorate jewelry worn by aristocracy. Given that the densest deposits of obsidian are found in Mexico and Guatemala, it is no surprise that the Aztecs utilized obsidian in virtually every aspect of their daily living. Obsidian may not be used to make weapons today, but the field of medicine has found a use for obsidian in the form of blades used in eye surgery. These blades produce a very even cut, which aids in faster healing time.

Extrusive rock is igneous rock formed when lava cools on the earth's surface. Sometimes the magma cools slowly at first and then it is thrust to the earth's surface, where it cools quickly. This cooling process produces large crystal grains embedded in smaller grains. Igneous rock with this crystal size mixture is porphyritic. Lava that cools too rapidly to create crystals forms the glasslike volcanic rock called *obsidian*. Pumice is another example of an igneous rock cooled too rapidly to form crystals. When pumice forms, gas bubbles escape from the molten material and become trapped in the rock. The bubbles make the rock porous and give it a low density.

LESSON REVIEW

1. What is igneous rock?
2. How does the cooling rate of magma affect the texture of igneous rock?
3. What are the mineral contents and textures used to classify igneous rock?
4. What is the difference between an intrusive igneous rock and an extrusive igneous rock?
5. Compare the formation of a large-grained igneous rock with that of a fine-grained igneous rock.

Pumice is an extrusive igneous rock.

1.3.2 *Sedimentary Rock*

OBJECTIVES

- Explain the process of compaction and cementation.
- Describe how the three types of sedimentary rock are formed.
- List and describe the major types of clastic sedimentary rock.
- Identify sedimentary rock and simulate its formation.

VOCABULARY

- **clastic rock** a sedimentary rock made of rock particles and fragments deposited by water, wind, or ice
- **lithification** the process that transforms layers of rock fragments into sedimentary rock
- **sedimentary rock** a rock formed from sediments that have been compacted and cemented together
- **sediments** particles of minerals, rock fragments, shells, leaves, and the remains of once-living things
- **shale** a clastic rock composed of silt- and clay-sized particles in flat layers

Unlike the earth's crust, which is dominated by igneous and metamorphic rock, the most common rock visible on the earth's surface is sedimentary rock. After igneous rock develops from cooled magma, it is often exposed to the atmosphere and hydrosphere. This exposure to wind and water causes fragments of the rock to loosen and break away into tiny particles called *sediments*. **Sediments** are particles of minerals, rock fragments, shells, leaves, and the remains of once-living things. Different sediments have different textures—from very coarse to very fine. Some examples of sediments include gravel, sand, silt, and mud.

Sediments form in a variety of ways. Water from rain or runoff soaks into pores of rocks. When the water freezes, the pores crack open and portions of the rock fall away, creating sediments. Acids dissolved in rainwater also break down rocks into tiny fragments. Another way that sediments form is when rocks are exposed to the heat of the sun, which causes rock molecules to expand and contract. This molecular movement can create cracks in rocks until at some point, fragments and particles completely separate from the original rock. Water, wind, or ice carry these fragments, along with organic sediments, away and deposit them. When sediments collect, sedimentary rock can form.

Sedimentary rock is rock formed from sediments that have been compacted and cemented together. The process that transforms layers of rock fragments into sedimentary rock is called **lithification**, which means "to turn into stone." Lithification occurs by two processes: compaction and cementation.

Many deposits of small pieces of earth collect on top of each other to form layers called *strata*. The weight of the upper layers

TRY THIS

Shifting Sediments

Fill a clear jar with sand, gravel, mud, large pebbles, and clay. Add 50 mL of Epsom salt. Add water until there is only about 5 cm of space left at the top. Place the lid on the jar and shake for several seconds. When all is thoroughly mixed, place the jar on a flat surface and allow it to sit undisturbed overnight. The next day, observe how the layers have settled. Carefully pour the water out and let the layers dry completely. The Epsom salt (magnesium and sulfur) acts as glue to hold the "rock" together.

Stratification of sedimentary rock

puts tremendous pressure on the bottom layers, compressing the sediments together until the bottom layers slowly turn into hard rock. During this compaction, as the sediments are pushed together, inner pore spaces become smaller and some of the water is squeezed out. The remaining water surrounding the sediments can contain dissolved minerals, which later recrystallize as new minerals in the pore spaces.

Cementation occurs following compaction and recrystallization. In cementation, the crystals interlock and connect the sediment grains. This process essentially glues the sediments together. The resulting strata layers range in varying degrees of thickness and color, which helps to easily distinguish the incorporated sedimentary rock. This visible stratification, or layering, of sedimentary rock gives geologists clues about how rocks formed. Most sedimentary layers are deposited in a nearly horizontal position. However, there are times when scientists examine a rock layer that is folded or tilted. Scientists then assume this folding or tilting is a result of a disturbance in the earth's crust.

Sedimentary rock is classified into three main groups: clastic, chemical, and carbonate, or organic. Geologists classify sedimentary rock depending on how it is formed. The most common sedimentary rock, **clastic rock** (from the Greek word *klastos*, meaning "broken into pieces"), is made of separate rock particles and fragments

Folded rock layers

that were eroded from an older rock. These fragments come together by wind, water, or ice to form a new rock by compaction and cementation.

Conglomerate rock

Clastic sedimentary rock is further classified by the sediment size from which it forms. A conglomerate rock is a clastic rock composed of rounded, gravel-sized rock fragments usually larger than 2 mm in diameter. Conglomerate rock forms where sediments are deposited, such as at the mouths of rivers and along beaches. Individual rock fragments can be seen in conglomerate rock. These rock fragments are usually cemented together by tiny mineral particles that form what is called *a clastic matrix*.

Breccia is a type of clastic rock composed of sharp-cornered, angular fragments larger than 2 mm in diameter that are cemented together with carbonate, silica, or silt material. Breccia often forms at the base of a steep cliff where rockslides have occurred.

Sandstone is a clastic rock composed of rounded, sand-sized grains usually between 0.063 mm and 2 mm in diameter. This clastic rock is the second most common sedimentary rock. It comprises 10%–20% of the sedimentary rock in the earth's crust. Sandstone has many pores through which water can easily move. One of the most common minerals in sandstone is quartz, which can comprise 90% of the rock.

The White Hoodoos near Wahweap Creek in Utah's Grand Staircase-Escalante National Monument are sandstone.

Shale is a clastic rock that forms in flat layers composed of silt- and clay-sized grains smaller than 0.004 mm in diameter. These layers are brittle and can be easily broken apart into flat pieces. Many of the particles are so small that they are barely visible without a microscope. Some geologists chew the sediments to estimate the size of their particles. (Silt is gritty, and clay is smooth.) Shale is the most abundant sedimentary rock, accounting for roughly 70% of sedimentary rock. These clastic rocks are often found with layers of sandstone or limestone. They typically form in environments where mud, silts, and other sediments were deposited by gentle transporting water currents. These sediments are then compacted in areas such as the ocean floor, basins of shallow seas, and river floodplains.

Chemical sedimentary rock is divided into two groups: allochemicals and orthochemicals. Examples of allochemicals include some limestone and chert. Examples of orthochemicals include bedded deposits of halite, gypsum, anhydrite, and banded iron formations. These sedimentary rocks do not form from separate rock pieces. They are composed of minerals that were once dissolved in water. Their structure is made up of interlocking crystals that result in a small, fine grain. As the water evaporates, the minerals that are left behind build up into rock masses. For example, some chemical sedimentary rock forms when dissolved salts in a body of water are deposited and the water evaporates away. Rock salt and gypsum are two examples of chemical sedimentary rock.

Carbonate sedimentary rock is composed of organic materials from decaying organisms. Coal, for example, is an organic sedimentary rock made of carbon from ancient plant remains. Other carbonate sedimentary rock is composed of the skeletal remains of marine creatures. Given that the skeletons are mineral and not technically organic, they are sometimes termed *biochemical*. An example of a biochemical rock is limestone, which forms from the mineral calcite. Limestone deposits often develop from the shells of clams, plankton, and other aquatic

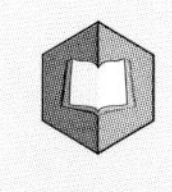

BIBLE CONNECTION

The Importance of Salt

Salt is mentioned in at least 36 places in the Bible. It was crucial in ancient cultures as a seasoning, preservative, disinfectant, component of ceremonial offerings, or as a unit of exchange. Salt was a necessity of life, both literally and metaphorically. In Matthew 5, Jesus uses salt as a metaphor, suggesting the children of God should preserve themselves from impurities just as salt preserves food.

FYI

Too Much Salt?

The Dead Sea in Israel is highly concentrated with various salts that allow individuals to easily float. On the western shore near Ein Gedi, one can find pebbles cemented with halite.

Dead Sea Composition

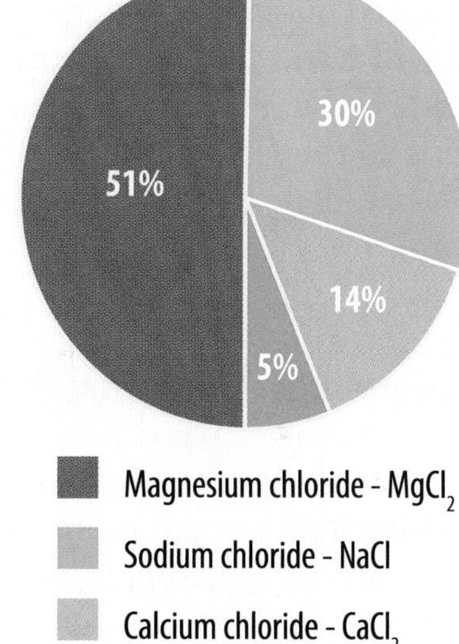

- Magnesium chloride - $MgCl_2$
- Sodium chloride - NaCl
- Calcium chloride - $CaCl_2$
- Potassium chloride - KCl

Composition of Most Oceans and Seas

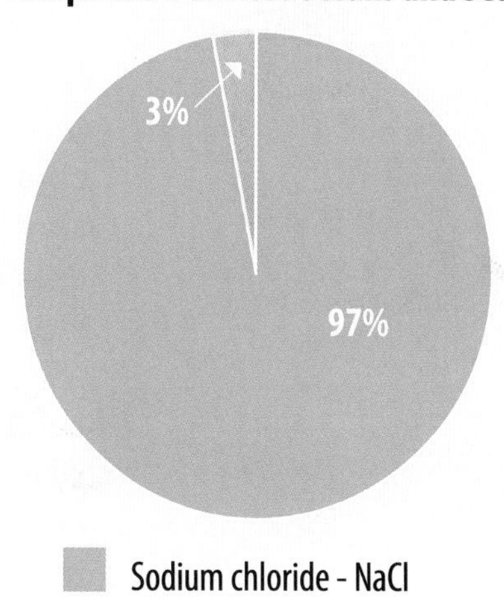

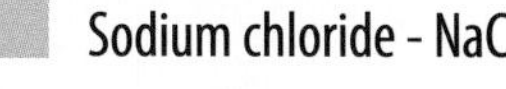
Sodium chloride - NaCl

Other components

CAREER

Sedimentologist

Sedimentologists are a specific group of geologists who study sedimentary rock and how it forms. They study the origin and deposition of sediments and their conversion to sedimentary rock. Sedimentologists look at sediment cores to determine how the process of sedimentation produces rocks that are in the process of forming at the bottom of oceans, deltas, and lakes. They are often involved in searching for and finding oil, natural gas, and economically important minerals.

creatures. Chalk is a fine-grained limestone made of microscopic shells, fragments of larger shells, and calcite. It is soft enough to write with because chalk particles are tiny and rather loosely packed.

Some limestone is created entirely by chemical processes instead of organic processes. For example, as rainwater lands on the earth, it has the opportunity to enter caves through the cracks in rocks. The rainwater will then pass through organic material and incorporate carbon dioxide gas along the way, creating carbonic acid. This weak acid passes through joints and cracks in limestone. The mineral calcite is dissolved from the limestone rock. This process is what forms a cave. When the water that holds the dissolved rock is exposed to the air in the cave, it releases the carbon dioxide gas, much like a fizzy drink does when it is first opened. As the carbon dioxide is released, calcite is redeposited on cave walls, ceilings, and floors. This redeposited mineral will build up after countless water drops complete the chemical process, eventually forming a stalactite. If the water that drops to the floor of the cave still contains some dissolved calcite, it can deposit more dissolved calcite there, forming a stalagmite.

By analyzing and interpreting the sedimentary rock record, scientists attempt to date and document many of the significant events that have occurred in Earth's history. This record provides information on ancient geography. A map of the distribution of sediments that formed in shallow oceans bordering rising mountains or in deep, subsiding ocean trenches will indicate past relationships between seas and landmasses. An accurate interpretation allows scientists to form conclusions about the evolution of mountain systems, continental blocks, and ocean basins. Some scientists also attempt to draw conclusions about the origin and evolution of the atmosphere and hydrosphere. Other scientists examine the sedimentary rock record containing fossils of once-living creatures in an attempt to document the theory of evolutionary advancement from simple to complex organisms in the plant and animal kingdoms.

A west Texas oil pumpjack

It is also important to understand the economic significance of sedimentary rock. For example, sedimentary rock essentially contains the world's entire supply of oil and natural gas, coal, phosphates, salt deposits, groundwater, and other natural resources. As good stewards, humanity is responsible for taking care of and preserving the many gifts God has entrusted to people.

LESSON REVIEW

1. How does compaction and cementation form layers of rock?
2. What are the three types of sedimentary rock?
3. How are the three types of sedimentary rock formed?
4. Would it be more likely to find fossils in an igneous rock or a sedimentary rock? Why?
5. Describe the major types of clastic sedimentary rock.
6. Assume that the volume of a layer of mud will decrease by 40% during deposition and compaction. If the original sediment layer is 25 cm thick, what will be the thickness of the shale layer after compaction?

Mount Sodom salt cave near the Dead Sea in Israel

1.3.3 *Metamorphic Rock*

OBJECTIVES

- Identify metamorphic rock and discuss how it forms.
- Identify the agents of change in the process of metamorphism.
- Discuss features and examples of two categories of metamorphic rock.
- Compare and contrast the different types of metamorphism.

VOCABULARY

- **contact metamorphism** metamorphism that occurs when the heat of magma comes in contact with existing rocks
- **dynamic metamorphism** metamorphism that is produced by mechanical force
- **foliated structure** a rock structure with visible layers or bands aligned in planes
- **metamorphic rock** a rock formed when the structure and mineral composition of existing rocks change because of heat, pressure, or chemical reactions
- **metamorphism** the process of change in the structure and mineral composition of a rock
- (*continued on next page*)

Rocks seem permanent and indestructible. Perhaps there is a boulder near your house or school that you see every day, and it never seems to change. We often use the word *rock* to describe something that is unchanging. However, God created a dynamic world where even rocks can change over time.

If you were a scientist and you decided to measure the pressure and temperature of the layers of the earth, you would find that both the pressure and temperature increase the closer you get to the center of the earth. At some point, the temperature and pressure reach high enough levels for rocks to melt and become magma. However, before reaching this point, there is a region where temperature and pressure are at high levels, but not so high that rocks will melt. When rocks are exposed to these conditions, their texture, mineral composition, or chemical composition can be affected. If one of these changes occurs, a new rock is formed. These new rocks have undergone **metamorphism**, which is the process of change in the structure and mineral composition of a rock.

The products of metamorphism are **metamorphic rock**, rocks formed when the structure and mineral composition of existing rocks change because of heat, pressure, or chemical reactions. During metamorphism, a rock changes form, but it remains solid. Metamorphic rock can form from any type of rock. The chemical and physical properties of the new rock are usually very different from those of the old rock.

Rocks within the earth's crust can be changed by three main types of metamorphism: contact, regional, or dynamic. **Dynamic metamorphism** is produced by mechanical forces. Direct pressure is the primary cause of this type of metamorphism. One example of dynamic metamorphism is the mineralogical changes

Metamorphic Rock

Gneiss—foliated structure

Pink quartzite—nonfoliated structure

that occur along the flat surface between two pieces of land that have shifted during an earthquake. **Contact metamorphism** occurs when the heat of magma, such as an igneous intrusion, comes in contact with existing rocks. This process produces a local effect, only changing the rocks that are near or touching the magma. In contrast, **regional metamorphism** occurs when large regions of the earth's crust are affected by high temperatures and high pressures. Regional metamorphism changes minerals and rock types and is often accompanied by folding and rock layer deformation in the area.

Regional metamorphism forms most metamorphic rock. It is not uncommon to find rocks formed through contact metamorphism near regional metamorphic rock. This connection becomes evident when observing any volcanic activity that accompanies plate movements. As the magma that is produced by the volcano comes in contact with rocks and changes them through contact metamorphism, the movement of tectonic plates can also affect a large region of the earth's crust, resulting in regional metamorphism. By studying how a rock metamorphoses, scientists can interpret the conditions inside the earth's crust.

VOCABULARY

- (*continued from previous page*)
- **nonfoliated structure** a rock structure with no visible layers or bands
- **regional metamorphism** metamorphism that occurs when large regions of the earth's crust are affected by high temperatures and pressures

Contact and Regional Metamorphism

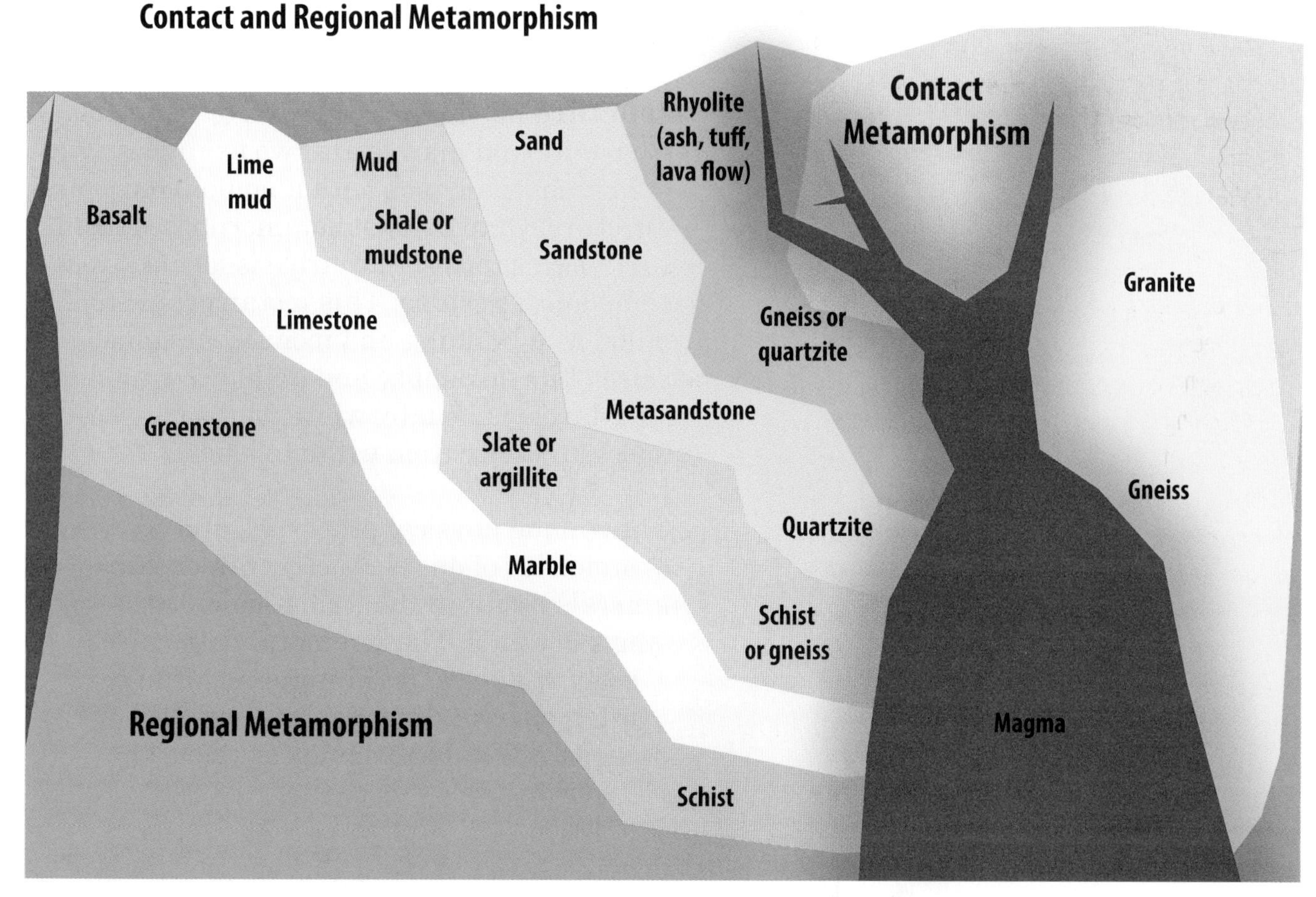

Garnet is a porphyroblast.

There are different grades of metamorphism. Lower temperatures and lower pressures produce a low grade of metamorphism. Higher temperatures and higher pressures produce a high grade of metamorphism. There is also an intermediate grade of metamorphism with varying temperatures and pressures.

Whether metamorphic rocks are formed by dynamic, contact, or regional metamorphism, the result is that the mineral crystals in the original rocks are converted and rearranged into new minerals that are stable under new temperature and pressure conditions. These new rocks will develop one of two basic structures—foliated or nonfoliated. Metamorphic rock with a **foliated structure** has visible layers or bands aligned in planes, similar to the pages in a book. Slate, schist, and gneiss are three common foliated metamorphic rocks.

How does foliation occur? Foliation is the product of pressure that has been applied from opposite directions. The foliation develops perpendicular to the pressure direction. By analyzing metamorphic structures and mineral composition, geologists are able to identify metamorphic rock.

Metamorphic rock with a **nonfoliated structure** has no visible layers or bands. Quartzite and marble are two examples of metamorphic rock with a nonfoliated structure. Quartzite is metamorphosed from quartz-rich sandstone. Marble is formed from limestone and dolostone. This metamorphic rock is valued as a building and monument stone because of its durability and ability to transmit light. Marble is usually white, but it may be almost any color from white to black.

The unique physical properties and symmetries of one class of metamorphic minerals result in the formation of large single crystals. These minerals are called *porphyroblasts*. It is interesting that other surrounding crystals may still remain small. A popular example of a porphyroblast is garnet.

Michelangelo's statue of Moses was chiseled from marble.

Many of the commercial products that are used throughout the world are the result of metamorphism of igneous and sedimentary rock. Three such products include talc and asbestos, which are minerals, and coal. The extreme softness of talc has been utilized in cosmetic powder products, in lubricants, and in textured paints. Asbestos easily separates into long, flexible fibers and has the useful property of being resistant to the effects of heat and fire. It has been used in fireproofing and insulating materials. Asbestos was also widely used in construction materials until in the 1970s it was discovered that asbestos poses a serious health risk. Regulatory agencies in the United States and abroad began placing tight restrictions on the use and exposure of asbestos. The metamorphism of coal, a sedimentary rock, may produce graphite, which is the main ingredient of the lead in pencils. Take time to observe the various uses of metamorphic rock in your area.

Shale is a sedimentary rock that can change into at least four different metamorphic rocks.

LESSON REVIEW

1. What is metamorphic rock?
2. How does heat change rocks?
3. How does pressure change rocks?
4. How are foliated and nonfoliated structures different? Name examples of each.
5. Compare and contrast the three types of metamorphism.

Coal, a sedimentary rock, may sometimes metamorphose to produce graphite, the main ingredient of "lead" in pencils.

1.3.4 *The Rock Cycle*

OBJECTIVES

- Demonstrate an understanding of the process that forms the basic substances involved in the rock cycle.
- Label a diagram of the rock cycle.
- Use the rock cycle to explain how rocks are classified.

VOCABULARY

- **rock cycle** the process by which one rock type changes into another

Earlier in the chapter, you learned rocks are classified according to how they are formed. Igneous rock forms when hot magma cools. Sedimentary rock forms from sediments that have been compacted and cemented together. Metamorphic rock is formed deep in the earth's crust where extreme pressure, temperature, and chemical reactions change them into different rocks. Any of these types of rocks can be changed into the other two types. The process by which one rock type changes into another is called the **rock cycle**.

The rock cycle begins with the cooling of magma to form igneous rock. Once a mass of igneous rock is exposed to the earth's surface, it begins to break down into smaller fragments. Rain, snow, sleet, and hail pound the rocks and wash away tiny fragments of the rock. The sun's heat cracks rocks open, and the freezing of water and the thawing of ice widens the cracks and breaks large rocks into smaller fragments. Pounding surf polishes jagged rocks first into smooth stones and then into small pebbles and sand. Even organisms can wear away rocks. The acidic excretions of lichen, for example, dissolve small depressions in boulders to open up spaces for fungus to grow. Over thousands of years, water and atmospheric forces erode igneous rock into small rock particles called *sediments*.

If rocks are continuously weathering, why are sediments not piled up everywhere? Wind, rivers, streams, and even glaciers carry sediments for hundreds of kilometers and deposit them in beds. These sediment layers build up over time, and the top layers put tremendous pressure on the bottom layers. The processes of compaction and cementation turn the sediments into sedimentary rocks.

Large rocks breaking apart through the process of freezing water and thawing ice

Sedimentary rock exposed to extreme pressure, heat, or chemical processes beneath the earth's surface can be transformed into metamorphic rock. The types of metamorphic rock formed depends on the amount of heat and pressure to which the rocks are exposed. If the heat and pressure become more intense, the metamorphic rock melts and reforms into magma. This magma can then cool and form igneous rock, starting the rock cycle over again. Most of the rocks in the earth's crust have probably passed through the rock cycle many times.

Rocks do not always complete the entire rock cycle. For example, igneous rock never exposed to the weather at the earth's surface will not be eroded into sediments. Likewise, not all rocks complete the cycle in a uniform order. Entire steps may be omitted. For example, igneous rock exposed to heat and pressure may change directly into metamorphic rock without first converting to sedimentary rock. Both igneous and sedimentary rock may melt into magma without first becoming metamorphic rock. The rock cycle is continually changing and remaking rocks.

Igneous intrusion

LESSON REVIEW

1. To what type of rock can all rock be traced? Why?
2. Explain the basic processes in the rock cycle.
3. What are the five basic substances involved in the rock cycle?
4. Use the rock cycle to explain how rocks are classified.

The Rock Cycle

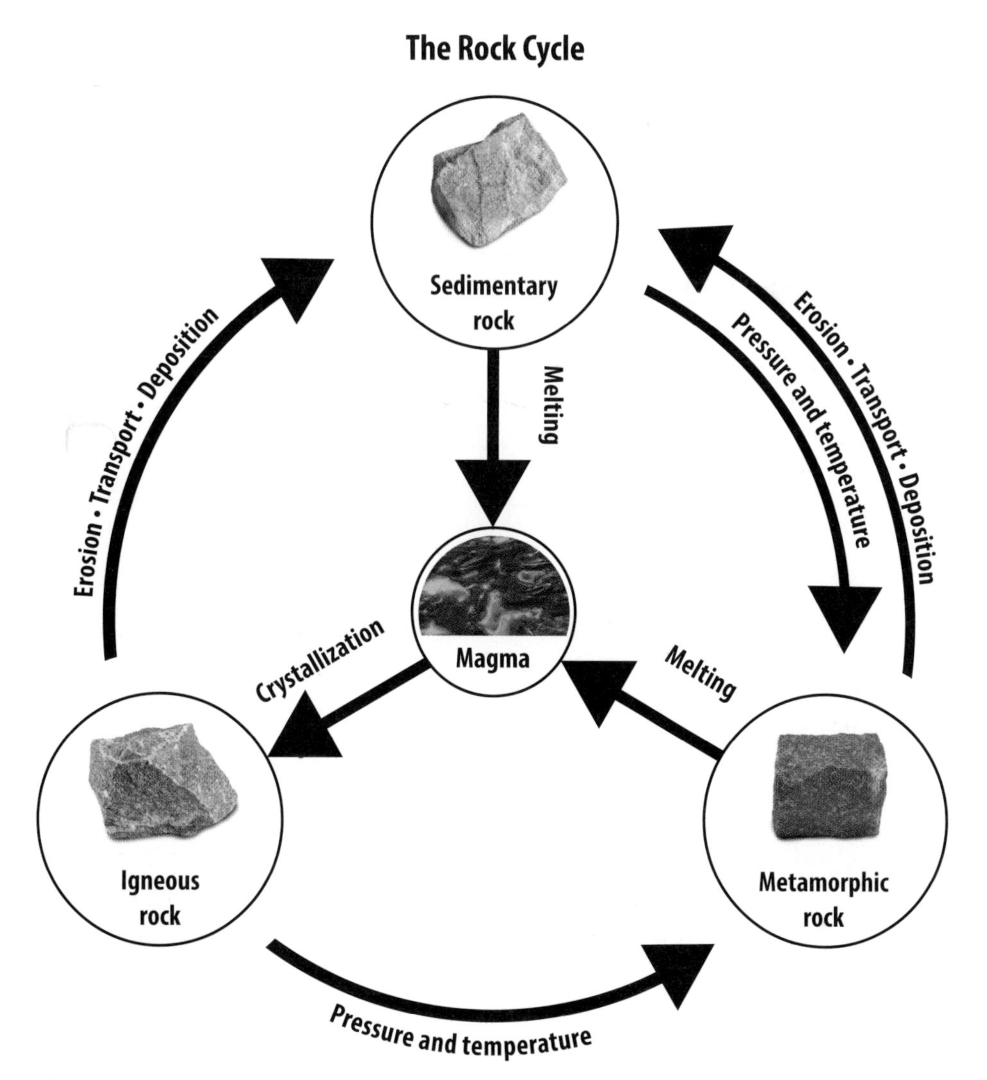

1.4.1 *Core*

OBJECTIVES

- Explain how seismic waves are used to determine the features of the core.
- Describe the two parts of the earth's core.
- Explain how the core generates a magnetic field.
- Describe the benefits of the magnetic field around the earth.

VOCABULARY

- **core** the central portion of the earth
- **inner core** the solid center of the earth
- **magnetosphere** the area around the earth that is affected by the earth's magnetic field
- **outer core** the liquid layer of the earth's core that surrounds the inner core
- **P wave** the fastest seismic wave, which travels through solids, liquids, and gases
- **S wave** the seismic wave that travels only through solids
- **seismic wave** a wave of energy that travels through the earth

God carefully planned the creation of the earth, even its deepest parts. He designed the deep layers to sustain the rest of His earthly creation. In Psalm 95:4, the psalmist says that the depths of the earth are in the Creator's hand.

Four hundred years ago, Galileo used a telescope to view the planets, which are millions of kilometers away, but geologists can only explore short distances into the earth. The world's deepest mine is only 3.9 km deep, and no drill has bored more than 12 km into the earth. Earth scientists have never come close to reaching the center of the earth.

Throughout history, people could only guess what the inside of the earth was like. In 1864, Jules Verne wrote an imaginative description of the earth's layers in his book *Journey to the Center of the Earth*. Verne described vast forests of giant mushrooms and great seas crawling with terrifying creatures. Since that time geologists have learned that the center of the earth is very different from what Jules Verne imagined.

During the 1970s, Russian scientists began drilling in the Kola Peninsula. After 20 years, they were able to penetrate the crust to 12 km. Although this may appear to be a great feat, the earth

Kola Peninsula drilling site

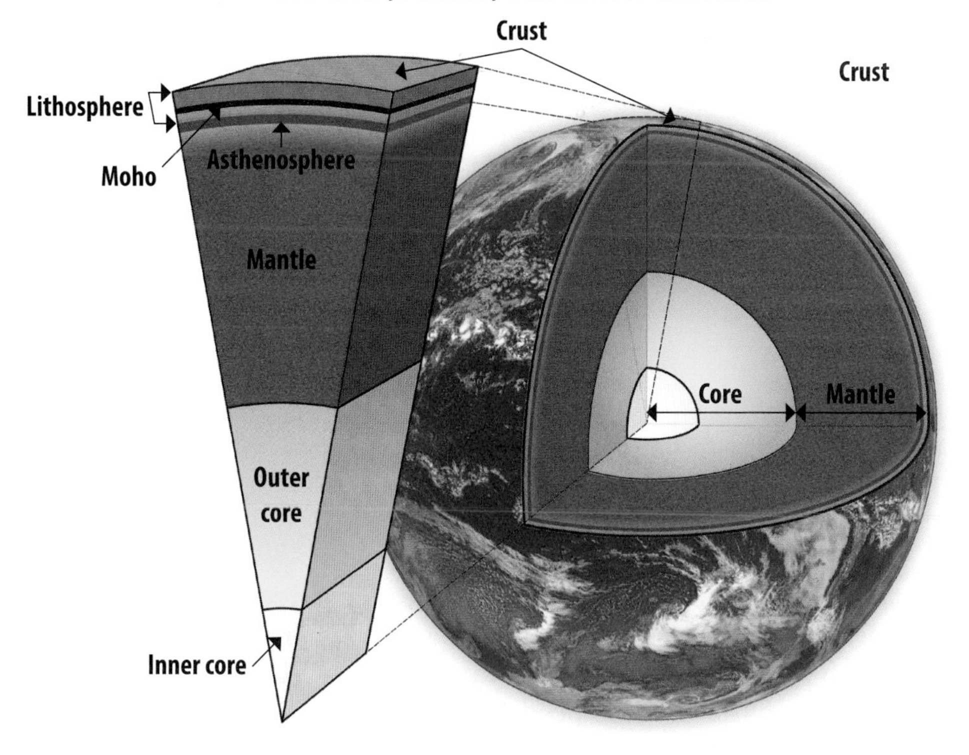

goes much deeper and can be divided into three major sections: the core, the mantle and the crust.

The **core** is the central portion of the earth. The diameter of the core is slightly larger than the diameter of the planet Mars, which is 6,787 km. The inside of this core is nearly as hot as the surface of the sun. Also, Earth's core is not a perfect sphere. Scientists have found evidence that the core has huge peaks that poke up into the mantle and that parts of the mantle carve deep valleys into the core.

Even though geologists have not drilled directly to the core, they have gathered information about the core by measuring the speed and behavior of **seismic waves** as they travel through the earth. Seismic waves are generated by a movement in the earth. There are two types of seismic waves: surface waves and body waves. **P waves** and **S waves** are body waves that carry energy from a movement in the earth through the interior of the earth. P and S waves behave very differently when they travel through a solid, liquid, or gas. P waves (primary seismic waves) are the fastest seismic waves. They travel through solids, liquids, and gases. S waves (secondary seismic waves) travel only through solids. The velocity of both types of waves is affected by the density and composition of the materials they go through. Using

TRY THIS

Pressure Practice

The inner core is solid and not liquid because the pressure of the earth at this depth counteracts the extreme temperature. To see how this could happen, take two large, soft marshmallows; leave the first one alone and place a book on top of the second one. Remove the book and compare the marshmallows. Now, place two books on top of the second marshmallow. Compare. Continue to add weight until you have a marshmallow that is completely solid. How much pressure did it take to solidify the marshmallow? How are the marshmallows like the earth's core? How are they different?

data gathered from observing the speed and behavior of seismic waves, scientists have established that Earth has both an inner and an outer core.

The **inner core** is the solid center of the earth. Scientists believe it is made of an iron-nickel alloy. Scientists know the inner core is solid because P waves speed up when they reach this layer. It may seem odd that the core is solid even though it is very hot. However, the pressure of the other layers is so great that the metal atoms in the inner core cannot move into a liquid state.

The **outer core** is the liquid layer of the earth's core surrounding the inner core. The outer core probably consists of iron and sulfur. Scientists know that the outer layer is liquid because it cannot transmit or conduct S waves.

Even though the earth's core is buried so deep, God gave it an important role. The heat inside the core keeps currents of molten iron and other metals constantly flowing throughout the outer core. This process produces electric currents, which in turn create magnetic fields (regions where magnetic forces

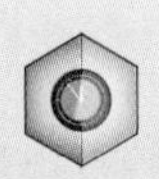

HISTORY

Quest to Drill Into Earth's Mantle

In the spring of 1961, geologists began drilling into the seafloor off the Pacific coast of Baja California. The expedition intended to penetrate the crust and reach the underlying mantle. Soon after the work began, President John F. Kennedy launched the race to the moon. By the end of 1972, several Apollo missions had landed on the moon and had brought back more than 363 kg of moon rocks and soil. The expedition to the earth's mantle ended as funding was diverted away from the drilling to the space program. Since then, more expeditions have tried to reach the mantle, but it is still beyond the reach of current technology and scientific expertise.

Seismic Waves

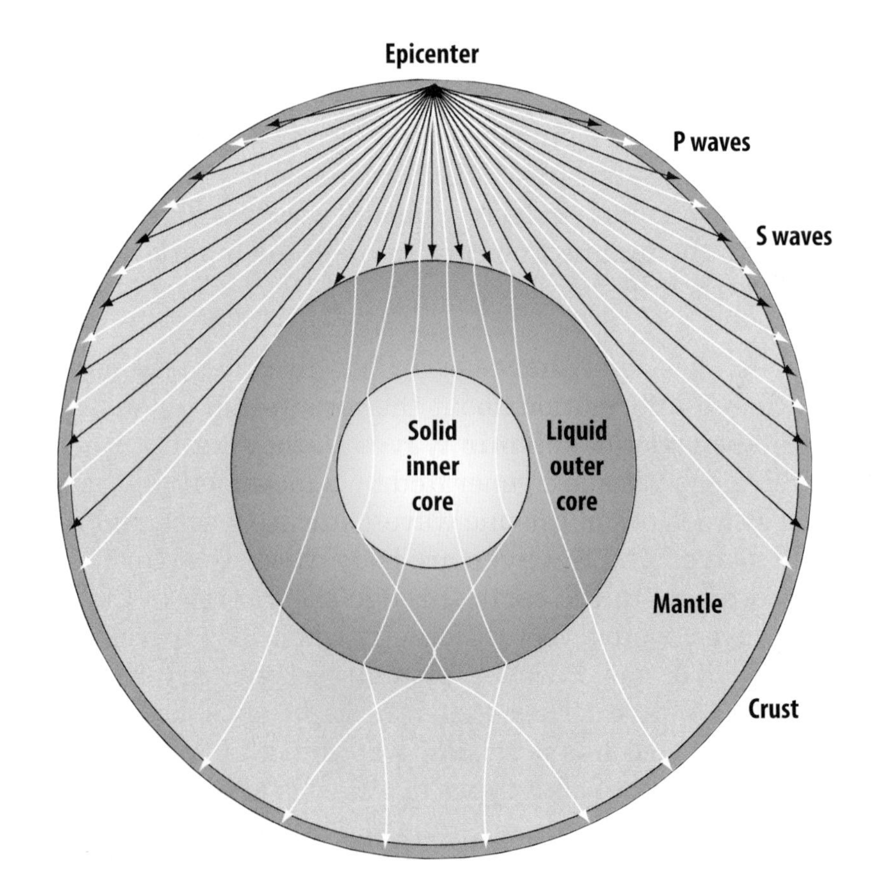

Core Knowledge

	Thickness (Radius)	% of Earth's Volume	% of Earth's Mass	Density (g/cm^3)	Temperature
Inner Core	1,220 km	<1%	2%	12.8–13.1	5,000°C–7,000°C
Outer Core	2,266 km	15%	30%	9.9–12.2	3,700°C–6,700°C
Total Core		15%	32%		

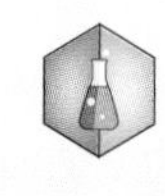

TRY THIS

A Magnetic Core
Cut off the top half of a foam cup. Place the bottom half upside-down on an 11" × 17" piece of cardboard. Sprinkle a thin, even layer of iron filings around the cup. Place a bar magnet on a table and carefully lower the cardboard and filings above the magnet until the cup is about a centimeter from the magnet. Tap the cardboard very gently, making the filings fall into a pattern. The earth's core is a magnet. How might this affect the earth and the area surrounding it? What might the magnetic field around the earth look like?

can be observed)—much like electricity flowing through copper wires creates a magnetic field around the wires. The magnetic fields cause the earth to act as a giant magnet. The entire earth creates an enormous magnetic field called the **magnetosphere**.

The magnetosphere has many important functions. It acts to shield the earth from solar winds and makes the use of a compass possible. The magnetic poles of the earth also help form the aurora borealis, or northern lights, which are beautiful displays of light and color sometimes seen in the Arctic night sky.

LESSON REVIEW

1. How are seismic waves used to determine the composition and features of the core?
2. What are the basic characteristics of the two parts of the earth's core?
3. How does the core generate a magnetic field?
4. What benefits result from the magnetic field around the earth?

Aurora borealis

1.4.2 *Mantle*

OBJECTIVES

- Describe the separate sections of the mantle, including the asthenosphere.
- Explain what convection currents are and how they are created.
- Compare and contrast direct observations with indirect observations.

VOCABULARY

- **asthenosphere** the layer of the upper mantle composed of low-density rock material that is semiplastic
- **convection current** the circular movement of heated materials to a cooler area and cooled materials to a warmer area
- **lithosphere** the outermost, rigid layer of the earth composed of the stiff upper layer of the mantle and the crust
- **mantle** the portion of the earth's interior extending from the outer core to the bottom of the crust
- **Moho** the boundary between the mantle and the crust

The **mantle** is the portion of the earth's interior that extends from the outer core to the bottom of the crust. It accounts for most of the earth's volume and mass. Earth's mantle is made of very hot rock. You would not be able to live if the earth's crust lay directly on top of the hot core. In fact, the land beneath your feet would melt! The mantle protects you from the core's intense heat. In later chapters, you will learn how the mantle's forces can give rise to continental drift, earthquakes, and volcanic eruptions.

The rock in the mantle has the property of plasticity, or flexibility. Plasticity means that the rock can flow or change shape. The rock flows at different rates, depending on its composition and temperature. Just as temperature differences in the atmosphere cause air to move and produce wind, the heat differences in the mantle's magma cause convection currents. A **convection current** is the circular movement of heated materials to a cooler area and cooled materials to a warmer area. As hotter fluid near the core moves up toward the crust, it expands, and the cooler rock near the surface sinks toward the core as it condenses. This cycle happens continuously.

The mantle is very complex, so scientists have divided it into separate sections to make it easier to study and to discuss. There is a lower mantle, a transition zone, and an upper mantle. All three parts of the mantle are formed with the same minerals rich in the elements iron, magnesium, silicon, and oxygen. But the density and temperature of the mantle sections change. The

Convection Currents in the Mantle

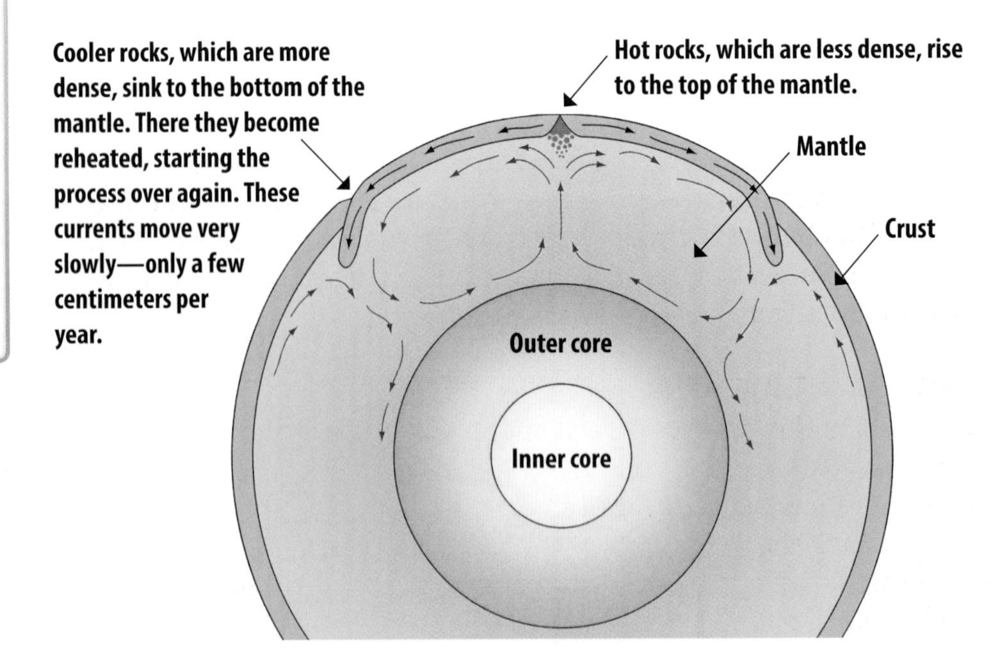

Cooler rocks, which are more dense, sink to the bottom of the mantle. There they become reheated, starting the process over again. These currents move very slowly—only a few centimeters per year.
Hot rocks, which are less dense, rise to the top of the mantle.
Mantle
Crust
Outer core
Inner core

Mantle Measurement

- Thickness: 2,900 km
- Volume: 83% of Earth's volume
- Mass: 67% of Earth's mass
- Temperature: 1,000°C–3,700°C
- Density: 3.4–5.6 g/cm^3

greater the depth in the mantle, the greater the density and temperature become.

The lower mantle is hot, flexible, and under great pressure. In the transition zone, the rock becomes less flexible. The upper mantle is solid rock except for the **asthenosphere**, a semisolid layer near the earth's crust. This layer of the upper mantle is composed of low-density rock material that is semiplastic, like putty. This region flows very easily and slowly—at about the speed that your fingernails grow. The **lithosphere**, the outermost, rigid layer of the earth, is the stiff upper layer of the mantle and the crust. It rides on the asthenosphere.

Geologists have spent decades attempting to make direct observations of the earth by drilling deep into the crust to reach the mantle. Scientists use many types of observations, but the preferred method is direct observation, where the object being studied can actually be seen and perceived with all five senses. Until the mantle is actually reached, scientists must rely on indirect observations of the mantle.

In October of 1909, Croatian scientist Andrija Mohorovicic recorded seismic waves at several different stations during an earthquake. From these indirect observations, Mohorovicic concluded that the unexpected changes in the velocity of the seismic waves marked a boundary between the mantle and the crust. This boundary was named *the Mohorovicic discontinuity*, or the **Moho** for short. Later studies using more sophisticated instruments confirmed his findings.

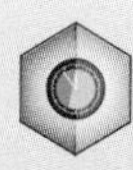

HISTORY

Drilling Continues

Between 2002 and 2011, several holes were drilled in the eastern Pacific. Scientists believed they reached rock just above the Moho, but they were unable to drill deeper. The SloMo project began drilling through the thinner crust in the Indian Ocean in an attempt to reach the mantle and possibly the Moho. Several setbacks slowed the project: the team got started late because supplies were not ready, a drill bit was broken, and a crew member had to be taken to shore for medical reasons. A week later, the crew and team of the ship, *JOIDES Revolution*, returned to the site to restart drilling. By January of 2016, drilling had reached a depth of 710 m, almost 610 m shy of the goal. However, the next phase of the project was planned and researchers believe they would achieve their goal of reaching the mantle in five years.

LESSON REVIEW

1. How are the three layers of the mantle alike? How are they different?
2. What is the asthenosphere?
3. What are convection currents and what causes them?
4. Compare and contrast direct observations with indirect observations.

Ophiolite rocks are thought to form in the upper mantle.

1.4.3 *Crust*

OBJECTIVES

- Describe the features of the earth's crust.
- Compare and contrast the continental crust with the oceanic crust.

VOCABULARY

- **continental crust** the crust on which the continents rest
- **crust** the thin, hard outer layer of the earth
- **oceanic crust** the crust beneath the oceans

FYI

Crust Counts

- Thickness: 6 km (oceanic), 40 km (continental)
- Volume: <1%
- Mass: <1%
- Temperature: 0°C–400°C
- Density: 3 g/cm^3 (oceanic), 2.7 g/cm^3 (continental)

The crust of the earth is the only layer that can actually be observed. The **crust** is the thin, hard outer layer of the earth. It is home to all life on Earth, and it has a great variety of features. A view from an airplane gives you the opportunity to see much of the varied scenery over the crust's different regions. Some regions are thick with trees. Other regions have farmland, deserts, or mountains. Flying over a river system gives a good outline of the design of watersheds, and flying over the ocean can make one feel very small indeed. Consider the vastness of the earth's continents. The earth's surface is truly a beautiful mosaic.

All of these wonderful features lie on the crust. This thin layer of rock is covered with soil, sediment, or water in many places. The crust is a very complex and varied layer, partly because of the action of the mantle that lies underneath. The hot mantle beneath the crust constructs and destroys the ocean floor, builds and splits continents, and rearranges land masses into towering mountain chains.

The crust is by far Earth's thinnest layer. The depth of the crust ranges from about 6–40 km. The crust is too thick in most places for drills to reach the mantle, however. The density of the crust varies depending on the individual rocks found in different locations. The temperature of the crust at Earth's surface is cool, but it is very hot near the mantle. Without this temperature difference, most life on Earth would cook.

Scientists divide the crust into two categories: continental and oceanic. **Continental crust** is the crust on which the continents rest. The continental crust has a more complex rock structure than the oceanic crust. Although there are many types of

Highest point on the earth: Mount Everest at 8,850 m in the Himalayan mountain range in both Nepal and Tibet

minerals and rock in the continental crust, granite is the most common component. The continents have an average height of 840 m above sea level. The highest point on the earth is Mount Everest at 8,850 m above sea level, and the lowest point is the Dead Sea at 420 m below sea level.

The continental crust can be further divided into three regions according to composition and formation: shields, fold belts, and sedimentary basins. Shields are large, stable land masses made of crystalline rocks. Shields occur on every continent and form vast plains. The high plateaus in Africa and Asia are lifted portions of these formations. Fold belts are folded rocks forming young mountains such as the Alps, Himalayas, Andes, and the North American Cordillera. Sedimentary basins are broad, deep depressions filled with sedimentary rock. Sedimentary basins form in shallow seas and other low spots on the continents.

The **oceanic crust** is the crust beneath the oceans. Basalt is the primary rock in the oceanic crust, which is thinner and denser than the continental crust. The oceanic crust sinks farther into the mantle than the continental crust, forming the basins for oceans. It is made of several layers and is overlaid by sediments that accumulate from continental erosion. These sediments include mud, sand, and even the remains of dead microorganisms. The average thickness of the sediment bed in the ocean is about 450 m.

The first layer of the oceanic crust, which is about 500 m thick, consists primarily of basalt-based lavas. The cooled lava can create pillow lavas, which are formations that look like large pillows, or sheet flows, which look like large sheets. In the second layer, the basalt forms sheeted dikes, or passages for lava to flow. The dike portion of this layer is about 1 km in thickness.

FYI

The Eighth Continent
Scientists have been intrigued with the prospect of an eighth continent since 1995. Sitting just below New Zealand is a large land mass that scientists have named *Zealandia*. The majority of the area is underwater and measures five million square kilometers. More focus has been placed on this area because it has a definite boundary, unique geology, and a thicker crust compared to the surrounding ocean floor. This discovery is important as scientists continue to explore continental crust placement and movement.

The lowest point on the earth is the Dead Sea at 420 m below sea level.

TRY THIS

"Eureka"

The Ancient Greek scientist Archimedes was once asked to determine whether someone had stolen the king's crown and replaced it with a fake. Archimedes knew he could not melt the crown to see whether it was pure gold, but he had to find its true composition. History tells us that Archimedes came up with the solution as he was bathing. He saw the bath water rise as he got in the tub. "Eureka!" he exclaimed as he ran down the street. Archimedes realized that a solid placed in water will displace its own volume of water. Use Archimedes' principle to determine the volume and ultimately the density of the main components of the continental crust and the oceanic crust. Measure the volume of a sample of basalt and a sample of granite using a graduated cylinder and water. Determine the mass of each by using a scale. Calculate the density of each rock sample using the formula: density = mass/volume. Record the results and observations about the properties of each rock. How are the samples similar? How are they different? How do you think these differences affect the earth's crust?

The third layer of the oceanic crust is composed of dikes made of gabbro, which is basalt rock with coarse mineral grains. This portion is about 4.5 km thick.

Most people think of the ocean floor as a place without interesting features, probably because people cannot see the ocean floor. But the oceanic crust is a work of art. Its features look much like the features of the continental crust. Undersea ridges form extended mountain ranges—in fact, the mid-ocean ridge in the Atlantic Ocean is perhaps the earth's single most dramatic feature. Individual volcanic mountains called *seamounts* rise from the ocean floor. The tallest mountain in the world begins on the ocean floor. The base of Mauna Kea is almost 6,000 m below sea level and the summit is about 4,000 m above. This makes the full height of Mauna Kea about 10,000 m!

Reynisdrangar, basalt sea stacks, in Iceland

The ocean floor has a flat region that extends hundreds of kilometers. Deep, steep valleys and ravines plunge into the oceanic crust. Submarine canyons in the ocean floor were cut by river water or shallow ocean currents flowing out to sea. The oceanic crust, like the continental crust, reveals God's creativity and love of variety.

LESSON REVIEW

1. Briefly describe the structure of the earth.
2. Describe the features of the earth's crust.
3. Even though the crust is thinner than the other layers, scientists have been unable to observe below it. Why?
4. Compare the continental and oceanic crusts.

UNIT 2

Geologic Changes

Chapter 1: *Weathering and Erosion*
Chapter 2: *Soil*

Vocabulary

abrasion
bedrock
carbonation
carbonization
channel
chemical weathering
deflation hollow
desiccation
drumlin
earthflow
erratic
fault
floodplain
fossil
geologic column
glacial drift
glacier
gully
horizon
humus
hydrolysis
ice wedging
index fossil
intrusion
landslide
law of superposition
mass wasting
mechanical weathering
moraine
mudflow
oxidation
petrifaction
pore space
regolith
rock pedestal
runoff
soil creep
soil profile
subsoil
till
topography
topsoil
trace fossil
unconformity

Key Ideas

- Systems, order, and organization
- Evidence, models, and explanation
- Change, constancy, and measurement
- Evolution and equilibrium
- Form and function
- Abilities necessary to do scientific inquiry
- Structure of the earth system
- Earth's history
- Energy in the earth system
- Geochemical cycles
- Origin and evolution of the earth system
- Abilities of technological design
- Understandings about science and technology
- Populations, resources, and environments
- Natural hazards
- Risks and benefits
- Science and technology in society
- Population growth
- Natural resources
- Environmental quality
- Natural and human induced hazards
- Science and technology in local, national, and global challenges
- Science as a human endeavor
- Nature of science
- History of science
- Nature of scientific knowledge

SCRIPTURE

Before the mountains were born or You brought forth the whole world, from everlasting to everlasting You are God.

Psalm 90:2

2.1.1 *Mechanical Weathering*

> **OBJECTIVES**
> - Identify and explain several processes of mechanical weathering.
> - Assess the effects that climate, rock type, exposed surface area, and topography have on mechanical weathering.
> - Apply concepts of mechanical weathering to technological designs.

> **VOCABULARY**
> - **ice wedging** the mechanical weathering process in which water in the cracks of rocks freezes and expands, widening the cracks
> - **mechanical weathering** the breaking down of rocks by physical processes
> - **topography** the surface features of a place or region

Some of Earth's features appear timeless. Mountains, cliffs, canyons, and valleys may look as though they have not changed for centuries. However, they are actually changing all the time. God uses tools such as wind, water, and chemical action to continuously shape the earth's surface. An example of how rocks change over time may be seen in stone monuments such as those used to mark graves or to commemorate important people, places, or events. New monuments have crisp inscriptions and sharp corners, but the lettering on old stone monuments is worn and smooth, and some may even be unreadable. This change is the result of weathering and erosion.

Weathering is the breaking down of rocks into smaller pieces by mechanical or chemical processes. Weathering works together with erosion to produce visible changes in the earth's surface. Erosion is the removal and transport of material by wind, water, or ice. Weathered material stays in one place, but eroded material moves.

Mechanical weathering, also known as *physical weathering*, is the breaking down of rocks by physical processes. Most of the weathering on monuments is mechanical weathering. The engraving is worn away, but the chemical makeup of the stone has not changed. Most mechanical weathering is caused by temperature extremes and the activities of living things, which is known as *biological weathering*. How fast weathering happens, known as its *rate*, is affected by the climate, the type of rock, the amount of exposed surface area, and the topography.

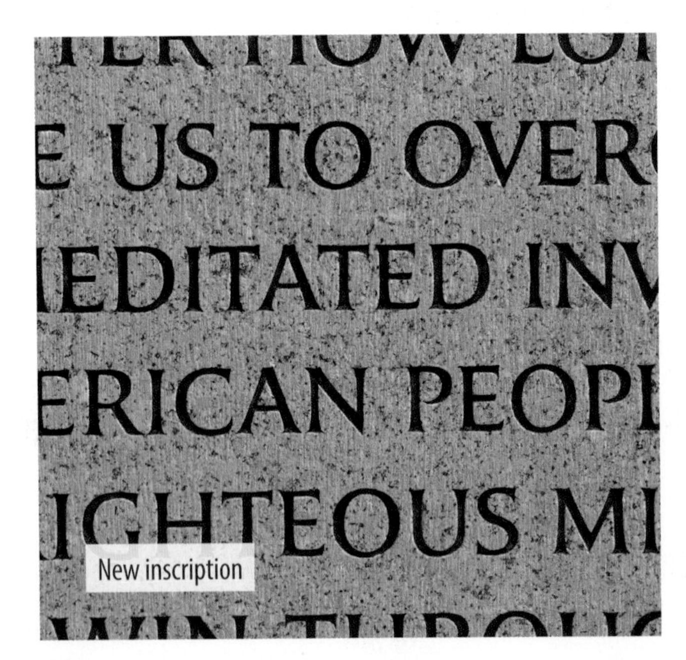

New inscription

Weathered inscription

Climate is probably the greatest factor in weathering. Ice wedging is common in climates that receive frequent precipitation and experience rapid temperature extremes. **Ice wedging** is the mechanical weathering process in which water freezes and expands in the cracks of rocks, widening the cracks. This process is common in mountainous regions during the spring and fall because temperatures can be warm during the day but drop below freezing at night. During the day, rainwater flows into cracks in the rocks and seeps into the rocks' pores. At night, the water freezes and expands. The pressure of the expanding ice is so great that it wedges the cracks apart. Through repeated thawing and freezing, the ice is wedged deeper into the rocks, widening the cracks. Over time ice wedging shatters the rock surfaces into angular fragments and blocks.

Hot, dry climates are free from ice wedging, but they still experience the mechanical weathering that comes from temperature differences. Even though deserts are often blistering hot during the day, temperatures can drop below freezing at night because the air has very little water vapor to hold in heat. The rocks expand in the heat and contract in the cold. This continuing cycle weakens natural cracks in the rocks, causing them to eventually split apart. Often, these splits separate surface layers from the layers underneath. When this process occurs on massive rock layers of granite or other hard rocks, the rocks weather into curved slabs in a process called *exfoliation*. Exfoliation is similar to peeling the layers off an onion.

Living things also contribute to mechanical weathering. Trees sometimes sink their roots into rocks. The roots follow cracks and crevices, splitting the rocks apart as the trees grow. Burrowing animals digging in the soil expose rocks, and some mollusks can

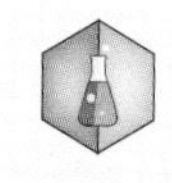

TRY THIS

Bean Power
Plant 2–4 lima bean seeds in about 2 cm of prepared plaster of paris in a small paper cup. Prepare a control cup of plaster of paris without bean seeds. Observe the cups for several days at the same time each day and sketch what you see. Create a hypothesis to explain the results.

Rock broken by repeated freezing and thawing

Exfoliated rock

even bore holes into rocks. This exposes new rock surfaces to the forces of weathering.

The type of rock, the rock's amount of exposed surface area, and topography affect how quickly a rock weathers in any climate. Certain rocks are softer than others. In general, sedimentary rocks are easily weathered, especially by mechanical processes. The particles in shale and sandstone are relatively loose and easily broken up into fragments of clay and sand. Igneous and metamorphic rocks are quite hard, so they weather more slowly than sedimentary rocks. Even after all of the sedimentary rock of a region has weathered or eroded away, igneous and metamorphic rocks often appear unchanged. The mineral in igneous and metamorphic rocks that is most resistant to weathering is quartz. Quartz often remains as tiny grains of sand after other minerals in a rock have eroded away.

The amount of rock that is exposed to the elements also determines the rate of weathering. The greater the exposed surface area, the greater the potential for weathering. Small rocks weather faster than large rocks, just as sugar grains dissolve faster than sugar cubes in hot tea. Surface area is

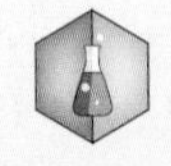

TRY THIS

Moving Mountains
Design an experiment to determine whether temperature changes can split rocks.

Roots can grow into cracks in rocks.

increased when cracks form or widen and when loose particles or soil erodes away.

Topography, the surface features of a place or region, also affects the rate of weathering. High elevation encourages weathering because of its greater temperature extremes. Also, gravity pulls weathered rock fragments from steep slopes, and the water from heavy rain helps gravity by washing away particles more rapidly. As particles are swept from the slopes of mountains, new rock is constantly exposed, speeding up the weathering processes.

Weathering and erosion affect structures people build as well as natural features. Architects and engineers have to take weathering factors into consideration as they choose building sites, select building materials, and design structures. They may need to reinforce a foundation, seal building stones, or improve drainage in order to prevent the erosion of a building site or a structure.

LESSON REVIEW

1. What is mechanical weathering?
2. How can water cause mechanical weathering?
3. Explain how climate affects weathering processes.
4. How do the following factors work together to affect the rate at which rock weathers: type of rock, exposed surface area, and topography?
5. What kinds of mechanical weathering might an architect need to consider when designing a house to be built on a forested mountain cliff?

Gravity erodes weathered rock from a cliff face.

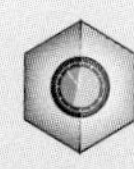

HISTORY

Measuring Weathering

Research on tombstone weathering has contributed to the general knowledge of weathering factors. In the late 1880s Sir Archibald Geikie of Edinburgh, Scotland, calculated the weathering rate for marble tombstones to be 8.5 mm per century. In the 1960s, professor E. M. Winkler measured a vein in a marble marker in Indiana and calculated the weathering rate for the marble surface to be 1.5 mm in 43 years. If all factors remained constant, Professor Winkler's calculations show marble weathering in that region to be 3.49 mm per century. Both of these studies were done in humid climates. A measurement taken in a dry climate showed a weathering rate of only 1 mm per century. The monuments on the Nile River in Egypt (a very arid climate) testify to the resistance of the granite there to weathering. In 1916, the American geologist D.C. Barton estimated a weathering rate of 1–2 mm every millennium for granite in dry climates. The greatest rate he calculated was only 0.5 mm per century.

2.1.2 Chemical Weathering

OBJECTIVES

- Identify and explain several agents of chemical weathering.
- Contrast the types of chemical weathering that involve water.
- Apply concepts of chemical weathering to technological designs.

VOCABULARY

- **carbonation** the process in which carbon dioxide from the atmosphere or soil dissolves in water to form carbonic acid
- **chemical weathering** the breaking down of rocks by chemical processes
- **hydrolysis** the breaking down of a substance by a chemical reaction with water
- **oxidation** a chemical change in which a substance combines with oxygen

Chemical weathering is the breaking down of rocks by chemical processes. Chemical reactions occur between the minerals in rocks and either water, carbon dioxide, oxygen, or acids. These reactions either break down or change the chemical structure of some of the minerals. The rate of chemical weathering is affected by many of the same factors as the rate of mechanical weathering. Certain rocks contain minerals that are more easily affected by chemical weathering. Rocks that have been broken up into fragments by mechanical weathering are more susceptible to chemical weathering because the smaller rock fragments have more exposed surface area. Rocks in warm climates are more susceptible to chemical weathering because high temperatures speed up chemical reactions.

Water is one of the primary agents of chemical weathering. Many people think of water as pure—not as something strong enough to be part of a chemical reaction. However, water weathers minerals in rocks in three main ways: hydrolysis, hydration, and carbonation. **Hydrolysis**, the breaking down of a substance by a chemical reaction with water, dissolves minerals, which then drain into lower layers of soil and rock. Rocks that are weathered by hydrolysis have rough surfaces and are often pitted or grooved. Feldspar weathers into kaolinite, a clay mineral, through hydrolysis.

Some minerals can change by absorbing water in a process called *hydration*. In these cases, the mineral's chemical formula changes

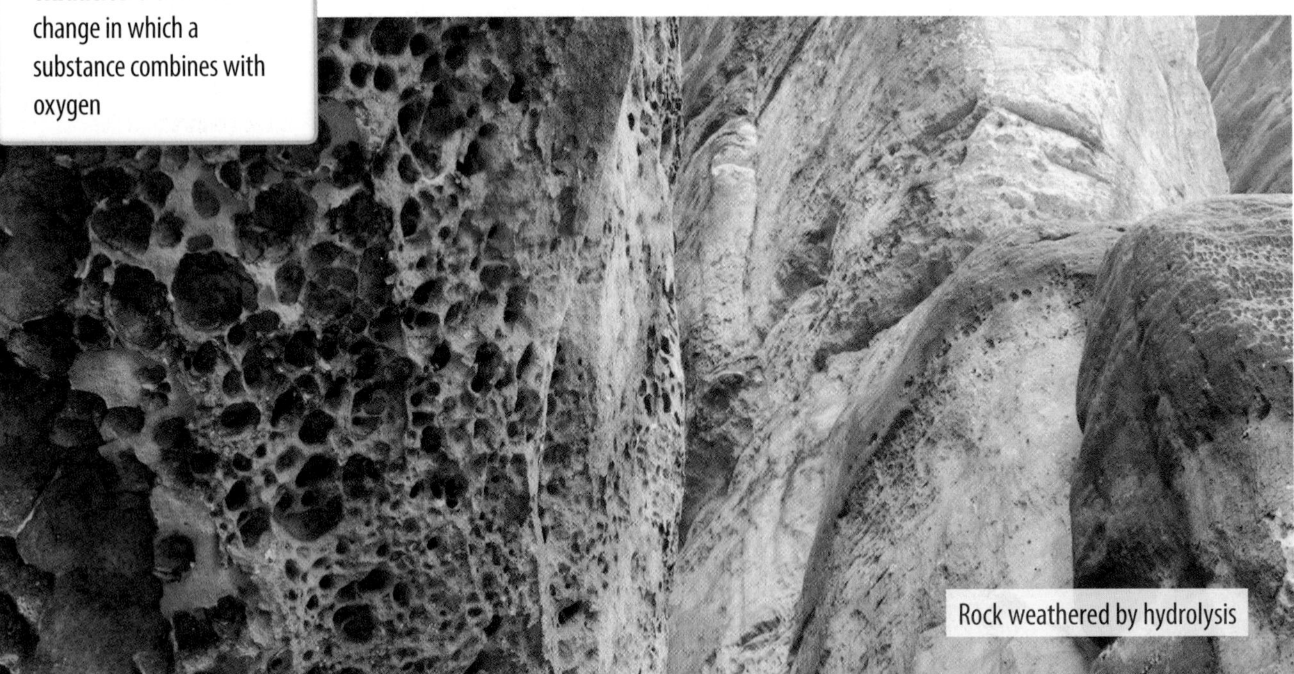
Rock weathered by hydrolysis

Slowly dripping water deposits dissolved calcium bicarbonate to form stalactites.

very little, but the crystalline structure is significantly changed. For example, anhydrite can absorb water and become gypsum.

Water can combine with other substances to form acids, which weather rocks. **Carbonation** is the process in which carbon dioxide from the atmosphere or soil dissolves in water to form carbonic acid. The interaction between carbonic acid and the calcite in limestone and marble produces calcium bicarbonate, which dissolves easily in water and washes away. Over time, acidic water can carve caves out of rock. The dissolved calcium bicarbonate can be deposited from slowly dripping water to form stalactites (mineral forms hanging from the ceiling of a cavern) and stalagmites (mineral forms rising from the floor of a cavern).

In addition to carbon dioxide, water in the atmosphere can form sulfuric and nitric acids when it combines with the gases sulfur dioxide and nitrogen oxide. These gases are commonly released into the atmosphere as a result of burning fossils fuels, such as oil or coal. Molecules of nitric and sulfuric acids increase the acidity of normal precipitation (rain, fog, snow, sleet, or dew), which is commonly called *acid rain*.

Oxygen is a component in another major chemical weathering process. **Oxidation** is a chemical change in which a substance combines with oxygen. For example, iron combines with oxygen to form rust. Iron oxide produced by oxidation provides the red, rusty color of soil in the southeastern United States, southeastern China, and the tropics of South America and Africa. Protection against rust is crucial in the industrial world. Preventative

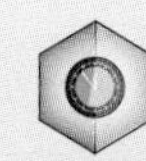

HISTORY

Climate and Weathering
A good example of a climate's influence on the rate of weathering is Cleopatra's Needle, an Egyptian granite obelisk. The obelisk stood exposed to the elements in the hot, dry climate of Egypt for 3,000 years. During this time its surface scarcely changed. In 1881 the obelisk was set up in Central Park in New York City. After a century of exposure to pollution and acid rain, Cleopatra's Needle has been weathered severely. Chemical and mechanical weathering processes in New York produced far more damage in 100 years than the desert climate of Egypt did in 3,000 years.

measures include blocking air and water from the iron surface by painting, oiling, greasing, or coating it with another metal.

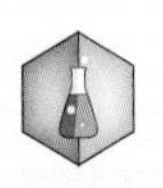

TRY THIS

Speed Up, Slow Down
Design an experiment that tests how the acidity of water affects chemical weathering. Then create a hypothesis that suggests how chemical weathering could be slowed down and design an experiment to test it.

Biological weathering can also contribute to chemical weathering. For example, lichen cause chemical weathering in the tundra. Lichen produce a weak acid. When lichen grow on boulders, the acid dissolves the rock surfaces, creating small depressions in the boulders. Such acids can also form cracks in rocks. Mechanical weathering further weathers these rocks as water flows into these cracks and freezes, breaking the rocks apart.

LESSON REVIEW

1. What are three agents of chemical weathering?
2. Explain the differences among the three types of chemical weathering caused by water.
3. What is oxidation?
4. How can plants contribute to chemical weathering?
5. Compare the rate of chemical weathering in moist, hot climates with that in dry, cold climates.
6. What agents of chemical weathering should be considered when building a bridge over a river?

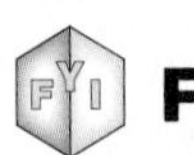

FYI

Chemical Weathering Turns Gas into Stone
An international team of scientists working in Iceland have discovered a promising method of storing carbon dioxide by turning it into calcite. Researchers discovered that carbon dioxide turns into calcite when it is dissolved in water and injected into underground basalt rock, which is plentiful throughout Earth. The water and carbon dioxide form carbonic acid, which reacts with the metal elements in the basalt, eventually forming a carbonate mineral called *calcite*. Hellisheidi Geothermal Power Station near Reykjavik, Iceland, tested the process on an industrial scale. At first, scientists thought it could take hundreds of years. However, in Hellisheidi's experiment, the carbon dioxide changed into calcite in less than two years. Scientists are optimistic that this technology will prove a cost-effective, permanent solution to the problem of capturing and storing carbon dioxide emissions from industrial facilities. Potential problems include the need for about 25 tons of water for every ton of carbon dioxide, the potential of the injection process triggering earthquakes near a fault, and a microbe that feeds off carbonate minerals and releases methane. These challenges can be addressed. Plentiful seawater can be used, basalt is abundantly found away from faults, and the presence of the microbe can be limited.

Weathering and erosion work together to slowly smooth broken or carved rock, create caves, or split boulders. These forces erode such tiny fragments and take such a long time to occur that they are difficult to notice. There is a form of erosion, however, that is hard to miss! **Mass wasting** is the downhill movement of rocks and soil caused by gravity. Mass wasting may affect only a few square meters, or it may involve an entire mountainside. **Regolith** is a loose layer of rock and soil that moves during mass wasting. Regolith soaked with water flows down a mountainside, but dry regolith tumbles or slides. Some of the regolith typically accumulates at the bottom of the slope in a bulge called *a toe.* The size and speed of the movement depends on the steepness of the slope, the type of rock, the presence of vegetation, and the amount of moisture in the ground.

OBJECTIVES

- Distinguish among various forms of mass wasting.
- Determine how various factors contribute to mass wasting events.
- Infer reasons why people might want to build in locations prone to mass wasting.
- Identify methods of reducing the risk of mass wasting.

You may have heard of a "landslide victory" such as when a candidate wins an election by a huge margin over an opponent. In nature, landslides are similarly dramatic mass wasting events. A **landslide** is a rapid, downhill movement of a large amount of rock and soil that separates from the bedrock beneath it. Landslides happen when the weight of materials on a slope can no longer resist the gravitational pull to slide downhill. If a landslide occurs as a large block of soil and rock that slides down a concave slope, it is called *a slump.* Often, the curved slope causes the sliding mass to tilt backward against the slope. The effect is similar to what happens when a large spoonful of pudding is slowly tilted upward; the pudding moves along the spoon's curved surface, and some spills over the end. Slumping

VOCABULARY

- **earthflow** the movement of wet soil down a slope
- **landslide** the rapid downhill movement of a large amount of rock and soil
- **mass wasting** the downhill movement of rocks and soil caused by gravity
- **mudflow** the rapid downhill movement of a large mass of mud and debris
- **regolith** a loose layer of rock and soil
- **soil creep** the extremely slow downhill slide of soil

Landslide

typically occurs along steep slopes. A slump block may measure up to 5 km long and 150 m thick. Landslides can be triggered by earthquakes, volcanic eruptions, spring thaws, or heavy rains.

On May 12, 2008, a tragic earthquake struck China's Sichuan province, about 80 km west-northwest from the city of Chengdu. The earthquake caused massive damage and loss of life, not only from the earthquake itself but also from the landslides it caused. In some places, landslides dammed rivers, creating new lakes, and in other places they blocked roads and destroyed property.

Landslides that primarily involve rocks are called *rockslides*. These typically start on steep slopes when huge chunks of rock come loose from the bedrock and slide downhill. Similarly, rockfalls are common on steep cliffs or hills where individual rocks and boulders occasionally break free. Rockfalls are not true landslides because they are an abrupt movement of rocks that

Mass Wasting

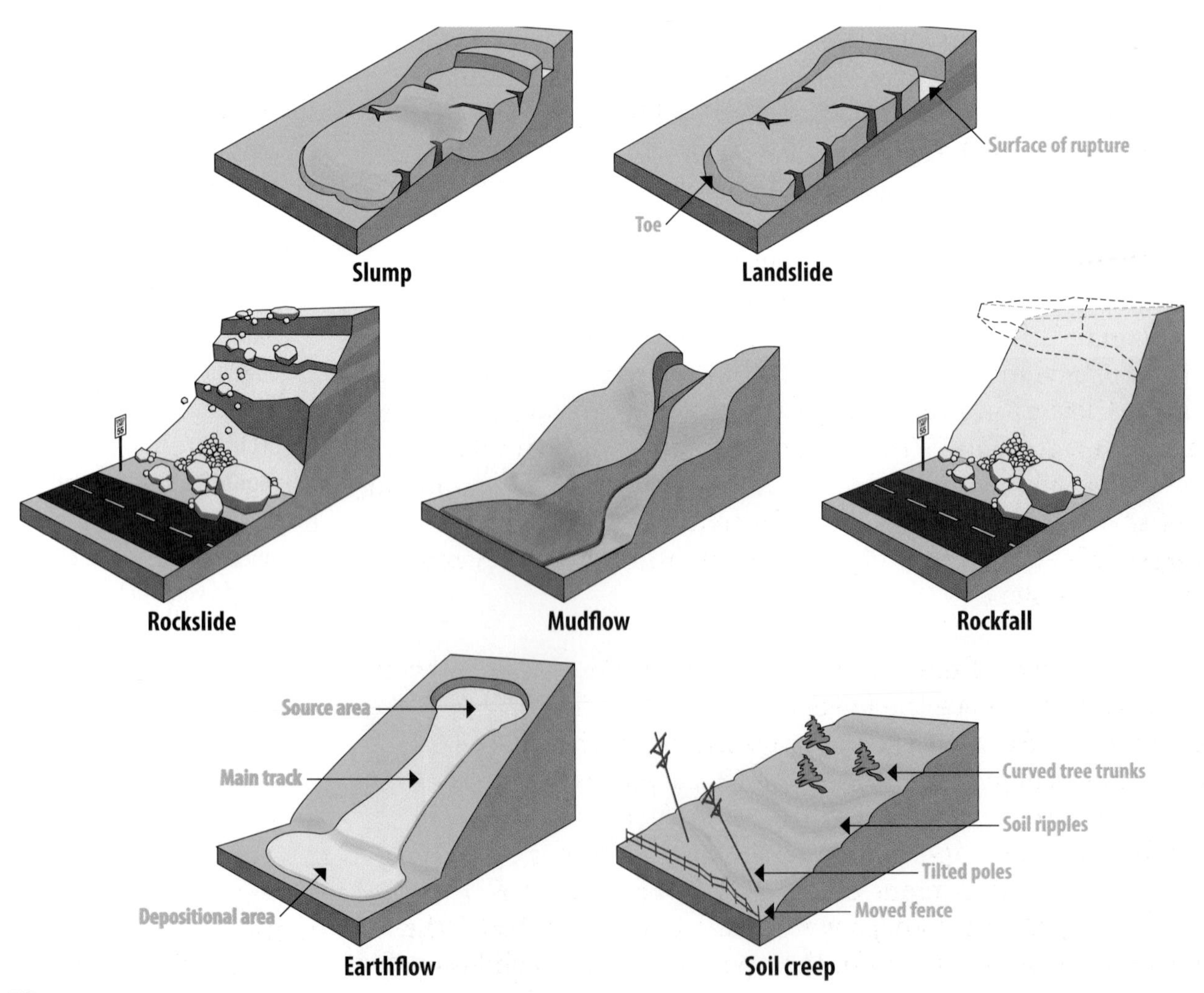

fall or bounce downhill from a cliff. The rocks in a rockfall do not slide down a slope. However, a rockfall could start a landslide by jarring rocks and soil free from their underlying bedrock.

A **mudflow** is the rapid, downhill movement of a large mass of mud and debris. This occurs when a large amount of water mixes with soil and rock. Mudflows are different from landslides because of their high water content, which causes them to behave more like rivers. Mudflows follow natural channels until they reach the base of a slope, where they spread out in fan-shaped patterns. Landslides move as a mass and have less fluid movement. Mudflows are particularly common in places where deforestation has occurred. The roots of trees and other plants help hold the soil together. Without them, the soil is exposed to greater erosion, which can be especially dangerous on mountainsides during heavy rains.

Mudflows follow natural channels.

Not all mass wasting is fast. **Soil creep** is the extremely slow, downhill slide of soil. This type of mass wasting is observed only by its effect on trees, fences, or displaced land marks. Many factors cause soil creep. Water lubricates rock particles, allowing them to move more freely, plants wedge particles apart, freezing and thawing cycles loosen soil, and burrowing animals displace soil particles. Once one or more of these forces starts the particles moving, gravity slowly pulls the soil downhill.

An **earthflow** is the movement of wet soil down a slope. It is faster than soil creep but can be slower than a mudflow. Although earthflows and mudflows can both move rapidly, they are different events. The main differences between an earthflow and a mudflow are water content and size. Earthflows have less water content than mudflows. Also, earthflows can be relatively narrow (approximately 100 square meters) or can include a broad area of several square kilometers. In contrast, mudflows are usually confined to clearly observable channels until they reach the base of the slope.

Another slow form of mass wasting, called *solifluction*, can occur in Arctic regions where the lower layer of soil, called *permafrost*, is permanently frozen. During the spring thaw, the upper layer of soil thaws, trapping moisture next to the permafrost. This trapped moisture causes the muddy upper layer of soil to slide downhill. A similar type of slide can occur in warmer climates where the lower soil is made of hard clay. The clay forms a waterproof barrier that keeps water from being absorbed. When the ground becomes saturated, the upper layer of soil slides over

BIBLE CONNECTION

Build on the Rock

Jesus' parable of the wise and foolish builders in Matthew 7:24–27 reflects the concept of mass wasting. In the parable, the wise man built his house on a rock. This rock was strong enough to resist rain, rising streams, and hard wind; the house built on it stood firm. The foolish man built his house on sand. As expected, this foundation was weak, and the house on it did not survive the forces acting against it. Jesus' point is that people should place their trust in Him, because He is the only sure foundation for life.

the clay. Depending on the angle of the slope and the moisture content of the soil, the speed of solifluction can range from very slow to fast.

Mass wasting can occur wherever there is a slope, but it is most common in areas prone to heavy rainfall, earthquakes, and volcanoes. Construction to accommodate home owners' desires, housing demands, industry, and road building can also increase the likelihood of mass wasting if building is done on or near slopes and proper precautions are not taken. The best way to avoid damage from mass wasting is to avoid building on or near locations prone to it. Sometimes, however, these sites cannot be avoided, such as when building a road through mountains. In these cases, engineers may be able to reduce the hazard of mass wasting through various methods including proper grading, building retaining walls, providing proper drainage, covering loose rocks with steel mesh, and planting vegetation. Rock sheds can sometimes be built in places where mass wasting is likely to occur near roads; these are designed to act as roofs or tunnels, enabling debris to flow over the road without harming the road itself.

This El Salvador landslide was caused by an earthquake.

LESSON REVIEW

1. What is a landslide called that slides along a curved slope?
2. How is an earthflow different from soil creep?
3. What factors might trigger a mass wasting event?
4. Describe a scenario in which people might build in a location prone to mass wasting.
5. What are some methods engineers can use to reduce the risk of mass wasting?

Have you ever sat on a beach when a strong wind was whipping across the sand? The strong wind pelts tiny grains of sand against your skin. The tiny grains can bite into your skin until it is raw. Wind is the most influential sculptor of dry landscapes. Its force can move large amounts of soil and sand over great distances. When these blowing particles rub against surfaces, those surfaces weather and erode.

The way in which wind moves particles depends on their size. Tiny dust particles can be suspended in wind and moved great distances. Wind can briefly lift grains of sand before they fall and bounce along the ground; this movement is called *saltation*. Bouncing particles and wind can also push or roll larger grains that are too heavy for the wind to lift in a movement called *creep*.

Deflation is a form of erosion in which wind carries away sand and soil particles. Wind deflates dry land more quickly than wet land because moisture weighs down soil and glues the grains together, making it harder for the wind to pick them up. Major deflation events come in the form of dust storms. Under the right conditions, strong winds can lift sand and soil over 1 km into the air and carry the dust 40–80 km. Some of these storms can stretch up to 160 km. Deflation can also occur in smaller events.

Deflation commonly produces two distinct landforms. *Desert pavement* is the hard, packed ground left after all the loose soil or sand has been washed or blown away. **Deflation hollows** are soil depressions scooped out by the wind. These can range in area

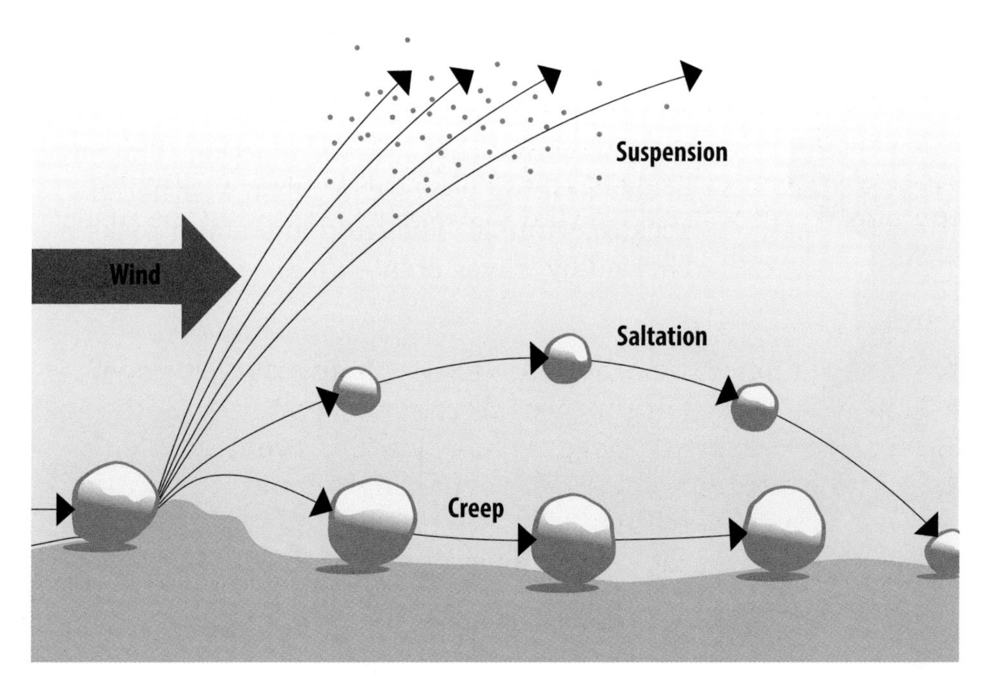

OBJECTIVES

- Distinguish between wind erosion through abrasion and deflation.
- Measure the process and effects of erosion caused by waves.
- Model the relationship between erosion and the formation of features.
- Summarize ways in which people accelerate or reduce the effects of wind and wave erosion.

VOCABULARY

- **abrasion** the wearing down of rock surfaces by other rocks or sand particles
- **deflation hollow** a soil depression scooped out by the wind
- **rock pedestal** a mushroom-shaped rock formed by the erosion of the rock's base

TRY THIS

Sea Stacks

Pour sand on a plate, making a mound in the center. Place several coins on the mound. Use a watering can to sprinkle water on the mound. Describe the results. Compare the results to ocean wave erosion.

from about 1 m^2 to several thousand square kilometers. Egypt's Qattara Depression, the world's largest deflation hollow, is about 18,100 km^2.

Abrasion is the wearing down of rock surfaces by other rocks or sand particles. Abrasion smooths or polishes the surfaces of rocks that face the wind. It can also help erode rocks into interesting shapes. For example, abrasion can help form **rock pedestals**, which are mushroom-shaped rocks. Blowing sand primarily chips away weathered material at the rocks' bases because the sand is too heavy to reach the top of the rocks.

Another effect of wind erosion is wind deposition. When wind takes soil or sand from one place, it deposits the particles someplace else to form either loess or dunes. Loess is a porous deposit of fine silt that is usually rich in minerals. These qualities make loess excellent for farming. The most well-known sand deposits are dunes, mounds of sand deposited by the wind. Dunes form in places where the wind is strong and the soil is dry and unprotected by vegetation, such as deserts or beaches. Wind carries sand until it comes against a barrier that traps or slows the grains, enabling them to collect in a pile. Barriers can include rocks, stands of grass, bushes, or even soft ground. The pile of sand grows and becomes sloped on the side facing the wind. Eventually, the sheltered side becomes too steep, and the top of the pile collapses away from the wind. This process of growing and collapsing causes the dune to move in the direction of the wind.

If you have ever tried to build a sand castle near waves or splashed water against a hill of dirt, then you know that water is also a force of erosion. One type of water erosion is wave action. The force of the striking waves can cause weathered rock to crumble. The sand and small rocks carried by waves create an abrasive force

Mushroom rock or rock pedestal

HISTORY

The Great Dust Bowl

During the Great Depression, the combination of poor farming methods, drought, and strong winds caused terrible erosion and dust storms throughout the United States' southern Great Plains. The primary states affected were Colorado, Kansas, Oklahoma, Texas, and New Mexico. This event was called *the Great Dust Bowl*. The Dust Bowl started in 1931 as drought killed wheat crops. These crops had replaced most of the natural grassland. Without the crops or the grass, the wind began to erode the deeply plowed land. The ensuing dust storms could be enormous. The worst ones reduced visibility to nothing, and a few even reached the east coast of the US. As the Dust Bowl continued, the federal government, under President Franklin Roosevelt, implemented several disaster relief programs. One such program was the Soil Conservation Service (SCS), which was established in April 1935. The SCS taught farmers conservation techniques such as strip cropping, contour plowing, and planting cover crops. In March 1937, the Shelterbelt Project began. This project encouraged farmers to plant native trees as windbreaks. These and other conservation measures reduced the wind erosion by 65%. Rain returned to the area in 1939, and the land began to recover.

similar to windblown sand. Waves can also carry and deposit sediment to both build up and erode beaches.

Waves battering a rock shoreline create steep cliffs called *sea cliffs*. The waves carve out the bottom of the cliff until the overhang drops into the sea. The cliff gradually wears back and becomes steeper. Soft rocks such as those on the coast of Dover, England, weather quickly, but cliffs of hard rock such as granite show little wear even after centuries of being pounded by waves.

Sea cliffs do not usually weather evenly. Waves often cut deep into the weakened rock at the cliff's base to form *sea caves*. If the cave forms in a promontory—a high piece of ground that juts out into the water—the waves will continue eroding the rock until the center of the cave is completely eroded and a *sea arch* is formed. Sea arches exposed to constant wave action may weaken until their middles collapse, leaving isolated columns of rock called *sea*

Sea cave, sea arch, and sea stack at Cliffs Porte d'Aval in Étretat, France

Sandbar

Contour farming

stacks. Eventually even the sea stacks undergo weathering until they no longer rise above the water's surface.

Pieces of rock that are broken apart by waves continuously grind against the shore and each other until they are reduced to small pebbles or sand. A beach forms when waves deposit sand or pebbles along an ocean shore or lakefront. Erosion changes beaches throughout the seasons. The large waves of winter storms carry enormous amounts of sand away from the beach, depositing it offshore. The deposits often form long, underwater ridges called *sandbars*. Sandbars may become exposed during low tides. In the summer, currents and waves return sand from the sandbars back to the shore, widening the beach once again.

Beach materials can be found in a variety of sizes and colors. The size of materials is largely determined by the force and frequency of the waves. Strong, frequent wave action has the ability to bring in pebbles, and it tends to carry lighter sand away. The color of beach sand depends on the materials in the sand. White sand is typically quartz or crushed shells. Black sand comes from basalt, a volcanic rock, or from heavy metals such as magnetite. Pink

A Room with a View

People are drawn to beautiful areas and frequently build houses on cliffsides and beaches so they can enjoy the beauty of creation. Unfortunately, such areas are prone to erosion and dramatic mass wasting events. In some parts of the world, available land is scarce, so apartment complexes, factories, and roads have even been built on hilly areas that are at risk for landslides or mudflows. Such construction can have serious consequences. For example, in India, heavy machinery that was used to build hydroelectric dams in the Himalayas contributed to huge mudslides in the region. Engineers and city planners work to balance the wants and needs of the population with the very real risks of building on potentially unstable ground.

sand generally comes from corals. Rare green sand typically comes from olivine, a mineral that erodes out of basalt. These materials can come from a variety of sources. Obviously, coral and marine shell fragments come from the sea. Minerals, however, may be deposited from rivers that carried the sand for many kilometers, or they may come directly from coastal rocks.

A jetty protects the coastline from erosion.

Erosion is a natural process, but human activity can accelerate or hinder it. People may encourage wind erosion by clear cutting large swaths of forest, by excavating or bulldozing sites in preparation for construction, or by tilling fields in preparation for planting. Various methods can help lessen human impact. Selective cutting and replanting in forests not only maintains healthy plants and trees, but also provides strong roots to hold the soil. Sprinkling water over construction sites helps prevent wind erosion, and laying gravel over machine paths and roadbeds helps keep soil in place. Farmers can plant windbreaks and plow along the contours in their fields to slow the wind and catch particles driven by the wind. By planting cover crops in dormant fields, farmers help return nutrients to the soil and limit wind erosion.

People can affect beach erosion too. In some places people build walls to either deflect waves and currents or encourage sand deposits. Care must be taken when building these because they can create different wave and current patterns, increasing erosion in other areas. Another way to maintain the size of a beach is to bring in sand from elsewhere. People can help protect structures from the effects of storms or sea surges by encouraging the formation of beach dunes by building fences or planting vegetation to hold the sand.

Erosion-control fence at a beach

LESSON REVIEW

1. Concerning wind erosion, what is the difference between abrasion and deflation?
2. Wind deposition forms what two land features?
3. How do waves erode cliffs?
4. What often happens to sand eroded from a beach during the winter?
5. Summarize the primary means by which people can accelerate or reduce the effects of wind and wave erosion.

2.1.5 *River Erosion*

OBJECTIVES

- Determine factors that affect river erosion.
- Evaluate the benefits and hazards of living on a floodplain.
- Explain how erosion and deposition can change the landscape.

VOCABULARY

- **channel** the path that a stream follows
- **floodplain** a flat area along a river formed by sediments deposited when a river overflows
- **gully** a narrow ditch cut in the earth by runoff
- **runoff** water from precipitation that flows over the land

Have you ever observed a river after a heavy rainstorm? The fast-moving water rises high on the banks, sweeping away soil and rocks. Sometimes its power can even overturn boulders. Rivers and the streams that run into them are significant movers of soil and sediments.

This complex transportation system begins with precipitation, such as rain or snow. Precipitation often soaks into the ground or evaporates. Any extra water that flows over the land's surface when the ground is saturated is called **runoff**. As a constant force of erosion, runoff washes away particles of silt and soil. These particles may be carried many kilometers downstream in a river before they are deposited in calmer waters. The process of depositing sediment is called *deposition*.

Another factor that affects river erosion is the slope of the land. Because of gravity, water always runs to the lowest point. So in areas where the slope is steeper, runoff will move with greater force and speed. Water follows the natural contours of the ground. Runoff deepens these contours through erosion if the ground is soft or if the force of the water is particularly strong.

River systems start in highlands and flow downhill to empty into lakes or oceans. A **gully** is a narrow ditch cut in the earth by runoff. Many gullies only carry water if runoff is present,

Water runoff and surface erosion

but some become permanent streams that empty into a river. A **channel** is the path that a stream or river follows.

The patterns of river erosion change with the topography of the land. In highlands, where slopes are steeper, streams tend to erode narrow and deep channels with steep, V-shaped banks. On gentle, lowland slopes, streams usually erode meandering, or curving, channels with U-shaped banks, and the channels can be much wider than those of highland streams.

Erosion can occur at a river's start, or head, and in its channel. The process called *headward erosion* occurs when the head of a stream or river becomes wider or moves uphill because of erosion. Water flowing through a channel erodes sediment from the banks and bed. Over time, this erosion can change a channel's

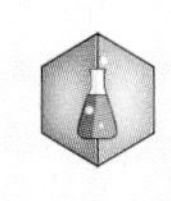

TRY THIS

A Changing View

Using sand, small rock fragments, chalk, and fine silt, form a landscape in a large, plastic tub. Make hills, valleys, and plateaus. Demonstrate how the landscape can be changed over time by different types of weathering and erosion.

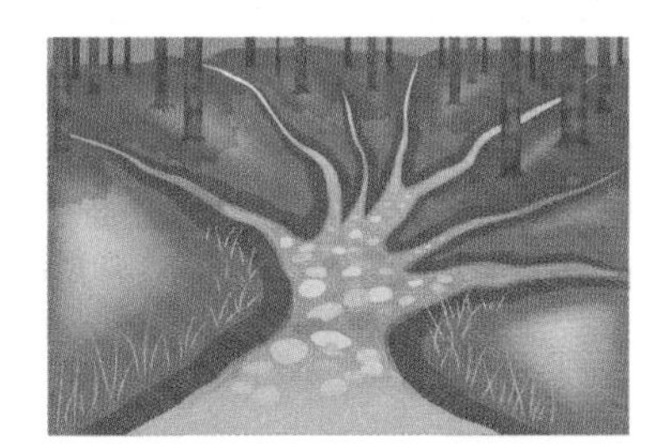

Headwater erosion

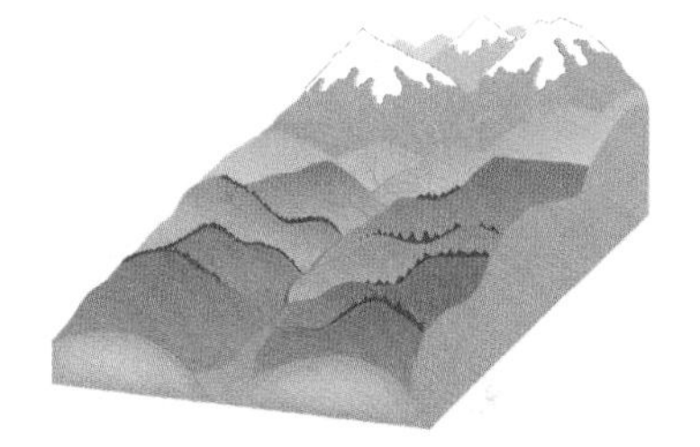

V-shaped mountain river

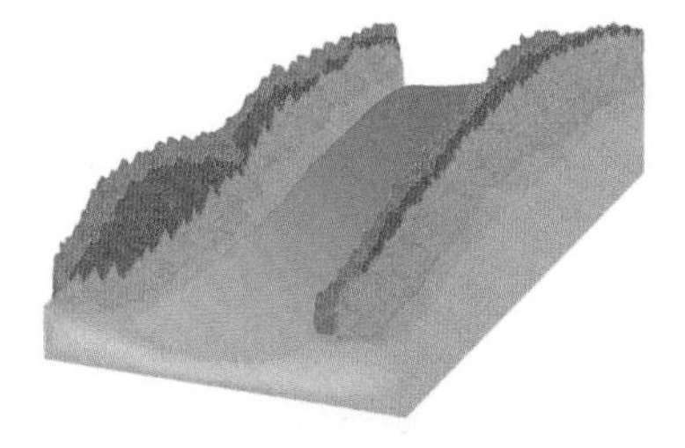

U-shaped lowland river

River sediment and erosion

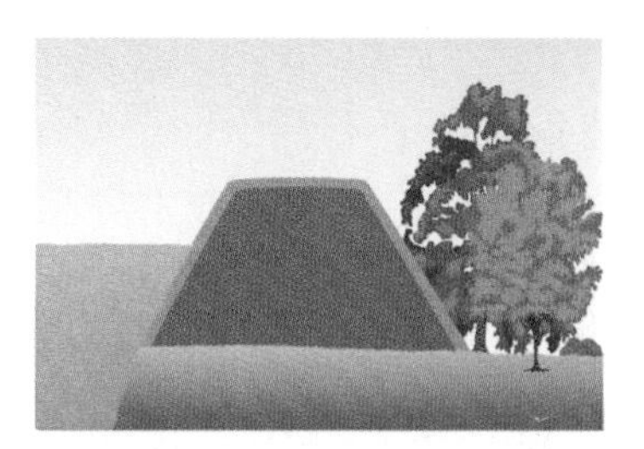

Levee

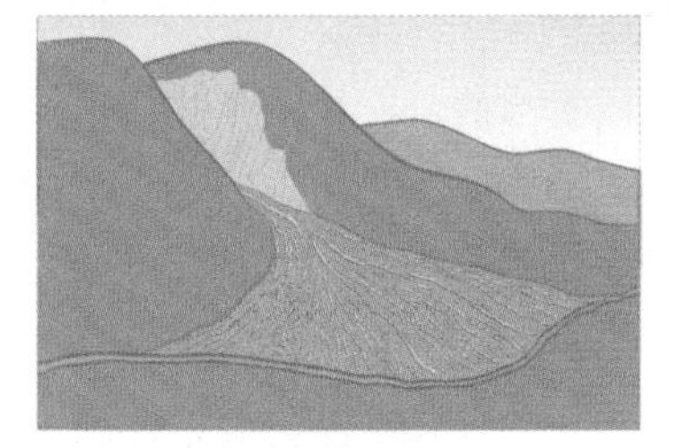

Alluvial fan

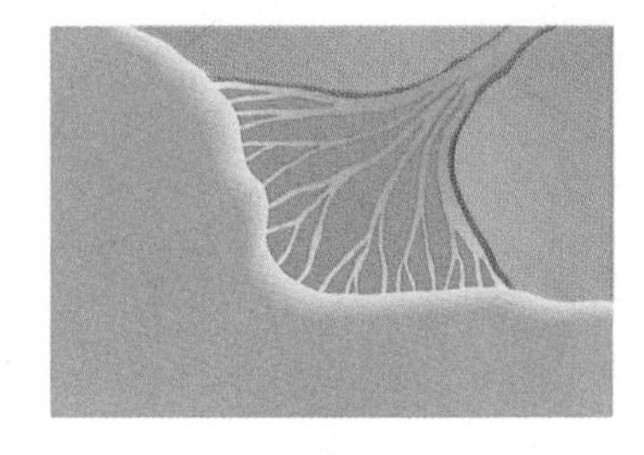

Delta

A levee breach

depth and shape. All the sediment carried by a stream or river is called its *load*. When quickly flowing water slows down, it deposits all or part of its load, which can change a channel's depth. In a meandering river, water flows slowly along the inside of the bends but flows quickly along the outer curves in a motion similar to that of a merry-go-round. A person on the edge of the merry-go-round travels faster than a person in the center. In a river, the difference in speed deposits sediment along the inside of a bend, but erodes the bend's outer curve. Over time, the shape of the river's channel is changed.

A river can also deposit its load after flooding. The increased volume of flood waters carries sediment over a river's banks, and the sediment is left behind as the flood waters slowly recede. After many years, these sediments build up what are called *floodplains* such as those found along the Nile River in Egypt, the Mississippi River in the United States, and the Ganges River in India. A **floodplain** is a flat area along a river formed by sediments deposited when a river overflows. Ever since ancient times, people have settled in floodplains to farm the soil, which is rich in minerals and soil deposits left by the floods. The Egyptians, for example, settled on the floodplains of the Nile.

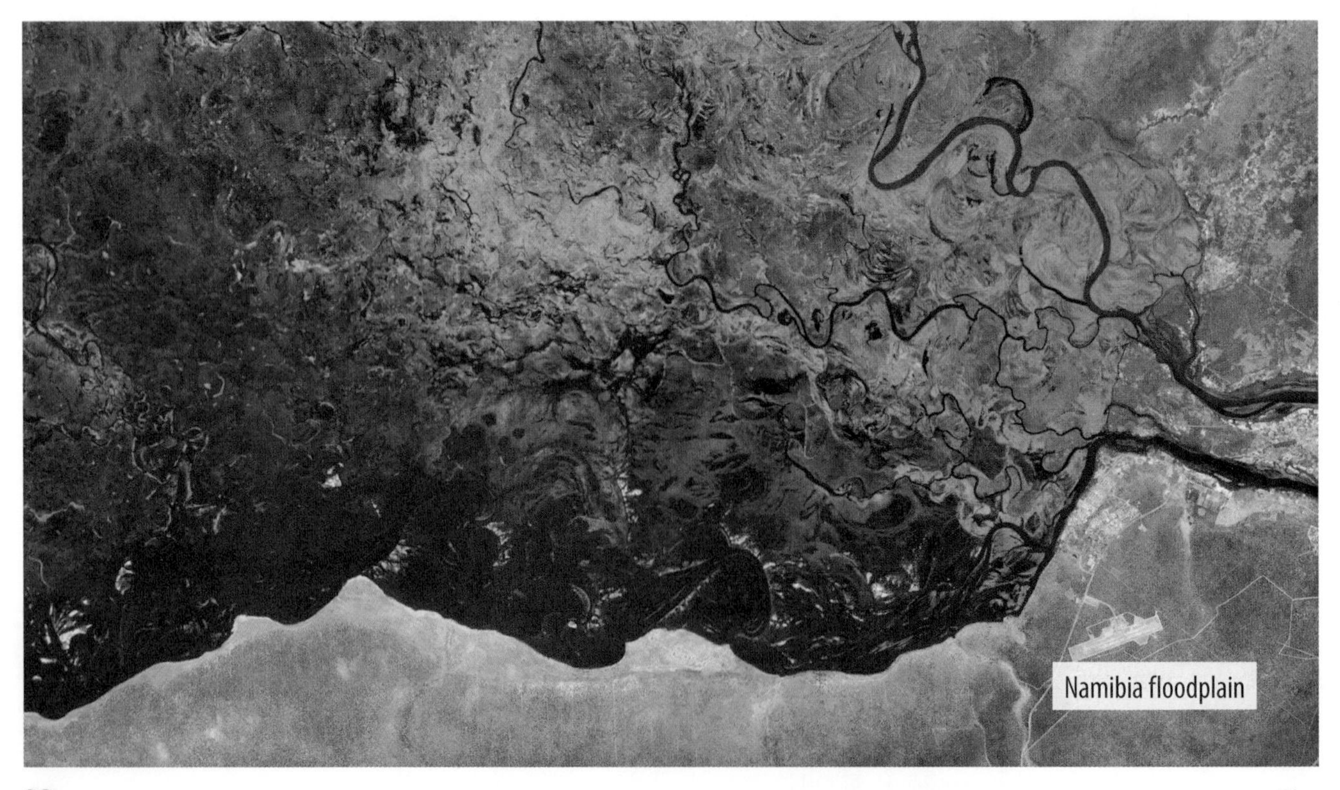
Namibia floodplain

Floodplains can be dangerous because they are naturally prone to flooding. Two elements of natural flood control are forests and wetlands. For example, wetlands absorb some of the floodwater, and they slow the speed of the water as it drains back to the channel. Human-made methods of controlling floods include dams and levees. Dams are structures built on a river to regulate its flow. Levees are earthwork constructions built to stop water from flowing in a specific direction. Levees must be maintained to keep them functioning properly. As floodwaters drain, the sediments are deposited along the levee and in the riverbed, which is the ground at the bottom of a river. These deposits build up the riverbed over time. The levee must then be made higher as the riverbed rises, or the river must be dredged to remove sediments.

Alluvial fan

River delta

Rivers slow down when their channels become wider. This slowing happens suddenly when a mountain stream enters a broad plain or when a river reaches a large body of water, such as a lake or an ocean. This sudden slowing deposits much of the river's load in one location. On land, this kind of deposit is called *an alluvial fan*. When a river empties into another body of water, the sediment deposit is called *a delta*. Deltas tend to form triangular shapes, and the term *delta* comes from the name of the triangular Greek letter that looks like this: Δ. Alluvial fans and deltas form in stages. Deposited sediments first split a river into channels of shallow water called *distributaries*. The distributaries change course as sediment builds. The changed course takes sediment to new locations and widens the alluvial fan or delta.

LESSON REVIEW

1. What factors affect river erosion?
2. How does erosion change a river's head?
3. Why does the inside of a river bend gain material while the outer side of the bend loses material?
4. How are the processes of erosion and deposition connected?
5. What benefits and hazards are associated with living in a floodplain?
6. What landforms can river deposits create?

2.1.6 *Glacial Erosion*

OBJECTIVES

- Determine how glaciers created various landforms.
- Explain what clues glacial landforms provide regarding the glaciers that formed them.
- Compare ice age theories.

VOCABULARY

- **drumlin** a long, tear-shaped mound of till
- **erratic** a piece of till that is not native to the place where it was deposited
- **glacial drift** the general term for any sediment deposited by a glacier
- **glacier** a large mass of moving ice that forms on land and remains from year to year
- **moraine** an accumulated deposit of till
- **till** unsorted rocks and sediments left behind when a glacier melts

Most people do not think of ice as something that shapes a landscape, but glaciers are tremendous forces of erosion. When you think of a glacier, you may think of a large chunk of ice that stays in one place. A **glacier** is a large mass of moving ice. Glaciers are commonly divided into valley glaciers and continental glaciers.

Valley glaciers gouge rugged features through mountainous regions. Some of the more obvious landforms include cirques, tarns, arêtes, and horns. A bowl-shaped hollow with an open end facing a valley is called *a cirque*. A lake inside a cirque is called *a tarn*. If two cirques form back-to-back, they can form a jagged ridge of rock called *an arête*. Sometimes cirques form on several sides of a mountain peak, and over time the cirques' sides closest to the peak erode, leaving only a tall pinnacle. This pinnacle is called *a horn*. One of the world's most distinctive horns is the Matterhorn in the Swiss Alps.

Continental glaciers spread out over large areas of land. As they move they scrape bedrock bare, scoop out deep depressions, and

Valley Glacial Landforms

Cirque in Altai Mountains, Russia

Tarn and arête in Alps, France

Matterhorn, Switzerland

U-shaped valley in Himalayas, India

carve U-shaped valleys. Some scientists theorize that retreating continental glaciers carved deep depressions in some places. Deep, narrow, U-shaped valleys that are partially submerged and open into the sea are called *fjords*. Fjords have a distinctive shape, which is why some scientists believe that they were at least partially eroded by glaciers. Fjords are common in Norway, Alaska, and other places near the Arctic Circle, but they can also be found in the far southern end of Chile.

Significant signs of continental glacial erosion are also found farther inland. Some geologists believe glacial erosion may be responsible for carving out lake beds. For example, some scientists theorize that the Great Lakes in Canada and the United States were formed by glacial erosion. Smaller round lakes called *kettle lakes* may have resulted from glacial erosion. Some kettle lakes may even have been formed by glacial deposition. If sediment covered a block of ice that was separated from a retreating glacier, the sediment would have fallen in on itself as the ice melted and created a water-filled pit.

TRY THIS

Kettle Lake

Kettle lakes are formed when till covers a block of ice that became separated from a retreating glacier. As the ice slowly melts, the till falls in on itself, creating a pit that retains the melted ice. Make your own kettle lake. Freeze water in a small paper cup. Peel the paper off the ice cube and place it on a tray. Cover the ice cube with sand. Observe what happens as the ice melts.

Continental Glacial Landforms

Tarn in Cascades, United States

Moraine in Rocky Mountains, Canada

Kettle lake in Isunngua, Greenland

Drumlin in Andechs, Bäckerbichl, Germany

Erratic in Alberta, Canada

Fjord in Norway

FYI

Icy Sculptors

Glaciers have shaped much of the landscape of the Northern Hemisphere, Antarctica, and many mountain ranges around the world. During ice ages, large sheets of ice moved south from the North Pole and north from the South Pole. The friction as they rubbed across the land slowed their journey across the continents, and the glaciers left behind dramatic patterns.

Glaciers deposit materials as well as erode them. As glaciers melt, they deposit all of the materials that they scooped up during their journeys. Glacial deposits can be identified by their unique shapes and composition. **Glacial drift** is the general term for any sediment deposited by a glacier; it is categorized into stratified drift and till. Stratified drift sediment was deposited by melting glacier water. The particles of stratified drift are about the same size and weight because they are sorted by streams running under a glacier or by lakes or streams at a glacier's edge.

Till is unsorted rocks and sediments left behind by a glacier. Till forms distinctive geologic features. A **moraine** is an accumulated deposit of till. Moraines commonly occur as large ridges or mounds. Moraines can form on the ground or on the glacier itself. They are often found on the sides of valley glaciers, at the place where two valley glaciers meet, or at the leading edges of both valley and continental glaciers. Moraines can even indicate where the boundaries of a glacier once existed. Another type of moraine, called *a ground moraine*, can yield fertile soil. Ground moraines are a widespread covering of till left behind by retreating glaciers.

A **drumlin** is a long, tear-shaped mound of till. How they form is unknown, but some scientists believe they were formed by deposits from the underside of glaciers as the glaciers advanced. Drumlins taper to a point in the direction the depositing glacier was traveling.

An **erratic** is a piece of till that is not native to the place where it was deposited. Erratics can be as small as a pebble or as large as a boulder. One erratic block in Alberta, Canada, weighs 16,500,000 kg or 16,500 metric tons! Erratics with distinctive minerals indicate areas from which a glacier traveled.

Most old-earth scientists believe that a majority of the erosion and deposition caused by glaciers happened during several long periods of time when sheets of ice covered large areas of Earth's surface. Such periods are called *ice ages.* Scientists disagree regarding the number and duration of ice ages that the earth has experienced. Some believe that there were more than four ice ages and that the most recent major ice age ended about 11,000 years ago. Most young-earth scientists believe that there was only one major ice age, which began shortly after the Flood.

The cause of an ice age remains a mystery. According to one theory, regular changes in Earth's orbit and in the tilt of its axis sparked the beginning of an ice age. These changes are thought to affect how much the sun warms the earth. If Earth's average temperature drops by even a few degrees Celsius, then glaciers could spread widely. This theory is called *the Milankovitch Theory*; it is named after Milutin Milankovitch, a Yugoslavian scientist who first proposed it in the 1920s.

Smoke from volcanic eruptions may have contributed to an ice age.

Another theory suggests that during the Flood the average ocean temperature rose because superheated water vented from beneath the crust. The warmer ocean water increased evaporation, which in turn caused more snow to fall during winter. Many young-earth scientists believe the Flood was accompanied by major volcanic eruptions. The smoke of these eruptions blocked energy from the sun and caused average temperatures to drop, which enabled glaciers to grow.

LESSON REVIEW

1. What features do valley glaciers create through erosion?
2. How did continental glaciers most likely form lakes?
3. Which glacial landform indicates where the edges of a glacier stopped?
4. What information about glaciers might drumlins provide?
5. What information about glaciers might erratics provide?
6. Explain two ice age theories.

FYI

Interpreting Erosion

Many old-earth scientists believe the theory of uniformitarianism helps people determine Earth's age. They believe that weathering and erosion rates have always been the same. Using these rates as constants, they work backward to calculate when Earth's features began forming. Uniformitarians conclude that different parts of Earth's topography must have developed over thousands or millions of years. In contrast, many young-earth scientists believe that cataclysmic events sped up erosion to shape Earth's features in a much shorter period of time. They base their theory on the observable effects of massive landslides, volcanoes, earthquakes, and powerful storms. Proponents of this view believe that many of Earth's features were shaped by the Flood.

2.2.1 *Soil Composition*

OBJECTIVES

- Distinguish among the three basic types of soil particles.
- Identify the inorganic and organic components of soil and compare their functions.
- Summarize how soil forms.

VOCABULARY

- **bedrock** the layer of solid rock beneath the soil
- **humus** the nutrient-rich, organic material in soil
- **pore space** the amount of space between soil particles

At first, you might not think of soil as important, but imagine a world without it. Life on Earth would not be sustainable. Healthy soil, along with water, air, and sunlight, is essential to the biosphere. Scientists have found that the world's soil is one of the largest reservoirs of biodiversity. It contains almost one-third of life on this planet including worms, insects, small vertebrates, fungi, and microorganisms. These organisms work with soil to provide nutrients to plants. When water flows through soil, it is purified by a natural filtering process. Soil absorbs nutrients like calcium, magnesium, and potassium, which prevents these elements from entering the water supply. At the same time, microorganisms found in the soil decompose the organic pollutants in the water and supply the nutrients absorbed by the soil to plants. This complex process also makes runoff far less toxic when it eventually reaches its destination.

Soil is a mixture of organic materials, rock particles, water, and gases. Organic materials are materials that are obtained from living or once-living things. Microorganisms, decaying plant and animal material, and living plant roots are organic materials. These organisms and materials turn lifeless fragments of rock into soil that is rich in nutrients. Without this mixture, plants could not grow, the food supply would be depleted, and most living things could not survive. Soil is the backbone of every land ecosystem on Earth. Current research indicates that unlike the moon or the other terrestrial planets where the top layer of crust is nothing more than tiny rock fragments, Earth's soil contains a mixture of nonliving and living things.

Soil teeming with life

The main ingredient of soil is small rock particles. These particles form the mineral content of soil. Soil can take thousands of years to form as most rocks break up into particles of different sizes. However, not all rocks disintegrate. Deep beneath the earth's surface lies a layer of solid rock that is not exposed to weathering processes unless it has been brought to the surface. This layer of solid rock beneath the soil is called **bedrock**. Bedrock is like a bowl that holds Earth's soil and groundwater. The loose layer of rock and soil above bedrock is regolith. The rocks near the bottom of the regolith are larger than the ones near the top because they undergo little weathering and erosion. The top layer of regolith is constantly exposed to weathering and erosion. Eventually these processes grind the rock particles into pieces that are small enough to become part of the soil.

Three basic types of soil are determined by the size of their rock particles. In a soil sample, the amount of each soil type depends on the "parent" rock that was weathered. For example, when the mineral feldspar goes through chemical weathering, small grains that contain aluminum and water are created. These grains form clay, which has a particle diameter of less than 0.002 mm. Individual grains of clay are so small that you cannot see them with the unaided eye or feel them between your fingers. When clay is squeezed, it can be easily molded and retains its shape. Clay becomes hard and loses its plasticity when heated. There are two categories of clay: residual clay and sedimentary clay. Residual clay is found where it formed. Most residual clay

BIBLE CONNECTION

The Potter and the Clay

In Isaiah 64:8, God's people are likened to potter's clay. Without any assistance, clay looks like a globule that lacks any form or purpose. As soon as the potter begins to work the clay, it starts to take shape. God is the potter. If people are ready, God will mold and shape their lives into something brand new that is better than they could ever have imagined.

God never makes mistakes. Clay on Earth will crack and break when exposed to heat if it was not formed properly. When God is allowed to be the potter, people can withstand the trials and pressures of this world. They will withstand the heat of evil with God by their side.

is formed by surface weathering. In contrast, sedimentary clay, or transported clay, was transported from its place of origin by erosion.

Silt particles are the next largest soil particles with particle diameters between 0.002 mm and 0.05 mm. These particles are not easily seen, and they feel like flour. Silt, which is composed primarily of quartz particles, is a product of the weathering and decomposition of preexisting rock. Silt is made from a variety of rocks. It is often carried by rivers and deposited on riverbanks. Hardened silt forms the sedimentary rock siltstone, which is deposited in thin layers. Siltstone is hard and flat, and it breaks into nearly rectangular slabs.

Sand particles are the largest soil particles. The rounded or angular particles of sand have a diameter between 0.05 mm and 2.0 mm. Most sand grains are large enough to be seen without aid, and their small crystals are easily felt. Sand is the product of the weathering and decomposition of igneous, sedimentary, or metamorphic rock. Most sand is made up of silica, usually quartz. However, sand grains may also be comprised of other

Magnified Size Comparison of Sand, Silt, and Clay Particles

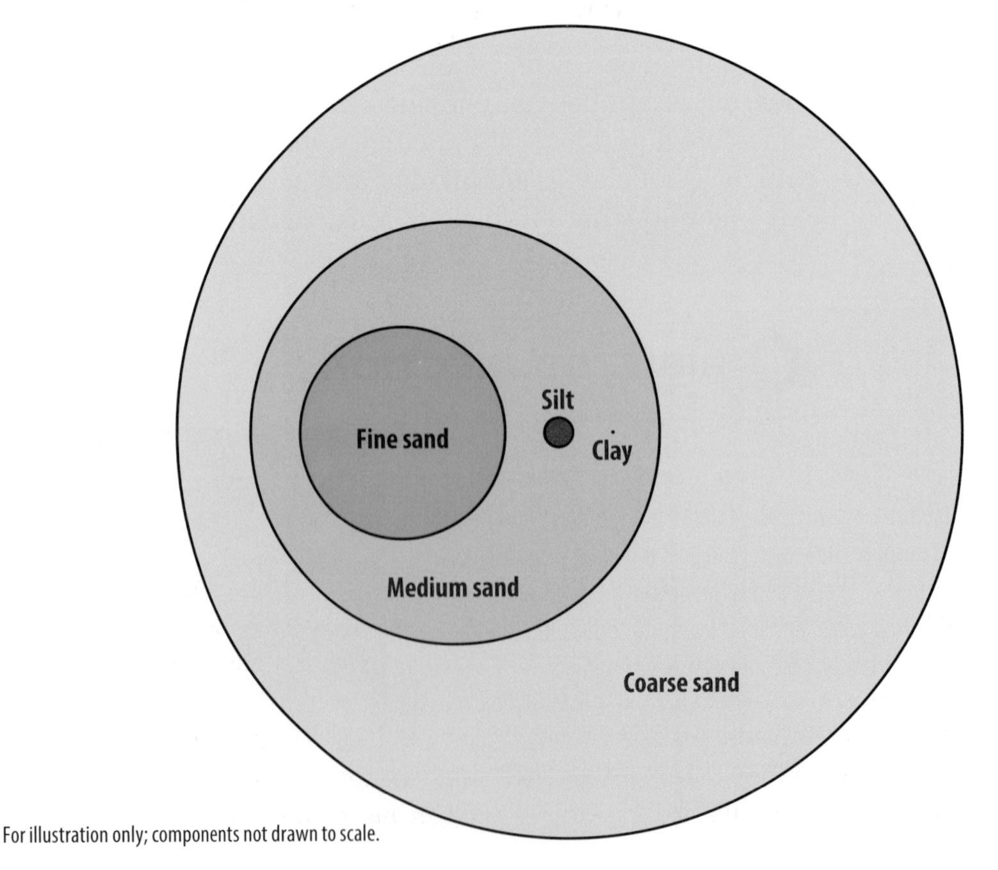

For illustration only; components not drawn to scale.

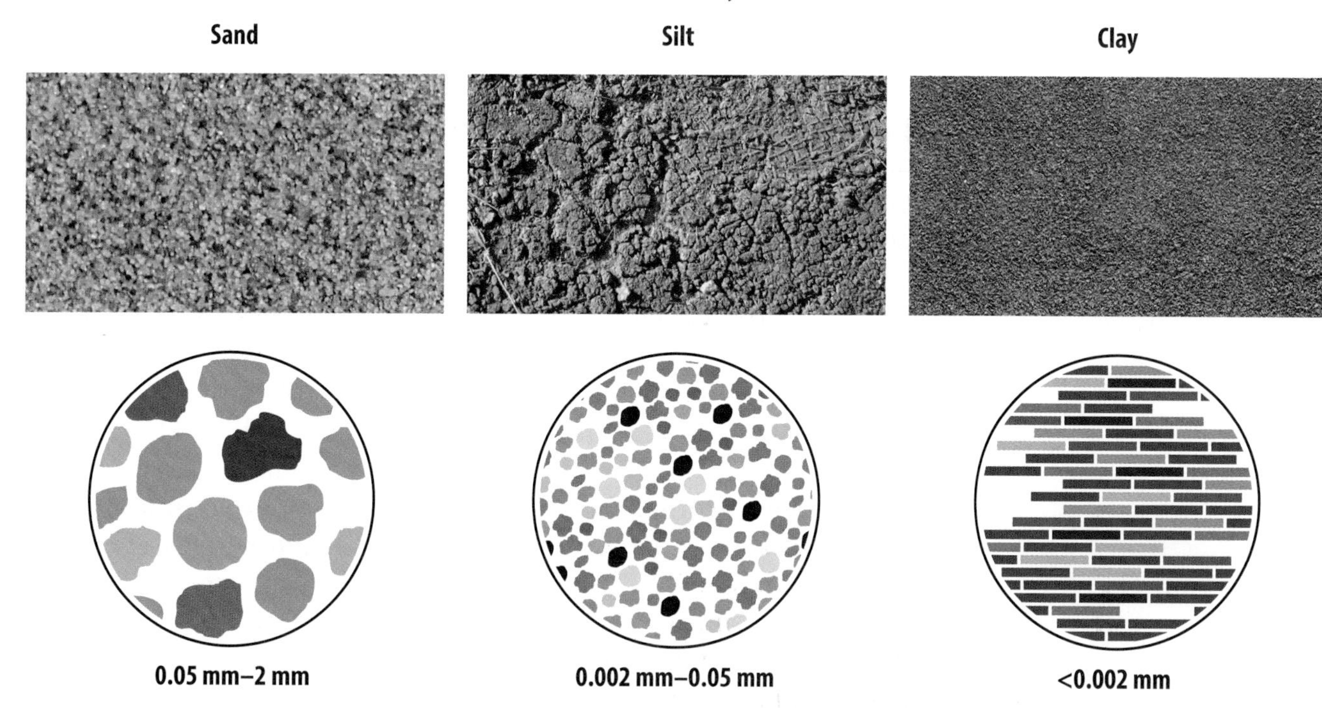

minerals. Sand may even be organic in origin. For example, organic sand can come from coral or shell. Sand deposits are formed by wind, running water, waves, and glaciers. Generally, sand makes poor soil. However, some sand in soil is helpful because it permits the free movement of air, improves drainage, and offers less resistance to roots.

Rock fragments that are larger than sand are not considered soil. These fragments are called *gravel*. Gravel consists of rock particles that are usually round with a particle diameter between 2.0 mm and 75.0 mm. Many kinds of rock comprise gravel, but quartz is the most common component. Gravel deposits are a product of the weathering of rocks and erosion by waves and running water. Gravel is useful when forming roads and concrete. In areas lacking natural gravel deposits, gravel is produced by quarrying and crushing durable rocks, such as sandstone, limestone, or basalt.

The mineral content of soil is generally made up of different proportions of clay, silt, and sand. Once the rock is broken into different-sized particles, air and water move in to fill the gaps between the larger particles. The amount of space between soil particles is called **pore space**. Different kinds of soil have different pore spaces. Fine soil particles, such as clay, have small pore spaces. Larger particles, such as silt or sand, have larger pore spaces. These spaces hold water and air. When soil is moist, the spaces hold the water that plants need to grow. During a drought, the spaces are almost entirely filled with air.

The organic material, rock particles, water, and gases found in soil are transformed by living things to create a rich ecosystem. Plant roots bind soil particles together to prevent erosion. Plant leaves shelter the soil from absorbing too much water. Roots draw minerals up to the surface. When plants decay, they form food sources for burrowing insects, worms, and larger animals. Bacteria and fungi thrive on dead plant materials and animal droppings. These ingredients comprise the dark, nutrient-rich, organic material called **humus**. Some scientists claim that humus makes soil more fertile. Others state that humus helps prevent disease in plants. Humus contains many useful nutrients such as nitrogen, which is a key nutrient for plants. Farmers depend on nitrogen and other nutrients found in humus for healthy crops. Although humus can be found naturally in many forests, it can also be created in a process known as *composting*.

LESSON REVIEW

1. Name and describe the three basic types of soil particles.
2. Name three things that comprise organic material in soil.
3. What inorganic components are found in soil?
4. How does pore space in clay compare to pore space in silt?
5. How does soil form?

Nutrient-rich humus can be found in many forests.

Soil thickness varies greatly across the world. Some regions have layers of soil up to 60 m thick; other regions only have a few centimeters of soil. Soil thickness depends on key factors, such as the climate, the slope of the land, the types of rock, the types of vegetation, and the amount of time that a rock weathered. For example, topsoil can be several meters deep on a flat plain but less than a centimeter on a steep slope because of erosion.

Soil scientists examine soil to gather information about the chemistry, biology, and physics of soil. Such experimentation and research give scientists the opportunity to be an influence or an advocate for important issues, such as agricultural production, biodiversity, climate change, environmental quality, and human health. To be able to examine the soil, scientists dig deep within the earth to inspect the **soil profile**, which is a cross section of soil layers and bedrock in a particular region. Imagine slicing into a cake. Just as a layer cake is made up of tiers of cake, frosting, and decorations, soil is made up of layers that vary in thickness and composition. Each layer in a soil profile is called a **horizon**. You have probably seen horizon layers when you pass a hillside that has been cut into or perhaps if you have ever dug a deep hole.

OBJECTIVES

- Model a soil profile and compare the properties of the different horizons.
- Explain how the activities of living things help form rich topsoil.

VOCABULARY

- **horizon** a layer in a soil profile
- **soil profile** a cross section of soil layers and bedrock in a particular region
- **subsoil** soil that is rich in minerals that have drained from the topsoil
- **topsoil** rich soil formed from mineral fragments, air, water, and organic materials

Soil Horizons

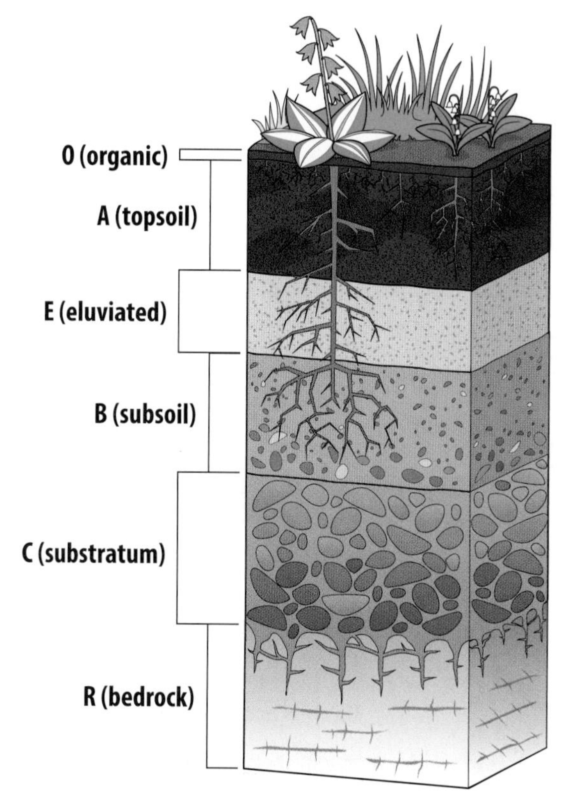

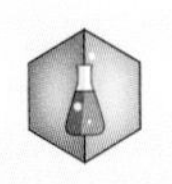

TRY THIS

Topsoil Versus Subsoil

Design an experiment that compares the effectiveness of topsoil and subsoil for growing plants.

There are six main horizons represented by the letters O, A, E, B, C, and R. Most soil has an A, B, C, and R horizon. Not all soil has an O or E horizon. The O horizon is the thin surface layer of soil composed of loose organic debris, which is usually only a few centimeters thick. The O horizon is formed mainly from decaying organic matter, such as dead leaves that pile up on the surface.

The A horizon is the topsoil. **Topsoil** is rich soil formed from organic materials, mineral fragments, water, and air. Most living things that make the soil their home live in the A horizon where plenty of organic material is available for food. Moles and earthworms burrow into this horizon, creating wide tunnels through which water, gases, and organic materials can travel. These materials feed plant roots, fungi, algae, bacteria, viruses, and protists. The microorganisms recycle dead animal and plant materials to form humus, which gives the A horizon a dark color. Much of the dissolved minerals in the A horizon leach, or flow, out of this layer to the layers below, which makes the A horizon thin.

If the E horizon is present, it is found beneath the A horizon. The E horizon has little or no organic matter and is light in color compared to the layers above and below it. Most of the silicate clay, iron, and aluminum minerals in the soil leach from the E horizon to the lower layers.

The next layer is the B horizon, or the subsoil. Plant roots extend into this layer. **Subsoil** is soil that is rich in minerals drained

Regional Soil Profiles

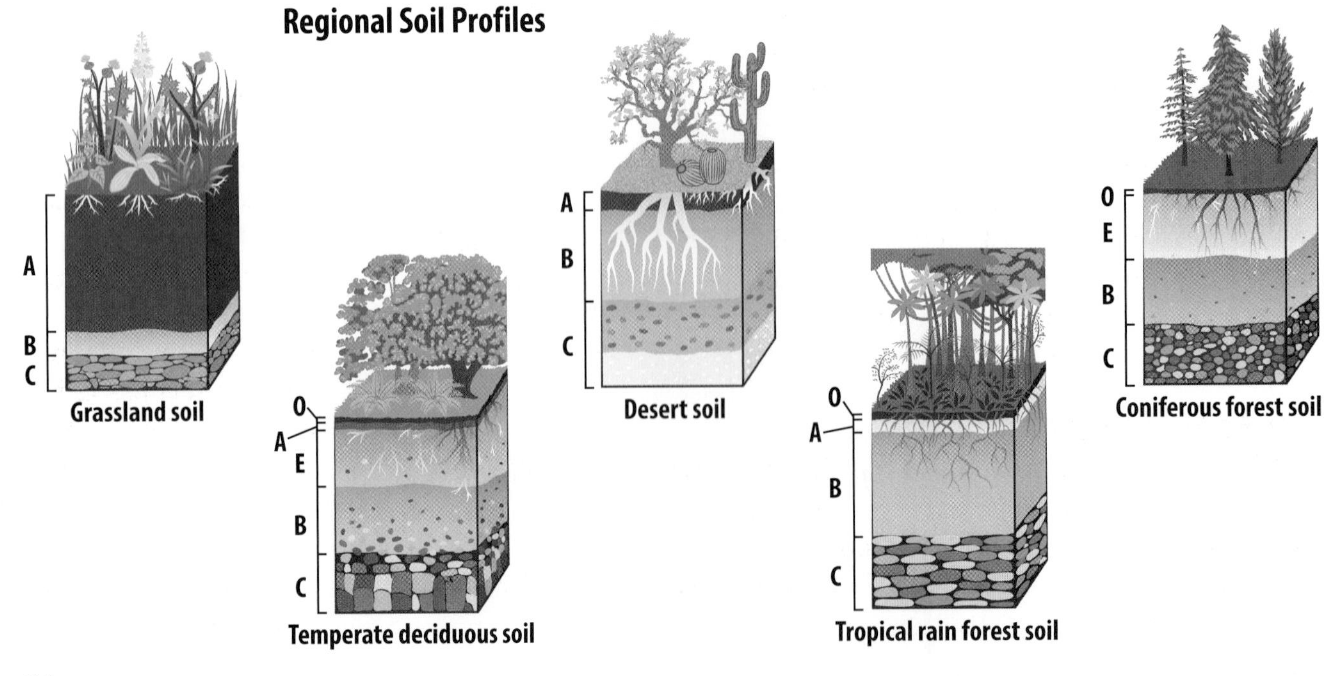

CAREER

Agronomist

Agronomists use science and natural resources such as soil, plants, and water to sustain the world's food supply and a quality environment. Agronomists seek to understand, manage, and protect Earth's vital resources and to address concerns about quality of life. Agronomy is basic to food production. Agronomy is an exciting career for those who are interested in food, feed, and fiber production. Agronomists work both in the lab and out in the field. An agronomist may focus on soil, water, the environment, crops, plants, or conservation. A soil agronomist, for example, focuses on soil's physical, chemical, and biological properties and the various uses of soil, its fertility and moisture, and soil management to ensure optimum crop growth. Soil studies may also include use for road and airport construction, waterways, building sites, and waste disposal. Soil and water conservation agronomists solve various soil and water problems such as air and water pollution, soil erosion, and proper land use.

from the topsoil by leaching. Even though it is rich in minerals, the B horizon is not nearly as fertile as the A horizon because the soil in the B horizon lacks most of the organic material found in the A horizon. The subsoil is also much lighter in color than the topsoil but it is darker than the E horizon.

The bottom layer of soil is the C horizon. The C horizon is composed of partially weathered pieces of bedrock that have changed very little from the time they were deposited. Below the soil layers is the R horizon, which is a layer of consolidated bedrock. Some examples of bedrock include granite and basalt.

Over time, natural processes degrade a C horizon to create a B horizon. Eventually this B horizon will form an A horizon of rich, fertile soil and humus. A typical soil profile has a top layer of dark topsoil rich in humus, a layer of pale subsoil beneath it, a thin layer of infertile rock fragments beneath the subsoil, and a bottom layer of bedrock. Few soil profiles fit this description perfectly.

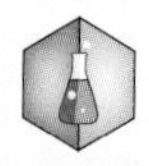

TRY THIS

The Layered Look

With a shovel, dig a hole 1 m deep in the following three regions: a wetland, a wooded area, and a grassy area. Mark where the soil changes color and indicate what each layer looks like. Measure and record the thickness of each layer. Measure and record the pH and temperature of each layer. What is the parent material of each soil sample?

LESSON REVIEW

1. What is topsoil? How do living things help form topsoil?
2. What is a soil profile?
3. Name and describe the different horizons.
4. Explain why A horizons often are darker than B or C horizons?

2.2.3 *Soil Types*

OBJECTIVES

- Analyze the effects of climate on soil type.
- Explain how a soil's fertility is connected to its formation.
- describe factors that affect the development of soil.

TRY THIS

Map the Soil
Locate your home on a local soil map. What type of soil is most common in your region? What do you think affects this?

Perhaps you have hiked through forests with rich, black soil or slipped on the red clay of a stream bank. Maybe you have noticed scrubby plants growing in sandy soil near a beach or planted vegetables in dark brown garden soil. In all of these situations, you have experienced different varieties of soil.

Scientists have several ways to classify soil. In fact, over the centuries, scientists have created and used a variety of soil classification systems. The earliest systems grouped soils by color or by how suitable they were for the production of certain types of crops. For example, soils were grouped as rice soils, wheat soils, or vineyard soils. Another system classified soils into sandy soils, clay soils, and loam, a fertile soil that is rich in humus. Over the years, many classification systems have been developed depending on the origin of the soil or its properties. However, there is not one system that has been designated as the best system for soil classification.

Characteristics of soil differ from place to place. The main factor that determines the type of soil found in a region is the climate. Climate factors, such as solar radiation, temperature, humidity, precipitation, atmospheric pressure, and wind, all play important roles in the development of different soil types. Specifically, the climate helps determine the acidity, fertility, and depth of soil. Climate also indicates the type of weathering processes that will occur to form the soil.

To measure the acidity of the soil in a particular region, scientists use the pH scale. This scale ranges from 0 to 14 with 7 being neutral. An acidic substance has a pH value of zero to less than seven. A basic, or alkaline, substance has a pH value greater than 7. Scientists have found that the soil in areas of

pH Scale

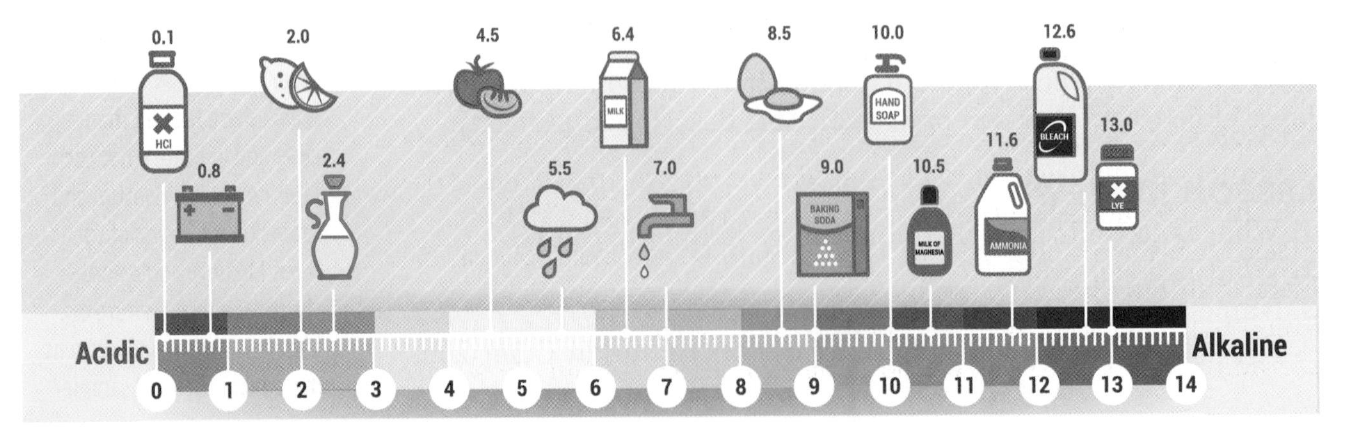

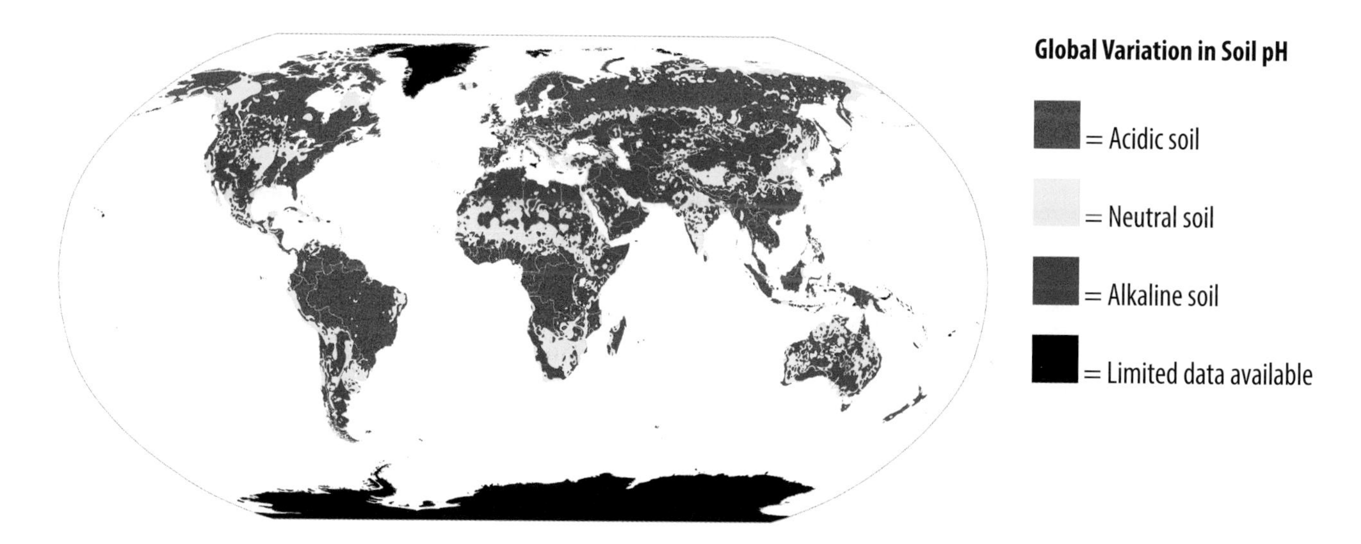

Global Variation in Soil pH

= Acidic soil

= Neutral soil

= Alkaline soil

= Limited data available

high rainfall is usually more acidic than the soil in areas with low rainfall. Rainwater is usually slightly acidic. When it comes in contact with soil, it leaches basic salts out of the soil. Soil acidity also depends on the type of parent rock the soil formed from. Rhyolite and granite are examples of acidic parent rocks.

Acidic soil can affect plants in different ways. Some plants undergo toxic reactions to high levels of aluminum, hydrogen, or manganese. Acidic soil can inhibit root growth or cause crinkled leaves. Plants in acidic soil may also be deficient in key nutrients, such as calcium and magnesium. Plant growth is also affected by pH ranges. Different plants grow best in different pH ranges. Azaleas, blueberries, and conifers thrive best in acidic soils with a pH range of 5.0 to 5.5. Vegetables and grasses flourish in slightly acidic soils that have a pH range of 5.8 to 6.5. These plants may not grow as well in soils outside of these ranges.

Tropical regions have high temperatures and heavy rainfalls. These conditions facilitate chemical weathering, which creates thick layers of soil. However, heavy rains also wash away the topsoil, which thins out the A horizon. Heavy rains leach most of the minerals out of tropical soils. Mineral leaching makes the soil in tropical regions less fertile. Ironically, many plants grow in tropical regions. Such plant growth is possible because most of the nutrients in tropical rain forests are found within the canopy of branches and vines in the forest. These organic materials are continuously added to the soil, creating a thin layer of humus. When rain forests are cut down by loggers or ranchers, the thin layer of humus becomes exposed to the direct impact of rainfall and quickly washes away. Without receiving the key nutrients stored in the now-absent canopy, the soil becomes infertile within

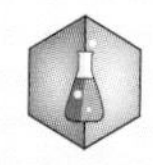

TRY THIS

Under the Weather

Fill five jars with a mixture of soil and vegetable matter. Label the jars as *Dry, Moist, Wet and Sunny, Shady and Warm*, and *Shady and Cool.* Cover the jars with plastic wrap, and poke holes in the plastic to allow for airflow. Place the jars in the locations described on each jar. Maintain the moisture levels in the jars. Record your observations for two weeks. Discuss your findings with the class.

Bom Futura tin mine in Brazil

two or three growing seasons. Because the land is no longer viable, more forests are cut down and burned.

The low rainfall of deserts slows the chemical weathering process that produces soil. Desert soil is composed mainly of regolith. Deserts are immature, weakly developed environments with mostly alkaline soil. Any water that falls on the desert evaporates quickly and leaves behind a white crust of salts. The high salt content of desert soil, along with the absence of rapid chemical weathering, water, organic materials, and vegetation, makes desert soil thin and infertile. Sometimes the soil's salt level can become so high that no plants, even desert plants, can grow there.

Arctic climates also slow down chemical weathering. Most of the weathering in the Arctic is mechanical weathering, which does not produce soil very efficiently. Similar to desert soil, the soil in Arctic regions is thin, composed mainly of rock fragments that are highly acidic and do not have suitable drainage systems. In addition, located above the mineral horizon in the Arctic is a layer of variable organic matter that has not decomposed. Depending on the season, the tundra soils of Arctic regions are often either frozen or waterlogged. The upper layer of tundra soil is rich in peat and looks like bluish mud.

Biological Soil Crusts

In arid regions throughout the world, crusts of soil particles are forming that are bound together by organic materials. Because vegetative production is very sparse in these areas, highly specialized communities of cyanobacteria, mosses, and lichens congregate in the open spaces. Biological soil crusts can be found throughout the United States, Antarctica, Australia, and Israel. Crust thicknesses can reach up to 10 cm. Usually, the crust is darker than the surrounding soil partly because of the density of organisms and the dark color of the enclosed organisms. In these dry climates, biological soil crusts help to stabilize the soil, prevent erosion, fix atmospheric nitrogen, and contribute nutrients to plants.

Temperate regions have moderate temperatures. These areas receive consistent amounts of rain. Both mechanical and chemical weathering processes in these regions produce forest soil that is rich in humus several meters deep. Soil in regions receiving more than 65 cm of rainfall annually have fertile soils made of clay, quartz, and iron compounds. Regions that receive less than 65 cm of rain a year have soil that is high in calcium carbonate, a compound that makes soil more alkaline and very fertile. The light rainfall in temperate regions helps to prevent essential minerals from being leached out of the topsoil.

Soil type is not only affected by climate. It is also influenced by the shape or slope of the land. For example, rainwater removes topsoil as it flows rapidly down steep slopes. The runoff produces a thick layer of soil at the bottom of a slope in comparison to the top or incline portions of the slope. Scientists researching soils in Manitoba, Canada, found that the flat portions of land have twice the thickness of topsoil compared to land with only a 10° slope. Any topsoil that clings to slopes is generally too thin and dry to support much plant life. Thick humus cannot form without the organic matter added by vegetation, so the soil on mountain sides is rocky, thin, and infertile. This soil quality makes growing crops on mountainsides difficult. In lowland valleys, soil retains water and rich organic materials that allow for the formation of a thick layer of humus. The soil in valleys is fertile and produces good farmland.

Three other factors that affect soil formation are parent material, type of vegetation, and time. Basalt minerals weather to form clay soils. Limestone, granite, and shale disintegrate to form sandy soil. Silty soil is composed of minerals such as quartz and fine organic particles. The local vegetation in an area tends to produce humus acids that are powerful erosion agents. Once the soil is formed, plants act as stabilizers for the soil profiles. The longer the parent rock has been exposed to weathering the less likely it is that soil will resemble the parent rock. However, if weathering occurred for a short period of time, the parent rock will determine the soil characteristics.

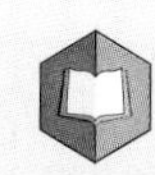

BIBLE CONNECTION

The Parable of the Sower

In Mark 4, Jesus taught a parable comparing the fertility of soil with the condition of people's hearts. Some people's hearts are like a worn path. Seed dropped there does not take root because the birds eat it. These people hear the Word, but Satan quickly steals it away. Other people's hearts are like rocky places, where seed springs up, but dies because it has no deep roots. These people's joy on hearing the Word lasts only a short time, especially when trouble comes. The third group of people in Jesus' parable have hearts like fields filled with thorns. Seed planted there is choked out, just as people's worries keep the Word from bearing fruit. But other people's hearts are like good soil. When the Word is planted there, it is heard, accepted, and produces a bountiful crop. Do not let the Word land in rocky or thorny places. Read the Word daily so your heart can produce a bountiful crop.

LESSON REVIEW

1. How does climate affect soil type?
2. Describe the soil of deserts and how the climate of deserts forms this soil.
3. Why is the soil on mountain slopes infertile and the soil in valleys fertile?
4. List four factors that affect soil development.

2.2.4 *Soil and Rock Layers*

OBJECTIVES

- Summarize how geologists apply the law of superposition.
- Explain how the principle of crosscutting relationships is applied to dating rock layers.
- Compare and contrast the three basic types of unconformities.

VOCABULARY

- **fault** a fracture in the earth's crust along which rocks move
- **geologic column** the order of rock layers
- **intrusion** a large mass of igneous rock forced between or through layers of existing rock
- **law of superposition** a law that states that layers found lower in the sedimentary rock formation are older than layers found closer to the top of the formation
- **unconformity** the eroded surface that lies between two groups of strata

Have you ever observed the rings in a cross section of a tree trunk? A tree produces one dark and one light ring in a single growth period, which is usually a year. The rings can provide a great deal of information regarding the environmental conditions during the tree's growth. For example, a very thin ring may indicate a year of drought. Sometimes portions of rings on one side of the tree show that the tree was burned and scarred. A tree's age can be determined by counting the pairs of rings. The rings on the innermost portion of the tree are older than those closer to the outermost portion.

In the same way, geologists study Earth's layers of sediment and soil to learn more about the age of the earth and to discover what may have happened throughout Earth's history. It may seem impossible for geologists to determine the age of layers of sediment when no one was alive to see them form. However, there are some methods that geologists are able to employ.

Sedimentary rock generally forms horizontal layers. The order of the rock layers is called the **geologic column**. Geologists have to make a few assumptions when attempting to determine the age of the geologic column. One common assumption made by old-earth geologists when observing strata is that layers found lower in the formation are older than layers found closer to the top of the formation. This principle is called the **law of superposition**. One problem with this law that young-earth geologists point out is that it assumes that layers of strata are formed one at a time. However, many layers of strata can be deposited at the same time.

Geologic column

HISTORY

The Mysterious Anasazi Migration

Geologists and archaeologists have been working together at the Davis Ranch site near the San Pedro River in Arizona to try to explain the mass migration of the Anasazi people. The Anasazi was a complex tribe of Native Americans who created a diverse community dedicated to native religious beliefs. About 700 years ago, this community migrated thousands of people to another location in the United States. Some scientists believe this migration happened because of a severe drought. Others believe it may have been because warfare was increasing in the region. A third school of thought proposed that the Anasazi people experienced a type of religious movement that they wanted to expand to southern regions. In an effort to study these hypotheses, scientists have examined varying widths of tree rings, the thickness of pollen layers, and ancient artifacts such as pottery. Evidence suggests that there was a dry spell and a cold climate environment during the last quarter of the 13th century when the Anasazi decided to migrate. However, additional evidence revealed that droughts had occurred in this region prior to the migration and the people had not moved during that time. In fact, when the Anasazi's crops began to suffer and they began to feel pressure from immigrating tribes, the people changed their practices to hunting and gathering and built fortified structures to protect against outsiders. The Anasazi seem fairly adaptable, which is why their complete relocation is a mystery. The real reason for the Anasazi migration may never be determined with certainty. However, an in-depth geological study may provide researchers with valuable clues to why the Anasazi moved.

Another problem that geologists may encounter when studying the geologic column is that not all sedimentary rock layers are horizontal. The varying orientation and unevenness of the layers indicate that these layers have been disturbed over the years. Sedimentary layers that do not lie horizontally may have been tilted by movements in the earth's crust. For example, the activity of the many earthquakes that occur over time cause older sedimentary layers to be transposed above younger layers.

Earthquakes and volcanoes not only transpose layers but also introduce faults or intrusions. A **fault** is a fracture in the earth's crust along which rocks move. An **intrusion** occurs when a large mass of igneous rock is forced between or through layers of existing rock. Intrusions form when hot magma is pushed into rock layers from beneath the earth's crust and it cools before reaching the surface. Geologists have determined that faults and intrusions that cut across layers of rock are younger than the layers of rock they cut across, a concept called *the principle of*

Intrusive rock

crosscutting relationships. The analysis of faults and intrusions that cut across existing rock is very complex. Geologists study and observe these formations very carefully before they attempt to assign dates to different rock layers.

Another phenomenon geologists have studied in nature is related to rock fragments called *inclusions.* As rocks are eroded, small parts of the rock break away. These small fragments may stay in the original rock layer or they may travel and become ingrained in a separate, nearby layer of rock. Geologists have concluded that rock inclusions that have traveled must be older than the new rock layer they are embedded in. This conclusion is called *the principle of inclusions.*

Shifting rock layers and the incorporation of faults and intrusions make it difficult for geologists to apply the law of superposition. In such cases, geologists search for other clues to determine the age of different rock layers. One clue they use is the particle size of each layer. Larger particles form the bottom sedimentary rock layers and small particles are generally located in the upper layers. Ripple marks—small waves formed by wind or water on the surface of sand—can also be used to determine the original order for sedimentary layers. Ripples are often preserved when sand is transformed into sandstone. When ripples form, the crest is located at the top of the ripple and the curved trough is located at the bottom of the ripple. If

Principle of Inclusions

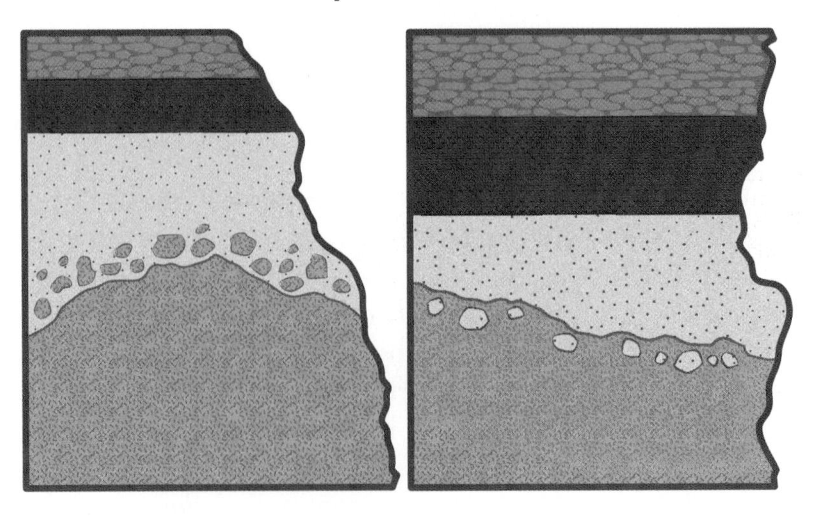

ripple crests are not facing upward in a disturbed layer of rock, many geologists conclude that they turned since their original formation.

Sometimes geologists come across a break in the geologic record where layers of rock are missing because they have been eroded away. The eroded surface that lies between two groups of strata is called an **unconformity**. Unconformities occur when movements in the earth's crust lift buried rock layers to the surface, exposing the layers to the effects of weathering and erosion. These eroded layers are eventually buried again under newly formed sedimentary layers. The portion of rock that was eroded leaves a gap of missing information.

There are three basic types of unconformities: disconformities, nonconformities, and angular unconformities. A disconformity occurs when there is an eroded portion of rock between two horizontal sedimentary layers. If the eroded portion is uneven, this type of unconformity is easily recognized. However, if the eroded portion is even, a disconformity is hard to discern.

Nonconformities occur when there is an eroded portion of rock between a sedimentary layer and a layer of igneous or metamorphic rock. When an igneous rock that is not layered, such as granite, is lifted to the surface, eroded, and buried by sediments, a nonconformity occurs at the boundary between the new sandstone and the old granite. This boundary indicates

Types of Unconformities

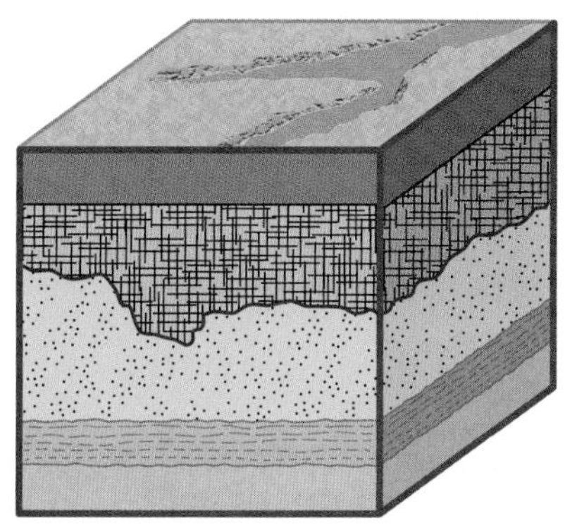

Disconformity

Angular unconformity

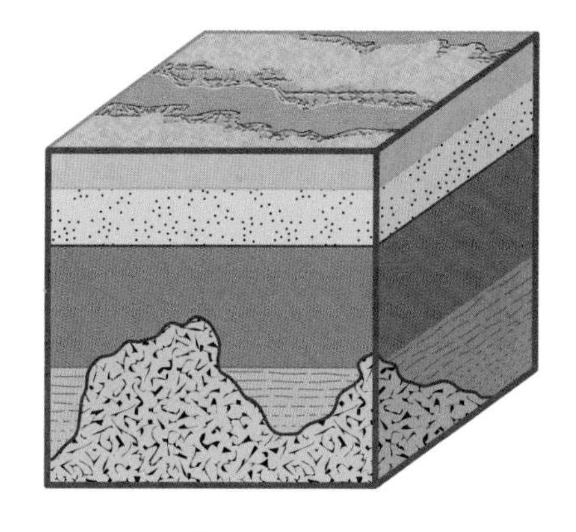

Nonconformity

Ripples in the desert sand

Angular unconformity

that the granite eroded for an unknown period of time. Nonconformities are often easy to recognize.

Angular unconformities occur when horizontal layers of rock that are brought to the surface tilt or fold and are exposed to the effects of erosion. The tilted layer of rock is then covered by a new horizontal layer of sedimentary rock. This type of unconformity frequently occurs when mountains are being formed.

Earth scientists are interested in understanding what was happening during some of Earth's most historic events. For decades, scientists have wrestled with trying to determine the age of the earth. Some scientists tried to determine the age of the earth by calculating how long it may have taken for Earth to cool from an original molten state. Others measured the depth of sediments and tried to determine the amount of time that it would take for those sediments to accumulate. Both of these methods have proven unreliable. With advances in technology and more detailed information, scientists are currently using three main methods to determine the age of the earth: radiometric dating, stratigraphic superposition, and the fossil record. The fossil record will be discussed in the next lesson.

The introduction of radiometric dating helped with some of the challenges early old-earth geologists faced as they attempted to determine the age of the earth. However, even though this system is widely used, it is not foolproof. Both young-earth and old-earth scientists will continue to study geologic columns and to develop new methods of determining the age of the earth.

LESSON REVIEW

1. What is a geologic column? How does the law of superposition apply to the column?
2. Using faults and intrusions to date a geologic record can be difficult. Why?
3. Compare and contrast the three basic types of unconformities.
4. What can the layers of the earth teach people about its history?

Have you ever hunted for fossils or seen fossils in a museum? Fossils provide people with a broadened view of God's creation. Without fossils of extinct animals like dinosaurs, you would never know about many of the amazing creatures God created.

The word *fossil* means "dug up." A **fossil** is the preserved remains or impression of an organism that lived in the past. The study of fossils is called *paleontology*. Scientists who study fossils to learn about Earth's history are called *paleontologists*. These individuals use fossils as clues to past events and to help determine the relative age of rock strata, or layers.

It is important to understand that fossil formation is a very rare event. The right conditions must be present to limit destructive physical and biological processes for a plant or animal to be preserved. There are two general conditions that must be met for an organism to be preserved as a fossil. First, the burial of an organism must be rapid to delay its decomposition and to prevent scavenging. In addition, hard components that are able to be fossilized must be present. Without these conditions, the organisms would decay and there would be no evidence of their existence. Significant portions of the fossil record have been completely eliminated because of the erosion, deformation, and metamorphism of the original rock. Many fossils may be hidden under the rock surfaces in areas that are not easily accessible or are located in geographic areas that have not been studied. Given

Ammonite fossil

OBJECTIVES

- Distinguish among different methods by which fossils are formed.
- Describe how scientists use fossils to interpret Earth's physical history.

VOCABULARY

- **carbonization** a process of converting organic material into carbon
- **desiccation** a type of fossilization where the organic material becomes dehydrated
- **fossil** the preserved remains or impression of an organism that lived in the past
- **index fossil** a fossil that is useful for dating and correlating the strata in which it is found
- **petrifaction** a process in which the organic portion of an organism is infiltrated or replaced with minerals
- **trace fossil** a fossil of a track, trail, burrow, or other trace of an organism

Fossil jewel beetle found in the Messel Pit of Germany

this information, it is easy to understand why only an extremely small percentage of species that once lived on Earth have been preserved and discovered in the rock record.

Fossils are usually found in sedimentary rock layers. Most fossils have been preserved in marine or freshwater environments where there are low oxygen levels, high salinities, or relatively high rates of sediment deposition. Most fossils are the skeletal remains of shells, teeth, or bone. Shells of marine animals are the most common fossils. Major storm events may account for the inclusion of shells into the sedimentary record by burial. Soft tissues and organisms with nonmineralized skeletons are rarely preserved as fossils. The majority of species in marine and freshwater communities have soft bodies. These species are able to be preserved because they typically are quickly covered by many layers of sediment. Interestingly, many preserved soft tissues have been found in recent years throughout the world. Some regions that contain very well-preserved soft tissues are the Burgess Shale in an area of the Canadian Rocky Mountains, the Chengjiang Maotianshan Shales in China, the Mazon Creek Formation near Morris, Illinois, and the Messel Pit in Germany.

Fossils form through a variety of processes depending on the physical and chemical conditions of the environment. Most organisms decay when they die. A lion that dies on the African savanna, for example, is quickly picked apart by vultures and decays in the sun. Such a lion does not form a fossil. Fossils form only when dead organisms are protected from decomposition, scavenging, mechanical destruction, transportation, and chemical dissolution and alteration. An organism that dies and is soon after buried by sand or mud may form a fossil. The soft tissues usually decay quickly, but the harder parts, such as those in a skeleton, gradually undergo chemical change and can be preserved in several different ways.

Some fossils form when dead plants and animals are buried by sediment on the seafloor. The hard and soft portions of their bodies chemically change or dissolve away, leaving no original or altered material. A hollowed-out impression, called *a mold*, is left in its place. Minerals may fill this mold to form a natural cast. If the mold is not filled, an imprint of the organism can be left in the rock layers. Magma intrusions can also naturally fill a mold, creating an igneous cast of the fossil.

Mold and cast fossil

The most common type of fossilization is the very slow process of **petrifaction** in which the organic portion of an organism is infiltrated or replaced with minerals. Eventually, the organism turns into a rock or a rocklike substance. You may have seen examples of this process if you ever visited the Petrified Forest National Park in the United States, which is famous for its petrified conifer trees. Petrifaction works best on the hard remains of an organism. It involves two processes: permineralization and replacement. Permineralization occurs when groundwater carrying dissolved minerals, such as apatite, calcite, and pyrite, infiltrates the pore spaces and cavities of bone, shell, or wood. The minerals precipitate out of the water and are deposited in the hard remains. Much of the original material of the specimen remains following permineralization. Replacement occurs when groundwater containing dissolved minerals removes the original organic material and replaces it with minerals such as silica, calcite, and pyrite. This gradual substitution results in a near-perfect replica of the original organism.

Petrified wood

Scorpion in amber

FYI

Fossil Formation

Fossils provide a fascinating glimpse of extinct parts of God's creation, such as the dinosaurs. Both old-earth and young-earth scientists study fossils for clues about the age of the earth. Both groups of scientists believe that in order for fossils to form, the animal or plant had to have been buried quickly. Old-earth scientists believe that the sedimentary rock layers where most fossils are found developed over thousands or millions of years, so fossilization likewise takes time. In contrast, young-earth scientists believe the key to fossilization is the presence of the right chemical conditions, such as cementing agents, rather than time.

Rarely, entire specimens are preserved by freezing soil and ice. Such specimens are one type of natural mummies. The organisms do not decay because the freezing temperatures delay decomposition. The remains of many mammoths have been excavated out of the ice in Alaska and Russia. These specimens were very well-preserved because of the climate. Woolly rhinoceroses have also been preserved in frozen soil.

Some fossilized organisms were preserved by tar. In some locations, tar pits resembled lakes of thick liquid oil oozing onto the earth's surface. Often these tar pits were covered with plant debris or water, making the pits invisible to unfortunate organisms that fell into them. It is not uncommon to find predator fossils in tar as well because when an herbivore became stuck in the tar, predators were often attracted to the site. During the wet season, the tar beds were covered with water rich in sediments, which added to the sedimentary fossil record. One of the most famous fossil sites is the La Brea Tar Pits in southern California. Bones of animals that lived thousands of years ago have been unearthed from these tar pits.

Fossils are also created when organisms become trapped in various types of natural resins. A resin is a viscous liquid produced by plants that can harden into a solid. One of the most common resins is amber, which is hardened tree sap. An entire organism can be preserved with this type of fossilization. Many insects and other small creatures that became trapped in sticky tree sap many years ago were perfectly preserved when the sap hardened into amber.

Sometimes there is only indirect fossil evidence that shows an organism existed in a particular area. Another name for an indirect fossil is a **trace fossil**. Trace fossils include burrows, tracks, trails, and waste products. When paleontologists examine trace fossils, they can glean a great deal of information regarding

Carbonization in Action

Place two leaves side by side between layers of wax paper. Set one heavy textbook on top of the wax paper. Place two more leaves between another set of layers of wax paper. Set five heavy textbooks on top of the second set of leaves. Leave the books undisturbed for two days. Remove the books and separate the wax paper layers. What do you observe? Which set of leaves produced the most liquid residue?

the behavior of an organism, its walking characteristics, and eating habits. Rarely are trace fossils found near the actual animal remains. This may create challenges when examining the fossil record, but paleontologists still value trace fossils because they provide more history regarding the life patterns of various creatures.

Many plants are preserved through another type of fossilization called **carbonization**. This process occurs when leaves, stems, and other plant materials are flattened between two layers of rock. Pressure from the rocks causes liquids and gases inside the plant material to be forced out. The liquids and gases go through a series of chemical reactions that produce a thin carbon residue on one layer of rock. The other layer of rock holds an impression of the plant material. Carbonization is not restricted to plants alone. Fish and jellyfish have also been fossilized by this process.

Desiccation, or mummification, is a unique and rare form of fossilization. This type of fossilization provides specimens that are second only to frozen fossils in quality. In very dry climates, the hard and soft portions of a deceased organism dry out before any method of decay can take place, forming natural mummies. In years past, Egyptians mimicked natural mummification with the use of natron, a drying agent, to preserve their loved ones and many animals. After an elaborate method of preservation was employed, the Egyptians buried their dead in the desert. The majority of these were simply buried in hollows in the sand rather than in tombs. It has been estimated that over 70 million people were mummified in Egypt.

Exploring the fossil record is not only interesting because new species are being uncovered all the time, but it also helps scientists in their attempt to explain and correlate different events in Earth's history. For example, paleontologists would be able to deduce the type of climate and environment in a particular layer if they found certain species of coral fossils that required an environment of warm, shallow water in that layer. Paleontologists have investigated what the climate was like during a particular period of time, how organisms interacted with one another, and what type of vegetation grew in a particular area.

Scientists also attempt to provide relative ages for different strata by studying the fossils that are found throughout the stratigraphic record. Many old-earth scientists assume that the particular layer that a fossil is found in is the same age as the

FYI

Baby Lyuba

In 2007, a reindeer herder discovered the extremely well-preserved remains of a female woolly mammoth calf on the banks of a frozen river on the Yamal Peninsula in Siberia. This specimen, named Lyuba, is an excellent example of a naturally formed mummy. Researchers determined that Lyuba had mud from a lake bottom in her trunk and airway by using a CT scan to examine the mummy. They theorize that she fell through a frozen lake, inhaled the mud, and died. The discovery of this one baby mammoth helped scientists learn more about normal mammoth biology, time in the womb, lifestyle habits, climate conditions, and mammoth migration.

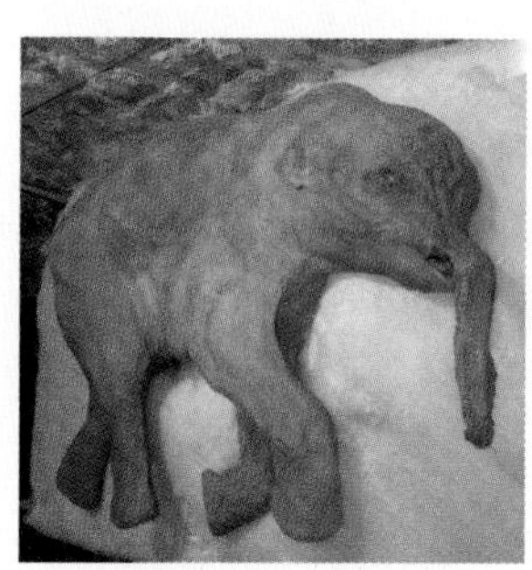

CAREER

Paleontologist

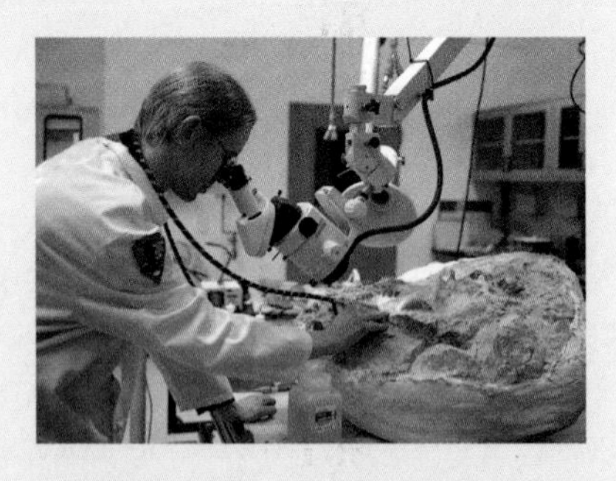

Paleontologists are scientists who study the history of life on Earth through the fossil record. Paleontologists may study microscopic fossils; fossil plants, including fossil algae and fungi; pollen and spores; processes of decay and preservation; fossil tracks and trails; or the ecology and climate of the past. It is estimated that more than 99% of all species that have existed on Earth are extinct, so the field of paleontology will be thriving for quite some time. The majority of paleontologists spend most of their time in the field collecting fossils. Some field assignments involve working in areas that are not easily accessible, such as a steep mountaintop. When not working outside in the field, paleontologists might be working at a university, in a museum, for federal or state governments, or for private industry.

fossil itself. Scientists cannot provide an exact age for the fossil or strata. They can only provide a relative age, meaning this layer and fossil are younger or older than another layer and fossil. Paleontologists also infer that the same fossils found in various locations around the world are roughly the same age. There are some fossils that are easy to recognize, plentiful, and found throughout much of the world. These fossils are referred to as **index fossils**. Another aspect of index fossils is that they are believed to have existed only for a relatively short period of geologic time. Old-earth paleontologists refer to index fossils in their attempt to make definite boundaries in the geologic time scale and to correlate different strata. Many young-earth scientists disagree with the use of index fossils for dating because some index fossils are found in different layers of the geologic column around the world, which indicates that the geologic time scale is incorrect. The ongoing study of fossils will continue to fascinate scientists as it reveals God's creation.

LESSON REVIEW

1. What two types of fossilization produce fossils that are the most well preserved?
2. What two assumptions do scientists make regarding fossils and rock strata?
3. Why have more fossils not been found?
4. How do scientists use fossils to interpret Earth's physical history?

UNIT 3

The Dynamic Earth

Chapter 1: *Crust Movement*
Chapter 2: *Earthquakes*
Chapter 3: *Volcanoes*

Vocabulary

aa
aftershock
caldera
compressional stress
continental drift
deformation
epicenter
faulting
fissure
focus
folding
footwall
hanging wall
hot spot
isostasy
liquefaction
Love wave
magnitude
normal fault
oceanic ridge
orogenesis
pahoehoe
plateau
plate boundary
plug
pluton
pyroclast
Rayleigh wave
reverse fault
rift
seafloor spreading
seismograph
sheering stress
subduction
subduction zone
tectonics
tensional stress
tiltmeter
trench
tsunami
volcanic bomb
volcano

Key Ideas

- Systems, order, and organization
- Evidence, models, and explanation
- Change, constancy, and measurement
- Evolution and equilibrium
- Form and function
- Abilities necessary to do scientific inquiry
- Understandings about scientific inquiry
- Structure of the earth system
- Earth's history
- Energy in the earth system
- Origin and evolution of the earth system
- Abilities of technological design
- Understandings about science and technology
- Populations, resources, and environments
- Natural hazards
- Risks and benefits
- Science and technology in society
- Natural and human induced hazards
- Science and technology in local, national, and global challenges
- Science as a human endeavor
- Nature of science
- History of science
- Nature of scientific knowledge
- Historical perspectives

SCRIPTURE

At that moment the curtain of the temple was torn in two from top to bottom. The earth shook, the rocks split and the tombs broke open. The bodies of many holy people who had died were raised to life.

Matthew 27:51–52

3.1.1 *Continental Drift*

OBJECTIVES

- Experiment with the theory of isostasy.
- Explain the theory of continental drift.
- Relate how scientific progress depends on the work of past scientists.

VOCABULARY

- **continental drift** the theory that the continents can move apart from each other and have done so in the past
- **isostasy** the equilibrium in the earth's crust maintained by a flow of rock material in the asthenosphere
- **tectonics** the study of the movement and changes in the rocks that make up the earth's crust

The continental crust consists of seven major continents—large landmasses that are completely surrounded by water, although sometimes a land bridge may link two continents. Europe and Asia have traditionally been considered different continents even though they are part of one landmass called *Eurasia*. Generally, continents are separated by deep oceans, not shallow seas. The Baltic Sea and North Sea, for example, are merely flooded portions of a continent.

If they think about it at all, most people probably assume that Earth's landmasses and oceans have always looked like they do now. However, scientists have made discoveries that indicate the earth has changed and is still changing. It seems the processes God set in place have been at work reshaping the land throughout history. For centuries, scientists have studied the earth, trying to understand these processes.

You know that some scientific data is gathered through direct observation and other data is gathered through indirect observation. Since scientists have no direct observations of how the continents may have moved, they must rely on data gathered through indirect observation. For example, Scottish geologist James Hutton believed that basaltic lava formed the continents

Volcanic Eruptions in Sumatra

Sumatra is located in the Pacific Ocean's Ring of Fire, and the country's 130 active volcanoes regularly contribute to the volatility of that region. Mount Sinabung has been erupting almost daily since 2013. In the summer of 2016, three of Sumatra's volcanoes, Mounts Sinabung, Rinjani, and Gamalama, all erupted over a few days, spewing ash, causing evacuations, and disrupting travel in and out of the country. The eruptions were preceded by earthquakes.

Mount Sinabung

and that the continents were part of a renewing cycle. Hutton theorized that God created a recycling world and volcanoes were pathways to a molten underworld. Hutton's theory was called *volcanism*. In 1807, the newly formed Geological Society of London accepted volcanism as the correct explanation for the formation of the continents. In the 1850s, volcanism was nudged a step further when British geologist Charles Lyell wrote *Principles of Geology* and pointed out that geologists are not able to look at the complete picture. Contrary to the young-earth belief that events like the Flood shaped Earth's landmasses, Lyell believed if geologists could see everything, they would discover that catastrophes had nothing to do with the earth's geological features. Lyell agreed with Hutton's theory of uniformitarianism, a belief that natural processes have acted on the earth in the same way and at about the same intensity throughout history.

Then in 1882, American geologist Clarence Dutton presented the idea of **isostasy**, the theory that the continents float on the asthenosphere, much like an iceberg floats in water. Dutton suspected that people can see only the tip of the mountains just as people can see only the tips of icebergs. Although not accepted at the time, most scientists today accept the theory of isostasy. Much like large ships float and move across the water in the oceans, the earth's crust floats and moves on the asthenosphere. Different parts of the crust float at different levels depending on their mass. Think about a heavy ship in the ocean; the heavier the load, the deeper into the water the ship sinks. As the ship is unloaded, it slowly rises in the water. The earth's crust behaves in the same way. The mountains that rise majestically above the

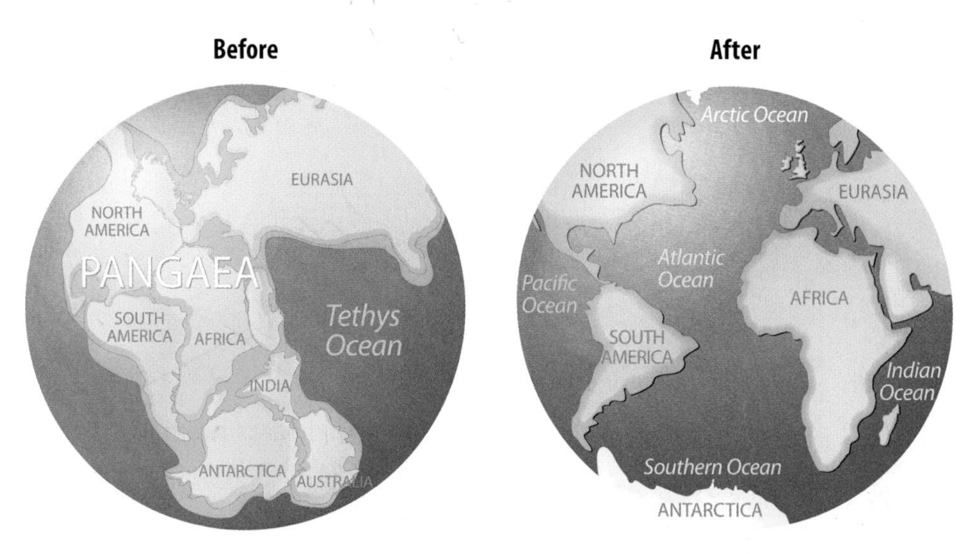

ground also sink deep into the asthenosphere because of their greater mass.

Isostasy accounts for the balance between the forces that raise landmasses and the forces that depress them. The thicker continental crust floats higher than the thinner oceanic crust because the rock that forms the continental crust is less dense than the very dense rock of the oceanic crust. Heavy sections of the crust, such as a section of crust that holds a mountain, sink farther into the asthenosphere. As rain, wind, and pollution erode the mountain, it becomes lighter and does not push as heavily into the asthenosphere. The crust slowly rises out of the asthenosphere as the crust erodes.

When accurate maps of the entire world became available, people noticed that the continents looked like pieces of a jigsaw puzzle that had been moved apart from each other. Scientists wondered if that was a coincidence or if the continents had once been connected. In 1911, German meteorologist Alfred Wegener made a discovery that indicated the continents had once been part of a larger landmass. By studying fossils, he determined that certain climate patterns had once been found only on the "matching" coastlines of Africa and South America. Wegener also found the same kinds of fossils—such as the fossil of the seed fern, a plant that is now extinct—on adjoining points on different continents. These findings added to the scientific evidence that the continents had once been joined in a larger landmass.

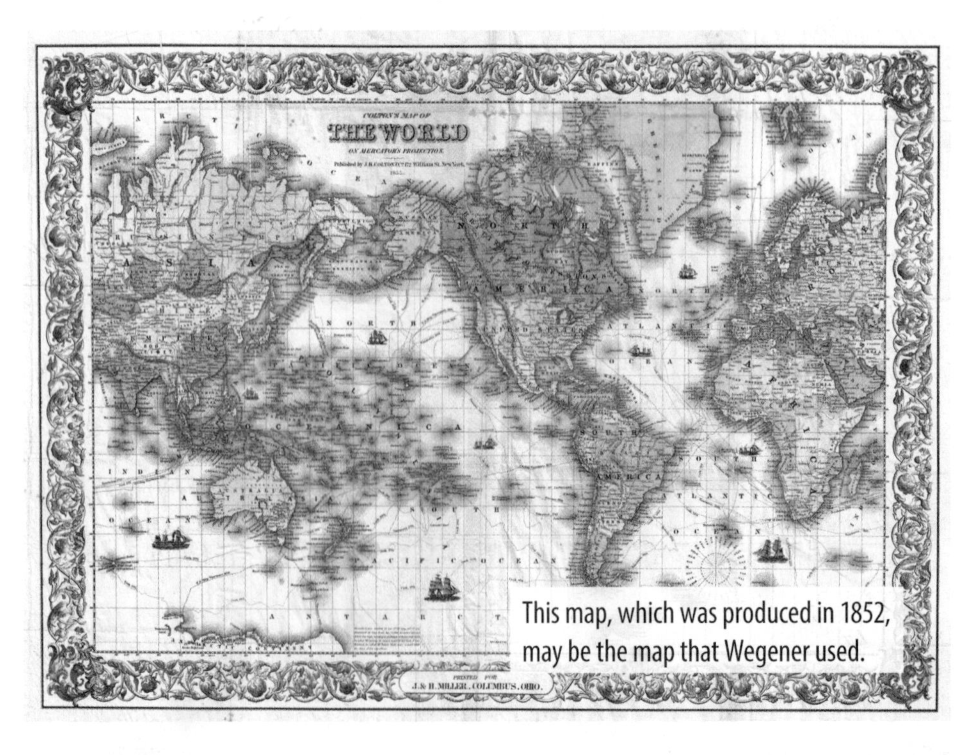

This map, which was produced in 1852, may be the map that Wegener used.

From his findings Wegener developed the theory of **continental drift**, which states that the continents can move apart from each other and have done so in the past. Wegener believed that the continents began as one supercontinent. He named this supercontinent *Pangaea*, which is Greek for "all lands." He named the water surrounding this mass *Panthalassa*, which is Greek for "all seas." He said that these continents had slowly separated into what are now the world's seven continents.

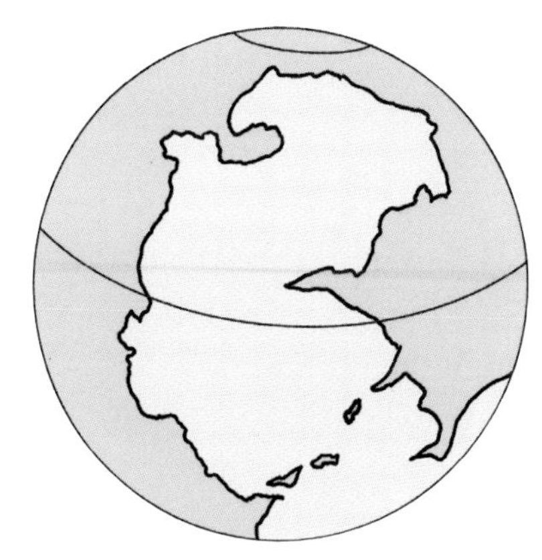

Wegener's Pangaea

In 1915, Wegener presented his ideas to the scientific community in his book *The Origin of the Continents and Oceans*. The evidence that Wegener cited included the unusual presence of coal deposits in south polar regions, glacial features near the equator, and the jigsaw fit of the opposing Atlantic continental shelves. He hypothesized that the earth's interior must include a plastic, or malleable, layer to allow for vertical adjustments caused by the creation of new mountains and the wearing down of old mountains by erosion. In addition, the earth's rotation horizontally adjusted rock in this plastic layer, causing the continents to drift. Friction along the leading edges of the drifting continents built the mountains.

Du Toit's continents

In the 1920s, South African geologist Alexander Du Toit's finding of similar geological and paleontological features on both sides of the Atlantic reinforced Wegener's theory. His later book, *Our Wandering Continents,* suggested that the supercontinent broke into two masses—the one to the north he called *Laurasia* and the one to the south he called *Gondwanaland*. In 1929, Scottish geologist Arthur Holmes suggested the continents moved by thermal convection in the mantle, a theory that is accepted by many scientists today. Many scientists had cast Wegener's ideas aside because he could not thoroughly explain how or why the continents could move. What kind of force on Earth was strong enough to push or pull something as heavy as a continent? Many old-earth scientists have theorized that the earth's rotation and convection form a self-sustaining dynamo that developed over millions of years and drives continental drift. In contrast, prominent young-earth scientists theorize that the decaying electrical current in the metallic core provides the energy for continental movement and indicates that Earth cannot be millions of years old.

In the 1950s, Canadian geologist Lawrence Morley and British geologists Frederick Vine and Drummond Matthews studied the

Convection Currents in the Mantle

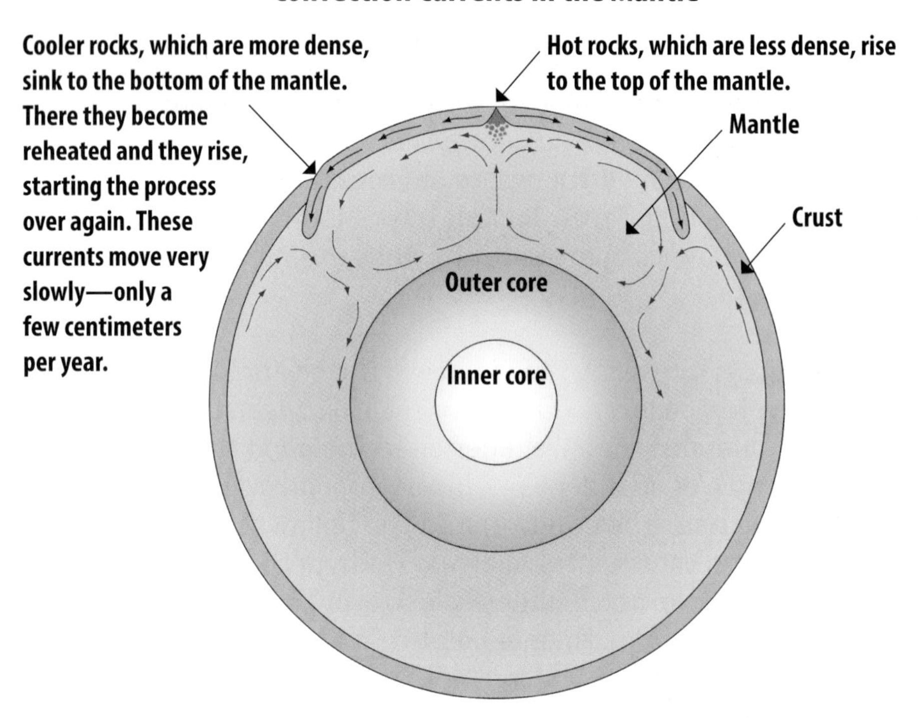
Cooler rocks, which are more dense, sink to the bottom of the mantle. There they become reheated and they rise, starting the process over again. These currents move very slowly—only a few centimeters per year.
Hot rocks, which are less dense, rise to the top of the mantle.
Mantle
Crust
Outer core
Inner core

magnetic characteristics of rocks from many different places. They found that the magnetic pole of each continent had changed direction many times. This discovery led them to conclude that the continents themselves had indeed moved. In the 1980s, NASA released a series of photos of the continents taken over 20 years. Measurements taken from the photos indicated that the continents were moving. The study of the movement and changes in the rocks that make up the earth's crust is called **tectonics**.

Nearly a century of such studies led to the current theory of plate tectonics, which states that the lithosphere is divided into plates, which are large sections of crust that float and move on the asthenosphere. There are seven major plates and about a dozen smaller plates, and they are approximately 100 km thick. The

Time Line of Crust Movement

Abraham Ortelius publishes world map.
1564

James Hutton's theory of volcanoes forming continents is accepted by Geologic Society of London.
1807

Sir Charles Lyell publishes *Principles of Geology.*
1830

Clarence Dutton's theory of isostasy.
1889

1560 1800 1810 1820 1830 1840 1850 1860 1870 1880

asthenosphere acts as a barrier between the lithosphere and the rest of the mantle. Scientists theorize that because this area is fluid, both the mantle and the crust can move. The crust moves easily across the mantle, just as your hands move easily across each other when you rub lotion on them. The continents, which are about 40 km thick, are embedded in some of the plates and move along with them. The plates move at different speeds. The fastest plates move at 15 cm per year; the slowest plates creep along at less than 2.5 cm per year.

The big question in plate tectonics, of course, is how plates move. One analogy is to picture conveyer belts. They carry groceries through the checkout line and keep luggage moving at the airport. The continents move across the earth through a similar method. The convection currents of the mantle are the conveyer belts that move the plates, and they are powered by heat from inside the earth. In the mantle, the currents of circulating magma turn in never-ending circles like the wheels under a conveyor belt. The lithosphere moves over these currents as a ship moves over the ocean currents.

Scientists still have much to discover about continental drift and plate tectonics, such as why some plates move faster than others, where the continents are headed now, and what forces may make the plates break up further.

LESSON REVIEW

1. What causes the different crusts to rise and lower?
2. Which sink lower into the asthenosphere—mountains or flatlands? Why?
3. What is stated in the theory of continental drift?
4. Starting with the idea of isostasy and ending with plate tectonics, explain how scientists' understanding of the earth's crust has changed.

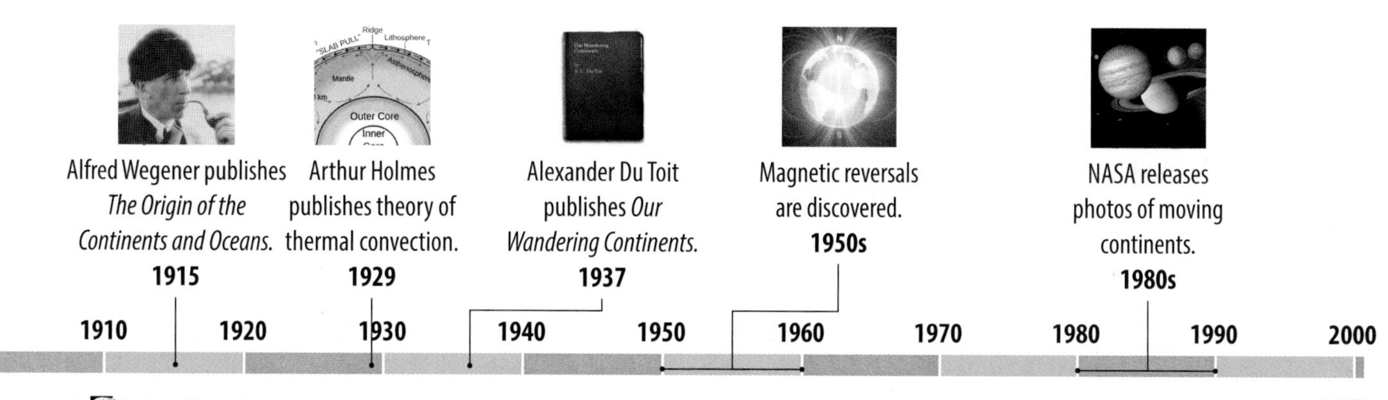
Mantle
Outer Core
Alfred Wegener publishes *The Origin of the Continents and Oceans.* 1915
Arthur Holmes publishes theory of thermal convection. 1929
Alexander Du Toit publishes *Our Wandering Continents.* 1937
Magnetic reversals are discovered. 1950s
NASA releases photos of moving continents. 1980s
1910
1920
1930
1940
1950
1960
1970
1980
1990
2000

3.1.2 *Plate Boundaries*

OBJECTIVES

- Describe the characteristics of different plate boundaries.
- Explain the process of seafloor spreading.
- Infer how seafloor spreading and subduction work together to recycle the earth's crust.

VOCABULARY

- **oceanic ridge** a mountain chain that forms on the ocean floor where tectonic plates pull apart
- **plate boundary** the point at which one tectonic plate meets another
- **seafloor spreading** the process by which a new oceanic lithosphere is formed at an oceanic ridge as older materials are pulled away from the ridge
- **subduction** the process of one tectonic plate being pushed under another tectonic plate
- **trench** a deep underwater valley

If you were to compare the land with the oceans, would you find more similarities or more differences? In many ways the two are opposites. The land and the ocean seem to have nothing in common. But like all parts of creation, they fit into one interconnected master design.

As scientists have studied continental drift, they have theorized that the continents are connected to a large section of the lithosphere and that the ocean floors are connected in the same manner. They have determined that some of the continents and oceans even share the same piece of the earth's lithosphere.

Most scientists believe the continents and the oceans rest on large, moving plates. Some plates, such as the North American Plate, support mostly land. Other plates, such as the Pacific Plate, support mostly ocean. Most plates support a combination of water and land. Each plate touches several other plates. The point at which one tectonic plate meets another is called a **plate boundary**.

Plates interact in many ways at the plate boundaries. To imagine the different ways that these tightly packed, moving plates interact, clap your hands in slow motion. Plates that are moving toward each other, like your hands, are said to be converging. The boundary between two plates that are moving together is called *a convergent boundary*. For example, the Nazca Plate and the South American Plate are converging at a rate of about 8 cm per year, which is considered an average speed. In comparison, other plates ram into each other at a rate of 5–10 cm per year.

Moving Plates

The current plate tectonics theory maintains that the earth's crust sits on huge plates of rock. These plates ride on the asthenosphere and move with the convection action of the mantle. Take a sandwich cookie and remove one side. Break that side into two pieces. Put those pieces back on the cookie. Hold the cookie with two hands. Now use your thumbs to move the broken pieces toward each other, then away from each other, and then sliding in opposite directions along the broken fault. How is the cookie like the plates of the earth? Describe which type of boundary is modeled with each movement of the cookie pieces.

Plate Boundaries

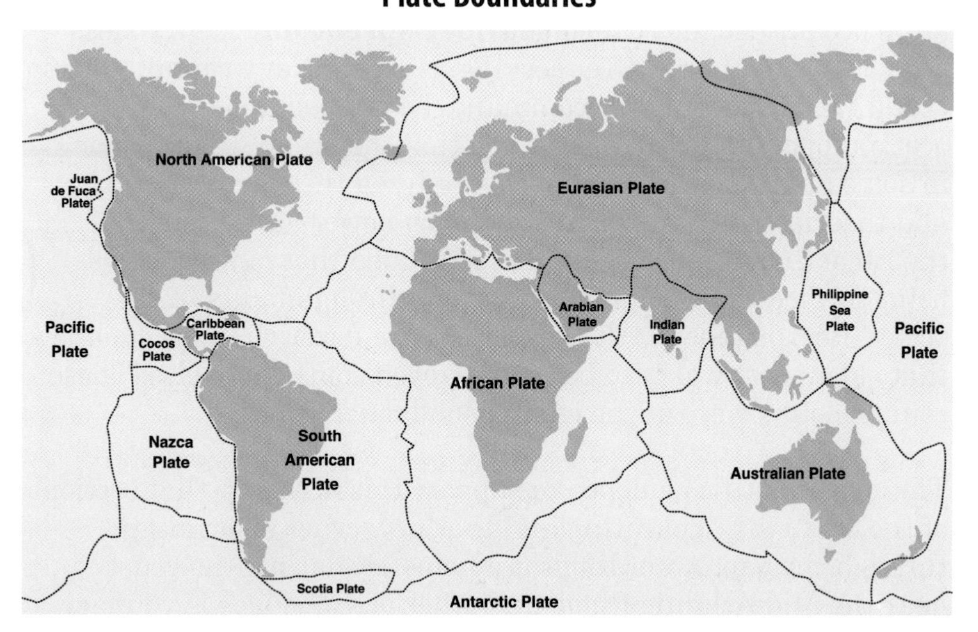

Scientists theorize that convergent boundaries occur because of the way Earth's internal convection currents power the movement of plates. According to scientific models, some convection currents are flowing downward. Downward-flowing currents pull together the plates that lie above them. This convergence may either form mountains like the Himalayas or pull one of the plates under the other. The process of an oceanic plate being pushed under a continental plate is called **subduction**. The descending plate, which slides under the other one, can release fluids and gases, which cause the hard mantle to partially melt. According to geologic data, the Andes Mountains of South America are currently undergoing this type of action on the boundary between the Nazca Plate and the South American Plate. On the continental side of the subduction, the Andes Mountains are slowly rising up. On the oceanic side, the oceanic crust is being pushed under the continental crust and a deep underwater valley, or a **trench**, is forming.

In other areas, plates are moving apart from each other, or diverging. Scientists call the boundary between two tectonic plates that are moving away from each other *a divergent boundary*. The North American Plate and the Eurasian Plate are diverging at a rate of 2.5 cm per year. Many scientists believe divergent boundaries occur above upward-flowing convection currents. At the boundary of divergent oceanic plates, magma flows up through the separation and forms new crust. The mountain chains that form on the ocean floor where tectonic plates pull apart are called **oceanic ridges**.

Henry Hess

The prevailing theory about how new oceanic crust is formed at an oceanic ridge is called **seafloor spreading**. Henry Hess developed this theory after serving as a U.S. Navy captain during World War II. During his command, he created a map of the ocean's topography. Hess observed that the ocean was warmer in some areas than in others. He analyzed the warmest crust and theorized that the crust was much newer at the center of the ridge than anyplace else. He concluded that new crust was being formed from magma flowing up through faults in the ocean. Because the earth's circumference never changes, he knew that older crust was also being destroyed somewhere else. These counterpoints were at the earth's subduction zones.

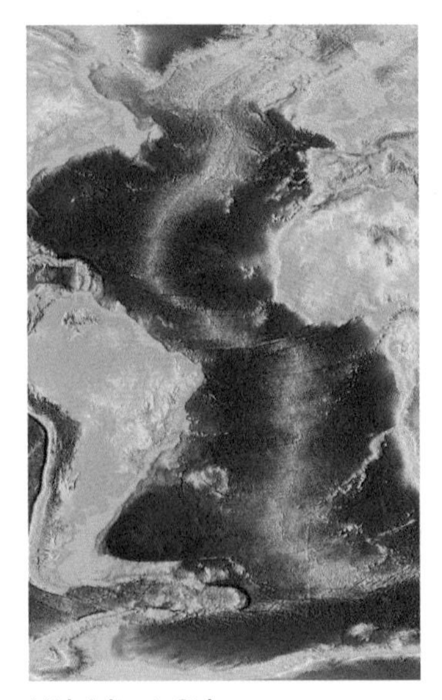

Mid-Atlantic Ridge

There is scientific evidence to support Hess's theory that sections of the earth are separating and that new crust is forming through the gap. According to radiometric dating, the crust near the Mid-Atlantic Ridge and other ocean ridges is younger than the crust farther away from the ridges. Old crust is pushed farther away from the ridge by new crust, and all crust is eventually recycled. This crust recycling explains why there is relatively little sediment on the ocean floor.

Magnetic studies offer additional evidence for seafloor spreading. The ocean floor is striped with magnetic fields. Canadian geologist Lawrence Morley and British geologists Frederick Vine and Drummond Matthews hypothesized that the magnetic striping was produced by repeated reversals of the earth's magnetic field. These stripes are different widths and are mirror images of each other across the ridge. The consistent pattern

Subduction

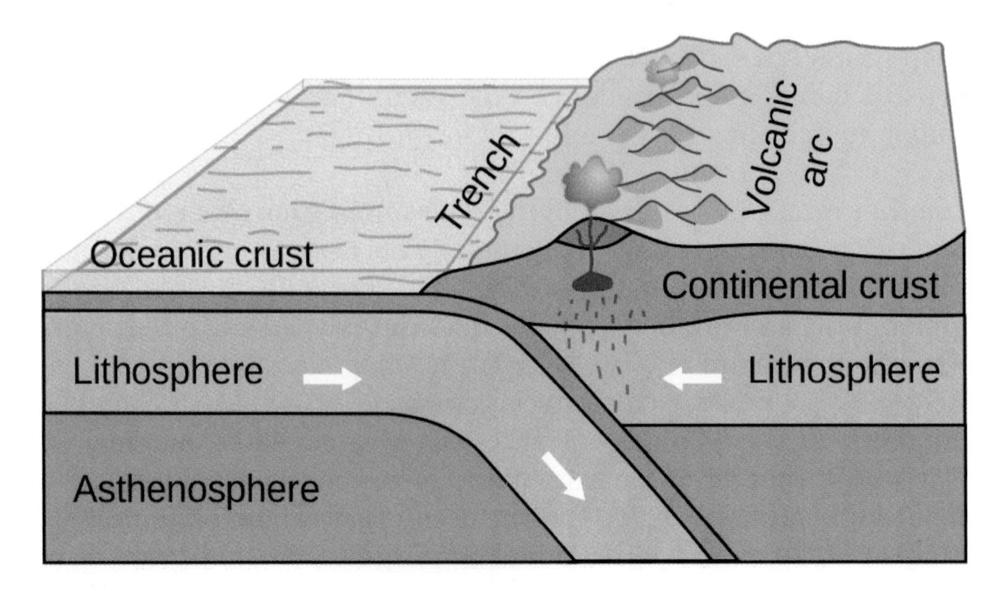

of magnetic reversals on both sides of the ridge suggests the seafloor spreads outward from the ridge. Seafloor spreading also explains how the continents move. German meteorologist Alfred Wegener had suggested that continents simply "plow" through the ocean floor, but this is physically impossible. The continents do not power themselves; they are carried along as the ocean floor spreads from the oceanic ridges.

The third type of plate boundary is called *a transform boundary*, which is the boundary between two tectonic plates that are sliding past each other horizontally. Crust is neither created nor destroyed at these boundaries. The boundary between the Pacific Plate and the North American Plate is considered a transform boundary. The North American and the Pacific Plates slide past each other at a rate of 4–6 cm per year.

LESSON REVIEW

1. What are the three types of plate boundaries? What is the direction of movement at each boundary?
2. What can result from each type of plate boundary movement?
3. What do many scientists believe causes the plates to move?
4. Using the terms *subduction* and *seafloor spreading*, explain how the earth's crust recycles.
5. What findings did Henry Hess discover that led him to the theory of seafloor spreading?
6. What other evidence exists to support the theory of seafloor spreading?

Seafloor Spreading

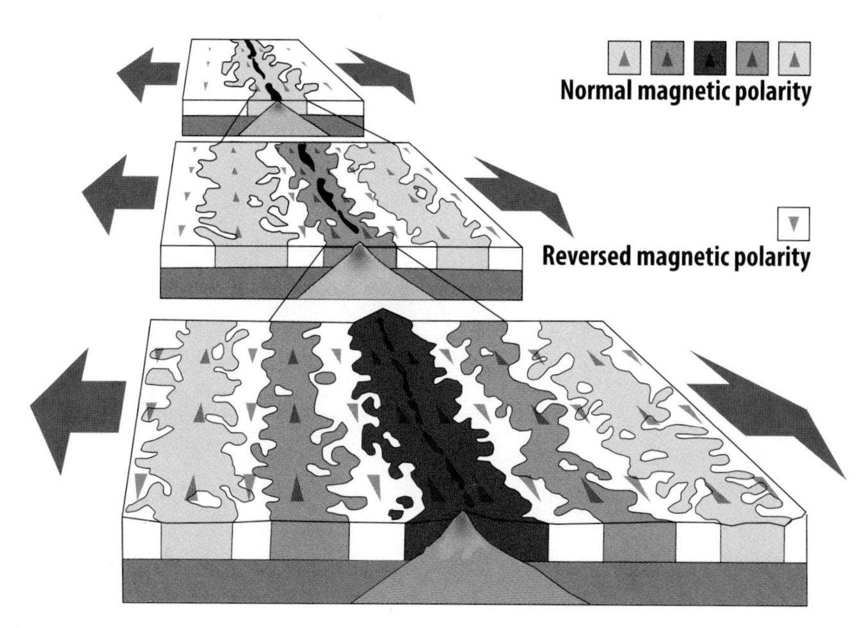

CHALLENGE

Earth's Polarity Reversals
The scientific community agrees that Earth's magnetic field has reversed polarity many times in the past, meaning that the north magnetic pole became the south magnetic pole and then changed back. What scientists do not agree on is how much time it takes for such a reversal to occur. Old-earth scientists contend that testing and dating of sediments indicate such a change takes thousands of years, and based on their models, such reversals happen millions of years apart from one another. Young-earth scientists point to recent findings using radiometric dating on lake sediments that offer evidence that the polarity reversed in less than 100 years in the past, which matches their models. Both interpretations are based on scientific evidence. In light of the differing scientific views, what gives an argument authority?

3.1.3 *Rock Stress and Deformation*

> **OBJECTIVES**
> - Describe the different types of tectonic stress.
> - Explain how the different types of stress can affect the earth's crust.
> - List the properties of rock that determine how it deforms under stress.

> **VOCABULARY**
> - **compressional stress** the stress produced by two tectonic plates coming together
> - **deformation** a change in the shape or volume of rocks
> - **faulting** the breaking of the earth's crust and the sliding of the blocks of crust along the break
> - **folding** the bending of rock layers from stress in the earth's crust
> - **footwall** the landmass below a fault
> - **hanging wall** the landmass above a fault
> - **shearing stress** the stress produced by two tectonic plates sliding past each other horizontally
> - **tensional stress** the stress produced by two tectonic plates moving apart

Have you ever been stressed? You feel stressed when pressure is being put on you. Maybe you feel a lot of pressure to score a goal at a soccer game, or to play your piano piece without any mistakes at the piano recital, or to get a good grade on your history project. How do you react to stress?

Just like you, the earth experiences pressure. And when the pressure becomes too intense, the earth reacts. In geology, stress is the force that causes Earth's crust to change its shape or volume. How can something solid undergo stress? According to scientists, the earth's crust is not one large section like an orange peel; it is more like the many sections of the outside of a soccer ball. The movement of the tectonic plates causes stress. Imagine what a soccer ball would look like if its sections shifted around. The sections would collide and separate. In the same way, the earth's plates would collide and separate. Most of the time you cannot feel this movement, although if the collisions are strong enough you may feel an earthquake.

According to the principles of plate tectonics, stress from the movement of plates can cause the earth's crust to move up, down, and sideways. Stress can even change the shape and volume of a mass of rock. Scientists have defined three basic types of stress that are caused by plate movement: tensional, compressional, and shearing.

Tensional stress is the stress produced by two tectonic plates moving apart. This kind of stress occurs at divergent boundaries. You see an example of this kind of stress when you grab a slice of pizza and the cheese stretches in an attempt to stay with the

Tensional Stress

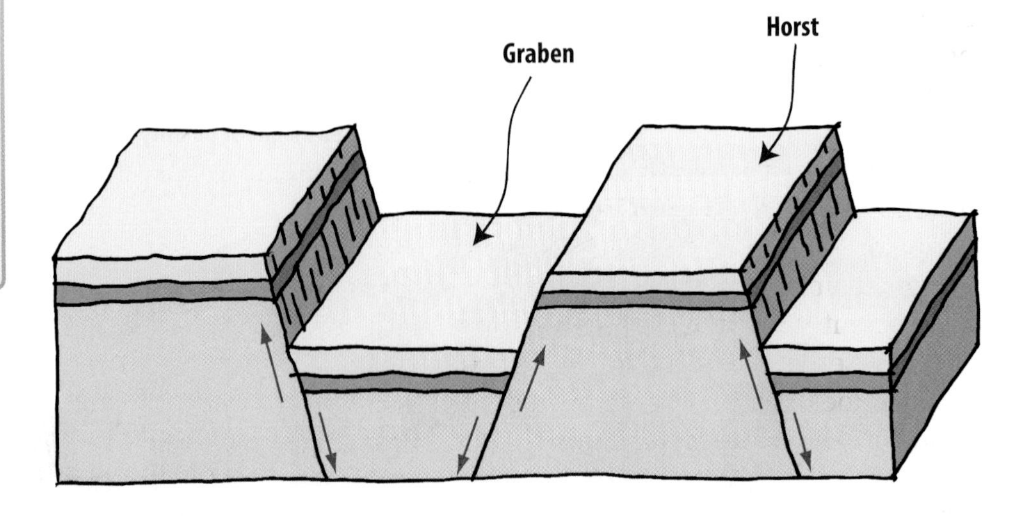

rest of the pizza. When two plates move apart, the rock increases in volume and decreases in density, becoming thinner in the middle than on the edges. In this way, tensional stress forms valleys. Iceland and Africa both have valleys formed by tensional stress. The land separates in sections called *grabens* and *horsts*. This makes the valleys look like they are made from large steps.

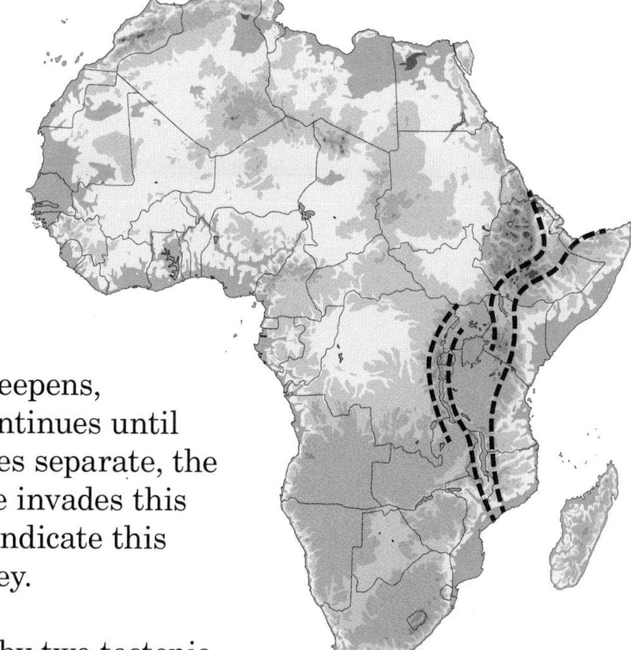

East African Rift Valley

As the plates continue to separate, the valley deepens, and water flows through this low area. This continues until the plates are free from each other. As the plates separate, the earth's crust gaps. Hot magma from the mantle invades this opening, forming new crust. Scientific studies indicate this process happened in the East African Rift Valley.

Compressional stress is the stress produced by two tectonic plates coming together. This kind of stress occurs at convergent boundaries. The particles of the rock squeeze closer together, increasing in density and decreasing in volume. Compressional stress is like a car crash in very slow motion. In fact, the mountains formed by such collisions look like the fronts of cars that have collided with each other. Scientists believe the Alps, for example, were formed by compressional stress.

Shearing stress is the stress produced by two tectonic plates sliding past each other horizontally. This kind of stress occurs at transform boundaries. Rocks that undergo shearing stress are not compressed or stretched—they simply break or bend apart. Obviously, shearing is very destructive to landmasses. Many violent earthquakes strike where shearing occurs. For example, the San Andreas Fault in California experiences a lot of shearing stress because the Pacific Plate is moving north along the state's coastline and the North American Plate is moving south.

Sometimes as the earth's crust undergoes stress, it experiences **deformation**, a change in the shape or volume of rocks. If the crust receives too much stress, it may get bent out of shape permanently. Or, the rock can return to its former shape after the stress has passed, much like gelatin does if you poke your finger into it. Two kinds of deformation are faulting and folding.

Traveling through the Alps

Fault line in Uzbekistan

Faulting is the breaking of the earth's crust and the sliding of the blocks of crust along the break. **Folding** is the bending of rock layers resulting from stress in the earth's crust.

Whether rock faults or folds depends on several things. One factor is the rock's point of deformation, or its breaking point. Robert Hooke, a 17th century British physicist, developed a formula and a measurement guide for specific rock deformation. Hooke stated that the earth's crust can be stretched or compressed depending on its elasticity. For example, chalk is very brittle and does not handle stress well; it snaps if you try to bend it. In the same way, brittle deformation causes a section of the earth to break away from the adjoining section. Granite is more ductile, or bendable, than chalk and can withstand a large amount of stress. A ductile deformation folds and bends like a foam mattress but does not snap apart.

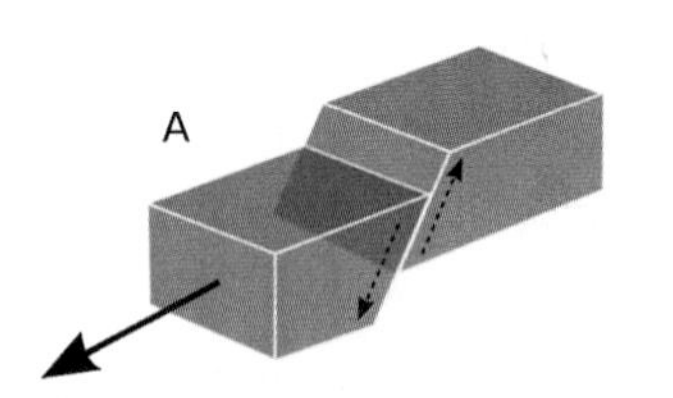

Reverse fault

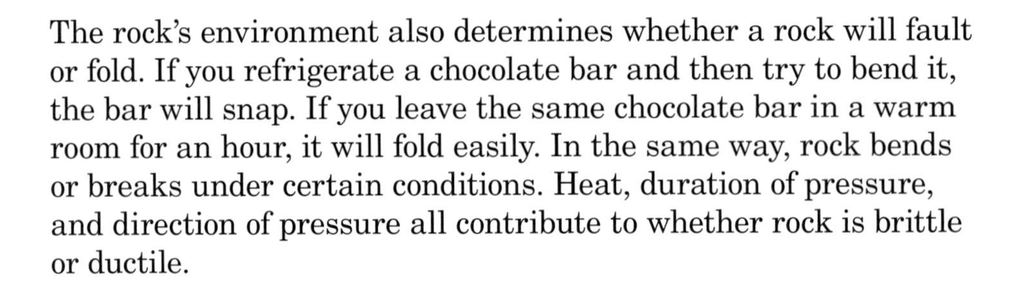

The rock's environment also determines whether a rock will fault or fold. If you refrigerate a chocolate bar and then try to bend it, the bar will snap. If you leave the same chocolate bar in a warm room for an hour, it will fold easily. In the same way, rock bends or breaks under certain conditions. Heat, duration of pressure, and direction of pressure all contribute to whether rock is brittle or ductile.

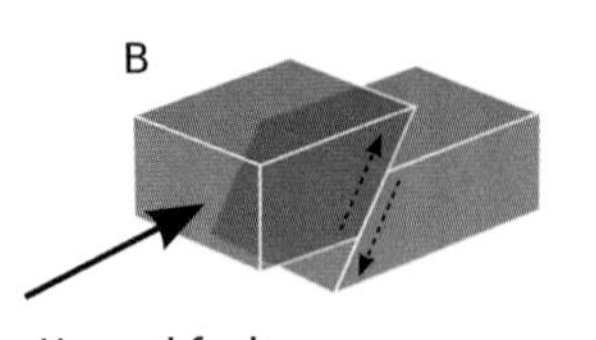

Normal fault

All faults are not alike. They depend on the kind of stress that is acting on that section of the earth. A normal fault involves downward movement caused by tensional stress. The **hanging wall**, or the landmass above the fault, slides down the **footwall**,

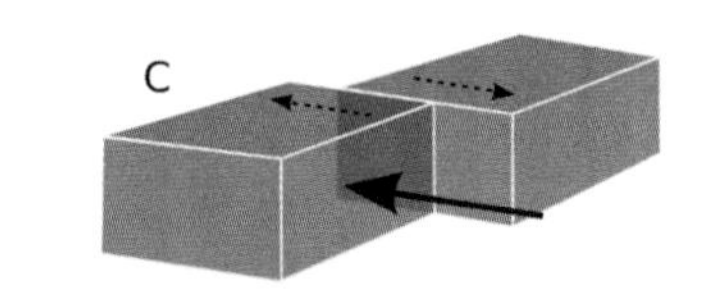

Strike-slip fault

HISTORY

Hooke's Law

In 1660, Robert Hooke discovered a law of elasticity, finding a direct correlation between the force applied to a solid body and the ability of that body to stretch. This law, which is written as $F = -kx$, helps scientists understand how a rock will respond to different types of stresses—shearing, twisting, and stretching. How much stress can a particular rock take before it breaks or becomes permanently deformed? Hooke's Law can help answer that question.

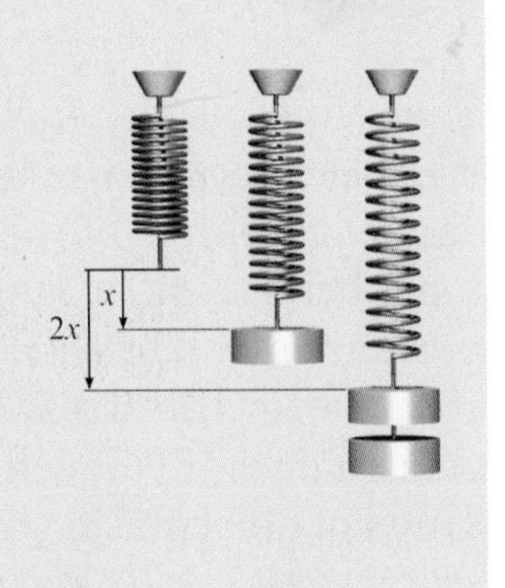

the landmass below the fault. The hanging wall is wide at the top and rests on what looks like the feet of the footwall.

Compressional stress causes a reverse fault. In a reverse fault the hanging wall climbs up the footwall. The two walls move toward each other, causing the landmass to compact.

Shearing stress causes a strike-slip fault. In a strike-slip fault, the hanging wall and footwall try to slide past each other. You can demonstrate this using your hands: if you push your hands together very hard and try to slide them past each other, your hands will slide, then stop, then slide, then stop. The earth behaves the same way in a strike-slip fault—it jerks and causes disturbances not only around the fault but farther out as well.

Folded rock, resulting from ductile deformation, decorates the earth with some of the most beautiful mountains in the world, including the Andes. The downward arches of folded rock are called *synclines*. The upward arches of folded rock are called *anticlines*. The series of synclines and anticlines in folded rocks look like large waves frozen in rock.

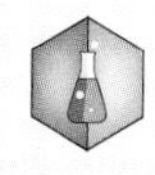

TRY THIS

Many Faults

Color several horizontal layers on a 10 cm foam block to represent layers of rock. Cut the block at an angle to represent a fault line. Label one piece as the footwall and the other piece as the hanging wall. Now move the walls to represent a normal fault, a reverse fault, and a strike-slip fault. What direction did the hanging wall move in each case? What type of stress is used to create each type of fault?

LESSON REVIEW

1. Describe three kinds of tectonic stress.
2. How does each kind of stress affect the earth's crust?
3. What is the difference between faulting and folding?
4. What properties determine whether a rock will fault or fold under stress?

The Andean fold in Argentina

3.1.4 *Mountains*

OBJECTIVES

- Compare and contrast the formation of folded mountains with fault-block mountains.
- Describe how a plateau is formed and how it is different from a mountain.

VOCABULARY

- **orogenesis** the process of mountain formation
- **plateau** a large area of flat-topped rock high above sea level

Perhaps you have heard someone reply to the question, "Why do you want to climb a mountain?" with the answer, "Because it's there!" That is the answer that British expeditionist George Mallory gave in 1924 when a journalist asked him why he wanted to climb Mount Everest, the world's highest mountain. It was not until 1953 that New Zealand native Edmund Hillary and his sherpa (local guide), Tenzing Norgay, reached the top of that mountain. They had climbed 8,848 m to the top of the world.

If you were to climb Mount Everest today, you would break that record. Why? Because Mount Everest is still growing. The latest measurement is 8,850 m. Since 1994, global positioning satellites placed on a plateau below the summit have measured the entire mountain range as moving 40–50 mm per year toward China. Scientists believe that as the Indian Plate moves steadily and slowly under the Eurasian Plate, Mount Everest gains height.

Typically, mountains are considered to be steadfast, unchanging parts of creation, but God-designed processes are constantly reshaping the earth with forces almost too great to understand. These forces result in changes over time and across the earth. Some of these changes produce mountains; some of these changes move mountains.

Orogenesis is the process of mountain formation. Old-earth and young-earth scientists disagree about the process. Old-earth

Mount Everest

BIBLE CONNECTION

Mountains

From the beginning of time, mountains have been an important part of human existence. The first mention of mountains is found in Genesis 7 where the Flood waters are exceeding the height of the mountains. In Exodus, Moses was called up the Sinai wilderness mountain to meet with God and receive the Ten Commandments. Mountains are a symbol of power, majesty, and refuge. God's dwelling place is often referred to as "His holy mountain." King David wrote in Psalm 15:1, "Lord, who may dwell in Your sacred tent? Who may live on Your holy mountain?" Mountains appear to be steadfast and immovable. However, the God who created the mountains also moves and changes them. The author of Job writes, "He moves mountains without their knowing it" (Job 9:5) and "A mountain erodes and crumbles" (Job 14:18). As scientists continue to study the earth, its mountains, and their constantly changing formations, the evidence bears witness to the truth of God's Word.

scientists believe that orogenesis occurs where the earth's plates collide and disrupt the earth's crust. Young-earth scientists assert that the strata laid down by the Flood was then folded, eroded, and uplifted, which resulted in mountains. Different mountains formed in different ways, but mountain formation is always a complicated process. According to old-earth scientists, land features that begin as small faults and folds when plates collide can grow into magnificent mountain ranges. A mountain range is a series of connected mountains. Most mountain ranges are found along the edges of tectonic plates.

The Appalachian Mountains are folded mountains.

Folded mountains are formed when converging rock layers are squeezed together and pushed upward. Folded mountains have zigzag folds or wrinkles where the rock has bent. The folding is especially evident in contrasting layers of rock that have folded. Some of these folds are visible only under a microscope, but others cover many kilometers. The tops of these folded rock formations are worn away by wind, water, and moving rock. Eventually the weaker layers are eroded more deeply, forming valleys. The regions that do not wear away as quickly form mountain ranges. Many scientists believe this is how the Alps and the Appalachian Mountains were formed.

Most scientists who affirm plate tectonics agree that fault-block mountains are formed at divergent boundaries. In regions where the plates move away from each other, large mountains form when rock blocks break or fault. The uplifted blocks can reach hundreds of meters into the air. Faulting usually occurs at lower temperatures than folding. When sedimentary rocks are tilted up through the faulting process, they produce mountains with sharp, jagged peaks. The Teton Range in western Wyoming and the Sierra Nevada mountains in California and Nevada were formed this way. This process is also occurring today in the East African Rift Valley.

Yosemite National Park in the Sierra Nevada mountain range

Sometimes when volcanoes erupt and spew molten rock onto the earth's surface, mountains form. Mount Fuji in Japan is a volcanic mountain of this kind. Many scientists believe volcanic mountains occur along convergent plate boundaries.

Plateau

Most mountain ranges are flanked by flat lands called **plateaus**, large areas of flat-topped rock high above sea level. They form on the earth's crust when hard, erosion-resistant rock caps other horizontal layers of rock. Plateaus are formed in much the same way as mountains. A largely accepted concept is that some plateaus are formed from colliding plates that are pushed together too gently to fold or crack into mountains; instead they remain flat. Other plateaus result from lava flows that build up on the land's surface.

LESSON REVIEW

1. What is orogenesis?
2. How is a folded mountain formed?
3. How is a fault-block mountain formed?
4. What conditions are different in the formation of a fault-block mountain and a folded mountain?
5. What are the two ways a plateau can form?
6. How is a plateau different from a mountain?

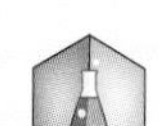

TRY THIS

Mountain Model

Research the dimensions and features of an actual mountain range. Make a model of the range with modeling clay or with clay made from 750 mL of flour, 750 mL of salt, 300 mL of water, and food coloring.

Mount Fuji rises over Tokyo, Japan.

3.2.1 *Earthquake Causes*

OBJECTIVES

- Summarize the connection between tectonic plate movement and earthquakes.
- Infer why earthquakes vary in magnitude.
- Indicate the causes of earthquakes.

VOCABULARY

- **magnitude** the strength of an earthquake

When people think of earthquakes, they typically think of feeling the earth moving. However, according to the plate tectonic theory, the earth's crust is always moving, even though people cannot feel the motion. The thousands of earthquakes that happen each year can be explained from an old-earth point of view as occurring because of Earth's plates moving against each other. Young-earth scientists believe that today's earthquakes are much smaller versions of what occurred when the "springs of the great deep broke forth" as stated in Genesis 7:11.

Many scientists believe earthquakes are caused by the movement of tectonic plates, which are moved at rates varying from 1–10 cm per year by convection currents in the mantle. The plates remain in constant contact with each other as they move away from each other, toward each other, and past each other. Because plates are not perfectly smooth, they tend to catch on each other. The sudden, jarring movement of the plates as they move produces seismic waves, which are waves of energy that travel through the earth. Seismic waves move the ground when they reach the crust's surface, and this motion is called *an earthquake.*

Thousands of earthquakes occur every year, yet the **magnitude**, or strength of an earthquake, varies greatly. Many earthquakes are so small that they do not produce any damage, and most cannot even be felt. However, sometimes the plates get caught for a long time and considerable pressure is built up. The release of this great stress produces great energy as the plates jolt past each other. Depending on the amount of stress released, the

Earthquake damage in Nepal

HISTORY

A Terrific Shock

American author, Samuel Clemens (better known as Mark Twain), experienced his first earthquake while walking along a California street in 1865. He wrote about it in his book, *Roughing It*: "Before I could turn and seek the door, there came a terrific shock; the ground seemed to roll under me in waves, interrupted by a violent joggling up and down, and there was a heavy grinding noise as of brick houses rubbing together. I fell up against the frame house and hurt my elbow. I knew what it was, now.... A third and still severer shock came, and as I reeled about on the pavement trying to keep my footing, I saw a sight! The entire front of a tall four-story brick building in Third Street sprung outward like a door and fell sprawling across the street, raising a dust like a great volume of smoke!"

plates may move between a few millimeters to several meters before their friction temporarily stops them. This movement and the large seismic waves produced can cause significant damage.

The causes of earthquakes are not limited to the interactions between plate boundaries. The stress of moving plates can create faults, or breaks, in the crust. These faults move similarly to the plates and create their own earthquakes. Earthquakes can be caused by any force that is strong enough to produce seismic waves including erupting volcanoes, explosions caused by humans, and collapsing buildings.

LESSON REVIEW

1. What is the connection between tectonic plate movement and earthquakes?
2. When do Earth's plates cause earthquakes?
3. What term is used to describe the strength of an earthquake?
4. What determines how large an earthquake will be?
5. Other than shifting plates, what else can cause earthquakes?

Part of the San Andreas fault zone in California, United States

TRY THIS

Causing Shocks

Place an empty paper cup on the ground. Then jump up and down one time next to the cup. Try jumping at different distances from the cup. Jump off a stool next to the cup, and hop next to the cup. Observe what happens to the cup after each jump or hop. What explains the difference in the way the cup behaves?

3.2.2 *Earthquake Zones*

OBJECTIVES

- Identify where earthquakes are most likely to occur.
- Describe the typical relationship between an earthquake's zone and its magnitude.
- Explain how the depth of an earthquake's focus affects how it is experienced on the surface.

BIBLE CONNECTION

Prison Break

Read Acts 16:16–40, which tells about the earthquake that freed Paul from prison. This earthquake occurred in Philippi, near the boundary between the African and Eurasian Plates. This region is one of the most seismically active areas in the Mediterranean. Statistically, most earthquakes are of low magnitude. Such quakes rarely generate much damage and cause few, if any, fatalities. The earthquake that freed Paul fits this description. It was strong enough to shake the prison's foundation and to skew the doorframes but not of a magnitude strong enough to destroy the prison.

Earthquakes can happen anywhere in the world. However, according to many scientists who support the tectonic plate theory, most earthquakes are caused by tectonic plate movement at the boundaries. When earthquakes are mapped, they appear to form a dot-to-dot outline of the plates. Earthquakes can be divided into zones according to the movement that causes them and their depth of origin.

The type of earthquake that strikes in a certain area depends in part on the relationship of the plates in that area. Plates move across the earth in several different directions. Divergent boundaries occur where tectonic plates are moving away from each other. Earthquake maps show numerous earthquakes along the Mid-Atlantic Ridge, which is the result of the North American and Eurasian Plates slowly separating. The ridge is often studied where it surfaces in Iceland, which straddles the two plates. Earthquakes along divergent boundaries generally have low magnitudes.

Earthquakes range from low to high magnitude at convergent boundaries where the plates are moving toward each other. Along these boundaries, the plates with greater density sink under the plates with less density. If the plates have similar densities, then they smash together to create folds and faults. Regardless of what happens to the plates, the convergent movement produces earthquakes. One such boundary is marked

Plate Boundaries

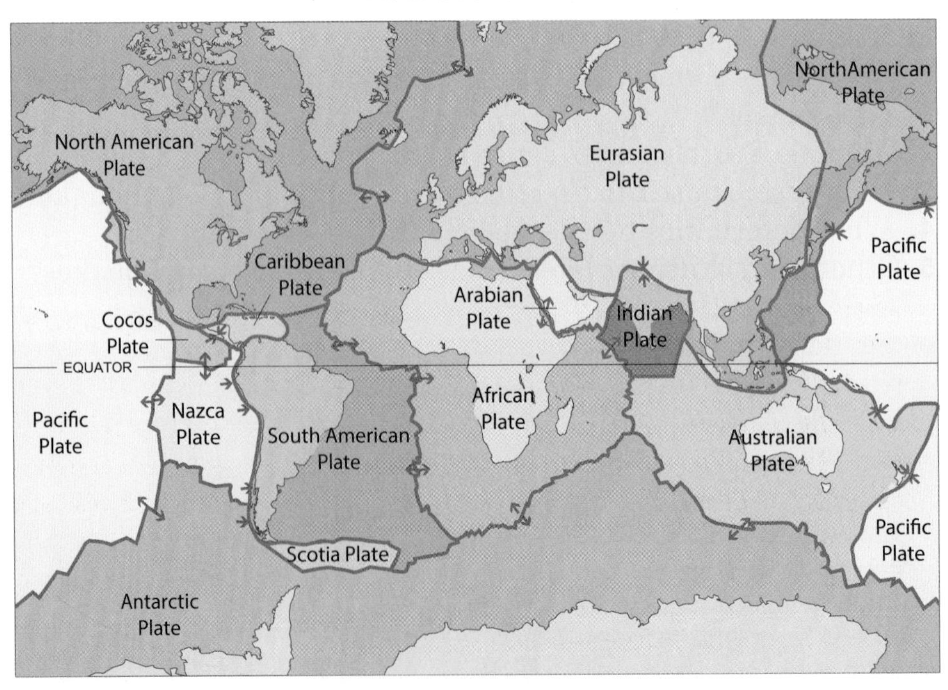

by the Southern Alps in New Zealand. Here, the Australian Plate is moving down and under the Pacific Plate.

The Mid-Atlantic Ridge passes through Thingvellir National Park, Iceland.

Transform boundaries, where plates are sliding past each other horizontally, often join sections of other types of boundaries. The earthquakes at these places can be highly destructive, partly because their magnitude can be moderate to high. A good example of a transform boundary is in New Zealand, which straddles the boundary between the Australian and Pacific Plates. The Pacific Plate is being forced under the Australian Plate near New Zealand's North Island, but the opposite is happening under South Island. The two convergent boundaries are connected by a transform boundary where the plates slide parallel to each other.

Earthquakes can also be zoned according to the depths at which they occur. An earthquake that occurs within 70 km of the earth's surface is considered a shallow-focus earthquake. Shallow-focus earthquakes frequently occur along divergent and transform

BIOGRAPHY

Inge Lehmann

Inge Lehmann (1888–1993) was a seismologist who determined that the center of Earth is a solid core around which a liquid mantle floats.

Lehmann grew up in Denmark. When she was a teenager, she and her family felt an earthquake tremor. This experience was her first introduction to a field of study in which she became notable.

After many years at the University of Copenhagen in Denmark and the University of Cambridge in England, she earned a master's degree in mathematics. She later studied in Germany, France, Belgium, and the Netherlands, earning a second master's degree. Her second degree was in a branch of mathematics called *geodesy*. This field applies mathematics to the study of Earth's exact shape.

Her work as a seismologist began in 1925, when she helped the director of the Royal Danish Geodesic Institute set up a network of seismic stations in Denmark and Greenland. These stations recorded any Earth tremors. Lehmann eventually became the head of the institute's seismology department, analyzing and recording seismograms coming from those stations.

Her study of P waves helped her determine that Earth's core has both inner and outer layers. Until that point, seismologists had thought that the unusual wave patterns they saw were a result of diffraction. Lehmann theorized that the waves' patterns made more sense if there were a solid inner core within the liquid outer core. Later in her career, she became an expert on Earth's mantle.

Inge Lehmann was blessed with a long, productive career. In 1971 at the age of 83, she was given the American Geophysical Union's highest honor, the William Bowie Medal. She also received honorary doctorates from Columbia University and the University of Copenhagen. Lehmann published her last professional paper when she was 99 years old.

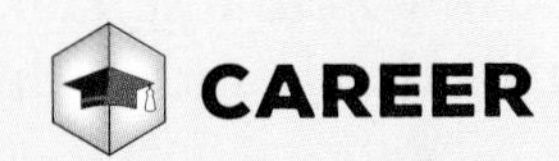

CAREER

Seismologist

A seismologist is a person who studies how energy waves from earthquakes travel through the earth and impact the surface. Seismologists examine these waves for a variety of purposes. They use waves to study large-scale issues including the composition of Earth's layers and the elasticity of different substances located below Earth's surface. On a smaller scale, seismologists use earthquake waves to locate possible oil deposits. Seismologists also examine seismic data to help governments determine where nuclear devices are being tested.

People interested in becoming seismologists should gain a strong background in mathematics, physics, and basic geology. They should also be skilled in working with computers. A bachelor of science degree may be sufficient to work in some oil industry careers related to seismology, but a master of science degree in geophysics is usually preferred. Typically, a doctorate degree is required to work as a researcher in seismology.

boundaries, such as in the mid-Atlantic region and in the middle of continents. Shallow-focus earthquakes are extremely common, but most of them have low magnitudes. Intermediate-focus earthquakes occur 70–300 km below the surface, and anything deeper than that is considered to be a deep-focus earthquake. Most intermediate-focus and all deep-focus earthquakes occur around the Pacific Plate along convergent boundaries. Deep-focus earthquakes typically have the greatest magnitudes.

Amatrice, Italy, after the August 24, 2016, earthquake

Great magnitude does not always equal great destruction. Deep-focus earthquakes tend to exert more initial force, which means their magnitude rating is higher compared to shallow-focus earthquakes, However, shallow-focus earthquakes tend to do more damage because their energy does not have as much distance to diminish before it affects the crust's surface. For example, when two unrelated earthquakes erupted on August 24, 2016, the depth of one earthquake greatly reduced its destructive power. One of the earthquakes erupted about 4–10 km beneath Norcia, Italy, with a magnitude of about 6.0. The same day, another earthquake erupted about 84 km below Chauk, Myanmar, with a magnitude of 6.8. Both earthquakes were damaging, but the shallower Italian earthquake caused much more damage than the deeper one in Myanmar, even though the Italian earthquake had a lower magnitude.

Epicenter of Myanmar August 24, 2016, earthquake

LESSON REVIEW

1. Where are earthquakes most likely to occur?
2. Identify the typical magnitude of earthquakes that occur along each of the three types of plate boundaries.
3. Identify the type of boundary along which earthquakes of each depth category typically erupt.
4. Using your answers to Questions 2–3, identify the likely magnitude of earthquakes occurring in each depth zone.
5. Explain how the depth of an earthquake's focus affects how it is experienced on the surface.

FYI

Differing Views

Scientists are trained to be independent thinkers even within a group. Although some young-earth scientists agree with the theory of plate tectonics and believe that it explains the formation of earthquakes, others do not. Both groups of scientists carefully examine the work of past researchers and their peers and construct intricate models to study the earth, but they arrive at different conclusions. For example, some young-earth researchers who believe plates are real structures and that they continue to move have pointed to earthquakes as proof that subduction zones exist in the lithosphere where rock is deformed and becomes ductile. Other scientists, who also believe the earth is young, refute this idea by saying that the models of plate movement are too simple, that measurements of many large features on the ocean floor do not indicate plate movement, and that the evidence for subduction zones is flawed.

3.2.3 *Faults*

OBJECTIVES

- Describe the three basic fault movements.
- Distinguish between the fault movement of an earthquake and fault creep.

VOCABULARY

- **normal fault** a fault in which the hanging wall slides down the footwall
- **reverse fault** a fault in which the hanging wall climbs up the footwall

You have already learned that a break in the earth's crust along which rocks move is called *a fault*. Your textbook slides easily over your desk, and skates glide effortlessly over ice, but Earth's plates do not move easily past each other. They scrape against each other like giant pieces of sandpaper. The movement can be sideways (horizontal) or up and down (vertical). A fault in which two fault blocks move past each other horizontally is called *a strike-slip fault*. The rock on either side of a strike-slip fault moves parallel to the line formed by the fault, known as *the strike*. As the fault moves, rocks that were once next to each other can be separated by many kilometers. The San Andreas Fault in California is a strike-slip fault that is part of a larger fault zone that extends over 1,200 km. This fault is responsible for the terrible 1906 earthquake in San Francisco, California.

A fault in which two fault blocks move past each other vertically is called *a dip-slip fault*. Dip-slip faults can be of several types. In each type, the rock above the fault surface is called *the hanging wall*, and the rock below the fault surface is called *the footwall*.

A **normal fault** is a fault in which the hanging wall slides down the footwall. Normal faults result from tensional forces that pull rocks apart, and they have steep dips, or slopes. Normal faults can create ridges, called *horsts*, and valleys, called *grabens*. In

People survey the damage after the April 18, 1906, earthquake in San Francisco, California. Smoke from the fires can be seen in the background.

Fault Terms

The terms used to describe faults can be traced back to English coal mines. Every so often, the veins coal miners followed would be disrupted by a fault. The miners would follow the fault up or down to find the vein again. If the fault continued in the direction the miners had been traveling originally, it was called *a normal fault*. If the fault backtracked from the miners' original direction, it was called *a reverse fault*. The terms *hanging wall* and *footwall* also come from mining. The hanging wall was the rock hanging above the miners' heads, and the footwall was the rock on which the miners walked.

California, the Sierra Nevada Mountains are a horst and the adjacent Owens Valley is a graben. A normal fault with a very gentle dip is called *a low-angle normal fault*. A good example is the Mai'iu Fault in Papua New Guinea.

A **reverse fault** is a fault in which the hanging wall climbs up the footwall. Reverse faults result from compressional forces that push rocks together. The Sierra Madre fault zone in southern California demonstrates reverse faults. In this system, the San Gabriel Mountains are thought to have been formed as the hanging walls of reverse faults were pushed up their footwalls,

Owens Valley and Sierra Nevada Mountains in California

FYI

Fault Facts

- One of the longest faults in the world is the Sunda Megathrust in Southeast Asia at 5,500 km long. The movement of this fault in 2004 caused a tsunami that killed 230,000 people.
- The Main Uralian Fault through the Ural Mountains reaches 15 km below the crust surface.
- The Alpine Fault in New Zealand moves very fast compared to other faults in the world.
- Istanbul, Tokyo, Seattle, San Francisco, and Los Angeles are all built on active faults.
- In October 2016, a new fault was discovered that runs parallel to the San Andreas Fault. Researchers theorize that this new fault may absorb stress from the San Andreas, which could explain why that fault has not had a major earthquake in 100 years.

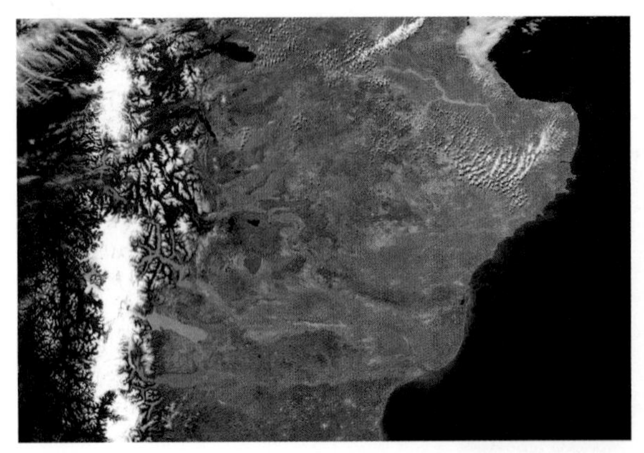

The Andes Mountains mark part of the boundary between the Nazca and South American Plates.

which are the San Fernando and San Gabriel Valleys.

A reverse fault with a slope measuring 45° or less is called *a thrust fault*. Scientists who favor the tectonic plate theory believe the subduction of the Nazca Plate under the South American Plate creates thrust faults above where the subduction occurs. These faults contribute to the height of the Andes Mountains. This process causes earthquakes that vary in both depth and intensity.

In general, the movement of faults jars the earth a little bit at a time. However, in some cases the rock on either side of the fault line moves fairly smoothly. This slow, almost continuous movement of rock along a fault is called *fault creep*. These faults experience fewer noticeable earthquakes than faults in which rock faces catch and temporarily hold each other.

One notable example of fault creep is the Hayward Fault, a strike-slip fault that runs from San Jose, California, up to San Pablo Bay. The effects are especially visible in the town of Hayward, where various features are misaligned because the town has straddled the fault for several decades. Until it was repaired in 2016, a section of curb at the corner of Rose and Prospect Streets served as a measurable example of fault creep. Two parts of the curb slowly moved out of alignment as the fault moved. Photographs taken in the 1970s showed the curb sections overlapping by approximately 2 cm. By 2004, a photograph of the same curb showed that the two sections were separated by at least 2 cm. Such pictures indicate the location and movement of the fault.

A section of offset sidewalk shows the effects of fault creep.

LESSON REVIEW

1. What term describes a fault in which the rocks move past each other sideways?
2. In which direction does the hanging wall slide in a normal fault?
3. In which type of fault does the hanging wall climb up the footwall?
4. What is fault creep?
5. How is fault creep different from fault movement in an earthquake?
6. What kind of fault movement does the Hayward Fault demonstrate?

OBJECTIVES

- Demonstrate seismic waves and how they are recorded.
- Explain the difference between intensity and magnitude.
- Compare different scales used to measure intensity and magnitude.

VOCABULARY

- **epicenter** the point on the earth's surface directly above an earthquake's focus
- **focus** the point inside the earth where an earthquake begins
- **Love wave** a fast surface wave that moves in a side-to-side pattern as it travels forward
- **Rayleigh wave** a slower surface wave that moves in an elliptical pattern as it travels forward
- **seismograph** an instrument that measures and records seismic waves

An earthquake has several parts. An earthquake's **focus**, or hypocenter, is the point inside the earth where an earthquake begins. It is where the built-up pressure in the earth is released. A focus can be at any depth in Earth's crust; some are as deep as 700 km below the surface. The **epicenter** is the point on the surface directly above an earthquake's focus. Ground movement is usually felt most strongly at the epicenter because it is the point on the surface closest to the focus.

When faults move or plates that are caught jar free, a great deal of energy is released. This energy travels in seismic waves. Seismic waves leaving an earthquake's focus flow much the same way as ripples from a pebble thrown into still water. The waves are tallest and strongest when they are closest to the focus. As they move out farther, they become shorter and weaker.

Earthquake waves are divided into two categories known as *body waves* and *surface waves*. Seismic waves that travel underground are body waves. They consist of P (primary) waves and S (secondary) waves. P waves are the faster of the seismic body waves. They can travel through solids, liquids, and gases. As P waves travel, they cause consecutive sections of the earth to push together, then spread back apart like a giant spring. P waves usually cause little to no damage. S waves are slower than P waves, and they travel only through solids. S waves move the earth perpendicular to the direction they are traveling. S waves can cause greater damage than P waves because they are stronger than P waves and because their motion can cause buildings to sway.

Seismic waves that travel on or just under the earth's surface are surface waves. They are detected after the body waves pass. Surface waves cause more damage than body waves because

P Waves

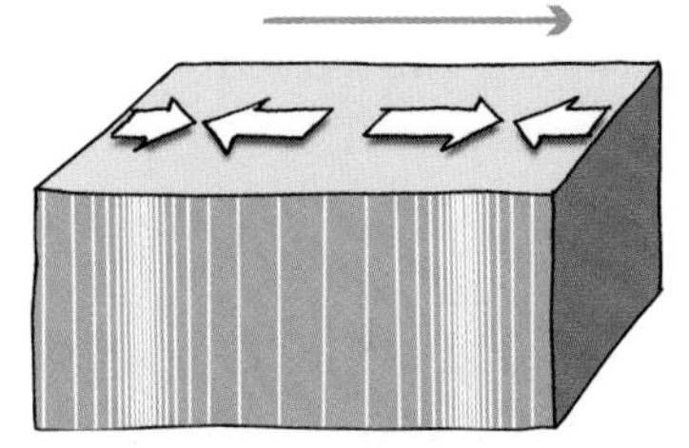

As P waves travel, they alternate between a compressed position and a stretched position.

S Waves

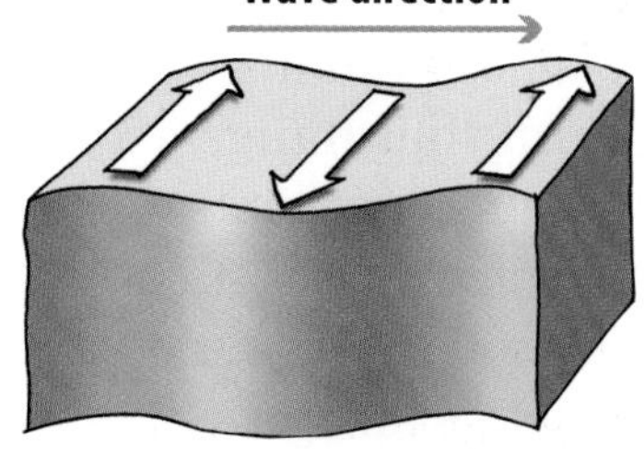

S waves travel back and forth, perpendicular to the direction they are traveling.

Love Waves
Love waves shake Earth's surface from side to side.

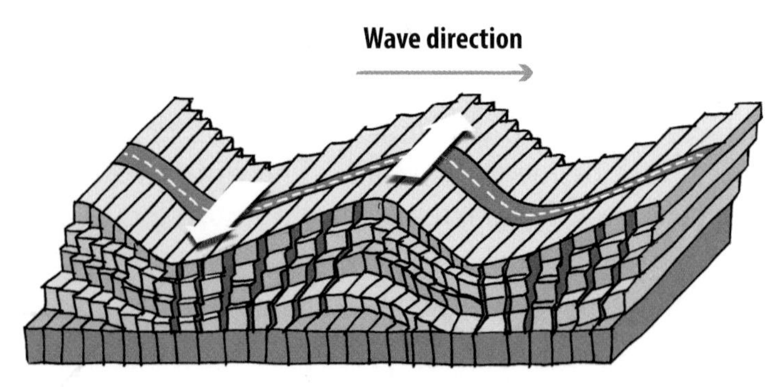

Rayleigh Waves
Rayleigh waves move in an elliptical motion as their energy travels forward.

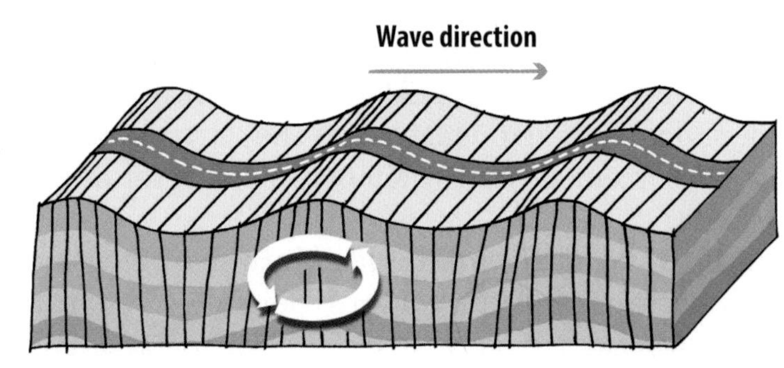

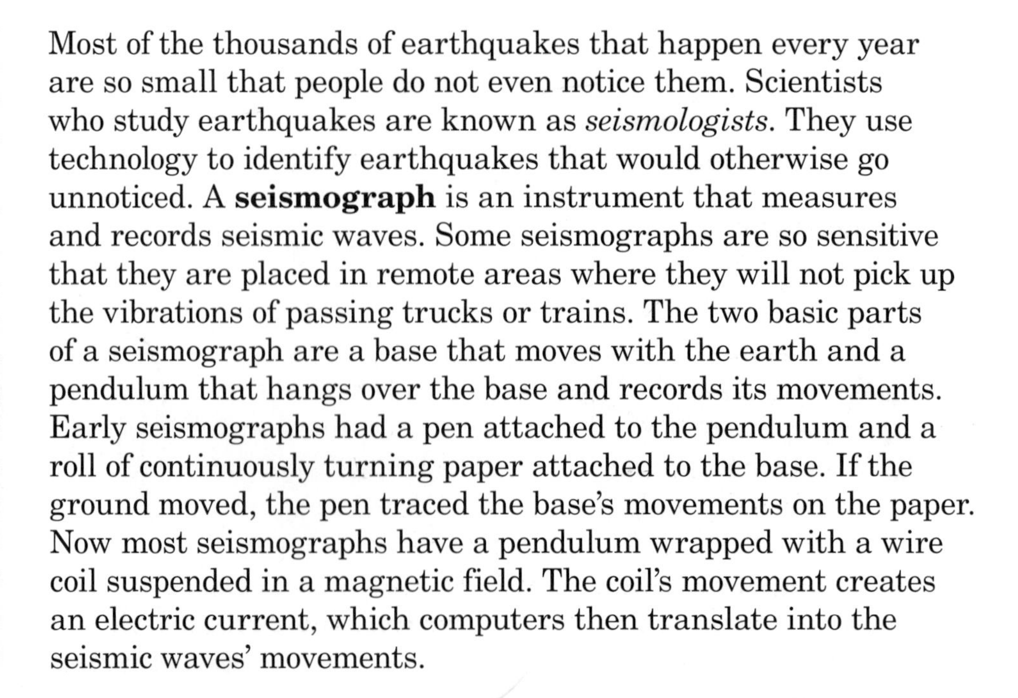

they have greater force and last longer. The two kinds of surface waves are Love waves and Rayleigh waves. **Love waves** are fast surface waves that move in a side-to-side pattern as they travel forward. Their pattern looks like a snake squiggling across sand. **Rayleigh waves** are slower surface waves that move in an elliptical pattern as their energy travels forward. Rayleigh waves feel like ocean swells; as they pass under a person, the person will feel the ground move up and down as well as back and forth.

Most of the thousands of earthquakes that happen every year are so small that people do not even notice them. Scientists who study earthquakes are known as *seismologists*. They use technology to identify earthquakes that would otherwise go unnoticed. A **seismograph** is an instrument that measures and records seismic waves. Some seismographs are so sensitive that they are placed in remote areas where they will not pick up the vibrations of passing trucks or trains. The two basic parts of a seismograph are a base that moves with the earth and a pendulum that hangs over the base and records its movements. Early seismographs had a pen attached to the pendulum and a roll of continuously turning paper attached to the base. If the ground moved, the pen traced the base's movements on the paper. Now most seismographs have a pendulum wrapped with a wire coil suspended in a magnetic field. The coil's movement creates an electric current, which computers then translate into the seismic waves' movements.

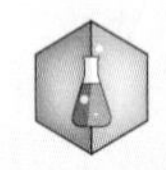

TRY THIS

Wave Refraction

Place a large coin in a bowl. Place the bowl on a table and have a partner move it away from you until the coin just disappears from your sight. Then have your partner pour water into the bowl until you can see the coin again. Trade roles with your partner and repeat the experiment. What does this experiment suggest about the way seismic waves behave when they encounter different substances in the ground?

Over the years, scientists have developed a variety of scales to chart earthquakes. These scales can measure either the intensity or the magnitude of an earthquake. An earthquake's intensity is a description of its effects on the earth's surface. A single earthquake often produces different intensity measurements depending on the materials in the ground. Tightly compacted materials will shake less than loose materials. Because the force of seismic waves lessens as they travel away from the epicenter, the location where the waves are measured also affects the intensity data.

TRY THIS

Energy Waves

Tie a piece of string to a desk. Wrap the other end of the string around your finger and hold it to your ear. Pluck the string. What kind of sound do you hear? Move the string away from your ear and pluck it again. What kind of sound do you hear? How do you think this is similar to earthquake waves?

Different places around the world use different intensity scales. For example, the Japan Meteorological Agency Seismic Intensity Scale, which is used in Japan and Taiwan, describes a level 3 earthquake as, "Felt by most people in buildings," but the term *Level 3* is described somewhat differently in the Modified Mercalli Intensity Scale, used in the United States, and the European Macroseismic Scale-98, used in Europe and other areas around the world. None of the scales can be called right or wrong; they are just different ways of categorizing what is seen or felt during an earthquake.

An earthquake's strength, its magnitude, is determined by measuring the energy released by an earthquake. Magnitude is a more consistent measurement than intensity because it measures force released at a single point instead of force experienced wherever seismic waves travel. However, two different people may arrive at different magnitude measurements depending on various factors, including how their seismographs are adjusted and how far away from the earthquake's focus their seismographs are.

In 1936, Charles F. Richter developed a mathematical formula that used printed information from seismograph machines, called *seismograms*, to calculate an earthquake's magnitude. This formula is called *the Richter scale*. Each level on the scale is 10 times greater than the level below it. For example, level 5 is 10 times greater than level 4, and level 8 is 10,000 times greater than level 4. Most earthquakes rate less than 4 on the Richter scale and cause little or no damage. Usually, only a couple earthquakes a year register over an 8. The Richter scale is not used much anymore because it was designed for earthquakes in California, which differ from those

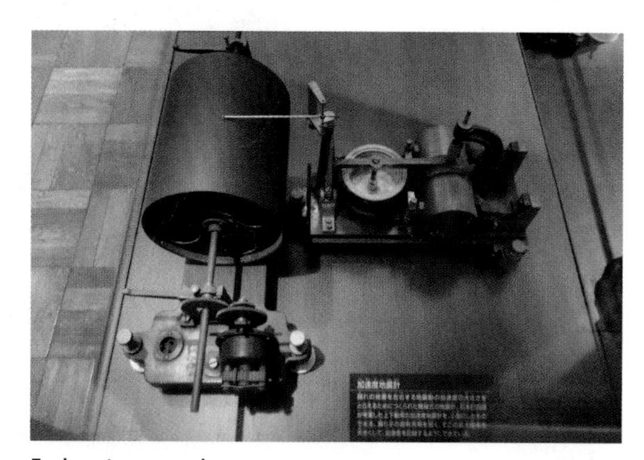

Early seismograph

Charles F. Richter

occurring in other parts of the world. It is also less accurate on very large magnitude earthquakes.

Consequently, the moment magnitude scale has become more widely used than the Richter scale. Like the Richter scale, the moment magnitude scale is a mathematical formula that is used to interpret the measurements recorded by a seismograph. The term *moment magnitude* refers to the distance a fault moved and the force used to move it. Unlike the Richter scale, the moment magnitude scale works with earthquakes of many sizes around the world. There are other scales that measure magnitude, including ones that measure local magnitude, surface-wave magnitude, and body-wave magnitude, but they are less reliable for measuring large earthquakes.

LESSON REVIEW

1. Which seismic waves travel through the earth, are detected first by seismograph machines, and have a compressional wave pattern?
2. Which seismic waves that travel through the earth are detected second by seismograph machines and move the earth perpendicular to the direction they are traveling?
3. Which seismic waves travel only on or near the surface and have a side-to-side motion?
4. Which seismic waves travel only on or near the surface and move the earth in an elliptical pattern as their energy continues to move forward?
5. What is the difference between intensity and magnitude?
6. Compare three scales that can be used to measure an earthquake's intensity, and two scales that can be used to measure an earthquake's magnitude.

Optical electromagnetic seismograph

Even if you have never experienced an earthquake, you may have seen or read reports of an earthquake or its aftermath. Smaller earthquakes may do minimal damage, such as knocking things off shelves and bookcases. Larger earthquakes can collapse buildings and bridges and leave people homeless. Even though only a small number of earthquakes cause damage, the ones that do can be devastating. An earthquake's effects do not stop with the initial tremors. The natural side effects of an earthquake can also be damaging.

When a fault releases its built-up pressure, there is typically one large, primary earthquake followed by one or more smaller earthquakes. These smaller earthquakes, or **aftershocks**, are tremors that follow a larger earthquake. They can topple buildings already destabilized by the initial earthquake. An earthquake's epicenter can have aftershocks for weeks as the fault continues to release its stress and readjust its position.

Another way seismic waves affect the earth's surface is through the creation of **fissures**, which are tears in the crust caused by the friction of a fault. Imagine chopping a pillow with the

Portable seismometer, Iceland

OBJECTIVES

- Relate various side effects of earthquakes.
- Interpret clues that suggest an earthquake may be about to occur.
- Summarize ways to reduce damage caused by earthquakes.

VOCABULARY

- **aftershock** a tremor that follows a large earthquake
- **fissure** a tear in the crust caused by the friction of a fault
- **liquefaction** the process by which soil loses strength and acts as a liquid instead of a solid
- **tsunami** a very large ocean wave caused by an underwater earthquake or volcanic eruption

CHALLENGE

Earthquake Resistant Construction

Use your knowledge of seismic waves to suggest ways a building could be designed to withstand earthquakes and their side effects. Consider both the structure of the building and the building's electric, water, and gas utilities.

BIBLE CONNECTION

Fissures

Earthquakes rarely cause large fissures, or tears in the crust. However, there is one record of God using a fissure to punish people who rebelled against Him. Numbers 16 tells the account of Korah, Dathan, Abiram, and their followers. These men refused to accept God's appointment of Moses and Aaron as their leaders. God punished these rebellious men by causing the ground to suddenly open and swallow them before closing over them again. Others who rebelled were burned by fire from heaven or killed by a plague. God's justice declares that the punishment for sin and rebellion is death and destruction (Genesis 2:17, Deuteronomy 28:15–68). God is also merciful. He accepts the death of a substitute in the sinner's place. God showed mercy to the rebellious Israelites by stopping the deadly plague when Aaron made atonement. Hebrews 10 explains that the Old Testament sacrifices pointed to Jesus. Just as Aaron's atonement saved the lives of the Israelites, so also Jesus' atonement saves all who trust in Him.

edge of your hand. The once-smooth pillow now has a large wrinkle in the center, with smaller wrinkles radiating from it. Those smaller wrinkles are like the fissures caused by the readjustment of the earth.

Seismic waves also affect the earth below the surface. Sometimes the soil loses strength and acts like a liquid instead of a solid, which is called **liquefaction**. Liquefaction only occurs in sandy, loosely packed soil that is saturated with water. As seismic waves pass through this soil, their energy increases the water pressure. The increased water pressure breaks the bonds between the soil grains and suspends them in the water. Once enough soil grains are suspended, the soil behaves like a liquid. If the water pressure becomes too great, the water will break through the surface, carrying sandy soil with it. These eruptions are called *sand boils*. Liquefaction can also cause landslides and tilt or collapse ground that was once flat.

Sand boils

Earthquakes can affect oceans too. A **tsunami** is a very large ocean wave that is caused by a sudden movement in the ocean floor. This movement could be an earthquake or a volcanic eruption. Picture what would happen if you were carrying a pan full of water and then stopped very suddenly. The water would keep moving at the rate you were going before you stopped. Earthquakes that strike oceanic crust or occur near the ocean have this effect on the water. When the ocean floor undergoes a sudden powerful shift, the water is forced to move. This movement of water turns into a tsunami.

Some of the effects of a tsunami caused by the March 11, 2011, earthquake in Japan.

Tsunamis are very powerful. In the open ocean, tsunamis may have wavelengths of up to several hundred kilometers and can travel at speeds up to 800 kph, yet their wave heights are less than 1 m, so people on ships at sea do not even notice them. But when a tsunami enters shallow water, the bottom of the wave slows down due to friction. As the wave's underside slows, the wave's length decreases and its height increases, sometimes reaching higher than 30 m. You can imagine the destruction of piers, buildings, beaches, and human life when such a wave breaks on shore. On March 11, 2011, a 9.0 magnitude earthquake struck Japan. It generated a tsunami that was felt as far away as the western coasts of North and South America. In Japan, the tsunami's waves reached up to 10 m high and swept up to 10 km inland.

Scientists have not yet discovered a dependable way to predict when earthquakes will strike. They have, however, developed

Tsunami emergency shelter

tools and methods that help them forecast the most likely places that earthquakes will happen. Scientists know that any fault can produce an earthquake. The main questions are when the earthquake will occur and how large it will be.

Time is a significant factor in an earthquake's size. The larger the time span between earthquakes in one location, the greater the probability that an earthquake will occur. The time period between earthquakes is called *a seismic gap.*

Another indication that an earthquake may be getting ready to occur is the formation of new cracks beneath the surface. One way these cracks are detected is by the sudden increase of radon gas emissions near faults containing uranium. Radon is created when the element uranium breaks down. Radon slowly makes its way through small cracks in rock and soil until it reaches the surface and dissipates safely. A sudden increase in radon emissions could indicate that old cracks widened or new cracks formed.

The sudden lowering of the water table can indicate new underground cracks as well. New cracks provide new places for underground water to flow, which reduces the amount of water held in aquifers and wells. When an area experiences an abrupt drop in the water table, an earthquake might be getting ready to strike.

Base isolators, similar to these, along with other technology enabled many Japanese buildings to withstand the March 11, 2011, earthquake.

HISTORY

Chilean Preparedness Saves Lives

On September 16, 2015, an 8.3 magnitude earthquake struck near Illapel, Chile. The earthquake created a tsunami with waves that reached up to 4.75 m. Despite the strength of both the earthquake and the tsunami, lives and property were saved because of high levels of preparedness. Chile's strict building codes have ensured that most modern buildings can withstand a major earthquake with minimal damage. Chile has also invested in sea-level monitoring systems and tsunami warning systems, which would enable people to evacuate to high ground before a tsunami hit.

Clues suggesting an impending earthquake can also be found aboveground. For instance, Earth's crust may expand slightly before an earthquake strikes. In addition, if a slow fault creep area stops creeping, pressure may be building up that will be released in an earthquake. Scientists track surface movements with satellites. These satellites include radar and lidar technology. Lidar means "light detection and ranging," and it works similarly to radar, but uses lasers instead of radio waves.

All of these clues are used by scientists to determine the likelihood of an earthquake in a particular location. However, none of the clues happen consistently enough to enable seismologists to predict exactly when an earthquake will strike. Nevertheless, knowing how faults and earthquakes work enables people to design buildings and technology that can save both lives and property. Some of these innovations include constructing bridges and buildings to sway with an earthquake, installing automatic switches to shut off electricity and gas lines when tremors are first detected, and establishing tsunami warning systems along coastlines.

FYI

Earthquake Warning

Located in the Pacific Ocean's Ring of Fire, Japan experiences frequent earthquakes. In order to protect people, Japan's Earthquake Early Warning system warns people about an imminent earthquake before tremors begin. When seismologists detect an earthquake's P waves, warnings are sent out to the media, businesses, schools, and even mobile phones before the S waves hit. Although less warning time is possible if a person is close to the epicenter, the system can warn people farther away about a minute before tremors occur.

LESSON REVIEW

1. List four naturally occurring side effects of earthquakes.
2. How can liquefaction change the earth's surface?
3. What causes a tsunami to become taller than a normal wave?
4. List several clues that seismologists consider when identifying the likelihood that an earthquake will occur at a fault. Which clue seems the most helpful? Why?
5. Summarize ways in which earthquake damage can be reduced.

3.3.1 *Volcano Formation*

OBJECTIVES

- Discuss three methods by which volcanoes can form.
- Explain how volcanoes grow.
- Infer the benefits of volcanoes.

VOCABULARY

- **hot spot** a place on the earth's surface that is directly above a column of rising magma
- **volcano** a vent in the earth's crust through which magma, steam, ashes, and gases are forced

Have you ever wished that you could peek through a window and see the inside of the earth for yourself? God did create windows to the inner earth—volcanoes. A **volcano** is a vent, or opening, in the earth's crust through which magma, steam, ashes, and gases are forced.

An erupting volcano shouts of God's astonishing design; the strength of a volcano shows a glimpse of His power. Volcanoes are an obvious example of God's awesome deeds. They not only put on a marvelous show, but they are also an important part of the framework of creation. God wisely planned for volcanoes to work together with the rest of creation. Still, volcanoes are one of creation's more mysterious and terrifying displays.

Magma beneath the earth's surface moves around in chambers, oozing through cracks in Earth's surface or melting through solid rock to reach Earth's surface. Magma that has reached the earth's surface is called *lava*. Lava reaches the earth's surface through volcanoes. Some volcanoes are little more than oozing cracks in the earth. Others—the kind that usually come to mind when you think about volcanoes—form cone-shaped mountains out of volcanic material. A circular depression called *a crater* often forms around the vents of these volcanoes.

Volcanoes may form in one of three ways. About 5% of volcanoes form over **hot spots**, places on the earth's surface that are

Tavurvur's 2009 eruption in Papua New Guinea

Mount Etna crater in Sicily, Italy

directly above a column of rising magma. Scientists believe that hot spots form when a portion of the deep mantle is heated. This part of the mantle, which is now less dense than the surrounding material, begins to expand and rise like a hot air balloon. The magma gathers in a porous region of rock called a *magma chamber.* The pressure builds from the expanding magma, which searches for cracks and weaknesses through which to escape. As it approaches Earth's surface, a hot spot can push up on Earth's crust. The pressure forces gas, ash, and magma through the volcano's vents.

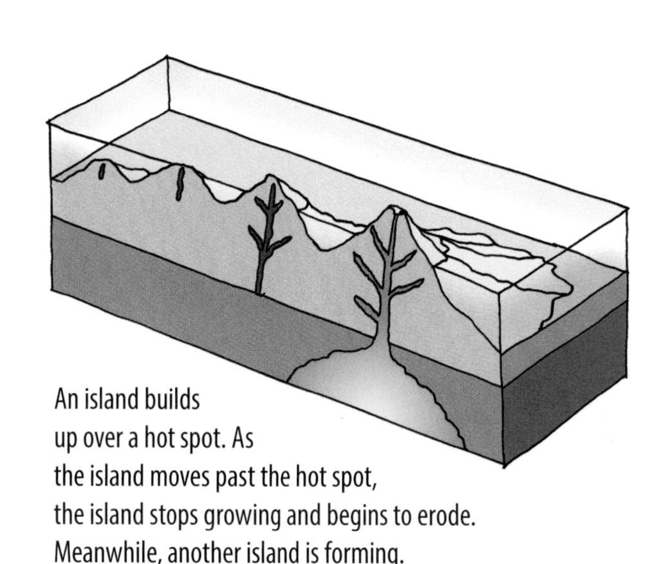
An island builds up over a hot spot. As the island moves past the hot spot, the island stops growing and begins to erode. Meanwhile, another island is forming.

Lava from the eruption hardens to form layers of rock and builds a volcanic cone as it cools. The Hawaiian Islands were formed by this process. Scientists believe the islands all formed over one hot spot because as the oceanic crust moved, each eruption formed a new island. If the crust had stayed in one place, only one island would have formed. In fact, the summit of the youngest Hawaiian

Fresh lava on the Hawaiian Islands

volcano, Lo'ihi, is still 970 m below sea level. Most hot spots lie beneath the ocean. However, two continental volcano systems are associated with a hot spot. One is in Yellowstone National Park in the United States, and the other is in the Cosgrove hot spot track in Australia, which is the world's longest chain of continental volcanoes.

Hot spots are not the only cause of volcanoes. About 80% of volcanoes form at plate boundaries when one tectonic plate is forced under another one. The subducted plate usually melts when the edges reach a depth greater than 100 km. With the increased temperatures, the plate releases water and gases. The melted crust and gases rise to Earth's surface under pressure and may erupt in a volcano.

Finally, a volcano may form at a divergent plate boundary. As the plates move away from each other, magma can rise through the gap. These rift volcanoes occur mostly below sea level and account for the other 15% of the earth's volcanoes.

Volcanoes grow in one of two ways. They can grow by intrusion, when magma moves up inside the cone and remains there without erupting through the vent. Volcanoes can also grow by

Volcano Formation

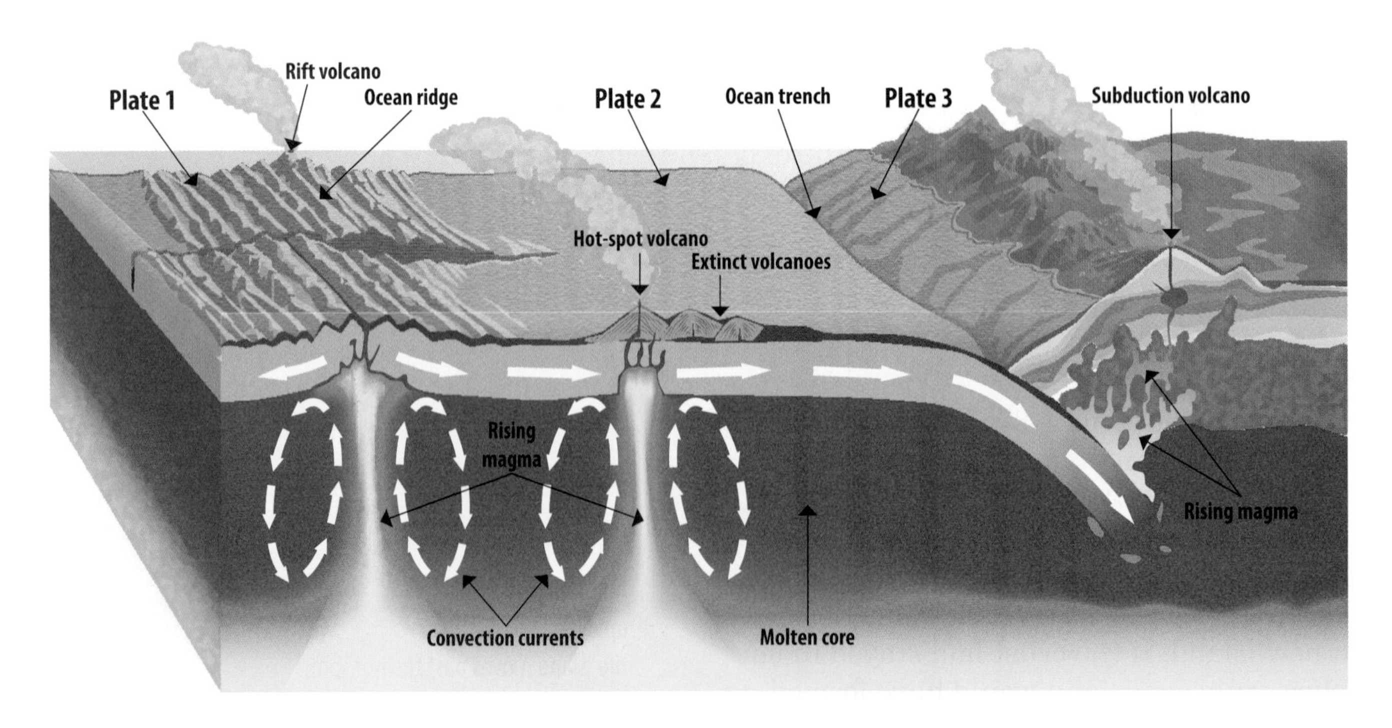

FYI

SAR and InSAR images

Satellite data helps volcanologists predict volcanic eruptions. Using SAR (Synthetic Aperture Radar) and Interferometric Synthetic Aperture Radar (InSAR), scientists have been able to measure the deformation of volcanoes prior to eruption. InSAR technology uses two or more SAR images to detect tiny surface changes and movements. The SAR image below shows Teide, a volcano in the Canary Islands. NASA and other space agencies monitor volcanic activity around the world using satellites with InSAR technology. InSAR can precisely map large areas that are difficult to reach on land. Knowing that a volcano is getting ready to erupt gives authorities time to alert citizens and get them to safety before the eruption occurs.

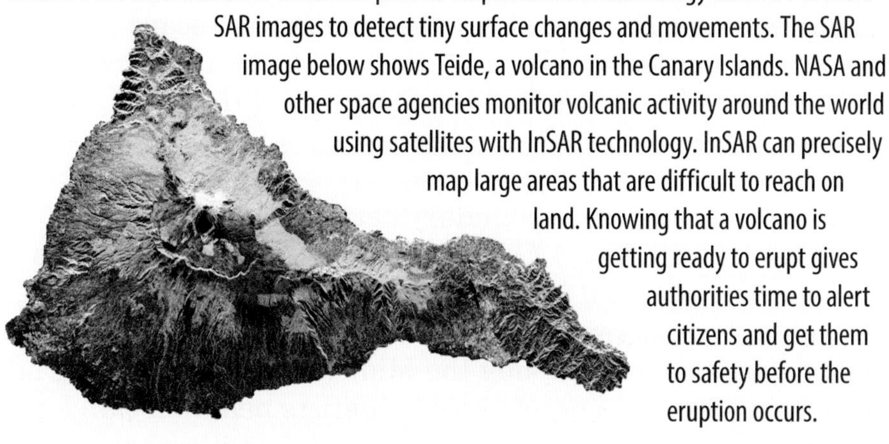

extrusion, when magma and other materials come through the vent and pile up as lava on the outside of the cone.

Although volcanoes are regarded as very destructive, they are actually an important process that God uses to sustain creation. Volcanic soil can be rich in minerals and good for growing grapes, coffee, and tea. Eruptions release gases that are trapped in the ground. Just as the vents of your house carry heat away from the furnace to every room of your house, volcanoes are part of the earth's intricate venting system. Think about the tremendous power and heat from all the volcanoes that have erupted since the time of creation. Imagine what would have happened if this heat and pressure had not been able to escape through volcanoes.

LESSON REVIEW

1. Describe three ways a volcano can form.
2. How do volcanoes help scientists study the interior of the earth?
3. How do volcanoes grow?
4. What important roles do volcanoes play in creation?

3.3.2 *Volcano Zones*

OBJECTIVES

- Explain where most volcanoes occur and why.
- Compare the volcanoes along the Mid-Atlantic Ridge with the volcanoes along the Ring of Fire.

VOCABULARY

- **rift** a deep crack that forms between two tectonic plates as they separate
- **subduction zone** a place where one tectonic plate is pushed under another tectonic plate

No matter where you stand on the earth, you are standing far above the mantle. The earth's entire crust lies above the mantle, which holds the heat that forms volcanoes. For that reason, you might expect to find volcanoes randomly scattered over the earth, but that is not the case.

Just like earthquakes, most volcanoes occur along plate boundaries, where the heat from the mantle can escape. According to the theory of plate tectonics, the plates do not rest quietly on the earth's surface; the edges of the plates are continuously being formed and destroyed.

One large divergent plate boundary between two oceanic plates is the Mid-Atlantic Ridge. One plate moves toward Europe, and the other moves toward North America. As the plates separate, heat, gases, and magma can escape through the **rifts**. Volcanic eruptions are fairly mild along the Mid-Atlantic Ridge where new land is being formed. For example, scientists believe Iceland was formed by magma that escaped and cooled, just like the nearby island of Surtsey. The mild volcanic eruption that formed Surtsey began in 1963. By 1967, the volcano had become the island of Surtsey, with an area of 2.5 km^2 and an altitude of 170 m.

On the other side of the planet, however, volcanic eruptions are not so quiet. Many subduction zones occur in the Pacific Ocean where the oceanic and continental plates meet. A **subduction**

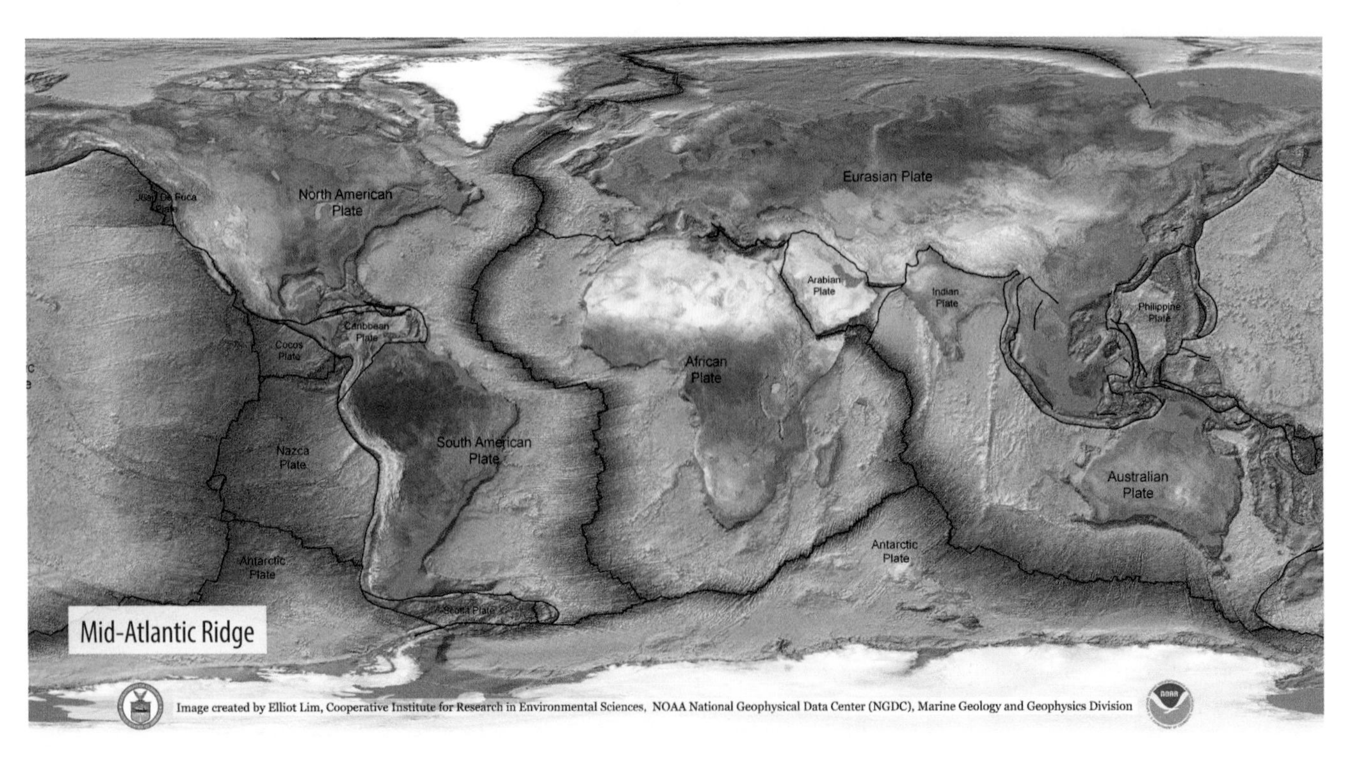

zone is a place where one tectonic plate is thought to push under another tectonic plate. The dense oceanic plate subducts under the continental plate because the basalt is heavier than the granite. The old crust of the earth is then destroyed as the plates grind into each other. Scientists have identified three types of plate collisions: oceanic-oceanic, oceanic-continental, or continental-continental. The heat generated by these collisions melts the mantle trapped above the subducted plate, which increases the pressure on the magma. The presurized magma is forced to the surface, and unlike the mild eruptions on the Mid-Atlantic Ridge, these eruptions roar.

Approximately 90% of all volcanoes form along the subduction zones bordering the Pacific Plate, the Cocos Plate, and the Nazca Plate, which subduct under the continental plates they touch. This rim of the Pacific Ocean is so famous for its volcanoes that it is called *the Ring of Fire*. Scientists noticed and described this fiery ring of volcanic activity even before the plate tectonics theory was developed. Other volcanoes in the Ring of Fire can form through oceanic-oceanic collisions. Because the magma in these volcanoes contains dissolved water and carbon dioxide, when the magma reaches the surface the gases are released in very explosive, lava-spewing eruptions.

In contrast, the rock on both plates of a continental-continental plate collision is too light to sink into the mantle, so instead of one plate subducting under the other, the edges of the plates crumble and fold. The Himalayan Mountains in central Asia are

FYI

Island Laboratory

The island of Surtsey offers a unique natural laboratory that is untainted by human population. Volcanologists, biologists, and botanists have the opportunity to study the genesis of a geological formation, the colonization of species, and the new growth of plant life. Three years after the formation of the island, birds were found nesting on the island, including the fulmar and guillemot. Lichen and mosses have been observed as well. The island has been protected since its formation and authorities only permit scientists onto to the island for research purposes.

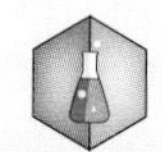

TRY THIS

Calm Volcanoes

Volcanoes formed along the Mid-Atlantic Ridge are not very violent. Because the plates are spreading apart instead of colliding, very little energy is added to the magma that escapes through the rifts. Fill a pan with thick mud and cut a piece of cardboard to fit the pan. Cut two slits in the cardboard, about 5 cm wide and at least 12 cm long. Press the cardboard down onto the mud. What does the cardboard represent? What does the mud represent? What did the mud do when you pressed on the cardboard? How is this like a volcano along the Mid-Atlantic Ridge?

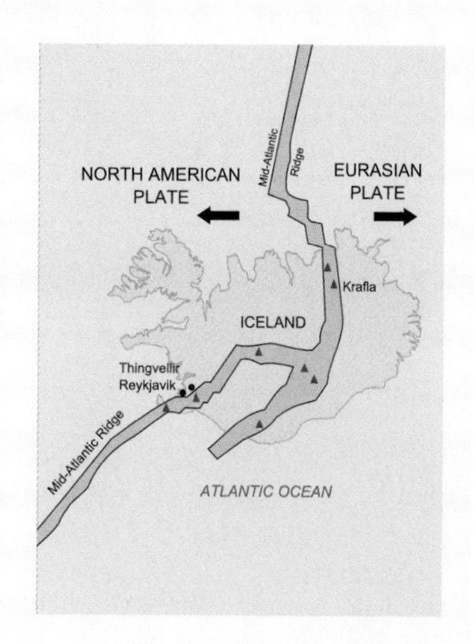

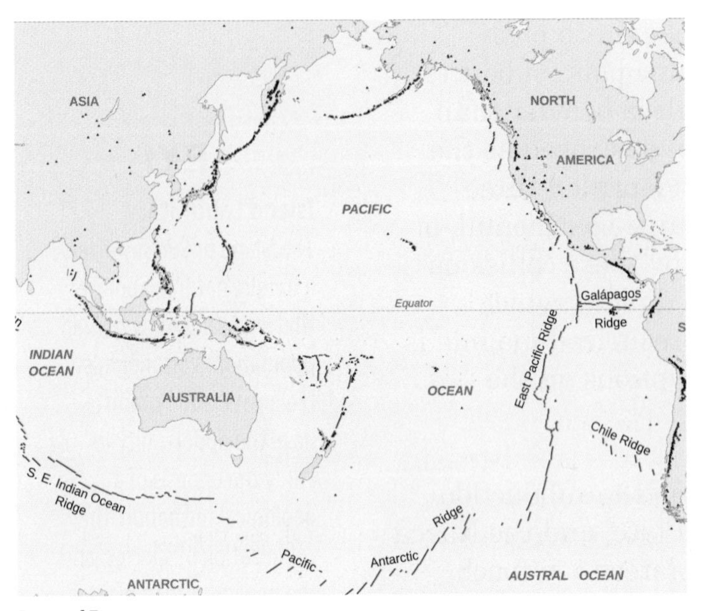

Ring of Fire

thought to have formed this way when the Indo-Australian Plate crashed into the Eurasian Plate.

Many volcanic islands resulted from plate collisions that produced violent eruptions. Three documented examples are Tambora, Indonesia, in 1815; Krakatoa, Indonesia, in 1883; and Mount Pinatubo, Philippines, in 1991. Volcanic islands are often part of an arc-shaped group. The arc shape is evident in the islands of Japan, the Aleutian Islands extending from the southwest coast of Alaska, and the Timor-Java-Sumatra chain in Indonesia.

LESSON REVIEW

1. Where do most volcanoes occur? Why?
2. How are volcanoes formed along the Mid-Atlantic Ridge?
3. How are volcanoes formed along a subduction zone?
4. Why are volcanoes along a subduction zone more violent than volcanoes on the Mid-Atlantic Ridge?
5. Why are volcanoes formed from oceanic-oceanic plate collisions the most violent?

Map of Indonesia

Volcanic Material 3.3.3

What is the first thing you think about when you picture a volcano? Most people think of boiling red lava shooting out of a mountain. It is hard to imagine how hot that melted rock is. Lava reaches temperatures of 1,200°C. The main ingredients in lava are silicate and gas. The more silicate in the lava, the less easily it flows. Lava is extrusive; it cools aboveground.

Pahoehoe is lava that has a smooth or billowy surface. This type of lava flows easily. Pahoehoe takes several forms. For example, it can be puffy layers of lava that look like large black clouds sitting on the earth. It can also be ropy-textured lava, which forms when the surface lava hardens but the lava beneath it continues to flow. As pahoehoe makes its way down the sides of the volcano cone, hot lava continues to flow under the cooled, hardened surface lava. After the hot lava has flowed past, the cooled crust forms a lava cave. Within the cave, the cooled cones of lava look like stalactites.

In contrast, **aa** lava has a rough surface. As it flows, it carries rough rock and cooled lava fragments from the volcano. If you walked across aa, its sharp edges would shred the soles of your shoes. The rough surface covers the dense, actively flowing core of lava. As this core of lava moves downhill, the rough fragments float along the surface until they eventually fall down. Some fragments are covered by the moving flow. A layer of rock and cooled lava fragments are found at the top and the bottom of an aa flow. Ancient peoples used aa to make weapons and tools.

Sometimes magma cools and hardens underground. The process is called *intrusive action* because foreign matter,

Pahoehoe on the coastal plain of Kilauea volcano in Hawaii

OBJECTIVES

- Compare pahoehoe lava to aa lava.
- Explain why intrusive rock has larger crystals than extrusive rock.
- Classify volcanic materials as plutons or pyroclasts.

VOCABULARY

- **aa** lava that has a rough surface
- **pahoehoe** lava that has a smooth or billowy surface
- **pluton** a body of magma that has hardened underground
- **pyroclast** a solid volcanic material such as ash and rock that has been ejected during an eruption
- **volcanic bomb** a fragment of molten rock that is shot into the air by a volcano

Pumice is so light it can sit on a rolled $20 bill.

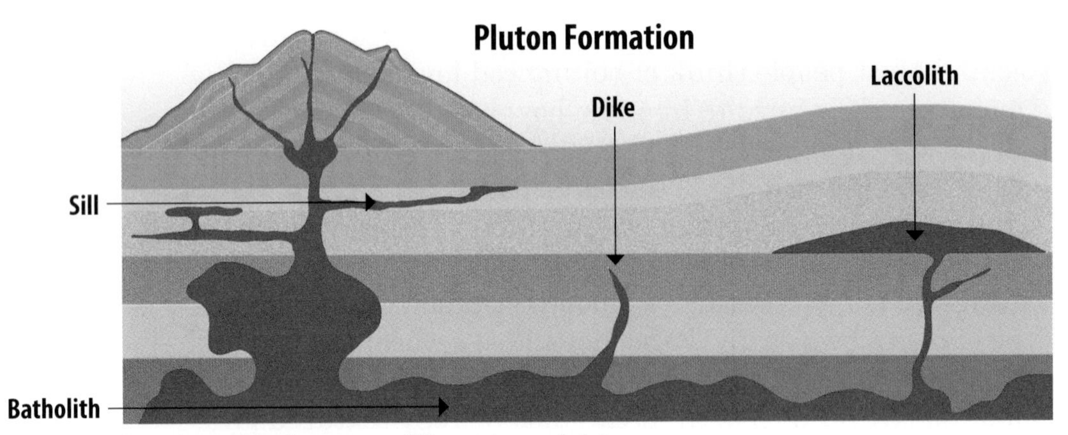

Intrusive activity forms many different types of plutons.

magma, intrudes into the existing rocks. As magma makes its way through the rocks underground, its heat changes the rocks around it. In contrast, lava's heat changes only the rocks underneath the lava. The crystalline textures of rocks differ depending on whether they are extrusive or intrusive. In general, rocks formed from lava, which is extrusive, have small or no crystals. However, the size of crystals in plutonic rock is quite a bit larger. This difference in crystal size occurs because plutonic rock is intrusive, and it takes a long time to cool, providing time for larger crystals to grow.

A body of magma that has hardened underground is called a **pluton**. Many plutons stay buried, but some are uncovered when the surrounding rock is worn away. Plutons form in different shapes. A long, horizontal pluton is called *a sill*. The Romans built part of Hadrian's Wall on a sill in Britain around 120 AD. Laccoliths also intrude horizontally. These plutons form from larger puddles of magma and are characterized by a dome shape. Plutons that run vertically and are usually straight are called *dikes*. Dikes can vary in thickness from a few centimeters to hundreds of meters. The largest intrusion, often made of several plutons, is called *a batholith*. Some batholiths extend to a depth of nearly 15 km and almost reach the base of the earth's crust. By their definition, batholiths must have a surface area of at least 100 km^2. In North America, the Idaho Batholith is about 40,000 km^2 and another large batholith forms the entire Sierra Nevada mountain range, including Yosemite National Park.

Dike in Makhtesh Ramon in Israel

Volcanic eruptions hurl materials other than lava into the air. **Pyroclasts** are solid extrusive materials such as ash and rocks that are thrown aloft. Ash clouds of finely broken rock fragments and gas pose a serious threat to living things. Volcanic ash is extremely fine but also very sharp. Winds can carry these clouds

FYI

Volcanic Ash

Volcanic ash is hard and does not dissolve in water; it is as abrasive as crushed glass. Although lava may seem to be the most frightening volcanic material, ash is the most deadly. Although it cools shortly after an eruption, it is very hot when it exits the volcano. It can obscure sunlight, creating complete darkness. Ash is slippery and can make roads and runways impassible. Its abrasive nature can damage machinery. It can clog automobile and jet engines, or melt in hot engines and fuse to engine parts. Roofs can collapse under its weight.

for thousands of kilometers from the volcano. For example, when Mount Saint Helens erupted in the state of Washington in 1980, the massive ash cloud grew to 24 km high in 15 minutes. Most of the ash landed within 180 km of the mountain, but some ash reached the opposite coastline within days. Ash from the volcano circled the earth in 15 days.

Volcanic bomb from the Mojave Desert

Ash is made of particles less than 4 mm in size. Other pyroclastic materials are larger. Pumice is a lightweight porous rock filled with holes that once held trapped gases. Depending on how large its holes are, some types of pumice can even float. Solid rock fragments greater than 64 mm in size are classified as volcanic blocks. Some eruptions have thrown large volcanic blocks as far as 20 km. **Volcanic bombs** are blobs of molten rock that are lobbed into the air by a volcano. They are also greater than 64 mm in size. As they fall to Earth, the outside cools, but the inside is still warm. When the bombs hit the ground, they squish, spreading out at the ends. The flight of the bomb, the cooling process, and the pressure of the fall give volcanic bombs distinctive shapes. Scientists name the bombs according to the shape they take after landing—such as spindle, pancake, ribbon, or bread-crust bombs.

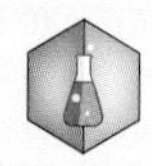

TRY THIS

Plutons

Cut a block of modeling clay into two pieces. Carve areas from the clay as molds for a type of pluton. Each half should be a mirror image of the other half. Make sure that a vent runs from each mold to the edge of the clay. Put the clay pieces together, matching the two pieces. Pour plaster of paris into the opening so it runs into the vent and fills the molds. Allow the plaster to dry and remove the clay to reveal the pluton. Identify the type of pluton and label it.

LESSON REVIEW

1. What is the difference between pahoehoe lava and aa lava?
2. Classify the different types of pyroclasts from smallest particle to largest.
3. What is a pluton?
4. Why are crystals larger in plutonic rock than in other volcanic materials like pyroclasts?

3.3.4 *Types and Eruptions*

OBJECTIVES

- Describe three categories of volcanoes.
- Relate the type of volcanic eruption to the kind of volcano produced.
- Identify the components of a volcanic eruption and how they affect the type of eruption that occurs.

VOCABULARY

- **caldera** a volcanic crater that is greater than 2 km in diameter and is formed by the collapse of surface rock into an empty magma chamber
- **plug** a structure of hardened magma that forms inside a vent

Around 1,500 volcanoes dot the earth. According to historical records, approximately 500 of these volcanoes have erupted. A volcano that has recently erupted or will soon erupt is called *an active volcano*. The sides of an active volcano show little erosion. Some active volcanoes release gases, smoke, and ash, and they heat up surrounding lakes, streams, and rocks. A volcano that is currently erupting is called *an alive volcano*.

Volcanoes can go dormant just as plants go dormant in the winter until warmer temperatures allow them to grow. A dormant volcano is a one that has not erupted for a long time but may erupt again. After a volcano unleashes its built-up pressure, it can sit for years without erupting. Volcanoes that have no recent history of eruptions and that show no signs of eruption are classified as *dormant volcanoes*. But these volcanoes are not dead—they are only sleeping. For example, in 1991, one of these sleeping giants awoke. Mount Pinatubo in the Philippines erupted after 600 years of being dormant.

Hardened magma can form a **plug** in the volcano's center. Weathering and erosion wear down the outside of the volcano, but the plug resists these forces. After the outer material has weathered and eroded away, the volcano's vent remains filled with a column of cooled magma sticking up out of the earth. When only a volcanic plug remains, the volcano is usually considered extinct. An extinct volcano is a volcano that can no longer erupt. However, it is hard to tell which volcanoes are truly extinct. The magma below the volcano might be gathering strength and preparing

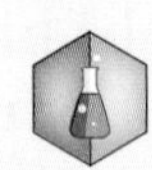

TRY THIS

Volcanic Plug

The existence of a plug in a volcanic vent can create large amounts of pressure inside the volcano. The gases build up pressure because they are contained under the plug. Eventually, so much pressure can build up that the plug is blown out of the vent. Create a simulation of an eruption with a volcanic plug. Pour 120 mL of vinegar into an empty 2 L bottle. Place 5 mL of baking soda on a 7.5 cm strip of bathroom tissue. Spread the baking soda in a line; roll the paper around the baking soda. Keep the baking soda secure by twisting the ends of the tissue. Drop the soda packet into the bottle and quickly place the cork in the opening, barely sealing the bottle. Stand about 1 m away from the bottle and watch what happens. Did the cork come out of the bottle? Did the "magma" erupt? Would you call the eruption gentle or violent? What caused the cork to come out of the bottle? What does the cork represent? What do the baking soda and vinegar produce that is similar to a product of a volcanic eruption?

to erupt again. Scientists are careful about declaring a volcano extinct.

Roque de Agando is an exposed volcanic plug on La Gomera in the Canary Islands.

Volcanoes erupt differently depending on the magma composition, the temperature of the magma, and the amount of pressure on the magma. Heat, pressure, gases, lava, and pyroclastic materials are all components of an eruption. Eruptions are classified into six different types according to their explosiveness and kind of volcanic material they emit: Icelandic, Hawaiian, Strombolian, Vulcanian, Peléan, and Plinian. The higher the amount of gas, the greater the violence. The varying action of the eruptions creates different sizes and shapes of volcanoes. As eruptions become more violent, cone shapes become steeper.

A shield volcano is a gently sloping volcano built almost entirely of lava flows. Some shield volcanoes have several vents. These vents spread the lava over wide areas. For example, Mauna Loa in Hawaii has an area of 5,271 km^2. Shield volcanoes form from Icelandic and Hawaiian eruptions. An Icelandic eruption has very little gaseous content with thin lava that pours out from several vents. A Hawaiian eruption is a mild to moderate eruption of gases and thin lava through one vent or several fissures. Neither of these eruptions is very explosive. The lava exiting the volcano has low viscosity and has very few gases mixed with it, so the

Mount Vesuvius and the City of Pompeii

Italy's Mount Vesuvius erupted on August 24 in 79 AD. Within two days, 6–7 m of ash and volcanic debris had choked the city. But this devastating ash also shielded the ruins from air and weather. The buried city of Pompeii was discovered in the late 16th century, and systematic excavations began in the early to mid-18th century. Excavators found the city preserved in the ash. When archaeologists uncovered the city, it was so well preserved that they could see the features of the victims' faces. Pliny the Younger witnessed the destruction of the city of Pompeii by Mount Vesuvius. He watched from a safe distance as most of the inhabitants of the city were buried in ash. Pliny wrote in his journal about the flashes of light and the flames. The preserved ruins of Pompeii, along with Pliny's eyewitness account, taught the world a great deal about volcanic activity, Roman culture, and how people lived in the ancient world.

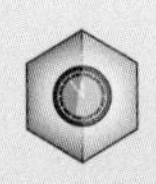

HISTORY

Birth of a Volcano

Parícutin, a volcano in Mexico, is a cinder cone. On February 20, 1943, smoke began to rise from a cornfield 320 km west of Mexico City. Several weeks prior, residents felt tremors and rumblings from the earth, hints of the tumultuous events to come. The newly formed volcano spewed lava and ash from a growing vent. It rose 50 m in one day; within a week it had more than doubled. When it was finished developing, Parícutin was over 350 m tall and had swallowed a town. By 1952, Parícutin was no longer erupting. But during those nine years, this fast and furious volcano excited the world and expanded volcanologists' knowledge of volcanoes.

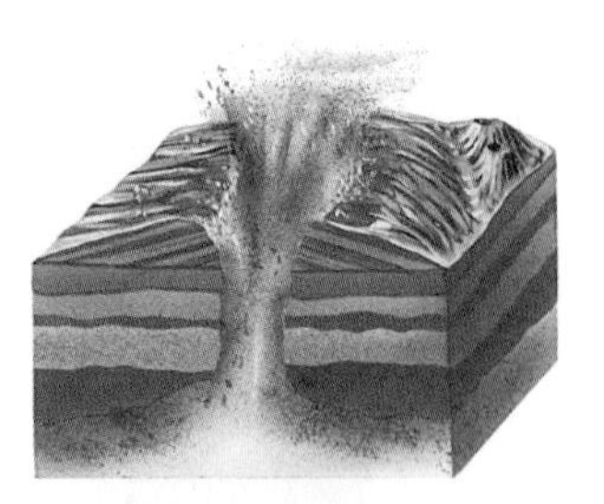

Shield volcano

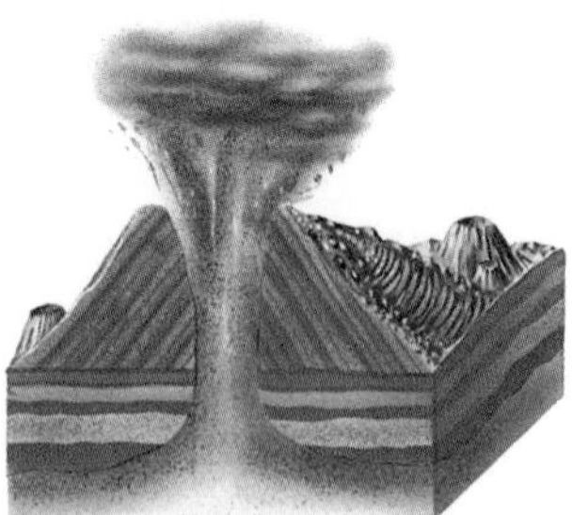

Cinder cone

Composite

lava flows easily from a shield volcano, oozing down like syrup over pancakes.

A cinder cone is a small, cone-shaped volcano built of ash and cinders. Cinder cones have a single vent. During an eruption, lava rushes through the vent and bursts up toward the sky. As it cools in the atmosphere, the fragmented lava falls back down and adds to the size of the cone. Each eruption adds more ash to the cone. Although the ash layers are thick, cinder cones are smaller than other volcanoes—rarely more than 300 m high. Cinder cones are sometimes formed from a Strombolian eruption, an explosive eruption of runny lava and steam or gases. Strombolian eruptions also shoot out rocky pyroclasts and volcanic bombs.

Composite volcanoes are the largest group of volcanoes. A composite volcano is a steep-sided volcano composed of lava, ash, and cinders, which are particles of burned material. Sometimes composite volcanoes shoot rock fragments and ash into the sky. At other times, thick lava flows down the steep sides of these volcanoes, so they have alternating layers of pyroclastic material and lava. The lava of composite volcanoes is thick and moves slowly, and it often carries large chunks of pyroclastic materials with it. Sometimes magma does not reach the surface, so it forms dikes within the volcano walls. The dikes add strength and structure to the walls, giving the volcano the support necessary to grow taller. Italy's Mount Vesuvius, Sicily's Mount Stromboli, Indonesia's Krakatoa, the Philippines' Pinatubo, and Japan's Mount Fuji are all composite volcanoes.

Composite cones form from Vulcanian, Peléan, and Plinian eruptions. A Vulcanian eruption is an eruption composed of bursts of dark ash, thick lava, steam, and gases. Vulcanian eruptions can shoot gases and ash 5–10 km into the air. Peléan eruptions are named after Mount Pelée, a volcano in the Caribbean. Peléan eruptions have a spectacular fiery cloud of fine ash, thin lava, gases, pyroclastic material, and superheated steam. Weighed down by its heavy load, this cloud does not float over the volcano peak but rather rolls swiftly down the volcano's sides like an avalanche. These clouds are extremely destructive.

A Plinian eruption is an eruption characterized by hot ash clouds, deadly pyroclastic flows, or both. The most violent eruption, Plinian eruptions often start unexpectedly after a long period of quiet volcanic activity. Thick magma and abundant gases explode deep in the volcano, and the gases shoot upward into a high cloud. The volcano's top collapses, forming a large crater.

Sometimes large circular depressions called **calderas** form at the top of a volcano. Exceeding the maximum diameter of a crater at 2 km or more, calderas form when magma is withdrawn or erupts from a magma chamber, leaving a void beneath the surface. The overlying rock collapses into the void, forming a caldera.

LESSON REVIEW

1. What are the three categories of volcanoes and how are these determined?
2. What is a shield volcano? Describe the two types of eruptions that can form shield volcanoes.
3. Compare a cinder cone to a composite volcano. Describe their physical features. Specify the eruptions associated with each.
4. List the eruptions in order from least violent to most violent.
5. What are the components of an eruption? Give three examples of eruptions and how their components affect the eruption.

The Aniakchak Caldera in Alaska is 10 km wide and 762 m deep, formed during a massive volcanic eruption 3,500 years ago.

Strombolian eruption, Italy

3.3.5 *Prediction and Effects*

OBJECTIVES

- Describe the changes volcanologists measure to predict volcanic eruptions.
- Identify the negative and positive effects of a volcanic eruption.

VOCABULARY

- **tiltmeter** an instrument that uses liquid to register changes in the earth

David A. Johnston

"Vancouver! Vancouver! This is it!" This radio transmission came from volcanologist Dr. David A. Johnston, who was monitoring Mount Saint Helens from a ridge about 8 km north of the mountain in the United States. It was 8:32 AM on May 18, 1980. Scientists knew that Mount Saint Helens was going to erupt; increased earthquake activity, small eruptions of steam and ash, and bulges on the surface warned that magma was rising. Unfortunately, scientists did not know the size of the coming eruption. If they had, Dr. Johnston would not have been on a ridge that close to the mountain. The radio transmission was the last anyone ever heard from him. He and his equipment were never found.

Volcanoes can be frightening, and their effects can be deadly. At times, scientists can predict their eruptions to some degree. Although scientists cannot predict exactly when a volcano will erupt or how large the eruption will be, knowing that a volcano is likely to erupt within a certain time frame can prepare people for when the eruption does happen. In the 1970s, scientists predicted that Mount Saint Helens would erupt before the year 2000. Dr. Johnston and other volcanologists warned that the eruption could be devastating. Careful preparation by local agencies and a public evacuation plan saved many lives.

A change in the type or volume of volcanic gases being released is one sign of a coming eruption. Such an alteration indicates a change in the magma within the volcano. Aircraft are used to fly over volcanic vents and to measure levels of gases like sulfur dioxide and carbon dioxide. Such flights can be risky, so scientists set up automated monitors to take readings as well.

Car covered in ash after 1991 eruption of Mt. Pinatubo

TRY THIS

Carbon Dioxide

Carbon dioxide (CO_2) is a gas that can be produced by volcanoes; it is also in carbonated beverages. In small concentrations, it is pleasant in a drink. But in large concentrations, it can be harmful to humans. If CO_2 levels are too high, people cannot breathe. Set a small candle on a candleholder inside a deep bowl. Pour about 240 mL of vinegar in the bowl to the top of the candleholder. Be careful not to get the candle wet. Light the candle. It should burn brightly. The lit candle represents a person who is breathing normally. Without getting it in the flame, carefully sprinkle 20–30 g of baking soda all around the vinegar. What happens in the vinegar? Wait a few seconds. What happens to the flame? The reaction of the vinegar and the baking soda produces CO_2. How is this similar to a volcano? How is the candle like a person breathing the gases given off by a volcano?

The upward movement of gases under the earth's surface triggers minor movements of the crust. Earthquakes are a sign that a volcano could be waking up. For example, more than 10,000 small earthquakes were recorded in the area before the eruption of Mount Saint Helens. Another clue that a volcano heats up, nearby streams, springs, and rocks also heat up. Steam or smoke

Near Mount Saint Helens, Spirit Lake was still filled with broken trees in 2012.

The bulge on Mount Saint Helens grew 2 m a day for three weeks.

Vulcanologist sampling lava on Kilauea, Hawaii

may even escape through Earth's crevices. One way to measure the temperature is through thermal imaging. Scientists mount infrared cameras on helicopters and fly near the volcano. The images provide temperature readings to monitor volcanic activity and indications of cooler areas where scientists can place their instruments.

Volcanologists also employ other technology to measure ground deformation. A **tiltmeter** is an instrument that uses water levels and laser technology to register changes in the earth. Rising magma can cause ground inflation or deflation prior to and during an eruption. The ground may bulge, as was noted before Mount Saint Helen's erupted. Water levels then change with the newly modified angle of the volcano's slope. Scientists measure deformations using information received from electronic distance measuring devices, global positioning satellites (GPS), and radio telescopes. All these instruments provide critical data about the activity inside a volcano.

Although these prediction methods can give people enough warning to leave the area, the effects of the volcanic eruption cannot be predicted. Volcanic ash can block out the sun for days and travel thousands of kilometers. Unlike soft, fluffy ash from burned paper or wood, volcanic ash is hard. It can blanket communities with a "snow" that does not melt and collapse rooftops with accumulations as little as several centimeters. The ash can cause breathing problems for people and animals, smother crops, and pollute rivers. When it mixes with rainwater or water from melted glaciers, it does not dissolve. Instead, it acts like a large mass of wet cement. In addition, pyroclastic flow can tear down trees and destroy buildings.

Volcanoes can change the climate temporarily, although some scientists contend that these changes are long lasting. As volcanic ash and gases from large eruptions reach the upper atmosphere and spread around the globe, they block sunlight, which can drop temperatures around the world. For example, after the Philippines' Mount Pinatubo erupted in 1991, the average global temperature dropped by 0.4°C.

TRY THIS

Expanding Volcano

A volcano can expand or develop a bulge on its side before it actually erupts as a result of magma motion and gas buildup. Take a balloon and stretch it out. Pour 230 mL of vinegar into an empty 2 L bottle. Place 20 g of baking soda into a small piece of bathroom tissue or paper towel and roll into a small package. Drop the baking soda package into the bottle and then quickly stretch the opening of the balloon over the mouth of the bottle. Be sure you have a tight seal. As the baking soda begins to react with the vinegar, what happens in the bottle? What happens to the balloon? Watch the system for about two minutes. What does the reaction in the bottle represent? What does the balloon represent?

Although volcanic eruptions are sometimes devastating, they also provide benefits. Volcanic soil is one of the most fertile types of soil. The lush foliage of the Hawaiian Islands offers proof of this. Rich with calcium, potassium, and magnesium, the volcanic fields are the ideal growing area for many types of plants. Indonesia's agriculture also benefits from its volcanic soil. Volcanic deposits also provide building materials, such as those used to make the concrete shields of nuclear reactors. Pumice, an abrasive pyroclast, is used as an ingredient in many hand soaps and household cleaners. Gems such as diamonds are pushed up to the surface by volcanic activity. Diamonds are popular in fine jewelry, but they are also utilized in industrial applications. The hardness of diamonds makes them ideal for cutting, grinding,

Benchmark installation for GPS surveys on the north flank of Mount Saint Helens, 2012

drilling, and polishing. Volcanic eruptions also provide scientists with the only visible information about the inside of the earth. And along with releasing built-up heat and pressure, volcanoes release atmospheric gases that have been trapped in the ground.

Although volcanoes can be terrifying and destructive, God is faithful to continue supporting the earth and the life on it. Five years after the Mount Saint Helens eruption, established plants were growing again. Within 10 years of the eruption, many animals had returned. Scientists predict that a forest will grow in that area within the next 100 years.

LESSON REVIEW

1. What changes do volcanologists monitor?
2. What causes a volcano to bulge?
3. What geologic event can precede a volcanic eruption?
4. What problems can be caused by heavy volcanic ash?
5. What other problems can be caused by volcanic eruptions?
6. What benefits come from volcanic eruptions?

The rich, volcanic soil in Bali, Indonesia, is perfect for growing rice.

UNIT
4

Water and Water Systems

Chapter 1: *Water*
Chapter 2: *Oceans*

Vocabulary

abyssal plain
adhesion
algal bloom
amplitude
aquifer
cohesion
condensation
continental glacier
continental margin
continental rise
continental shelf
continental slope
Coriolis effect
crest
dead zone
desalination
divide
eutrophication
evaporation
geyser
groundwater
hydroelectric power
levee
mature river
neap tide
old river
porosity
rejuvenated river
reservoir
salinity
seamount
sinkhole
spring tide
sublimation
submersible
surface tension
tidal range
transpiration
tributary
trough
valley glacier
water budget
watershed
water table
wavelength
youthful river
zone of aeration
zone of saturation

Key Ideas

- Systems, order, and organization
- Evidence, models, and explanation
- Change, constancy, and measurement
- Evolution and equilibrium
- Form and function
- Abilities necessary to do scientific inquiry
- Understandings about scientific inquiry
- Structure of the earth system
- Energy in the earth system
- Geochemical cycles
- Abilities of technological design
- Understandings about science and technology
- Populations, resources, and environments
- Natural hazards
- Risks and benefits
- Science and technology in society
- Natural resources
- Environmental quality
- Science as a human endeavor
- Nature of science

SCRIPTURE

Whoever drinks the water I give them will never thirst. Indeed, the water I give them will become in them a spring of water welling up to eternal life.

John 4:14

4.1.1 Water Properties

OBJECTIVES

- Describe various life-sustaining properties of water.
- Explain how polarity affects water's physical properties.

VOCABULARY

- **adhesion** the force of attraction between different molecules
- **cohesion** the molecular attraction between particles of the same kind
- **surface tension** the force that pulls molecules on the surface of a liquid together to form a layer

Water is an amazing substance! God created water with unusual physical properties that sustain life on Earth. How would life be different if water did not behave in the way God intended? For example, water is the only substance on Earth that can naturally exist in all three states—solid, liquid, and gas. On average, an adult human body is made up of 50%–65% water. About 71% of earth's surface is covered by water, most of which is found in the oceans. Less than 3.5% of water on Earth is found in freshwater sources, such as icebergs, ice sheets, glaciers, ice caps, ponds, bogs, lakes, rivers, streams, and aquifers.

One of the main reasons water has special physical properties is because of its chemical structure. One oxygen atom bonds with two hydrogen atoms to form a covalent bond. The electrons are unequally shared between the oxygen atom and the two hydrogen atoms. The covalent bonds are not formed in a straight line. Rather, a water molecule has a bent structure where the two hydrogen atoms are pushed toward each other on one side of the molecule, which creates a partial positive region. A partial negative region is created near the oxygen atom. The partial positive and partial negative regions of the water molecule make the entire molecule polar, similar to a magnet. The polarity of a water molecule determines many of the physical properties of water molecules observed in nature.

Cohesion is the molecular attraction between particles of the same kind. The partial negative region of an oxygen atom from one water molecule can be attracted to the partial positive region

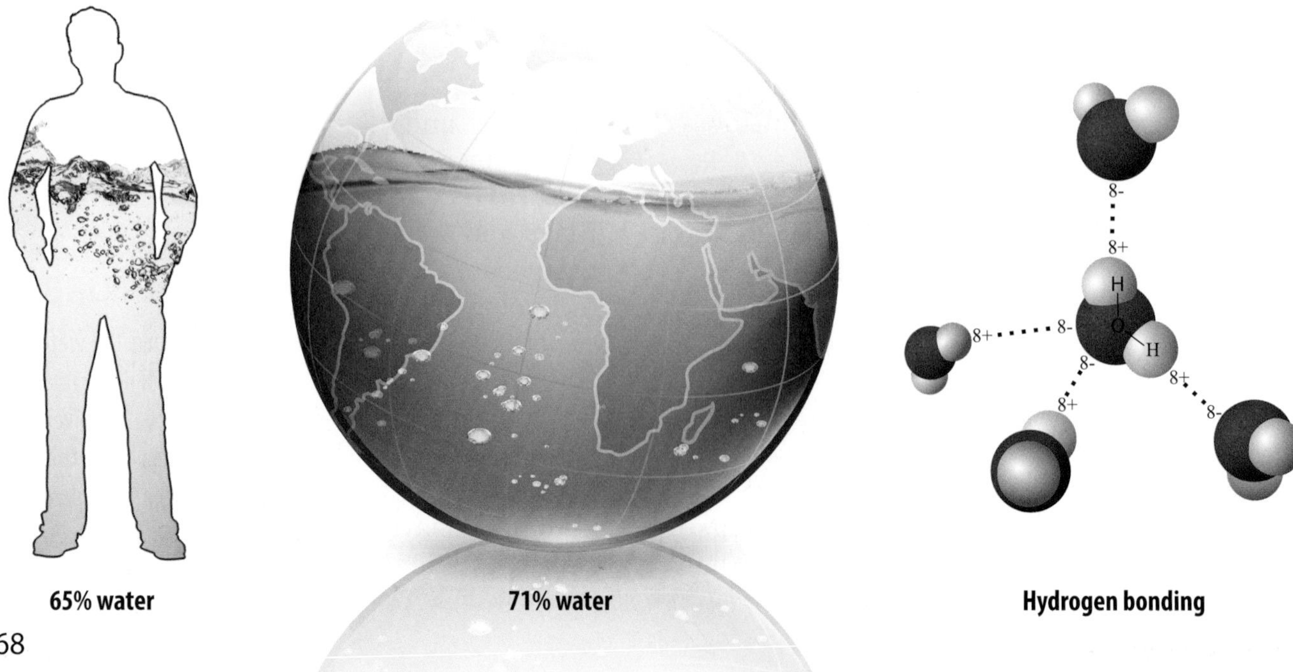

65% water

71% water

Hydrogen bonding

of a hydrogen atom in another water molecule. When these two water molecules come near each other, a hydrogen bond is formed. An example of water cohesion in nature is the shape of a raindrop. The cohesive forces between multiple water molecules pull them closer to one another and reduce the amount of surface area, forming the raindrop into a spherical shape.

Cohesive forces

Surface tension is the cohesive force that pulls molecules on the surface of a liquid together and creates a layer. Cohesion is strongest between water molecules on the surface of water because the molecules cannot form as many hydrogen bonds. Fewer bonds means the bonding force is concentrated and stronger. The layer created by surface tension allows certain things, such as water striders or leaves, to float on the water.

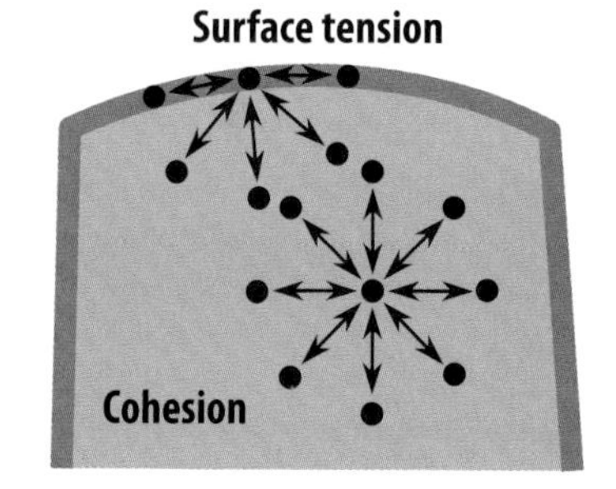

The polar structure of water molecules also attracts them to other kinds of molecules. **Adhesion** is the force of attraction between different molecules. When water is placed in a glass tube, the water's surface does not form a straight line. Instead, a concave line, called *a meniscus*, is created. The meniscus forms because the water molecules are attracted to the molecules on the sides of the glass tube. Adhesion explains why a towel can soak up water. The towel molecules attract the water molecules, drawing them into the narrow spaces between the towel's fibers.

The forces of adhesion and cohesion work together to move water through plant roots. When water reaches plant roots, adhesion attracts the water molecules to the root cells. Adhesion keeps the water molecules moving from cell to cell up the root and into the plant. As the water molecules travel upward,

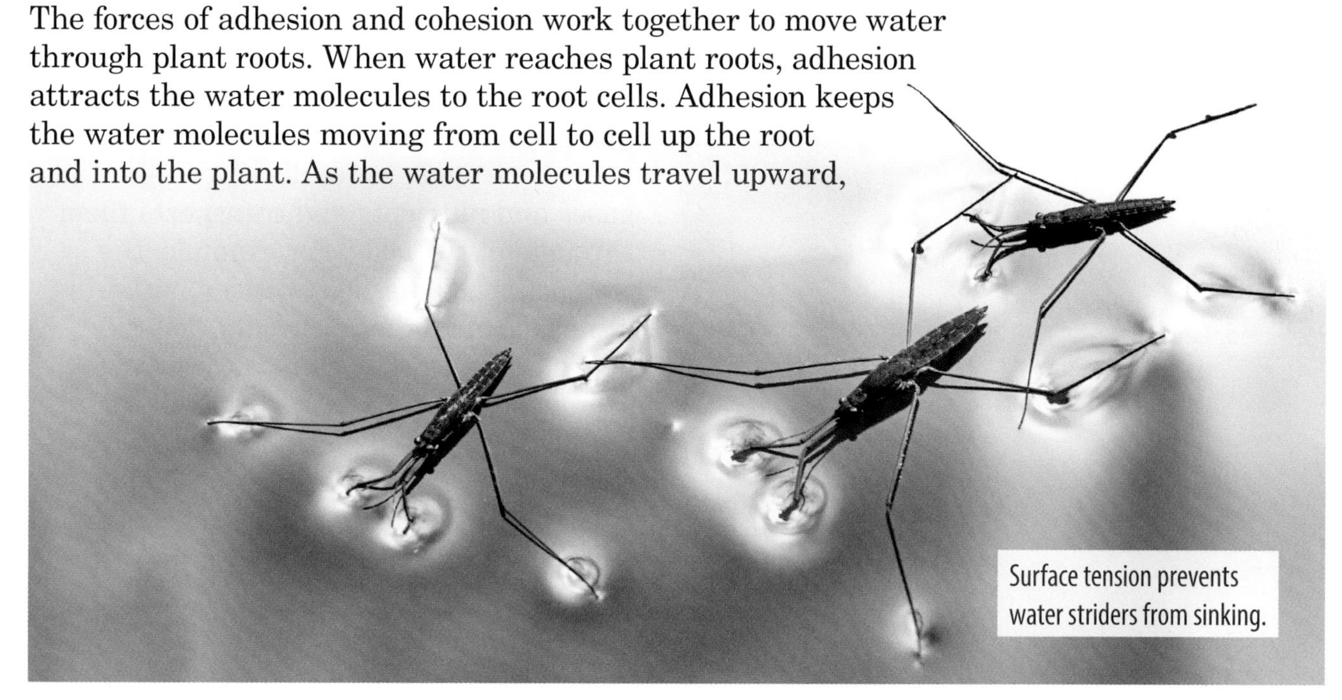

Surface tension prevents water striders from sinking.

Meniscus formed from adhesive forces

other water molecules follow behind since they are attracted to each other because of cohesion.

Another physical property connected to water's chemical structure is water's ability to store and release heat energy. Separating hydrogen bonds between water molecules requires energy, often in the form of heat. Likewise, forming hydrogen bonds between water molecules releases energy. If liquid water is to change into water vapor, the hydrogen bonds must be broken. Since many water molecules form multiple hydrogen bonds at a time, these bonds require a great deal of energy to break. So to change the temperature of a body of water, a tremendous amount of heat needs to be added or removed. A substance's ability to absorb heat energy is called its *specific heat*. Water readily absorbs heat energy. The high specific heat of water minimizes drastic temperature changes in bodies of water like lakes and oceans. For example, during the day, water vapor above the ocean absorbs heat, creating a cool environment. The heat that was absorbed during the day is slowly released in the evening, creating warm night air. As a result, the temperature of the ocean stays stable. Water also regulates or stabilizes the temperatures of various organisms. For example, plants with a large amount of water have internal temperatures that are not easily affected by environmental changes.

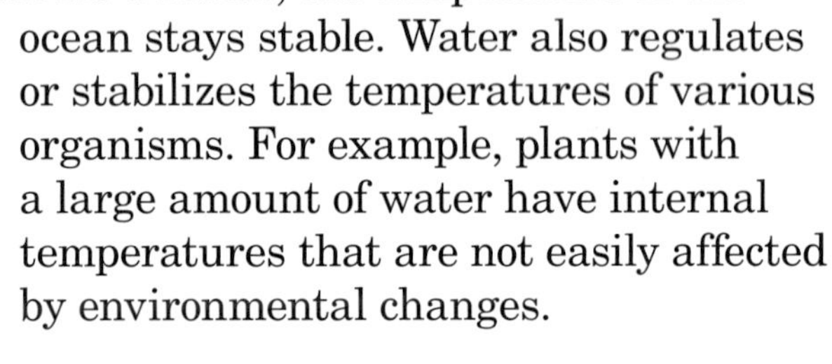

Ice floats.

Water is often referred to as *the universal solvent* because it is capable of dissolving more substances than any other liquid. In living things, water dissolves essential gases and nutrients and transports them throughout the body. For example, the water in blood dissolves oxygen, vitamins, minerals, and other nutrients that are needed. The bloodstream carries these chemicals throughout the body. Water also dissolves the salt in oceans by breaking the bonds between the sodium and chlorine atoms. The sodium and chloride ions that form remain dissolved in water because the water molecules surround each of the separated sodium and chloride ions to form a barrier.

FYI

High Specific Heat

Because changing water's temperature requires so much heat, scientists say water has a high specific heat. This property helps regulate body temperature. As a person's temperature rises, sweat is produced. The skin's heat is transferred to the water molecules in sweat until enough heat energy is absorbed to change the liquid water to water vapor in a process called *evaporation*. This process is why people feel cooler when they sweat.

TRY THIS

Which Property

Inflate a balloon and rub it with a piece of wool cloth. Turn a water faucet on to produce a thin stream of water. Slowly bring the balloon near the thin stream of water to observe the "bending" of water. Which property of water does this demonstrate?

Water cannot dissolve all substances. It can only dissolve substances that have a polar molecular structure. Water is repelled by oil and soap because they both have nonpolar molecular structures. The inability of water to dissolve such substances can cause problems ranging from laundry issues to an oil spill in the ocean. Animals, plants, and people are all affected because water cannot dissolve nonpolar oil molecules.

The structure of solid water, or ice, demonstrates another important physical property. Unlike most other substances, water is less dense as a solid than as a liquid. This unique feature allows ice to float on liquid water. If ice acted like other natural substances on Earth that are more dense in their solid state, aquatic life would be greatly affected during the winter months. As soon as a layer of ice formed on the surface of a lake, it would sink, crushing aquatic organisms below it. The solid block of ice would not melt and would remain frozen for the majority of the winter. Instead, God protected His creation by allowing ice to freeze on the surface of a body of water, where is acts as insulation for the organisms living there.

LESSON REVIEW

1. If the human body is made up of 65% water, how many kilograms of water are in a 41.52 kg person?
2. How does the polarity of water affect the cohesive physical property of water? Give an example of water cohesion.
3. Why is it important that God created ice to be less dense than liquid water?
4. Select three properties of water and explain how they help sustain life.

4.1.2 *The Water Cycle*

OBJECTIVES

- Explain the major components of the water cycle.
- Determine the factors that affect a region's water budget.

VOCABULARY

- **condensation** the change of a substance from a gas to a liquid
- **evaporation** the change of a substance from a liquid to a gas
- **sublimation** the change of a substance from a solid to a gas without passing through the liquid state
- **transpiration** the loss of water by plants
- **water budget** the relationship between the input and the output of all the water on Earth

The marvelous physical properties of water would not be very useful if all water stayed in one place. God created a water transportation system that stretches to every ecosystem on Earth. The continuous cycle that stores water and moves it from the atmosphere to the earth's surface and back to the atmosphere is called *the water cycle* or *hydrologic cycle*. The water cycle consists of five main processes: evaporation, transpiration, condensation, precipitation, and sublimation.

The main way that water enters the atmosphere is through **evaporation**, when liquid water is converted into water vapor. A large amount of energy, often in the form of heat, is required for evaporation to occur. During this process, heat is removed from the environment, creating a cooling effect. Scientists attest that about 90% of the water in the atmosphere evaporates from oceans, lakes, rivers, and streams. Most of the water in the atmosphere evaporates from oceans because of their large surface area. However, most of this water does not travel across land but instead falls back into the ocean water. A very small fraction of evaporated water is actually transported over land to fall in the form of precipitation.

Transpiration is the loss of water by plants. It represents the way that about 10% of the water in the atmosphere enters the water cycle. Transpiration rates are greatly affected by weather

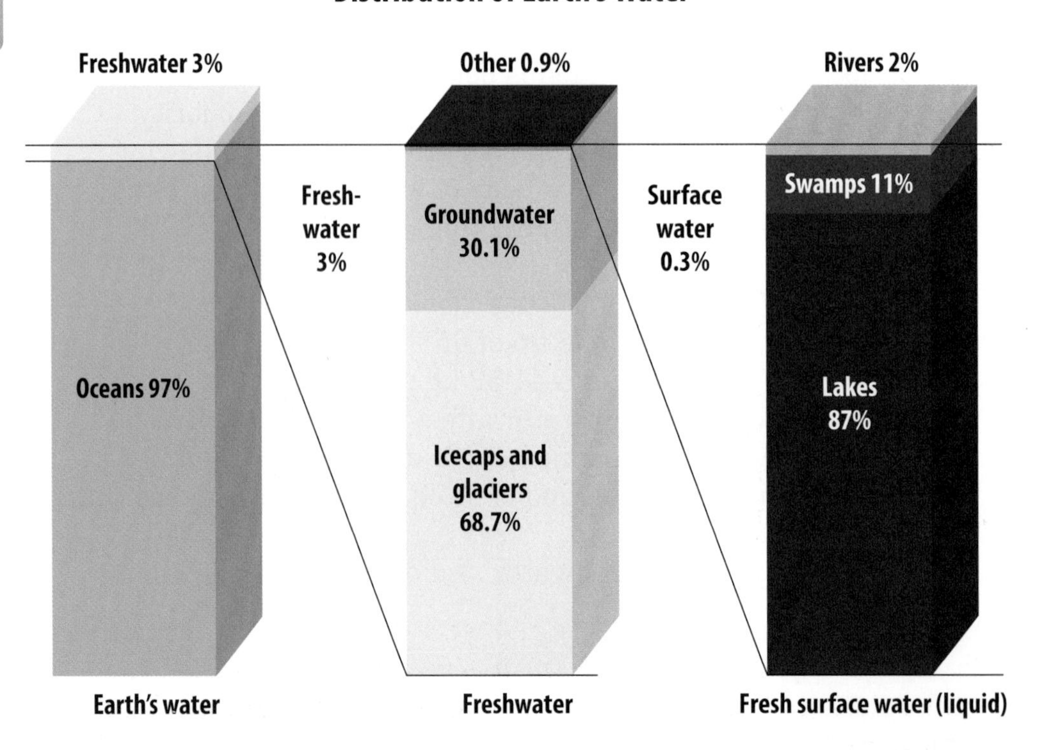

conditions, such as temperature, humidity, wind, precipitation, soil composition, land slope, and plant type. As temperature increases, plant transpiration also increases, especially during the growing season. The warmer temperatures cause plant stomata to open and release water vapor. In contrast, when the temperature is cooler, plant stomata tend to remain closed, keeping the water contained in the leaves. When it is humid, the atmosphere contains excess water vapor, so transpiration rates are low. Transpiration rates tend to increase if wind replaces more saturated air with dryer air. Water that is transpired during dry periods can contribute to soil dryness. When there is not a enough water in the soil, plants transpire less water in an attempt to stay hydrated. Precipitation, the composition of the soil, and the land's slope are other factors that can impact the amount of water in the soil. Different plant types also affect transpiration rates. For example, in more arid regions, plants such as cacti and succulents tend to conserve water by transpiring less.

The next stage in the water cycle is **condensation**, which is the change of a substance from a gas to a liquid. Water molecules are grouped randomly when water is in a vapor form. As condensation occurs, the water molecules group in a more uniform pattern. Condensation is the opposite of evaporation. Evaporation requires a lot of heat. In contrast, condensation releases a lot of heat, so it occurs more frequently at higher elevations where the air is cooler. Depending on its temperature, air can hold a limited amount of water vapor. Warm air can hold more water vapor than cooler air. When air contains all the water vapor it can possibly hold, it is saturated. Scientists use the saturation point of air to determine what is called its *relative humidity*. Saturated air has a relative humidity of 100%, so air that is holding only half the water it can has a relative humidity of 50%.

Condensation is a crucial process of the water cycle because it creates clouds. When the invisible water vapor in the air cools to the point that visible drops of water form, it has reached the temperature called *the dew point*. At the dew point, clouds form because the water-saturated air condenses. Condensation can occur high in the sky to form clouds and at ground level to form fog and dew.

Clouds may eventually release the condensed water in the form of precipitation. Precipitation is water that falls from the atmosphere to the earth such as rain, snow, sleet, or hail. Most

BIBLE CONNECTION

Who Sends the Rain?

Evaporation. Transpiration. Condensation. Precipitation. Do these processes all just happen by chance?

In Psalm 147, the psalmist makes plain that the water cycle is under God's dominion. Verse 8 says, "He covers the sky with clouds; He supplies the earth with rain and makes grass grow on the hills." These words were written long before the complex balance that forms Earth's water budget was understood by scientists, and yet the cycle is clearly depicted. Water vapor condenses in the clouds, falls as rain on the grass, and is transpired by the grass to return to the clouds once again. Jeremiah echoes this certainty when he says, "Do any of the worthless idols of the nations bring rain? Do the skies themselves send down showers? No, it is You, Lord our God. Therefore our hope is in You, for You are the One who does all this" (Jeremiah 14:22).

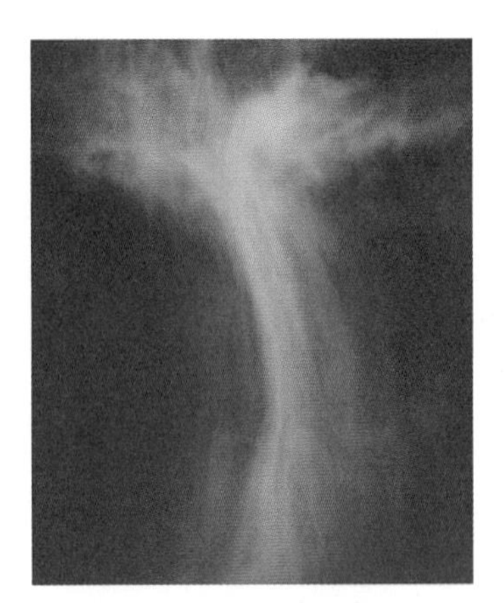

Wisps of precipitation that evaporate before they reach the ground are called *virga*.

of the condensed water in clouds will not precipitate, or condense and fall, because updrafts of air keep the droplets suspended in the atmosphere. You may have seen wispy trails called *virga* extending from clouds. Such trails of moisture do not reach the ground. Most precipitation falls in the form of rain.

Sublimation is the change of a substance from a solid to a gas without passing through the liquid state. For example, when warm, dry winds flow over the mountains, snow is vaporized before it can melt. This process releases a very small amount of water vapor into the atmosphere. Without energy to fuel the process, sublimation could not occur. Sunlight often provides the energy needed for sublimation, which requires more energy than evaporation or transpiration because the step of changing to a liquid is skipped. It takes about five times more energy for water to move from ice to water vapor than it does for liquid water to become ice. Sublimation occurs more readily in areas with a low relative humidity, plenty of sunlight, low air pressure, and abundant dry winds. Many high altitude regions provide these requirements, including unique regional dry winds. For example, sublimation regions include the North American Rocky Mountains that experience Chinook winds; the Alps, where foehn winds frequent; the mountains in Libya, where ghibli winds occur; and the Andes Mountains, which experience zonda winds.

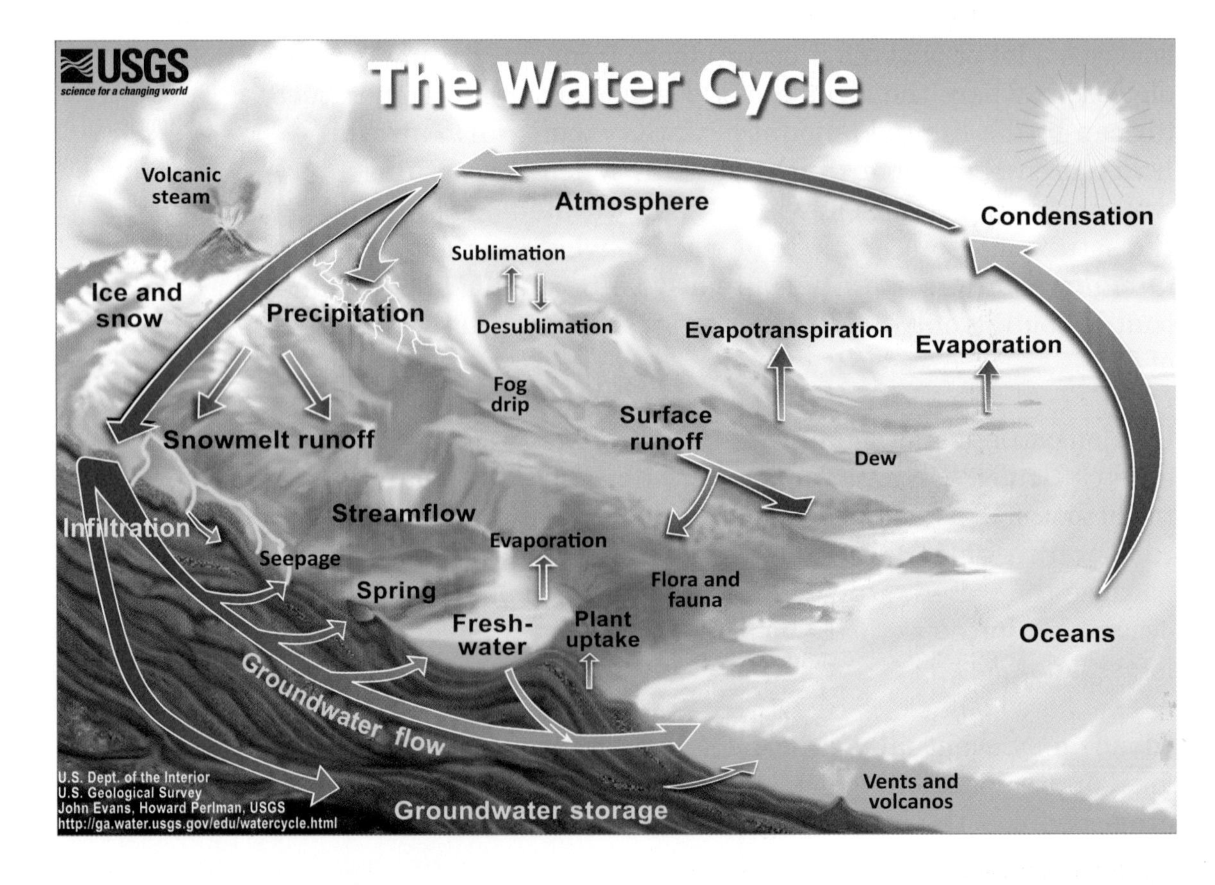

The **water budget** is the relationship between the input and the output of all the water on Earth. Earth's water budget can be compared to a financial budget. For example, each month, you may earn a certain amount of money from a job or be given an allowance; money entering your budget is called *income*. The ways you spend your money are called *expenditures*. Expenditures can be divided into categories, such as tithing, saving, housing, food, clothing, and recreation. When your income equals your expenditures, then your budget is balanced. In Earth's water budget, precipitation and condensation represent income, and evaporation, transpiration, sublimation, and water runoff represent expenditures. Earth's water budget is balanced because the amount of water it uses equals the amount it receives.

Sublimation on Lhotse in the Himalayas

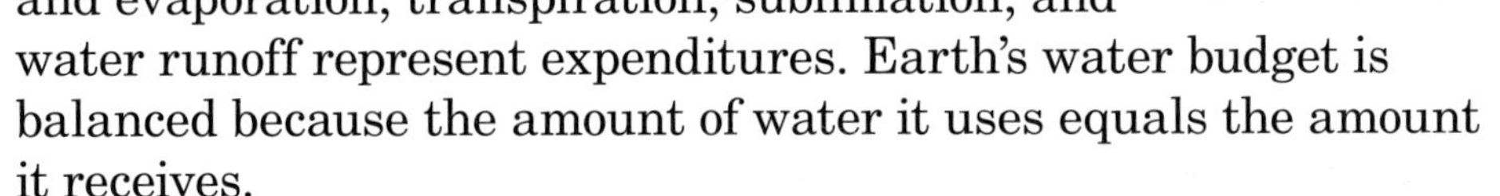

CHALLENGE

Design an experiment that tests an aspect of transpiration. Some questions to consider include the following: How much water does one plant transpire? Do different types of plants transpire different amounts of water? Do plants transpire different amounts of water under different conditions?

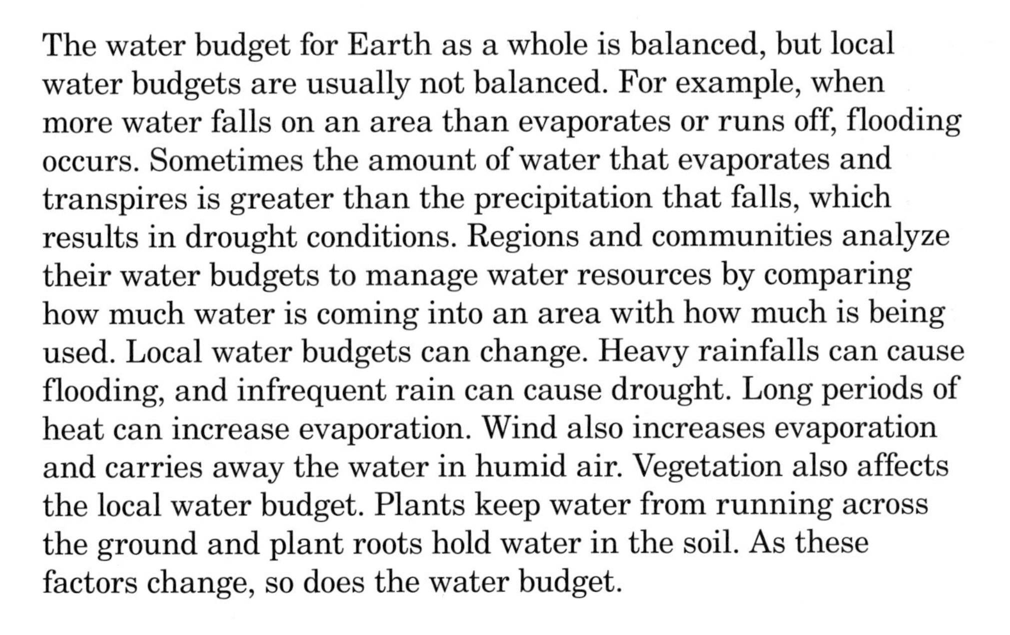

The water budget for Earth as a whole is balanced, but local water budgets are usually not balanced. For example, when more water falls on an area than evaporates or runs off, flooding occurs. Sometimes the amount of water that evaporates and transpires is greater than the precipitation that falls, which results in drought conditions. Regions and communities analyze their water budgets to manage water resources by comparing how much water is coming into an area with how much is being used. Local water budgets can change. Heavy rainfalls can cause flooding, and infrequent rain can cause drought. Long periods of heat can increase evaporation. Wind also increases evaporation and carries away the water in humid air. Vegetation also affects the local water budget. Plants keep water from running across the ground and plant roots hold water in the soil. As these factors change, so does the water budget.

Researchers study local and regional water budgets to gain a better understanding of how water is stored and how water flows in and out of a particular ecosystem. They can calculate the water availability and analyze and predict water shortages. A study of the water budget aids the decision-making processes and helps researchers address natural resource management issues.

LESSON REVIEW

1. What is the main contributor to the water cycle?
2. Name and explain the major components of the water cycle.
3. What factors affect a region's water budget?
4. Why is Earth's water budget considered balanced?

4.1.3 Glaciers

OBJECTIVES

- Explain how glaciers form.
- Analyze how glaciers contribute to the water cycle.
- Contrast the two main types of glaciers.

VOCABULARY

- **continental glacier** a glacier that covers a large area of land in a continuous sheet
- **valley glacier** a long, narrow, U-shaped mass of ice that takes shape as ice moves down a mountain and through a valley area

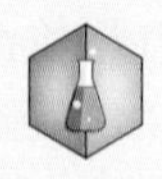

TRY THIS

Ice Melt

Predict which colored ice cube will melt the fastest. Pop out the colored ice cubes and place them on individual petri dishes. Set the petri dishes next to each other in direct sunlight and record how long it takes for each cube to melt. Was your prediction correct?

Many scientists believe the earth was cooler in the past and had much more ice than it does today. During an ice age, it is estimated that about one-third of the earth's land mass was covered with glaciers. Today, glaciers exist on every continent except Australia. A large mass of moving ice that forms on land and remains from year to year is called *a glacier.* Glaciers form at high altitudes or in polar regions where snow remains throughout the year. As the seasons change, snow partially melts, compacts, and recrystallizes. This process forms a grainy ice called *firn.* The pressure from the deep layers of snow squeezes the air from between the ice grains, reducing the pore space. The increased density changes the color and structure of firn from white snow to steel-blue, solid ice. Compacted glacial ice appears blue because when it becomes dense, it absorbs all colors in the light spectrum and reflects only blue. White glacier ice is less dense and contains many tiny air bubbles.

Snow converts to firn in a region near the head of a glacier called *the zone of accumulation.* Near the foot of a glacier in a region called *the zone of ablation*, glacial ice reduces by melting, evaporating, or calving. The process of calving involves portions of a glacier breaking off to create more glaciers. The accumulation zone is separated from the ablation zone by the equilibrium line.

Glaciers are constantly shrinking and growing. Glaciers increase in size when the rate of precipitation is faster than the rate of evaporation. When the layered snow evaporates at a faster rate

Glacier Zones

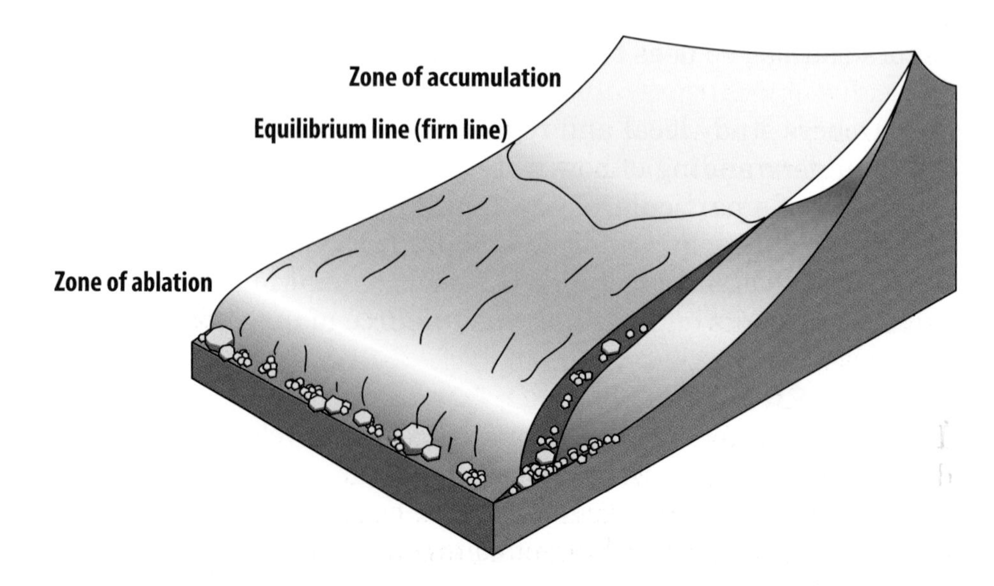

than the precipitating snow, the size of a glacier decreases. The development of a glacier is affected by many factors, such as the amount of snowfall, the amount of sunlight, and the slope of the land. For example, if a mountain has a steep incline, snow has difficulty sticking to the surface and accumulating.

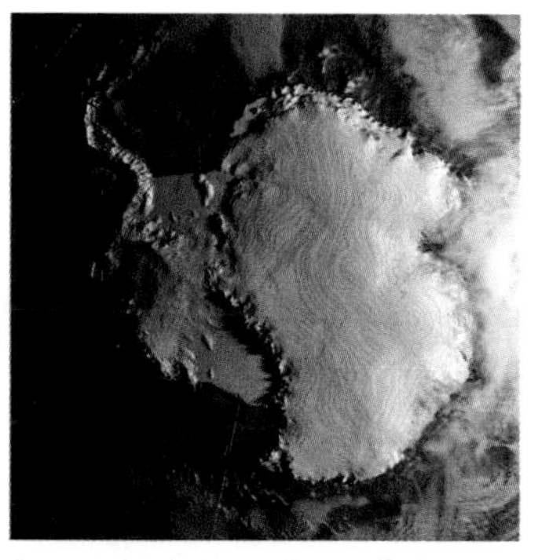

Antarctica is a continental glacier.

When a mass of ice reaches a thickness of about 40 m, it becomes so heavy that it begins to deform and move. Glacial movement is very slow. On average, glaciers move a few millimeters to a few meters each day. However, there are times when glaciers move rather quickly. During these surges, glaciers can move up to 6 km in a year. The stress of such movement causes glacial ice to form fractures called *crevasses* near the top of the glacier. Many crevasses form during glacial surges. In contrast, the lower portions of a glacier flow more like a thick fluid. The underside of a glacier tends to slip over the surface. Friction between the glacier base and the land reduces the speed at which the bottom of the glacier can move. This friction is why the underside of a glacier moves more slowly than its upper portion. As glaciers move, some glacial ice reenters the water cycle as glacial ice breaks off, melts, and sublimes.

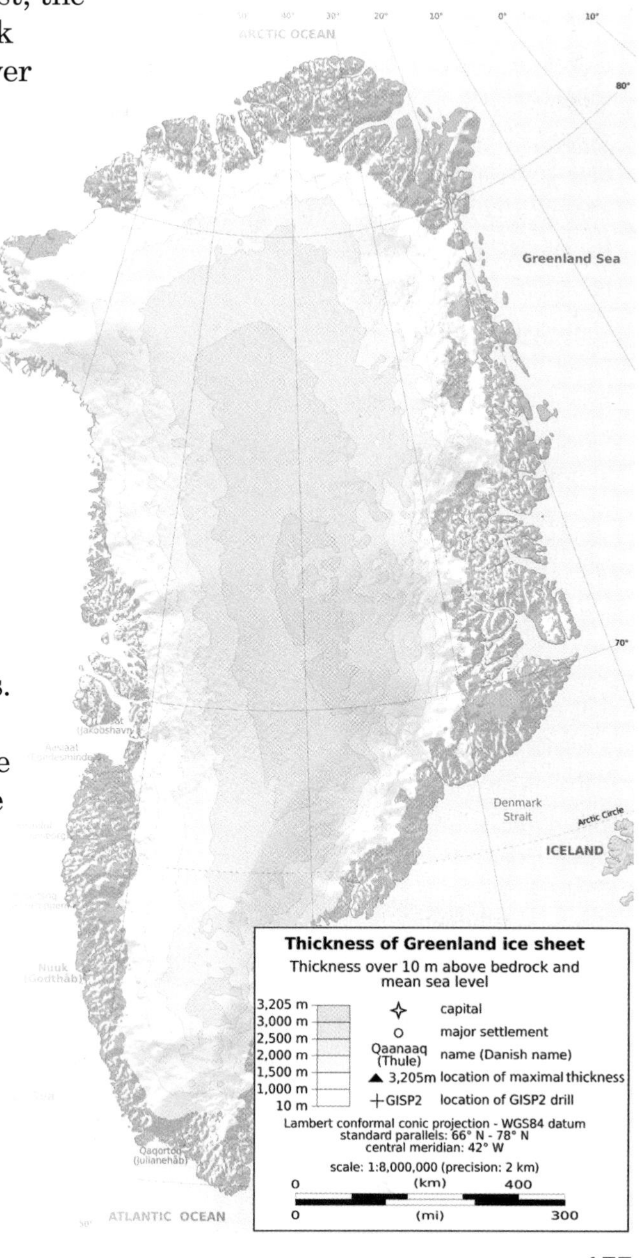

Glaciers are an important component in Earth's water cycle because much more water is in storage on the planet than is moving through the water cycle at any one time. Freshwater on Earth is stored for short periods of time in lakes, longer stretches of time in groundwater, and even longer periods in glaciers. Much of the water that is now a liquid was once frozen in continental glaciers. Scientists estimate that in the past these larger glaciers lowered the sea level more than 100 m.

A **continental glacier** is a glacier that covers a large area of land in a continuous sheet. Today, continental glaciers cover about 11% of the earth's land mass. Continental glaciers are largely unaffected by underlying topography. They move out from a central region in all directions. Examples of continental glaciers are the Greenland and Antarctic ice sheets. Continental glaciers hold amazing amounts of

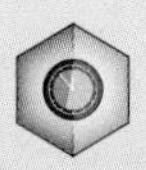

HISTORY

Greenland

If roughly 80% of Greenland is covered with ice, why is the word *green* in its name? Erik the Red, a Norwegian exile, settled on the island in 982 AD, where he had hopes of developing a large Norse settlement. In an attempt to lure potential settlers, Erik gave the island the appealing name *Greenland.* This tactic actually worked for some time. Erik's son, Leif Eriksson, arrived on the island during the 11th century and was responsible for introducing Christianity to the local populations. Scientists believe that the climate may have been more hospitable at that time than it is today. However, Greenland's climate began to cool in the 14th century, and many of the Norse settlements began to dwindle. By the 15th century, there was no evidence of Norse habitation. Although some Dutch and English whalers visited the island during the next two centuries, it was not until 1721 that Greenland was colonized by Denmark. Today Greenland is a self-governing part of Denmark, which granted Greenland greater autonomy in 2008.

Earth's water. It is estimated that if the Greenland and Antarctic ice sheets melted, the sea level would rise about 80 m, and most coastal areas would experience flooding. In comparison, if the entire amount of ice on Earth melted, the sea level would rise about 90 m. Smaller continental glaciers are called *ice caps.*

A **valley glacier** is another type of glacier. Much smaller than continental glaciers, valley glaciers are also known as *alpine glaciers.* A valley glacier is a long, narrow, U-shaped mass of ice that takes shape as ice moves down a mountain and through a valley area. It originates in the snow or ice fields of a mountainous area. The speed at which a valley glacier travels is affected by the temperature and thickness of the ice, the slope of the valley floor, and the shape of the valley walls.

LESSON REVIEW

1. How do glaciers form?
2. Explain how glaciers move.
3. What part do glaciers play in the water cycle?
4. What is the difference between a continental glacier and a valley glacier?

Valley glacier

Groundwater 4.1.4

Lakes, rivers, and glaciers hold an enormous amount of water. However, 30% of the earth's freshwater supply is locked up in the ground. **Groundwater** is water that seeps down into soil and rock crevasses to be stored underground.

When water falls on the land, it travels through the earth as far as possible until it reaches clay deposits. Water first seeps through the **zone of aeration**, which is the upper permeable layers of rock and soil. The pore spaces of this underground region contain both air and water, so the ground is not saturated. Beneath this area is the **zone of saturation**, which is an area of rock and soil with pore spaces completely filled with groundwater. The **water table** is the region that separates the zone of aeration from the zone of saturation. Water located in the zone of saturation does not remain stagnant because it moves and travels to new locations. However, water cannot move down through the saturated soil and rock located just above the clay layer. Clay particles have very little pore space, making clay impermeable.

The water in rivers can flow several meters per second, but groundwater may move only a few meters per day or a few centimeters in a decade. The movement of groundwater is a slow process because it must seep through varying pore spaces. Groundwater movement is measured according to flow velocity and permeability. Groundwater flows downhill along the water table. When the water table is steep, the gravitational force that pulls groundwater down is greater and the flow velocity, or

CAREER

Hydrogeologist

Hydrogeologists study the distribution, movement, and quality of water found underground. They interpret data and information from maps and historical documents to develop a conceptual model of groundwater flow. The models are created to make predictions about future trends and impacts on groundwater movement and quality. Most of the work is completed in an office setting. However, designing and completing investigations in the field is also critical in order to test and develop models. Investigations in the field may incorporate various measurement and sampling techniques that can allow the hydrogeologist to collect data over a short or an extensive period of time. The work of a hydrogeologist leads to better management of natural resources and better protection of groundwater.

OBJECTIVES

- Describe the different zones and features of groundwater.
- Identify geological features formed by groundwater.
- Illustrate how groundwater storage and movement are related to the water cycle.

VOCABULARY

- **aquifer** a permeable underground layer of rock
- **geyser** a hot spring that periodically erupts
- **groundwater** all the water found underground
- **porosity** a measure of the open space in rocks
- **sinkhole** a hole in the ground that forms when an underground cave collapses
- **water table** the boundary between unsaturated and saturated ground
- **zone of aeration** the underground region where pore spaces contain air and water
- **zone of saturation** the underground region where pore spaces are saturated with groundwater

speed, increases. Rock layers containing similarly sized sediment grains are porous and allow water to flow freely. In contrast, sediment grains of different sizes often block the flow of water. Loosely packed grains have high permeability, but tightly packed grains have fewer spaces and slow or even block the flow of water.

An **aquifer** is a permeable underground layer of rock that can hold a large amount of groundwater. The amount of water that an aquifer can hold depends on its **porosity**, which is the percentage of open spaces in rocks or sediments that will hold groundwater. The greater the porosity of the rocks and sediments, the more water an aquifer can hold. Aquifers are made up primarily of fractured sandstone and limestone rock. Groundwater travels through aquifers and eventually reaches land, where the water table cuts across Earth's surface. As water emerges from underground, it produces a small stream known as *a spring*. People can also tap into underground aquifers by digging or drilling wells. Water is not accessible unless the wells reach beneath the level of the water table. The level of the water table fluctuates seasonally because of different amounts of precipitation. For example, an extremely rainy season may cause the water table to rise, but during a dry season, springs or wells might dry up. If an aquifer dries up, water from precipitation will eventually refill the aquifer, which is a very slow process. In

Yellowstone Volcanoes

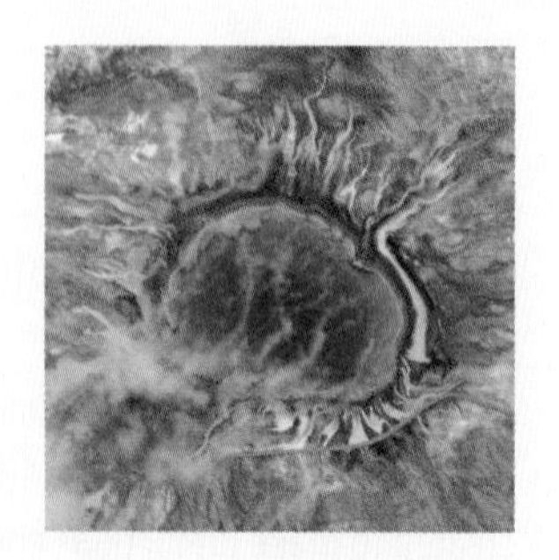

The majority of the world's known geysers are found in Wyoming, most notably in Yellowstone National Park. There are about 500 geysers and 10,000 thermal features located in this area. What do the geysers indicate? Geysers indicate the presence of magma under the surface of the earth. The Yellowstone area experiences 1,000 to 3,000 earthquakes each year, which indicates activity belowground. Scientists believe there were three major volcanic eruptions in Yellowstone's past. One of the major eruptions is believed to have created the West Thumb of Yellowstone Lake. Some scientists consider Yellowstone to be a supervolcano capable of an eruption that would cover more than 386 cubic miles. An eruption is theoretically possible, but it is very unlikely to occur within the next thousand years. Geologic activity at Yellowstone has remained relatively constant for the past 30 years. Scientists continue to monitor the region closely for any sudden or strong movements or shifts in heat that would indicate increasing volcanic activity.

fact, deep aquifers may take hundreds of years to regain their original water quantity. Aquifers may also be refilled with the use of rapid-infiltration pits or groundwater injection. To create a rapid-infiltration pit, water is spread over the land in furrows, pits, or ditches and allowed to seep into the aquifer. Recharge wells may also be constructed for direct water injection into the aquifer.

Old Faithful

Spring water is usually the same temperature as the surrounding land area. Spring water found in cold climates may average 10°C, but warmer climates may have spring water that averages 24°C. Interestingly, spring water is usually warmer in the winter months and cooler in the summer months. Aquifers that are located near volcanic activity absorb a large amount of heat. Springs produced from extremely warm aquifers can form some interesting features on the earth's surface. When hot groundwater rises to the surface, it is called *a hot spring.* A **geyser** is a hot spring that periodically erupts. A narrow tube under a geyser connects the earth's surface to underground chambers. Heat from magma warms the rocks that surround the narrow tube and the water in the chambers. Over time, the heat causes the water to boil. When the water boils, tremendous pressure begins to build at the base of the chambers. The pressure forces water upward until it erupts through an opening in the earth's surface. During an eruption, liquid water is converted into very hot water vapor. The eruption continues until most of the tube and storage chambers are empty. This process can be repeated multiple times throughout a day. For example, Old Faithful in Yellowstone National Park in the United States erupts every hour or so throughout the day.

Another interesting feature forms when groundwater dissolves and carries away underground minerals such as salt, gypsum, or limestone. Land areas that have experienced large amounts of chemical weathering by groundwater are said to have a *karst topography.* Karst topography can be found around the world in such places as China, France, Mexico, Slovenia, and in the United States in parts of Florida, Indiana, and Kentucky. This type of topography is usually characterized by caverns, sinkholes, and gaps in rock that swallow streams. Occasionally, these streams will run underground for several kilometers until they come out through another gap in the rock.

Limestone mountain karsts

Sinkhole in Didyma, Turkey

If a water table drops too low, hollows in the limestone can collapse to form sinkholes. A **sinkhole** is a circular depression in the ground that forms when the roof of an underground cave collapses. Sinkholes also form when limestone under the soil dissolves. In September 2016, a massive sinkhole in Florida opened up underneath a storage pond near a fertilizer plant. More than 750 million liters of contaminated wastewater leaked into the Floridan aquifer, one of the state's main underground resources of drinking water. The Floridan aquifer is one of the highest water-producing aquifers in the world. It lies beneath the entire state of Florida and extends into southern Alabama, Georgia, and South Carolina. The sinkhole was about 14 m in diameter. Representatives from the fertilizer plant diverted the storage pond water to an alternate holding area and recovered the water by pumping the contaminated water through on-site production wells. To date, the largest natural sinkhole in the world is the Qattara Depression in Cairo, Egypt. It measures 80 km long by 120 km wide and is 133 m deep. Other naturally occurring sinkholes have become ponds or lakes.

Water is essential for the survival of humans, animals, and plants. The more than 7.4 billion people who live on Earth use more water than can be supplied by lakes and rivers. As a result, people tap into the groundwater supply to meet their water needs. Areas with large populations or large areas devoted to agriculture can use up the water in aquifers faster than the water is replaced. When aquifers near the coasts are drained of water, saltwater seeps into them. Another issue affecting the groundwater supply occurs in regions where vegetation is lacking. Plant foliage that covers a large amount of the ground slows the movement of runoff and allows it to seep into aquifers. Plant roots prevent the collapse of pore spaces in soil and absorb harmful chemicals. Without vegetation, contaminated water can enter aquifers where salt and other pollutants can remain for years.

LESSON REVIEW

1. Describe the different groundwater zones. How do rock and soil pore spaces affect the path of groundwater?
2. Explain two geologic features that are formed by groundwater.
3. Why do geysers have such intense heat?
4. Describe why groundwater is an important component of the water cycle.

OBJECTIVES

- Summarize how a stream forms.
- Assess potential problems associated with contaminated runoff.

VOCABULARY

- **divide** a ridge or other elevated region that separates watersheds
- **tributary** a stream or river that flows into a larger stream or river
- **watershed** an area of land that drains into a particular river system

Have you ever watched water rushing down a street or pouring from your roof during a heavy rain or as snow melts? Precipitation that falls to the earth usually soaks into the ground or evaporates. But when the ground is fully saturated and can no longer absorb any more water, the water begins to flow over the land in the form of runoff.

Streams begin as runoff that travels down a hill or a mountain. The runoff erodes the soil to a depth of at least 30 cm to form a narrow ditch cut in the ground called *a gully*. Gullies often become empty and dry shortly after precipitation stops. Runoff from nearby slopes flows into the gully, producing even more erosion. Eventually, all of the flowing water widens and deepens the gully into a valley with a permanent stream.

The path that a stream follows is called *a channel*. A channel is generally long and narrow and is confined by banks and a streambed. Channels branch out and widen upstream as water carries sediment downstream. As streams gradually grow wider and deeper, the banks above the water level that do not have vegetation and the streambed below the water level erode.

The flowing water in streams and rivers constantly cuts into the stream's banks, washing away more sediment. Gravity always pulls running water to the lowest elevation. The surface features of a place or region, known as *the topography*, determine the way water drains from an area. Topography includes the shapes and patterns formed by height differences in the landscape. In some locations, rivers follow lines of rock, turning at sharp angles. Stream channels are somewhat straighter when they cut into bedrock because the channels tend to follow joints, faults, or other weak structural elements. Mountain streams form a deep V-shape with steep sides, and they flow quickly in relatively straight lines. Flatland streams have rounded banks. They spread out into broad floodplains and gradually meander to the river's mouth. A bluff may develop from this type of water passage. Bluffs consist of high banks with broad, steep, sometimes rounded cliff faces overlooking plains or bodies of water.

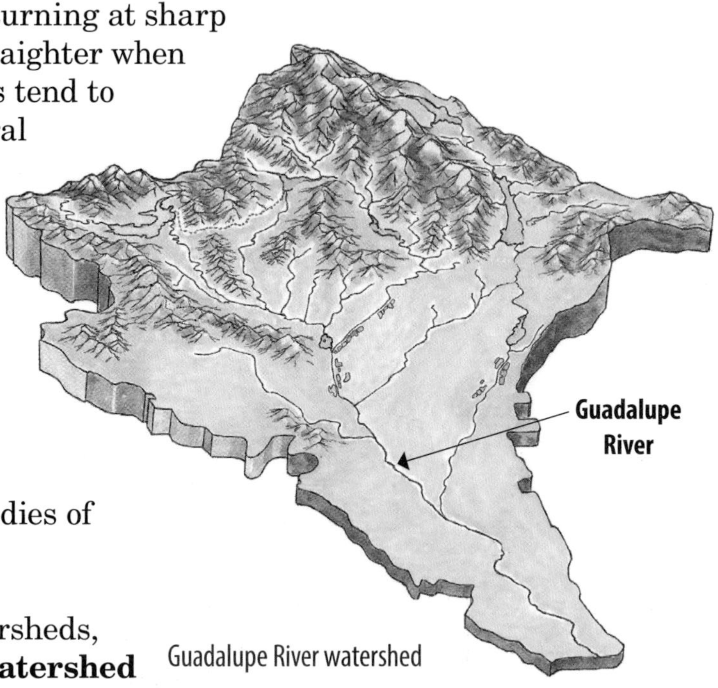

Guadalupe River watershed

These water systems are examples of watersheds, which are also called *drainage basins*. A **watershed**

Big Horn River and its tributaries in Wyoming and Montana as seen from space

is an area of land that drains into a particular river system. It includes the main river and all of the streams that flow into it. One of the largest watersheds in the world is the Amazon Basin, which covers over 7 million square kilometers. The largest watershed in the United States is the Mississippi River Basin, which covers more than one-third of the United States. A **tributary** is a stream or river that flows into a larger stream or river. In the United States, hundreds of tributaries stretch from the Allegheny Mountains in the east and the Rocky Mountains in the west as part of the Mississippi River watershed.

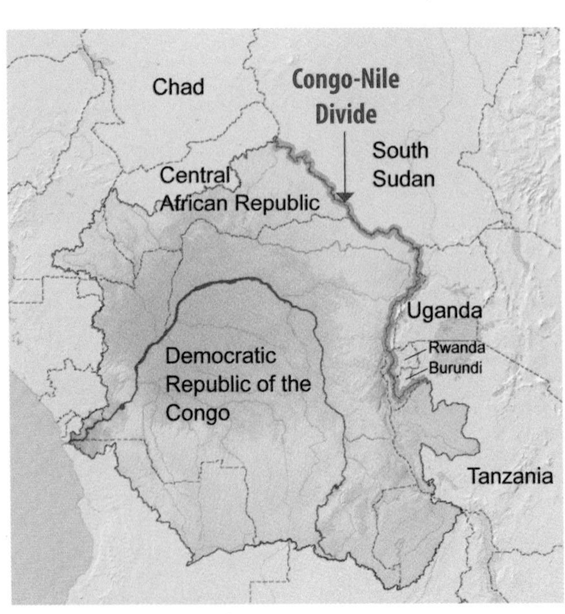

Geographic divide in Africa

A **divide** is a ridge or other elevated region that separates watersheds. Every continent has a continental divide. Some divides span multiple continents. The continental divide in North America, also known as *the Great Divide*, runs through the Rocky Mountains and extends into portions of South America along the Andes Mountains. It separates the watersheds that flow into the Pacific Ocean from those that flow into the Atlantic Ocean and the Gulf of Mexico. Some divides form country borders, such as the Congo-Nile Divide in Africa.

Runoff dissolves minerals and soil as it flows across the land toward a stream. Runoff or stream water that flows over soft rocks like limestone may become what is called *hard water*, which is water that contains a high concentration of dissolved minerals such as calcium and magnesium. The hardness of water is measured by determining the amount of calcium carbonate found in a water sample. Water that flows over rocks that are not easily weathered does not pick up many, if any, dissolved minerals. This water is called *soft water*—water that does not contain dissolved minerals. Water is considered soft if the concentration of calcium carbonate is between zero and 60 mg/L.

Effects of hard water

Much of the rainfall in watersheds with forests and fields is absorbed into the soil. This water becomes groundwater and slowly makes its way into streams and rivers. In most rural areas, the majority of rainfall does not enter the streams and rivers all at once because of vegetation. The gradual infiltration helps prevent flooding, even during heavy rains.

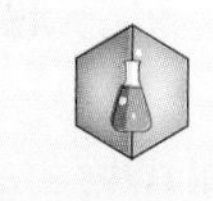

TRY THIS

Water Softeners

Design an experiment to test the effectiveness of water softeners.

In contrast, in urban areas, much of the absorbent topsoil and vegetation has been replaced by surfaces that water cannot penetrate, such as roads, parking lots, buildings, and other hard surfaces. Instead of being absorbed into the ground, rainfall flows over the hard surfaces to storm sewers, which redirect the runoff into local streams. These streams cannot handle large amounts of runoff all at once, so they often flood during storms. This type of runoff can harm streams. The water that flows across a parking lot or down a street during a heavy rain picks up pollution, such as oil, garbage, and possibly salt and sand used to melt snow and ice. The runoff carries these pollutants into streams. In summer, water that flows over hot pavement can raise stream temperatures, killing fish and other aquatic life.

Towns and cities can reduce the harmful effects of runoff in various ways through the elimination of pollution. For example, industrial waste and untreated sewage should not be dumped into water systems. To melt ice on roads during winter months, alternatives to salt can be used. In addition, reducing regional deforestation ensures that water can be absorbed by the soil and not create excess runoff. These are just a few ways towns and cities can reduce the harmful effects of runoff to benefit the entire ecosystem.

LESSON REVIEW

1. How does a stream form?
2. What is the difference between hard and soft water?
3. How can runoff harm a stream?
4. How can urban areas reduce harm to streams from runoff?

4.1.6 Rivers

OBJECTIVES

- Compare the four main stages of rivers.
- Relate the structure and function of rivers.

VOCABULARY

- **mature river** a meandering river located at a low elevation
- **old river** a slow-moving, flat river
- **rejuvenated river** a river with an increased stream gradient and power to erode
- **youthful river** a fast-flowing, irregular river with a steep, V-shaped channel

Rivers play an important role in society. Explorers charted routes along the paths of rivers. Rivers provided the energy for the first mills, and great port cities have been built on rivers. Transportation needs are met along river waterways. Drinking water is often supplied by rivers. Rivers keep underground aquifers full. Many recreational activities are facilitated by the flow of river water. All of these benefits are possible because the different types of rivers function in various ways. Think about the rivers in your area. Do they flow from the mountains or across flat land? Is the river path straight, or does it snake around in a winding path? Are rivers broken with rapids and waterfalls, or are they calm? Why are rivers so different?

In the late 19th century, a model was developed to describe stages in the development of rivers. At that time, rivers were thought to develop from a youthful stage to a mature stage to an old stage. Today, this model is no longer used. However, scientists still use the terms *youthful*, *mature*, and *old* to describe rivers. These terms do not identify the literal age of a river. Rather, the names describe river characteristics that depend on factors such as climate and the shape and erosion patterns of the land.

A **youthful river** is a fast-flowing, irregular river with a steep, V-shaped channel. Youthful rivers flow through hard rock, such as granite, that does not easily erode. The channels that develop from youthful rivers are deeper than they are wide. Given that the sides of these rivers are steep, water flows quickly and with force. The water in this type of river often tumbles over rocks in rapids and waterfalls. Youthful rivers carry relatively small volumes of water because they do not have very many tributaries. An example of a very important youthful river in Spain is the Ebro River. This river has the greatest discharge, or volume, and the

Youthful river

Mature river

Old river

largest drainage basin in Spain. Tributaries that flow into the Ebro River provide hydroelectric and thermoelectric power and are used for irrigation purposes.

A **mature river** is a meandering river located at a low elevation. Eroded channels that develop from mature rivers are wider than they are deep. Mature rivers are fed by many tributaries. Rain from watersheds flows from the tributaries into mature rivers. This enables mature rivers to carry more water than youthful rivers. Mature rivers are not as forceful as youthful rivers. They eventually lose their waterfalls and rapids, and they sometimes break their banks and flood the surrounding land. Instead of flowing in straight lines, mature rivers bend to form wide curves. Some of these curves may become cut off from the main river to form lakes or ponds, called *oxbow lakes*. The River Thames in southern England and the Mississippi River in the United States are examples of mature rivers.

An **old river** is a slow-moving, flat river. The slow pace of water prevents further land erosion. When water slows down, old rivers build up sediments in their channels and along their banks to form a broad, shallow plain. They are not as efficient as mature rivers at draining water from a watershed. Old rivers do not have as many tributaries as mature rivers because numerous smaller tributaries combine. The Tigris and the Euphrates rivers in the Middle East and the Indus River in South Asia are old rivers.

A **rejuvenated river** is a river in which the stream gradient, or slope, and power to erode have increased. Rejuvenated rivers develop when the river's base level falls because the amount of seawater decreases or the land rises. The land may rise when a tectonic plate uplifts, elevating a section of Earth's crust. When the land rises, the river channels become steeper. The river then cuts more deeply into the floor of the valley. For example, a rejuvenated river may cut a new V-shaped valley into an old river. The remains of the old floodplains may be present in steplike structures called *terraces*.

Rivers are a gift from God, but people have not always treated these gifts as they should. For a long time, many people thought that mighty rivers, such as the Mississippi, were self-cleaning machines that rushed pollution out to sea. In the 1960s, every major waterway in the United States was polluted with industrial waste and sewage. Laws were passed to reduce the pollution of waterways. These government actions have helped, but pollution is still an issue in many rivers.

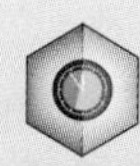

HISTORY

The Role of Rivers

Rivers have played an important role in the history of many countries. They have defined both geographic and political boundaries. During the Civil War in the United States, many of the necessary resources needed by the Confederate Army were transported along the Mississippi River. In 1862, the Union Army decided to cut off all Confederate access to the Mississippi River. This action would eliminate a key supply route for the Confederate Army and affect its ability to defend certain positions. Ulysses S. Grant directed a fleet of gunboats to follow the Mississippi south while David G. Farragut's squadron in the Gulf of Mexico traveled north along the river. The two Union forces met at Vicksburg, Mississippi, and after a 40-day siege, successfully gained complete control of the Mississippi River. The Union's tactical decision to control the river was a major contributing factor to its victory over the Confederate Army.

An oxbow lake at Horseshoe Bend in Arizona

LESSON REVIEW

1. Compare the characteristics of the four stages of rivers.
2. How do people benefit from the fast-moving water found in youthful rivers?
3. Mature rivers bend to form wide curves. What is the name of the structure that is formed when these curves are cut off from the rest of the main river to form lakes or ponds?
4. Explain how the structure of a river and its functions are related.

Terrace development at the San Juan River in Goosenecks State Park, Utah

Ponds and lakes are places of wonder. Perhaps you have searched for frogs and turtles in the mud or looked for salamanders under rocks. The murky bank of a neighborhood pond is a great place to begin a lifelong discovery of God's creation.

OBJECTIVES

- Compare features of ponds and lakes.
- Determine how sunlight infiltration affects pond and lake ecosystems.
- Explain how ponds and lakes form.

Ponds and lakes contain standing or slowly moving water and are surrounded by land. Generally, ponds are smaller and shallower than lakes. However, this is not always true. Echo Lake in New Hampshire has a water surface area of about 5.6 hectares and is 3.35 meters deep. In contrast, the water in Island Pond in Vermont covers an area of 202.3 hectares and is 18.29 meters deep. Lakes and ponds can be found in a variety of sizes and depths.

Ponds and lakes are unique habitats, separate from the surrounding meadows or forests. Their ecosystems consist of freshwater organisms that depend on each other and the environment to survive. Algae, flagellates, plants, invertebrates, fungi, and fish are examples of the producers, consumers, and decomposers in these ecosystems. These organisms reside in one of the following four habitats: the shore, surface film, open water, or bottom water. The most plants and animals are found in the shallow depths of ponds and lakes where sunlight can penetrate.

Rooted plant life diminishes with lack of sunlight.

The temperatures of lakes and ponds are affected by the depth of sunlight infiltration. If a pond is very shallow, the sun's rays can reach to the bottom, enabling rooted plant growth throughout the pond. Without sunlight, rooted plant growth does not occur on the floors of ponds or lakes. Plant growth is further inhibited on lake shorelines that experience excessive wind and wave erosion.

Pond temperatures are relatively uniform throughout, but deep ponds or lakes can contain multiple thermal layers during the summer months in temperate regions. This layering, called *thermal stratification*, happens because the water's density changes with the temperature. Warm water is less dense than cold water. Spring winds help circulate lake water. As summer's heat warms a lake from the surface down, three layers of water form. The temperature of each water layer decreases moving downward. Wind circulates the less dense surface water, but the deeper water is relatively unmixed. Since water circulation moves oxygen through the water, the lake bottom has less oxygen in summer. Algae grows, preventing sunlight from reaching the lower layers in deep bodies of water. As temperatures cool in fall, the pond or lake water begins circulating again.

Thermal Stratification

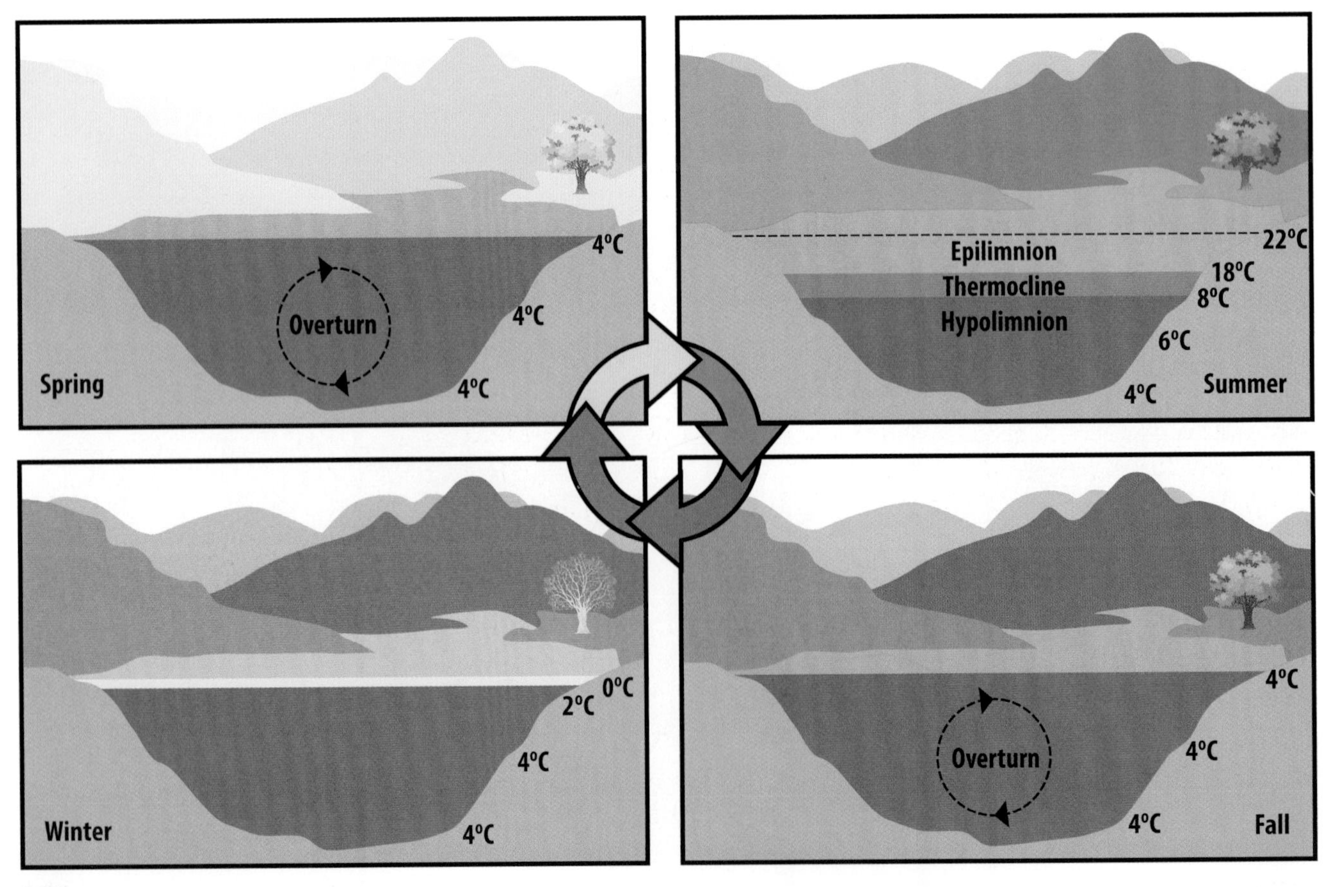

Dissolved oxygen and carbon dioxide quantities in shallow bodies of water also fluctuate with temperature variation. During the day, water plants and algae capture sunlight for photosynthesis. As they photosynthesize, plants give off a lot of oxygen, which means the oxygen level in the water peaks in the late afternoon. Plants stop producing oxygen when the sun sets, but animals continue to take in oxygen and expel carbon dioxide throughout the night. As a result, overnight the oxygen level in the water declines and the carbon dioxide level increases. Bacteria also give off carbon dioxide when they decompose organic substances in the water. Unlike shallow lakes and ponds, a deep lake's temperature, dissolved oxygen level, and carbon dioxide level remain about the same throughout the day.

Beaver dams can create ponds.

Not all ponds form in the same way. Many ponds formed thousands of years ago when glaciers receded, leaving holes in the ground. Some ponds form as rivers erode and change course. Some ponds form when landslides block the streamflow in steep valleys. Beavers can make ponds by damming up sections of a stream. Alligators sometimes hollow out small ponds as they search for water. Strong winds and meteorites can even carve out deep impressions in the soil, which later fill with water and form small ponds. Some ponds form in depressions in a forest during the wet season but evaporate during the dry season. People also dig new ponds that supply water for farm animals or for irrigation. Ponds generally have a short lifespan. Over time, they develop into marshes and then meadows.

Lake formation is very similar to pond formation, but requires a greater amount of force. Rivers can form oxbow lakes, and delta lakes can form at the mouth of a river when sediments dam up the current. In North America, thousands of both small lakes and deep lakes, such as New York's Finger Lakes, formed in deep depressions left by glaciers. The movement of the earth's plates has also formed enormous lakes. Scientists theorize that a crustal plate rose from the sea and isolated Florida's Lake Okeechobee and that tectonic rifting formed Lake Tanganyika in Central Africa. Deep, clear lakes often form in the craters of volcanoes, such as Quilotoa Crater Lake in Ecuador. Some lakes are formed when rivers are dammed. For example, dams along the Columbia and Colorado rivers resulted in a series of large lakes. Lake Nasser is a reservoir, or artificial lake, that lies behind the Aswan Dam in Egypt. Lakes have a longer lifespan than ponds. They can flourish for thousands of years.

The Great Lakes, which scientists believe were formed by glaciers, make up the world's largest surface area of freshwater. The United States and Canada share all of these lakes except for Lake Michigan, which lies entirely within the United States. The Great Lakes are unique among the world's freshwater lakes. All five lakes form a single watershed with one common outlet to the sea, which is the Saint Lawrence Seaway.

Although ponds and lakes only make up a small percentage of water on Earth, they are important sources of freshwater. In fact, many scientists consider lakes to be the best available freshwater source on Earth's surface. Ponds and lakes not only create habitats for plants and animals, but are also used by people for recreation, industry, and agriculture. These bodies of water and their contributions can be enjoyed for many years if the environment is purposefully protected.

LESSON REVIEW

1. How are ponds and lakes alike? How are they different?
2. Why is water depth an important physical characteristic of most ponds?
3. Explain why there is a small percentage of plant and animal life at deeper water depths in ponds and lakes.
4. Why is there less dissolved oxygen in pond or lake water at night than during the day?
5. Describe two ways that ponds and lakes form.

Kelimutu Crater Lake in Indonesia

In order to take advantage of rivers for transportation needs, energy sources, recreational activities, and drinking water resources, many cities and towns have been built on floodplains. With an increasing number of individuals building houses near rivers, flood prevention has become an important topic in many areas. However, it is important to realize that not all flooding is bad. In fact, flooding is a natural and even necessary occurrence in the life of many rivers. Flooding can even be beneficial because floodwaters leave behind sediments that produce flat, fertile plains for farming. To limit flood damage, scientists now believe it is best to leave floodplains undeveloped and in their natural state. If that is not possible, limiting or restricting how development occurs in floodplains helps lessen the devastation from floods. In regions where extensive development has already occurred on floodplains, scientists and engineers continue to research and develop plans that will prevent devastating floods.

God provided natural flood control systems in the environment. Natural flood control involves using forests, wetlands, and soil conservation methods to prevent excess runoff during heavy rains. Some human methods for controlling floods include levees and dams. A **levee**, also called *a dike*, is a structure built to prevent a river from overflowing. Most levees are built alongside a river. Levees offer temporary protection from flooding. As a river deposits sediment, the height of a levee must be raised. In contrast, a dam is a permanent structure built across a river

Levee breaks in New Orleans during Hurricane Katrina

OBJECTIVES

- Evaluate ways that flooding can be prevented.
- Indicate advantages of using dams and hydroelectric power.
- Explain disadvantages of using dams and hydroelectric power.

VOCABULARY

- **hydroelectric power** the electricity produced from the power of moving water
- **levee** a structure built to prevent a river from overflowing
- **reservoir** a natural or artificial lake used to store and regulate water

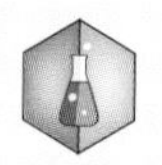

TRY THIS

Build a Dam

Work with a team and fill a rectangular plastic container with gravel or small rocks that must not be removed. Using the provided materials, construct a dam that can hold back five liters of water and allow for a controlled release of some of the water. Test the dam for its ability to allow water to flow, stop, and flow again. Make adjustments as needed.

Hetch Hetchy Reservoir formed behind the O'Shaughnessy Dam in Yosemite National Park.

to regulate water flow. By regulating the water flow, engineers can control flooding. Some of the largest structures on Earth are dams. Dams can be found on almost every continent.

Most dams are constructed for flood control or to allow navigation on a river. However, many large-scale dams were built in the 20th century to provide **hydroelectric power**, which is electricity produced from the power of moving water. To produce energy, the water level behind a dam is raised and then diverted over the turbines of a generator to create electricity. Hydroelectric power supplies nearly 16% of the world's electric power. This type of power is the most widely used renewable resource in the world.

Hydroelectric dams have many advantages compared to other energy sources. Unlike burning fossil fuels, this power source does not produce air pollution. Hydroelectric power is also one of the most economical sources of energy. Tens of thousands of dams around the world are used to generate hydroelectric power. Dams and hydroelectric power plants use technology that is well

BIBLE CONNECTION

God-Given Power

The first hydroelectric power plant was designed and built by Nikola Tesla and George Westinghouse in 1895. In Tesla's speech at the Niagara Falls power plant opening ceremony, he stated that such monuments "exemplify the power of men and the greatness of nations." Tesla placed his focus on the power and capabilities that people possess without giving proper attention to the one—God the creator— who provides people with the power to build such a marvel. More important, God supplied people with His power because individuals are created in His image. In Exodus 4:21, God tells Moses to "perform before Pharaoh all the wonders I have given you the power to do." Everything people have is a gift from God. With these gifts come great responsibility. Tesla shared later in his speech that the hydroelectric power station "signifies the subjugation of natural forces to the service of man." As good stewards of God's kingdom, people are directed to protect and utilize the resources wisely. These resources are not just for human gain.

understood, and they cost less to maintain than nuclear or coal-burning power plants.

Hydroelectric power station in Naberezhnye Chelny, Russia

Frequently, a reservoir is created behind a dam. A **reservoir** is a natural or artificial lake used to store and regulate water. People use reservoirs for drinking water and for recreation.

However, dams change the natural environment, and sometimes these changes are not beneficial. God's creation is complex, and people must respect how the different facets work together. Constructing a dam across a river can disrupt the ecosystem, putting the native species at risk. Dams can harm fish or prevent them from reaching their spawning habitats. Scientists have determined that dams can lower the temperature of warm rivers by drawing in cooler water from deep reservoirs. Dams can also raise the temperatures of cold rivers by trapping the water in shallow reservoirs where energy from the sun is absorbed. Fish and other creatures cannot always adapt to such temperature fluctuations, so these changes may lead to lower population numbers.

Downstream from dams, the beds and banks of rivers often erode because the sediment needed to rebuild what erosion removes is stopped by the dam. Dams trap debris, which can clog reservoirs. Water pollution and heavy metals, such as boron, arsenic, and uranium, can accumulate in sediments and reservoir water. Polluted drinking water can create serious health hazards.

Caring for God's world is an intricate task. There are many factors that must be considered when people attempt to alter the flow of a waterway by building a dam, including the environmental impact, the economic impact, and the overall community impact. As with many human endeavors, the needs of the community should be weighed against the effects on God's creation.

LESSON REVIEW

1. Is flooding always harmful? Why?
2. Describe one method of flood prevention and explain why this method is the best.
3. What are the benefits of building dams for hydroelectric power?
4. How might dams have a negative effect on the environment?

4.1.9 *Eutrophication*

OBJECTIVES

- Explain the process of eutrophication.
- Analyze the effects of eutrophication.
- Discover solutions related to eutrophication issues.

VOCABULARY

- **algal bloom** an explosive growth of algae caused by too many nutrients in the water
- **dead zone** an area that has been depleted of oxygen by eutrophication
- **eutrophication** the process by which nitrate or phosphate compounds overenrich a body of water and deplete it of oxygen

Aquatic plant and animal life requires the right amount of nutrients and minerals to thrive. During different periods in time, water sources can become saturated with an influx of nutrients and minerals. When this happens, plant and animal life is adversely affected. This overabundance of resources actually harms organisms rather than helps them. Their systems become overwhelmed and cannot function properly, and death is often a result. As the saying goes, "Everything in moderation."

The overenriching process begins not in the water but on land. Nitrogen and phosphorus are the two most common minerals required by plants, so most fertilizers contain these two minerals. Sewage also contains a significant amount of nitrogen and phosphorus. Rainfall can wash fertilizer and sewage into rivers, lakes, and other surface waters. Over time, a surplus of this fertilizer and sewage can build up in waterways and completely change the dynamics of the water system.

Eutrophication is the process where a body of water becomes overenriched with nitrate or phosphate compounds and is depleted of oxygen. The process begins with **algal bloom**, which is an explosive growth of algae caused by too many nutrients in the water. Algae feed on the extra phosphate and nitrate compounds and begin to reproduce at a dramatic rate. Large numbers of algae develop to form a layer that covers the water's surface. This layer blocks light from passing through the water. Without light to photosynthesize, aquatic plants beneath the water's surface quickly die. Bacteria and other microorganisms digest the dead plants and algae. With all this extra food, the bacteria reproduce quickly. The large bacteria population uses up much of the water's dissolved oxygen. Fish and other animal

TRY THIS

Too Much of a Good Thing

Using pond water, distilled water, and liquid fertilizer, design an experiment that tests the effects of phosphorus and nitrogen on water.

Bactrian camels relaxing in algal bloom

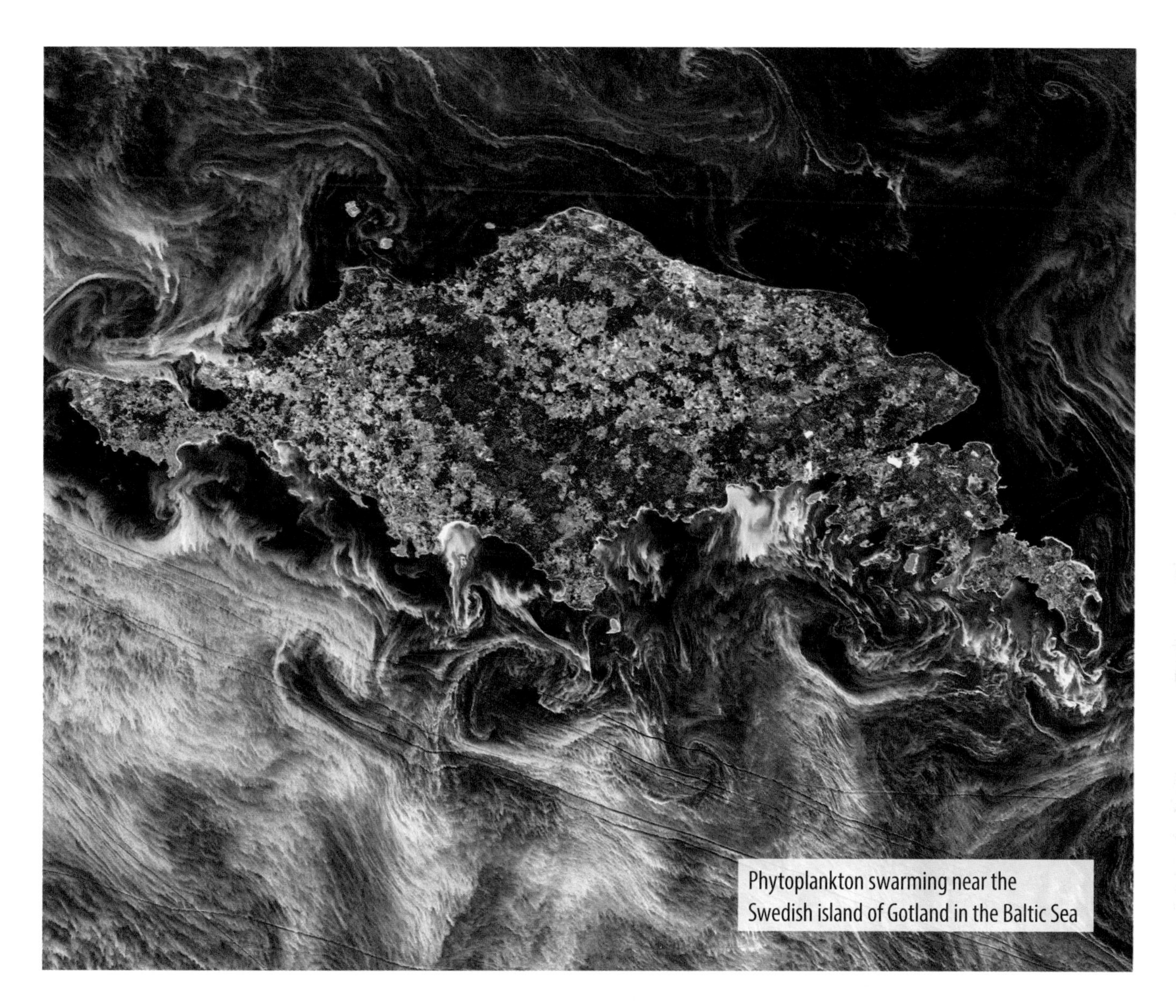
Phytoplankton swarming near the Swedish island of Gotland in the Baltic Sea

populations decrease in number because they do not receive sufficient amounts of oxygen to live.

Such an occurrence can happen in large bodies of water as well. A common example of algal bloom that occurs along the coast is called *red tide*. The seawater is often colored red because the dinoflagellate population increases. Dinoflagellates are aquatic, single-celled organisms that can release toxic substances that are harmful to marine life. Red tides kill many fish, so they are accompanied by the strong odor of dead fish. Brown tides may also develop with increases of *Aureococcus anophagefferens*, a particular type of algae that lives in areas where there is little sunlight and high concentrations of nitrogen and phosphorus.

Between the late 1850s and 1920, towns throughout North America and Europe designed sewer systems that pumped human waste into storm sewers that distributed the waste to nearby bodies of water. This practice led to surface water contamination and eutrophication. Waste treatment processes developed between 1880 and 1940 helped remove suspended particles and disease-causing microorganisms from the sewage, but these methods did not remove the phosphates and nitrates. The combination of fertilizers with sewage and the phosphates from detergents made the problem of eutrophication worse. Algal blooms turned waters green, brown, and red and killed aquatic plants and animals. However, eutrophication was not recognized as a major problem in North America and Europe until the late 1960s when Lake Erie was declared a dead zone. A **dead zone**, or a hypoxic zone, is an area that has been depleted of oxygen by eutrophication. Marine life either dies off or leaves dead zones.

Today, eutrophication is a major problem in nations such as China where human populations are growing at an exponential rate and pollution control is not viewed as a priority. Scientists estimate that the human impact on nature is about eight times higher today than it was 40–50 years ago. Industry and farm production increases with human population. Technological

FYI

Soap or Detergent

Before 1916, people used soap to wash their clothes, clean their homes, and bathe themselves. When soap combines with the minerals in hard water, it forms an insoluble scum called *soap curd*, which builds up on surfaces. The first detergent was developed when a shortage of the fats needed to make soap occurred during World War I. People liked detergents because they did not create soap curd. However, detergents left heaps of foam in waterways. Newer detergents do not create foam, but they are more toxic to fish and other aquatic life.

Dinoflagellate Bioluminescence

Occasionally, a dinoflagellate population will multiply to create a red tide. Some dinoflagellates contain bioluminescent genes that enable the creatures to produce a blue glow when physically disrupted. Scientists have determined this glow is emitted by the dinoflagellate in an attempt to startle predators enough to disrupt their feeding pattern and to prevent further ingestion. This glow also attracts secondary predators that can eat the primary predator. Any physical disruption can cause the dinoflagellate to luminesce. Examples of physical disruptions include the forces of waves, animals swimming nearby, or the commotion a paddling surfer.

Farmer spraying crops

advances designed to solve problems often cause other issues. For example, farmers can produce more crops with modern methods, but rely on fertilizers and pesticides to get high crop yields.

By being good stewards, individuals can reduce or prevent the effects of eutrophication and prevent dead zones from developing. Regulating fertilizer use and wastewater runoff is a first step, as is using efficient flood control. Wetland restoration should be a priority because these regions capture and filter excess nutrients and pollution. By working together to prevent eutrophication, communities can protect their water supplies and the lives of aquatic plants and animals.

LESSON REVIEW

1. What two main chemical elements contribute to eutrophication?
2. Describe the roles algae and bacteria play in the eutrophication process.
3. How does eutrophication affect aquatic life?
4. What is an area that has been depleted of oxygen called?
5. Name two methods that can reduce or prevent the effects of eutrophication.

4.2.1 *Ocean Water Properties*

OBJECTIVES

- Explain what affects ocean water salinity.
- Examine what affects ocean water density and how density affects ocean water.
- Illustrate how life-sustaining gases cycle through the ocean environment.
- Model why heat and light from the sun extend only to certain depths.

VOCABULARY

- **salinity** the amount of dissolved salt in a given quantity of liquid

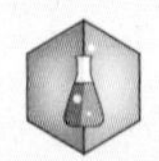

TRY THIS

Bubbles Out, Bubbles In

To observe that hot and cold water hold different amounts of dissolved oxygen, let a glass of cold water stand at room temperature for several hours. Observe the bubbles that form on the inside of the glass. Then carefully (without disturbing the bubbles) put the glass in a refrigerator and leave it there for several hours. What happens to the bubbles? Why? How might temperature changes in ocean water affect the creatures that live there?

If you were to observe Earth from space, you would notice how vast the oceans are compared to the continents. In fact, ocean water covers over 70% of the Earth; this water accounts for 97% of Earth's water. Ocean water is a careful recipe created to support a wide variety of life.

Ocean water is a complex solution of pure water, solids, and gases. It is 96.5% pure water. The other 3.5% is dissolved salts from at least 72 different elements. However, only six of these elements make up approximately 99% of the ocean's salt content.

Rivers are one source of the elements in oceans. The place where freshwater from a river meets salty ocean water is called *an estuary*, which often takes the shape of a wide, shallow bay. As river water flows over rocks, it dissolves some of the minerals in the rocks and carries them along. Each year, rivers carry 400 billion kg of these minerals to the ocean. Once in the ocean, elements may combine to create various salts. Sodium and chlorine, in their ionic forms, make up more than 90% of the elements that enter the ocean. These ions combine to create table

"The sea is His, for He made it, and His hands formed the dry land." Psalm 95:5

salt, which explains why ocean water tastes salty. Minerals in ocean water also come from the rocks on the ocean floor or from openings in the sea floor called *hydrothermal vents*. These vents emit heated water from inside the crust that carries dissolved minerals.

People easily float on the Dead Sea because of its high salinity.

Salinity is the measure of dissolved salt in a given amount of liquid. It is usually expressed in parts per thousand. The amount of salt in ocean water varies. Normal ocean water ranges from 34–37 parts per thousand. Ocean water in drier, hotter climates usually has more salt compared to ocean water in more humid, cooler climates. Less freshwater runs into the ocean and more water evaporates in drier climates. In contrast, places where large rivers drain into the ocean usually have low salinity because such rivers add large amounts of freshwater to the ocean.

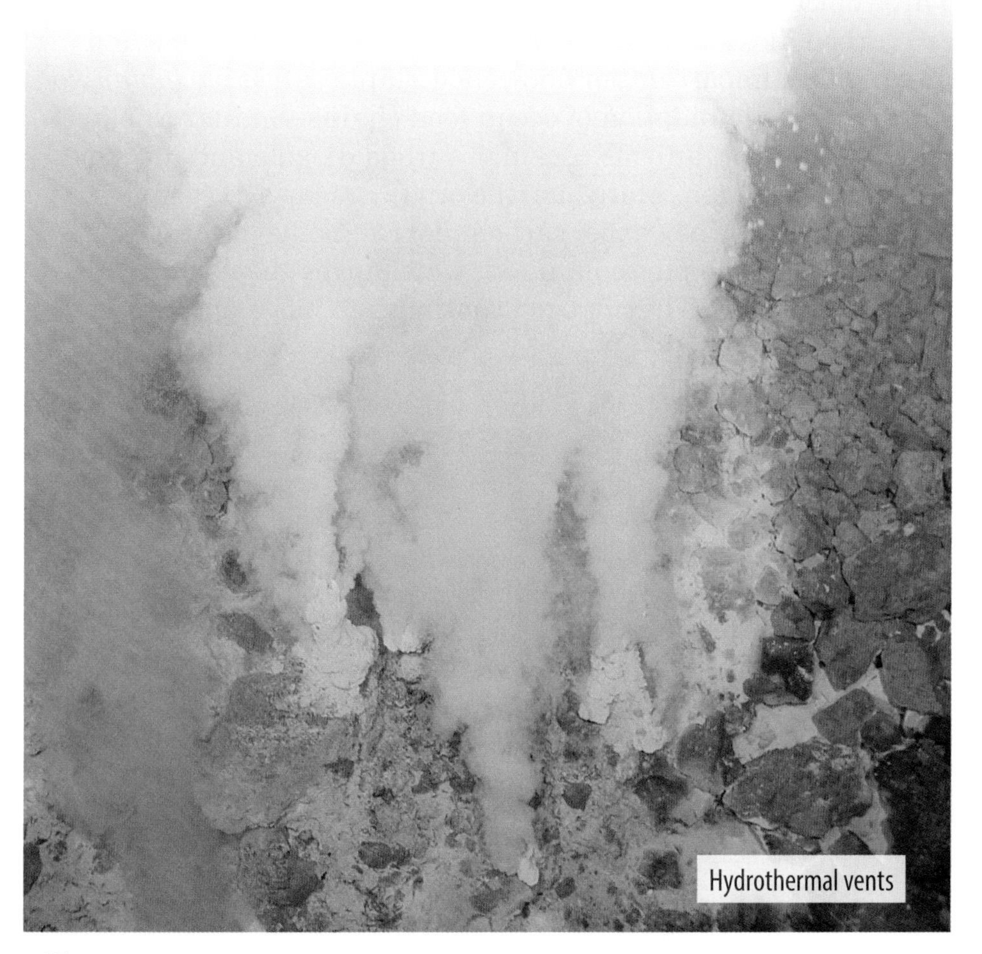
Hydrothermal vents

TRY THIS

Freezing Point

Design an experiment to find out how the salt in ocean water affects the temperature at which it freezes.

FYI

Pile it On

If the salt in the oceans could be removed and spread evenly over Earth's land surface, it would form a layer more than 150 m thick, about the height of a 40-story building!

Some species of phytoplankton glow under certain conditions.

Differences in salinity and temperature create ocean currents. Water is more dense when it is cold or salty. More dense water sinks, forcing warmer or less salty water to the surface. This process creates currents called *thermohaline currents*. (*Thermo* refers to temperature, and *haline* refers to salt content.) These currents move nutrients and gases throughout the oceans.

Some of the properties of ocean water determine the amount of dissolved gases it can hold. For example, ocean water with low salinity can hold more gases than saltier seawater. Cold water can hold more gases than warm water, which is important for the aquatic life throughout the ocean that depends on oxygen and carbon dioxide for survival. The surface region of the ocean, where photosynthesis takes place, is the most oxygen enriched. However, the deep cold waters of the ocean are also filled with oxygen because the greater density of the cold water carries the gas into the deep sea.

FYI

Lights Please

At 600 m deep, the light available in ocean water is about the same as starlight.

Around 690 m deep, the light intensity is about one ten-billionth as strong as the light on the surface.

Below 1,000 m deep, the ocean is totally black. Since most of the ocean is deeper than 1,000 m, most of this ocean zone never receives any light.

Three of the most abundant gases dissolved in ocean water are carbon dioxide, nitrogen, and oxygen. Carbon dioxide and nitrogen are important for one-celled plants called *phytoplankton*, which are the foundation of ocean food chains. Similar to plants on land, these organisms consume carbon dioxide and nitrogen and give off oxygen. Many marine organisms use oxygen for respiration, and they expel carbon dioxide. Some of these same organisms eat the phytoplankton, which gives them the nitrogen their bodies need. The nitrogen continues to move up through the

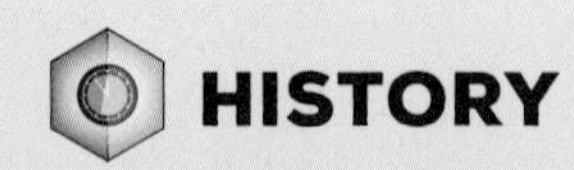

Controlling Pollution

On January 19, 2013, more than 140 nations adopted the Minamata Convention on Mercury to address the worldwide problem of mercury poisoning resulting from various forms of pollution. The agreement was named after a significant outbreak of mercury poisoning coming from Minamata Bay, Japan, in the 1950s. Mercury entered the ocean through factory waste that was improperly disposed of. The mercury particles in the waste worked their way up the ocean food chain and severely contaminated various fish and shellfish. People who ate these creatures suffered from a variety of symptoms including mental retardation, paralysis, and death. Japan worked diligently to clean up the area, and Minamata Bay was declared free of mercury by July 1997. Japan also played a key role in drafting the agreement and helping other nations address the problem of mercury poisoning.

More or Less Salty

Enclosed seas such as the Red Sea and the Persian Gulf have a high salt content, with a salinity of approximately 40 parts per thousand. Coastal areas near large rivers have a lower salt content because of dilution from freshwater.

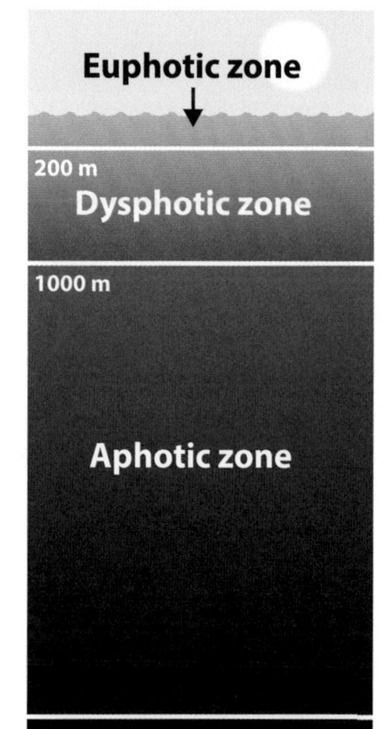

food chain as predators consume prey. When phytoplankton and other organisms die, they sink to the bottom of the ocean where bacteria decompose them and release the nitrogen back into the water. Currents bring this nutrient-rich water back to the surface for the cycle to begin again.

Even though so many solids and gases are dissolved in it, ocean water is clear. Because of this, sunlight can penetrate the water. However, the sun's power to warm and illuminate the ocean decreases with greater depth because energy loses intensity as it passes through matter. The sun actively warms the top 1 m of ocean water, and wave action distributes that warmth to a depth of about 100 m. This means that at any given location the water's temperature is fairly consistent through the top 100 m.

The intensity of sunlight effectively divides the ocean into three layers. Light waves lose intensity and scatter when they enter water. Therefore, only about 1% of sunlight reaches 150 m below the surface, which is the greatest depth where plants can perform photosynthesis. However, there is still enough light for most organisms to see down to about 200 m. This upper 200 m of ocean is called *the euphotic zone*. The middle zone is called *the dysphotic zone*, or *the twilight zone,* because very little light reaches it. The dysphotic zone extends from about 200–1,000 m below the surface. Below 1,000 m is known as *the aphotic zone*, commonly called *the midnight zone*, because no light reaches it.

LESSON REVIEW

1. Where does the ocean's salt come from?
2. Explain why the salinity of ocean water is likely to be greater in a hot, dry climate than in a cool, wet climate.
3. What two factors especially affect ocean water density?
4. How does density affect ocean water?
5. How do carbon dioxide and nitrogen cycle through the ocean environment?
6. Why do heat and light from the sun not travel to the lowest depths of the ocean?

4.2.2 Ocean Motion

OBJECTIVES

- Illustrate the parts of a wave.
- Describe how waves are formed and what affects their growth in the deep ocean and close to shore.
- Compare types and behaviors of currents near the shore.
- Demonstrate the flow of major ocean currents.

VOCABULARY

- **amplitude** a wave's height or depth measured from the surrounding water level
- **Coriolis effect** the curving of moving objects from a straight path because of Earth's rotation
- **crest** the highest point of a wave
- **trough** the lowest point of a wave
- **wavelength** the distance between identical points on two back-to-back waves

Waves are a familiar sight. You see them on the ocean, in lakes, and even in swimming pools. From the smallest ripple across a pond to the largest, most powerful ocean wave, all waves have common features. All waves have a crest and a trough. The **crest** is the highest point of a wave; the **trough** is the lowest point of a wave. The **wavelength** is the distance between identical points on two back-to-back waves, such as from crest to crest or from trough to trough. The vertical distance between the wave crest and wave trough is called *the wave height*. The **amplitude** is a wave's height or depth measured from the surrounding water level; it is one-half the wave height.

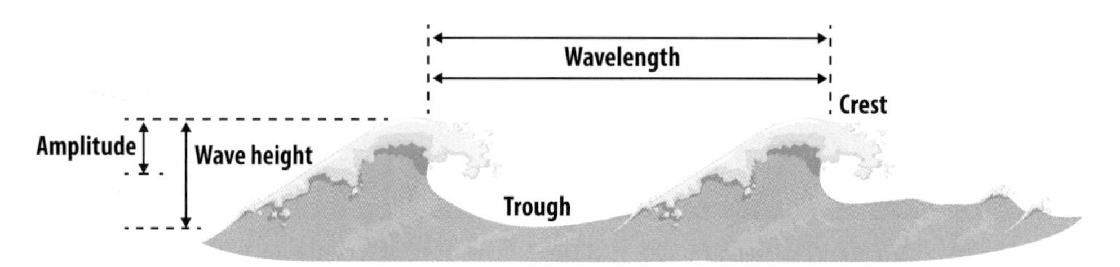

The ocean has several different types of waves. Ripples in the water are called *capillary waves*. These waves are caused by winds blowing gently across the water's surface. Waves become taller as winds become stronger, and their crests become steeper. Storms with high-speed winds form waves whose crests have been blown off, known as *whitecaps*. Intense storms may whip up waves measuring higher than 10 m! Waves are not only created by wind. A tsunami is a very large ocean wave that is caused by an underwater earthquake or volcanic eruption. Most tsunamis are generated in the Pacific Ocean around the Ring of Fire. A tsunami can rise up to 30 m above normal sea level.

Whitecaps

Other forces cause a wave to change shape as it approaches the shore. Friction against the ocean floor slows the wave's underside, which shortens its wavelength while increasing its amplitude. Because the wave's top section does not slow down, it gets farther and farther ahead of the underside until the wave topples over. The toppling wave is called *a breaker.*

A rip current is a narrow current flowing away from the shore.

Waves are not the only motion in the ocean. The continuous flow of water in a certain direction is called *a current*. Currents can occur in the ocean's depths, on its surface, and even along beaches. On a beach, the rapid flow of water back to the ocean after a wave breaks on shore is sometimes called *an undertow.* This force pulls lightweight objects like shells back toward the ocean. Undertows do not usually pull objects out to sea because the force of incoming waves tend to push those objects back onto the beach.

Narrow currents flowing away from the shore are called *rip currents.* They often form near structures or where a shallow trench has been carved in the sand. Rip currents can be dangerous because they are powerful enough to carry even strong swimmers out to sea. People who are caught in a rip current should swim parallel to the shore until they escape the current's pull and can safely swim back to the beach.

Surface currents are created by winds that blow over the ocean's surface, just like someone blowing air across a cup of water. Unlike blowing on water in a cup, however, ocean currents do not flow in straight lines. They curve away from the wind's general direction because of the Coriolis effect. The **Coriolis effect** is the curving of moving objects from a straight path because of

Tsunami

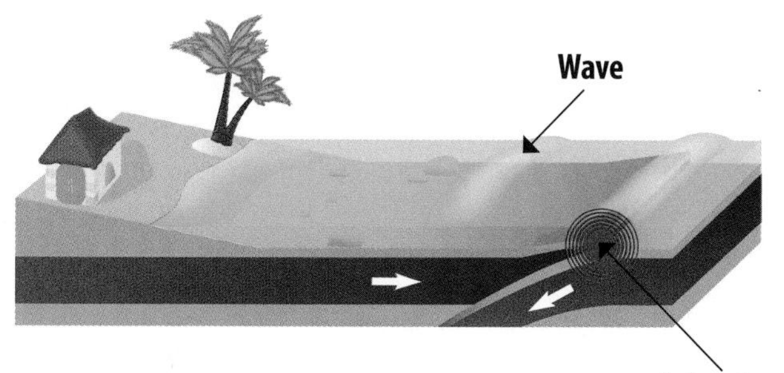
Wave
Epicenter
of an earthquake

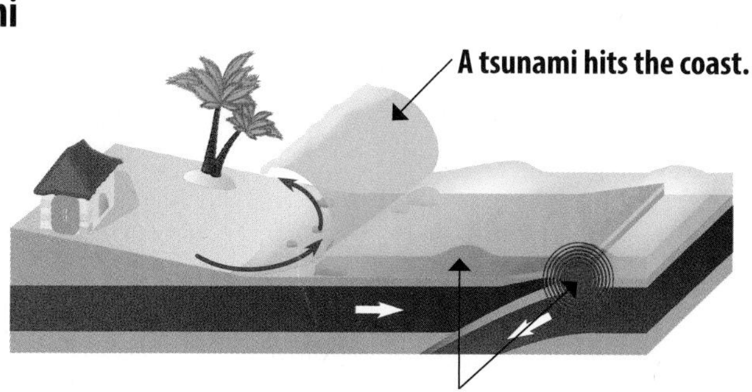
A tsunami hits the coast.
A tsunami starts during an earthquake.
The giant waves travel across the sea.

TRY THIS

Saline Density

Pour 250 mL of water in each of four 500 mL beakers. Add 4 drops of yellow food coloring to 2 of the beakers and 4 drops of blue food coloring to 2 of the beakers. Add table salt to the yellow water in 5 g increments until the water is saturated with salt; stir after each addition of salt. The water is fully saturated when no more salt will dissolve.

Slowly pour the water from one of the beakers of yellow water into one of the beakers of blue water. What happens? Why? Then slowly pour the remaining beaker of blue water into the remaining beaker of yellow water. What happens? Why?

Earth's rotation. Picture what would happen if a person tried to roll a ball across a spinning merry-go-round; the path of the ball would curve before it reached the other side. Because of the Coriolis effect, ocean currents in the Northern Hemisphere turn clockwise, but ocean currents in the Southern Hemisphere turn counterclockwise.

The Gulf Stream is a warm surface current in the Atlantic Ocean that flows up the eastern coast of North America and then east to Europe. This current travels 25–75 km per day. A steady wind blows the warm air from this current over Europe, producing unusually high temperatures for a region so far north. However, the Gulf Stream has little effect on the east coast of the United States and Canada because the west winds blow the warm ocean air away from the coast.

Deep currents are movements of water deep beneath the ocean's surface. These currents form because of differences in water density, which is influenced by temperature and salinity. Encircling Earth is a great thermohaline ocean current that travels through the oceans like a river. The current begins near Greenland as water cools and sinks. The cold water flows southward deep in the Atlantic Ocean toward Antarctica. From here it flows northward into the Indian or Pacific Oceans where it begins to rise and warm. The warmer water moves back around southern Africa, and up through the Atlantic Ocean to where it began. Scientists call this current *the global conveyor*

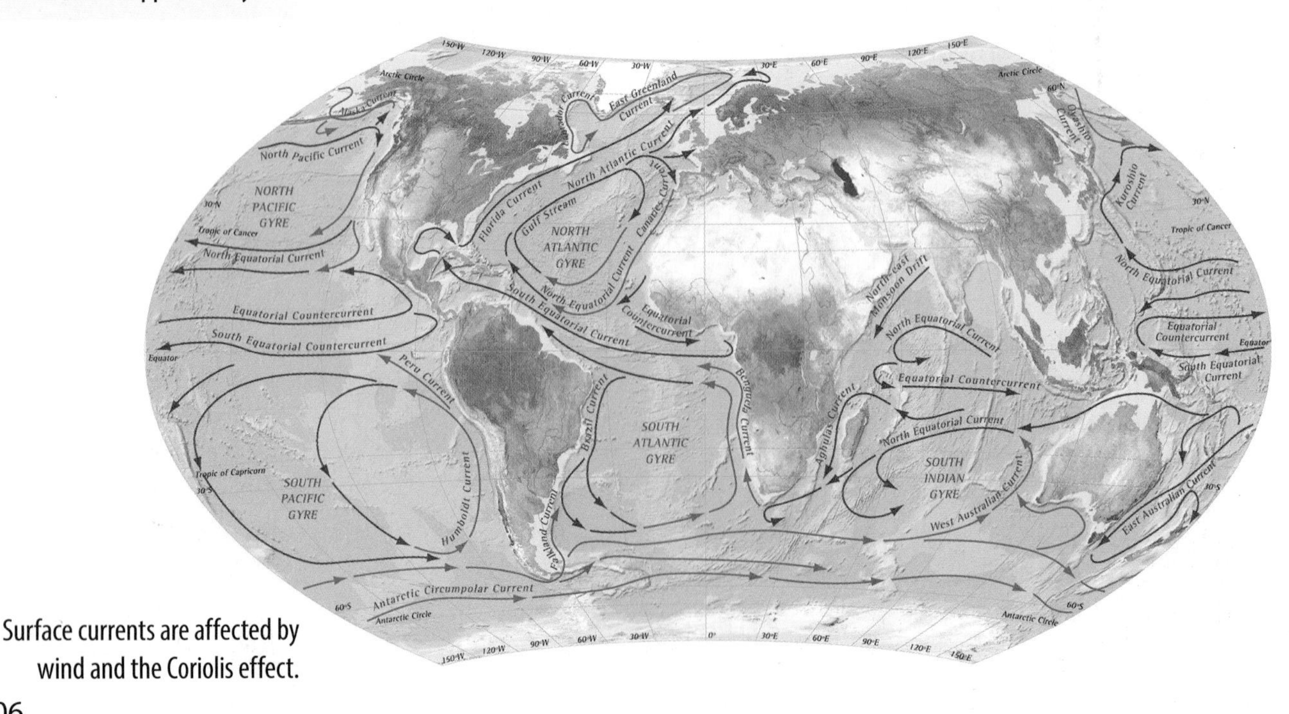

Surface currents are affected by wind and the Coriolis effect.

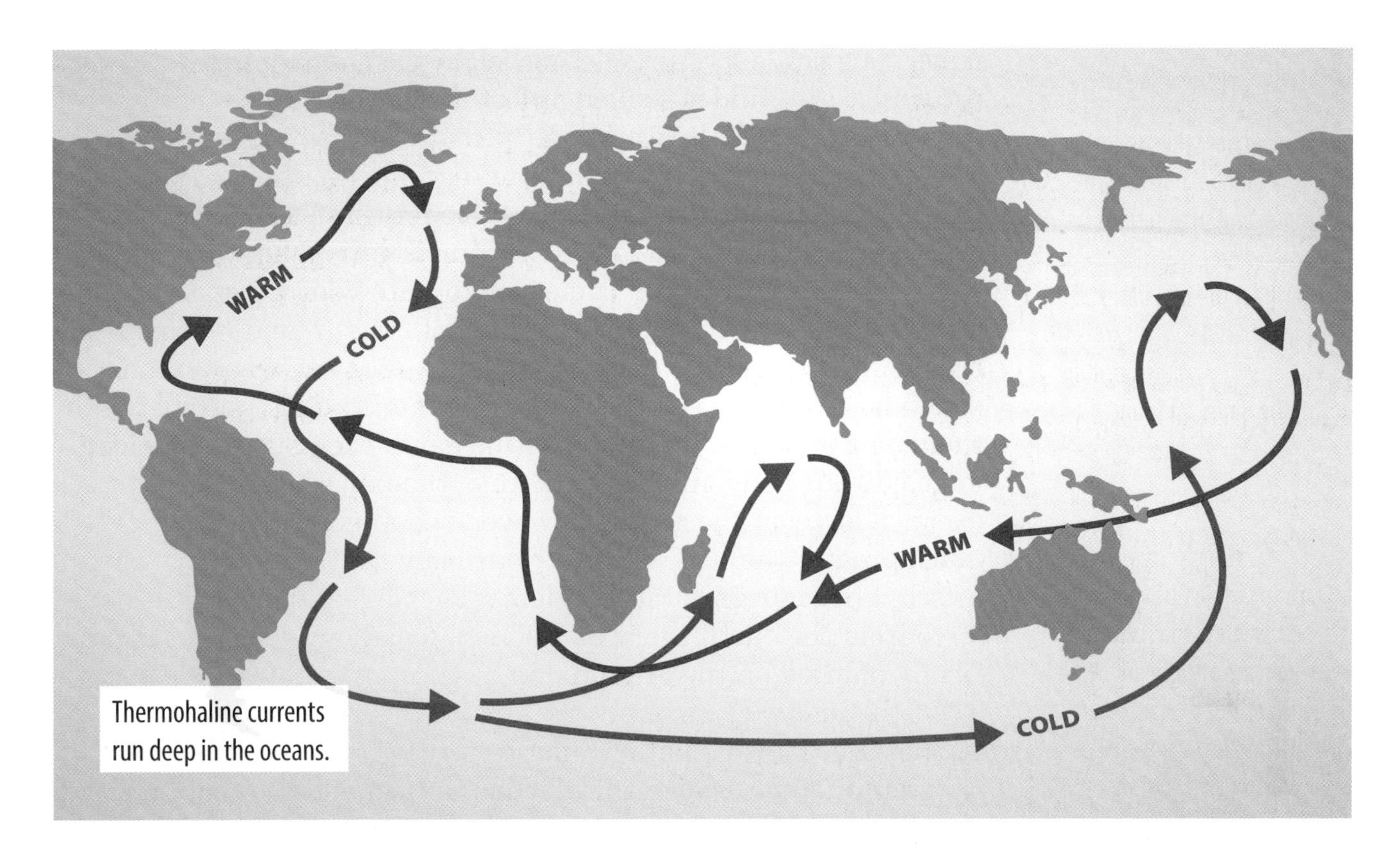

Thermohaline currents run deep in the oceans.

belt because of the way it moves. The round trip of this ocean current takes up to 1,000 years.

LESSON REVIEW

1. Draw a wave and label its five parts. Then, define the different parts of a wave.
2. What forces create waves?
3. What happens to a wave as it nears shore?
4. How are rip currents different from undertows?
5. What two forces produce ocean currents?
6. Why do ocean currents not flow in the exact same direction as the wind that creates them?

Lituya Bay, Alaska

The largest recorded tsunami in history occurred in Lituya Bay, Alaska, on July 9, 1958. The tsunami was the result of an enormous 30.6 million m^3 rockfall, which was caused by the eruption of a 7.7 magnitude earthquake. The tsunami cleared trees from a nearby slope up to 524 m high and swept the entire 11.3 km length of the bay. Eyewitnesses described the wave as spanning the full 3.2 km width of the bay. The wave was strong enough to knock over trees up to nearly 1,100 m from the normal waterline.

FYI

Progress of a Wave

A wave is a transfer of energy. A seagull floating on water bobs up and down but does not actually move forward. The wave transfers energy through the water, but the water itself does not move toward shore. The gull rides up the crest and down the trough but does not move forward unless the wind moves it over the surface. Only after a wave breaks in shallow water will it propel objects to shore.

4.2.3 *Tides*

OBJECTIVES

- Explain how the gravitational forces of the moon and sun produce ocean tides.
- Contrast the two basic types of tides.
- Relate tides to the position of the moon and sun.

VOCABULARY

- **neap tide** a tide that occurs when the sun and moon are at right angles to each other
- **spring tide** a tide that occurs when the sun, moon, and Earth are aligned
- **tidal range** the difference in water height between high and low tide

Have you ever left your beach towel on the shore only to return later to find it soaked or lost to the tide? Tides touch coastlines all over the world. For years, philosophers and scientists attempted to explain the movement of tides. Pytheas of Massilia, an ancient Greek philosopher, first recognized that tides were related to the moon, but this relationship was not well understood until Sir Isaac Newton provided an explanation involving the gravitational attraction of the sun and moon on the oceans. Newton's laws indicate that the force between two objects depends on the mass of the two objects and the distance between them. For example, the center of the earth exerts a gravitational force on your body. At the same time, the mass of your body exerts a force on the earth. However, the mass of the earth is so much greater than the mass of your body that the earth is barely affected by your gravitational force. People feel the gravitational force from the earth every day. This force allows your feet to stay firmly planted on the ground.

In the same way, planetary masses exert forces on each other. Einstein further developed this idea in his general theory of relativity. Massive objects impact the geometry of space-time. Imagine a bowling ball placed in the middle of a trampoline. The bowling ball would cause the center of the trampoline to dip and bulge. If a smaller object was placed near the curvature of the trampoline, it would move in toward the bowling ball. The earth, moon, and sun behave in much the same way as the bowling ball. Smaller masses that are near the space-time curvatures created by a larger mass would be drawn toward the larger mass.

Low tide

The gravitational forces acting along the curves in space-time allow the moon to pull on every molecule on Earth. This force is most noticeable with matter in a liquid state. The moon exerts a force on all bodies of water, but it is only visible in very large bodies of water. You do not see tides appear in a glass of water because the sample is too small. Gravitational forces are most evident on large lakes and oceans.

Space-time curvature

The moon's gravitational force is a major contributor to the formation of tides. Inertia acts to counterbalance the pull of this force. Inertia is a property of matter that keeps matter at rest or moving in a straight line. On the half of the earth closer to the moon, the moon's gravitational force pulls strongly on the ocean water. As the gravitational force draws the water closer to the moon, inertia pulls to keep the water in place. The gravitational force is stronger than the inertia on this side of the earth, so the water ends up bulging on the side near the moon. On the opposite side of the earth, inertia is more powerful than the moon's gravitational pull because the moon is farther away. Inertia is what causes the movement of the water to create a bulge on this half of the earth. These two bulges form the earth's high and low tides. Because water is fluid, the two bulges stay aligned with the moon even as Earth rotates.

High tide

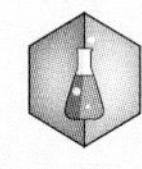

TRY THIS

Moon Waves

Compare a tide chart to an almanac chart of the positions of the moon. Plot the position of the moon relative to high and low tides for a lunar cycle.

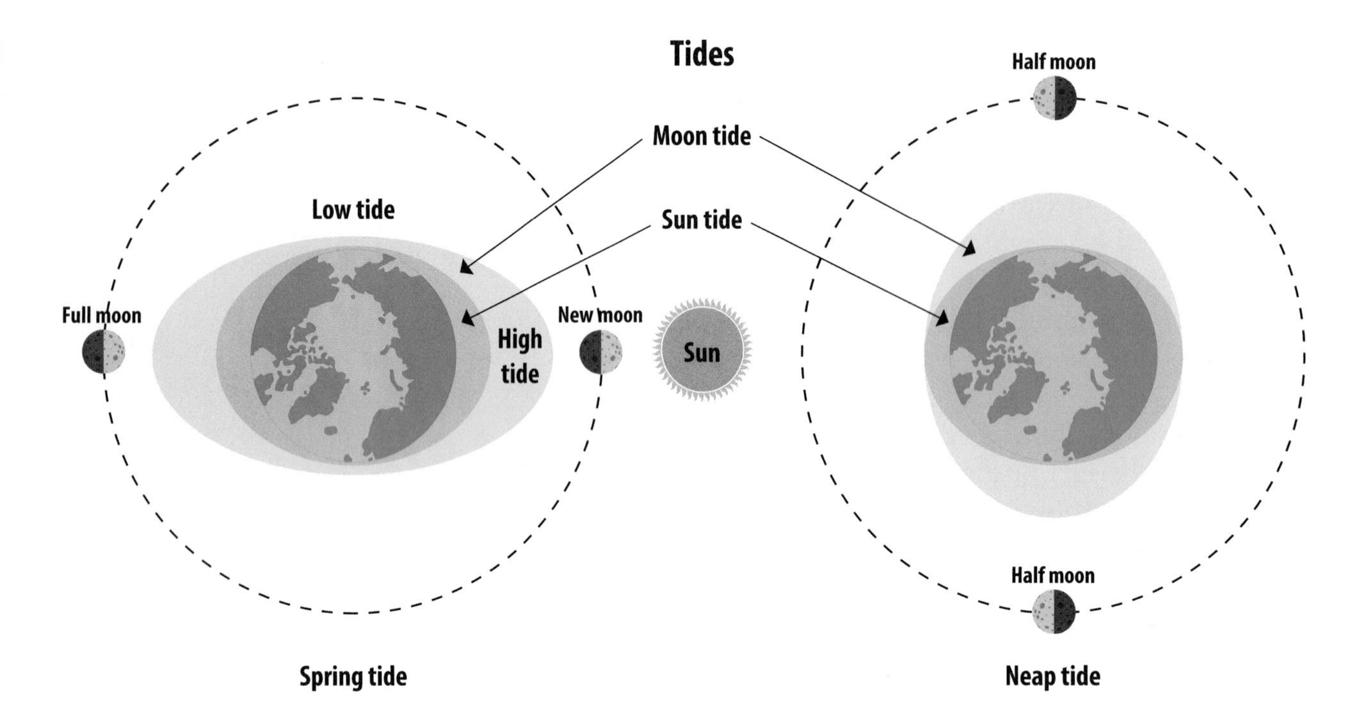

The bulge of the tides appears slightly ahead of the moon's actual position. As water tides move across the bottom of the sea, friction is produced. Tidal friction, caused by the earth's rotation, prevents the ocean bulge from being located directly in line with the moon.

Tides are produced as the earth spins and different regions of the world are facing the moon at various times throughout the day. Two high tides and two low tides occur every 24 hours and 50 minutes. A lunar day lasts 50 minutes longer than a standard 24-hour day because the moon orbits the earth in the same direction that the earth is spinning on its axis. It takes an additional 50 minutes for the earth to catch up to the moon.

The sun also exerts a gravitational pull on Earth's oceans. You might think that the sun's pull would have an even greater influence on the earth, but it does not. Even though the sun is much more massive than the moon, the sun's gravitational force does not have as great of an impact because sun is so much farther away from Earth. In fact, the sun's tide-generating force is about half of the moon's force.

The gravitational forces of the sun and moon often act in conjunction with one another to produce higher tides. The **tidal range** is the difference in water height between high and low tide. When the sun, moon, and Earth are aligned, the sum of the gravitational forces produces a **spring tide**. Spring tides have a wide daily tidal range, so the ocean rises and falls more than usual. Spring tides occur twice a month, during the new moon and full moon. The term used to describe this type of tide is not related to the season. It was first used because tides were said to be *springing forth.*

During the moon's first and third quarters, the sun and the moon are at right angles to each other. At this time, the gravitational pull of the sun partially cancels the gravitational pull of the moon. Consequently, moderate tides are produced called **neap tides**. During neap tides, high tides are lower and low tides are higher, resulting in the lowest daily tidal range.

Tides vary from place to place. For example, the tides of the Atlantic Ocean are different from those of the Pacific Ocean. This difference occurs because the earth is not smooth. Ocean waters are not free to flow over the earth's entire surface in a continuous pattern. Large continents create natural barriers that ocean tides must travel around. Ocean water is also trapped by ocean basins and blocked by mid-ocean ridges and other underwater landscape features. Earth's rotation and the resulting Coriolis effect also influence the oceans' movement. These variations combine to produce different patterns of tides in different regions. Some ocean basins have complex waves that result in no tides. In other places tidal ranges may vary 1–3 m. In bays that are partly enclosed, such as Nova Scotia's V-shaped Bay of Fundy, the tidal range can reach 16 m.

Each day, two high tides and two low tides occur along most of the Atlantic Coast. Other regions, such as the Gulf of Mexico, experience one high tide and one low tide a day. Tides along the Pacific Coast have a mixed pattern, so the high and low tides differ in height along the coast.

LESSON REVIEW

1. How do the gravitational forces of the moon and the sun produce tides?
2. Why do ocean bulges occur on Earth?
3. Compare spring and neap tides.
4. When the sun and moon are at right angles to each other, how are tides affected?
5. Why do tides not appear the same in different regions of the world?

FYI

Tidal Bore

When ocean tides are exceptionally high, some of the water can rush into the narrow channels of rivers and estuaries along the coast. This wall of water is called *a tidal bore*. It is a true tidal wave. Tidal bores only occur at spring tides, never at neap tides. As the ocean tide flows in, it meets the resistance of the river water that is stagnant or flowing in the opposite direction. Significant waves can be created that travel up the river at speeds of up to 24 kph. The largest tidal bores on Earth can be found on the Qiantang River in China. These bores can reach heights of nearly 9 m.

4.2.4 Ocean Floors

OBJECTIVES

- Model ocean floor features.
- Relate floor features in the Atlantic Ocean and the Pacific Ocean.

VOCABULARY

- **abyssal plain** a large, nearly flat region beyond the continental margin
- **continental margin** the part of the earth's surface beneath the ocean that is made of continental crust
- **continental rise** the base of the continental slope
- **continental shelf** a broad, relatively shallow underwater terrace that slopes outward from the shoreline
- **continental slope** the steepest part of the continental incline located at the edge of the continental shelf
- **seamount** an underwater volcanic mountain that rises at least 1,000 m above the abyssal plain

How much of the earth's surface do you think you could visit if you could only travel by car? Less than one-third of Earth's surface can be explored this way because about 70% of Earth's landscape is under ocean water. Oceanographers have mapped about 5%–15% of the ocean floor, but in this small fraction of the space, a variety of landscapes has been discovered.

You may think continental land stops abruptly where it meets the ocean. However, a gradual incline of sediment stretches to the bottom of the ocean floor. The flattest part of this incline is called the **continental shelf**. A broad, relatively shallow underwater terrace, the continental shelf forms on the edge of a continental landmass as the land gradually slopes away from the shoreline. The waters on the outer edge of the continental shelf are rarely greater than 150 m deep.

Unlike the ocean floor's deeper regions, the continental shelf is filled with life. God uses living things to transform some ocean landscapes on the continental shelf. In tropical regions of the world, tiny coral animals build small shelters out of calcium carbonate, a hard substance similar to limestone. Layers of coral homes form massive underwater rock structures called *coral reefs*. For example, the Great Barrier Reef in Australia stretches for 2,000 km along Australia's northeastern coast. A barrier reef is a wall of coral that lies several kilometers off the coast. Eventually, some of these towers build up hundreds of meters high to form islands called *cays*.

At the edge of the continental shelf is the **continental slope**. The continental slope is the steepest part of the continental incline. The slope represents the transitional area between the continental shelf and the continental rise. It lies at depths between 100 m and 2,500 m. At a depth of about 130 m, the underwater landscape drops steeply down to the ocean floor several kilometers deep.

Great Barrier Reef

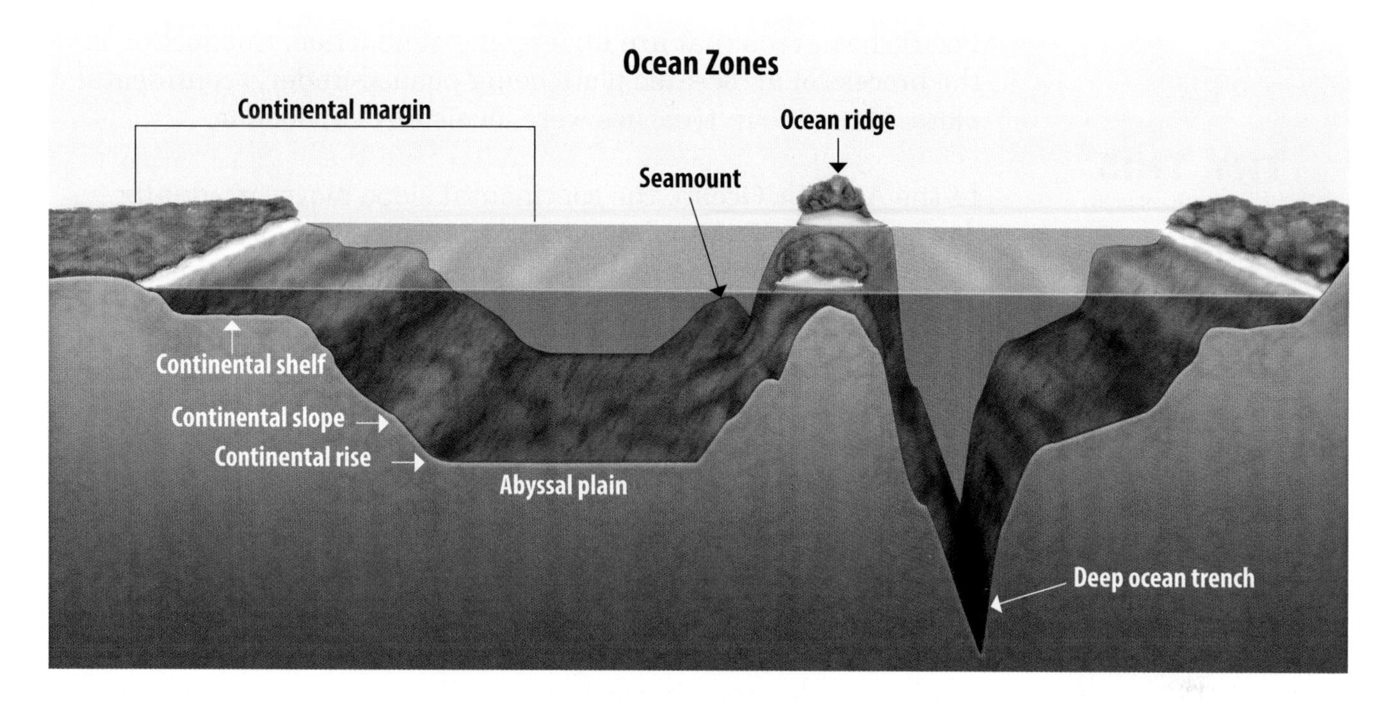

At the base of the continental slope is the **continental rise**. This region marks the transition from continental crust to oceanic crust. As sediment erodes from the continental crust, it travels down the shelf and slope and forms a thick deposit layer. Essentially, mass wasting occurs below the water's surface in this region. The rate of the erosion process is accelerated during storms as the waves and currents stir up layers of sediment.

The continental shelf, continental slope, and continental rise are known collectively as the **continental margin**, which is the most studied part of the earth's continental crust beneath the ocean. Because it is made of continental crust, the continental margin is considered to be part of the continent, even though it is underwater. Continental margins on the leading edges of tectonic plates are usually narrow and have steep continental slopes and poorly developed continental rises. Margins on the trailing side of tectonic plates are broad with gentle continental slopes and well-developed continental rises.

In the Atlantic Ocean, where earthquakes and volcanos are relatively rare, the continental shelves are wide. In the Pacific Ocean, where earthquakes and volcanoes are more common, the continental shelves are narrow and are separated from the ocean floor by deep trenches. Long, narrow underwater valleys are called *trenches*. Most of these trenches are 8,000–10,000 km deep. The deepest ocean trench is the Mariana Trench in the Pacific Ocean, which reaches a depth of 11,034 m. The majority of Earth's ocean trenches are found in the Pacific Ocean because the

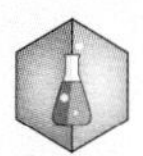

TRY THIS

Ocean Floor Features

Choose the Pacific, Atlantic, Indian, or Antarctic Ocean to study. Tally the number of ridges and trenches in the ocean. Note the different depths of the ocean. Compare your results with results collected by other students who studied another ocean. Create a chart comparing the features of the four main oceans.

Pacific has areas that are undergoing subduction. Subduction is the process of an oceanic plate being pushed under a continental plate. Many ocean trenches were formed by subduction.

TRY THIS

Ocean Vacation

Design a postcard featuring a section of one of the ocean floors. Draw a scenic picture on the front of the postcard. On the back of the postcard, write a letter to a friend describing your underwater vacation to that section of the ocean. Include details about scenery, temperature, light availability, ocean life, and other interesting facts.

In the Atlantic Ocean, the continental slope moves gradually down to form a fast underwater plain. The irregular landscape found in the Pacific Ocean often forms mountain ranges instead of plains. Underwater mountain chains that form where tectonic plates pull apart are called *oceanic ridges*. Many scientists believe that magma from Earth's mantle oozes through the crust to further develop the mountain ranges. Over time, as more magma is deposited, the ridges form mountain ranges. A rift, or small indentation, can be found on both sides of oceanic ridges. The most prominent oceanic ridge can be found in the Atlantic Ocean rather than the Pacific Ocean.

Beyond the continental margin lies a massive expanse of nearly flat land called the **abyssal plains**. Some of the larger plains can be thousands of kilometers long and hundreds of kilometers wide. They are normally located next to a continent. The abyssal plains—the flattest places on Earth—cover 54% of the earth's surface and about 75% of the deep ocean. If it was possible to roam across the abyssal plains, you could potentially travel 1,300 km without climbing or dropping more than 1 m during the entire trip.

Abyssal plains are formed from thick sediment layers that originate from the continental margins. In the Atlantic Ocean basin, the plains are uninterrupted. The Pacific Ocean is laden with more trenches, making the presence of vast abyssal plains much less common. Occasionally, ocean crust irregularities called **seamounts** protrude out of the plain surface. Seamounts are underwater volcanic mountains that rise at least 1,000 m above the abyssal plain. These features dot all major ocean basins but do not appear above the water's surface. An estimated 10,000 seamounts are located in the Pacific Ocean alone.

LESSON REVIEW

1. What three regions comprise the continental margin?
2. Where does the transition from continental crust to oceanic crust occur?
3. What are oceanic ridges?
4. How do many scientists believe oceanic ridges are formed?
5. Describe the continental margin in the Atlantic Ocean.
6. Where are a majority of Earth's major ocean trenches located? Why?

OBJECTIVES

- Discuss the history of ocean exploration.
- Identify technologies that advanced the study of the oceans.

VOCABULARY

- **submersible** a small underwater vessel

Around 100 BC, Posidonius, a Greek philosopher and geographer, set sail to the middle of the Mediterranean Sea. He was not a merchant carrying precious cargo, a fisherman, or a warrior sailing to meet an enemy. Posidonius was seeking to answer the age-old question of how deep the ocean is. In the middle of the Mediterranean Sea, Posidonius's crew fastened a stone to 2 km of rope and threw it overboard. The men were overjoyed when the rope stopped unwinding, indicating that the stone had reached the bottom of the sea. By subtracting the remaining length of the rope from the total rope length, the explorers were able to determine how deep the Mediterranean Sea was in that particular location. For 2,000 years, the line and sinker method was the only way to plumb the depths of the oceans.

In 1872, the modern science of oceanography emerged when the HMS *Challenger*, a British naval ship, set out on a 1,000-day oceanography journey to cross the Atlantic, Antarctic, and South Pacific Oceans. The journey covered more than 68,000 nautical miles. Researchers were able to identify many new marine organisms and gather temperature, ocean current, water chemistry, and ocean floor deposit data at 362 oceanographic stations.

In the 1800s, small underwater vessels known as **submersibles** were created to act as military crafts. The first submersible was a one-person wooden US submarine named the *Turtle*,

CAREER

Oceanography

Oceanography is the study of all aspects of the world's oceans and seas. This field can be divided into four major branches. Physical oceanography focuses on properties of ocean water (density, pressure, and temperature), the movement of ocean water (tides, waves, and currents), and the water-atmosphere interaction. Chemical oceanography studies the chemical composition of ocean water and biogeochemical cycles. Marine geology delves into the topography of the ocean floor. Marine ecology focuses on the plants and animals in the ocean. The study of oceanography aids scientists in making more accurate predictions regarding long-term weather changes. Scientists also gain a better understanding of the effects of ocean pollutants and discover more efficient ways of preserving natural resources.

which was used in the American Revolutionary War against the British. Submersibles were also used during the American Civil War. Many of these early vessels were not very effective. They often were destroyed as they attempted to demolish enemy craft. Andrew Campbell and James Ash built a submarine, the *Nautilus,* in 1886. The *Nautilus* was driven by electric motors that were powered by a storage battery. On January 21, 1954, another vessel named *Nautilus* was deployed by the US Navy. This submarine was the first to be nuclear powered, and it was the first ocean craft capable of prolonged submersion. In addition, it could reach speeds of more than 20 knots (37 kph) and could maintain the speed for an extended amount of time.

Another technological advancement was the invention of echo sounders, which were instruments used by ships to determine the depth of water. The first echo sounders were developed by oceanographers in the 1920s. Echo sounders measured the time it took for a produced sound to return, or echo, from the ocean floor. Once again, military needs encouraged advancements in this technology as echo sounders were designed to detect submarines during World War II. An added benefit of the advancements was the mapping of undersea areas that had been hidden. This technology gave scientists a picture of the ocean floor. On the civilian front, echo sounders have been used

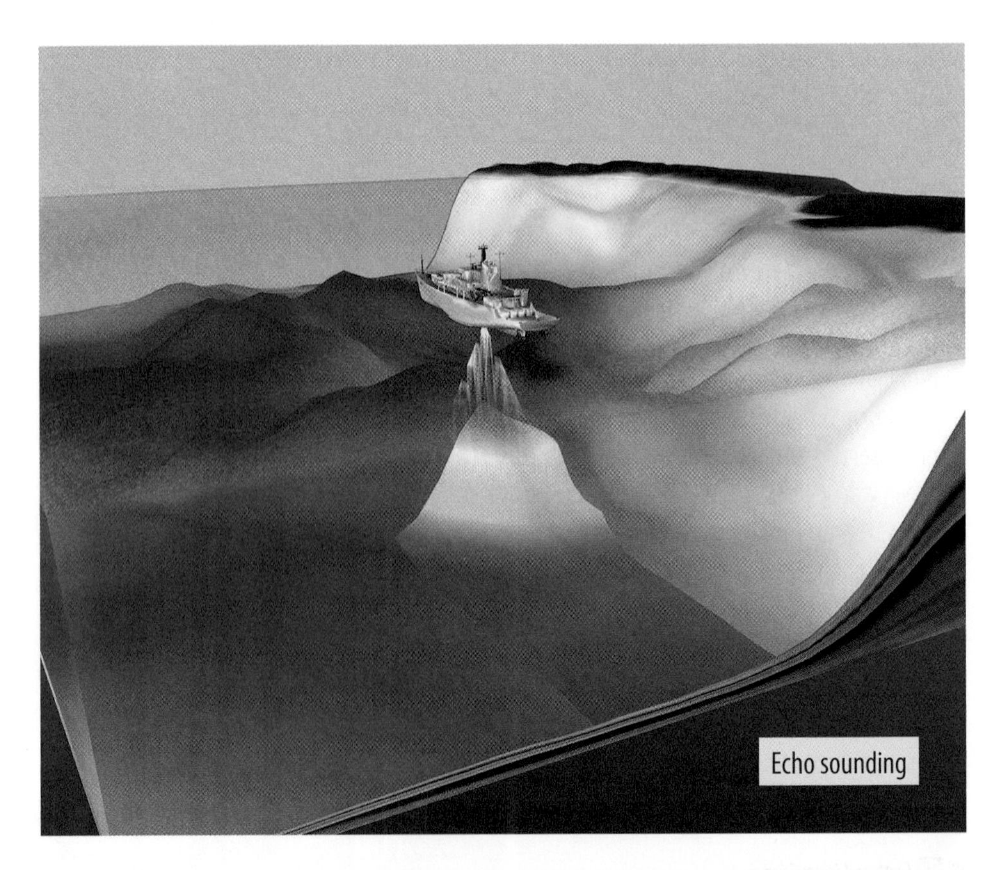
Echo sounding

FYI

ROV *Hercules*

Very few remotely operated vehicles (ROVs) in the world are specifically designed for scientific purposes. One such vehicle is *Hercules,* first launched in 2003. This machine can descend to depths of 4,000 m where it recovers shipwreck artifacts and gathers biological and geological information in the deep ocean. *Hercules* was designed with two manipulator arms, a high-definition camera, and acoustic sensors. One important feature of this ROV is the ability to measure depth, which can be used when mapping the ocean floor. *Hercules* can also measure water temperature, salinity, pressure, and oxygen concentration. The machine's cylindrical titanium pressure housings can undergo extreme water pressure. The electrical components that are not in pressure housings are immersed in mineral oil because mineral oil does not significantly compress under high pressure, does not cause corrosion, and does not conduct electricity. *Hercules* is operated by external pilots, who send signals through a long fiber-optic cable.

to locate fish, measure the thickness of Arctic ice, and record information for oceanographic charting.

Multibeam sonar, developed in the 1960s and 1970s, was used to accomplish the mapping of the ocean floor. This technology uses sound waves, which reflect off the ocean floor. A computer then creates images of the ocean landscape. This method of mapping is precise but slow. Scientists estimate that it will take an additional 125 years to map the entire ocean floor using this method. In addition to multibeam sonar, radar from satellites has also been used to detect large features on the ocean floor, including mountains. Currently, the most accurate, detailed method of exploring the ocean floor is the use of underwater cameras attached to a remotely operated vehicle (ROV). This method is useful in ocean depths up to 4,000 m where artificial light can penetrate.

Recently, the National Oceanic and Atmospheric Administration (NOAA) mapped more than 1 million km^2 of ocean floor in the Atlantic Ocean, Pacific Ocean, and Gulf of Mexico. Although this is a significant number, the ocean covers 335,258,000 km^2, which means the study of the ocean floor has only begun. Obviously there is still much to learn about this part of God's creation.

Ocean exploration has greatly advanced over the past century. Still, most of the ocean remains a mystery. For comparison, so far 12 people have been to the moon, but only three people, one of whom was James Cameron, have visited the Mariana Trench. In fact, Cameron broke a record in 2012 when he reached a depth of 10,898 m at the Mariana Trench's Challenger Deep area. While the ocean is a very important part of God's creation, support for ocean research has been lacking. Perhaps as more of this hidden world is mapped, support for ocean research and exploration will be expanded.

LESSON REVIEW

1. Discuss the importance of three events in the history of ocean exploration.
2. Explain how a line and sinker were used to determine the depth of the ocean.
3. What two inventions significantly advanced the study of oceans?
4. Describe how echo sounders work.
5. What technological advancement improved the process of echo sounding?

Jacques-Yves Cousteau

One of the major contributors to the study of the ocean was Jacques Cousteau. His love of the ocean and diving sparked an interest in expanding ocean exploration. However, prior to 1943, divers did not have any way to remain underwater for an extended period of time. Cousteau and Émile Gagnan developed the first fully automatic compressed-air Aqua-Lung to solve this problem. With this invention, divers could remain underwater longer. Cousteau also invented a small, easy-to-operate submarine and underwater cameras. Cousteau and his colleagues filmed their explorations so people could see what was beneath the ocean's surface. These films allowed people to see a part of God's creation that had been hidden. Later in his career, Cousteau founded a number of research and conservation organizations to help preserve the ocean world. During his career, which lasted to the early 1990s, he changed the way people viewed and understood the ocean.

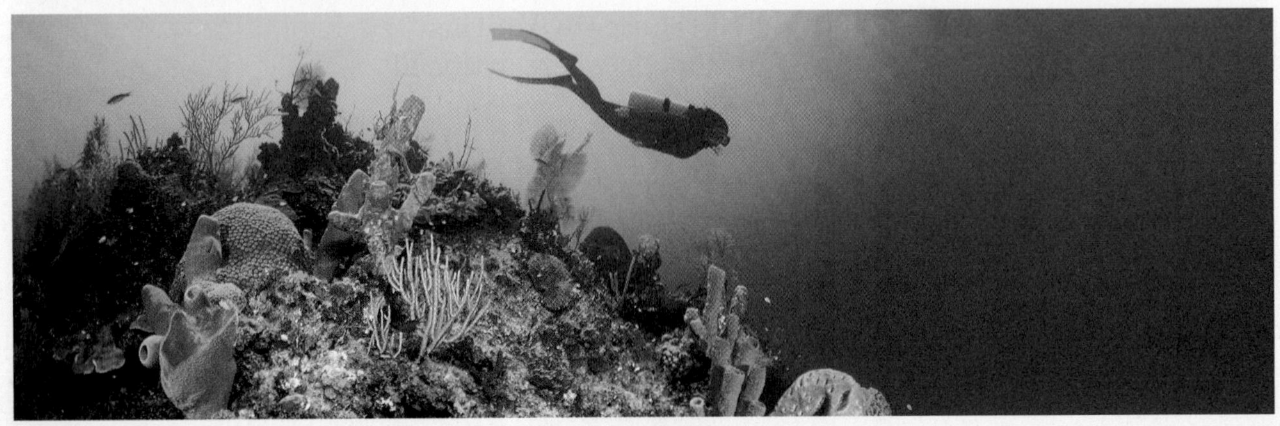

OBJECTIVES

- Summarize different types of ocean resources.
- Explain the process of desalination and other distillation methods.
- Analyze the risks and benefits related to harvesting ocean resources.
- Investigate alternative ocean energy sources.

VOCABULARY

- **desalination** the process of removing salt from ocean water to obtain freshwater for drinking, irrigation, or industrial use

Can you imagine swimming in water filled with gold and precious minerals? If you have ever been in the ocean, you have already had this experience. Living things are not the ocean's only resources. Gold, diamonds, zinc, and copper are hidden in ocean water and under the ocean floor. Currently, extracting these treasures from the ocean is expensive. A great investment in the areas of research, engineering, infrastructure, and operational equipment are necessary for such an endeavor. However, some of the ocean's resources are more easily obtained.

The most important nonfuel ocean mineral resources are sand and gravel. Sand and gravel form in the ocean as a result of land erosion. Currents and water action disrupt and transport both sand and gravel and deposit them in layers on the ocean floor. By using mechanical dredges, companies bring these resources up from the ocean floor. Sand and gravel are often used in construction, and sand is also used to replenish eroding beaches. Beach replenishing projects are designed to replace sand that waves and tidal currents have carried off. Such projects are very important to countries with land below sea level, such as the Netherlands, and to barrier islands such as Ocean City, Maryland. In addition, sand and weathered coral reefs are an important source of construction materials for many tropical countries.

In 1873, the HMS *Challenger* brought back another ocean resource, although crew members did not initially recognize its

Beach nourishment

importance. At first glance, the strange black lumps seemed insignificant. However, scientists determined that these lumps were actually manganese nodules. A large number of these nodules are scattered across the ocean floor, especially in the Pacific Ocean. Copper, iron, nickel, and cobalt can also be extracted from the nodules. Manganese is used to make products such as steel and fertilizers. The nodules are found in very deep water, which makes collecting them both difficult and expensive. However, scientists may develop better technologies to retrieve mineral resources from the ocean to supply the increased demand for these limited land resources.

Salt pan

Salt is an important ocean resource as well. Countries such as France, some African countries, and those in hot, dry climates produce salt using an economical process. Seawater is directed through a series of gates to several shallow ponds that are separated by dikes. The seawater is allowed to concentrate in these ponds. Then it is transferred to a number of crystallizing pans where the salt forms deposits as the water evaporates. In developing countries, the deposited salt is formed into rows and allowed to dry for several days. Individuals then rake the salt into piles and the salt is drained again. This process occurs a few times before the salt is finally dry. In contrast, industrialized countries complete the separation of salt from seawater using machines. The deposited salt is washed in a saturated brine bath, drained, washed with freshwater, and stored for future use.

Salt from ocean water is valuable, but the water itself is even more precious. The process of removing salt from ocean water to obtain freshwater for drinking, irrigation, or industrial use is called **desalination**. One common method to remove salt from the water is through reverse osmosis. This process uses a semipermeable membrane to separate the salt from the water. Another method that is frequently used is distillation. In distillation, water is boiled, the water vapor is gathered, and the vapor is condensed back into a liquid. The salt remains in the original container, so the condensed water is pure. However, this method is very expensive.

A more cost-effective process to separate salt from water is called *direct contact membrane distillation*. This process uses a hydrophobic membrane. (*Hydro* means "water" and *phobic* means "a strong dislike.") The water temperature is increased on one side of the membrane, which raises the water vapor pressure. The low vapor pressure on the other side of the membrane attracts water molecules in the high-pressure zone. As a result, distilled water is collected on the low-pressure side. Very little heat energy is required to produce the vapor pressure difference, so the cost is much lower than traditional desalination processes.

Manganese nodule

Much of the world depends on oil and natural gas for energy. Both of these resources are found under the layers of rock that make up the ocean floor. Engineers can drill through this rock to reach these resources, but it is a huge endeavor. In addition, drilling through ocean rock can cause pollution and sometimes results in major oil spills, which can harm or kill living things in the ocean. There is much controversy surrounding the practice of drilling into the ocean floor. Some people do not think that offshore drilling is a responsible way to use the resources that God created. Others believe that people should take advantage of any resource available for use.

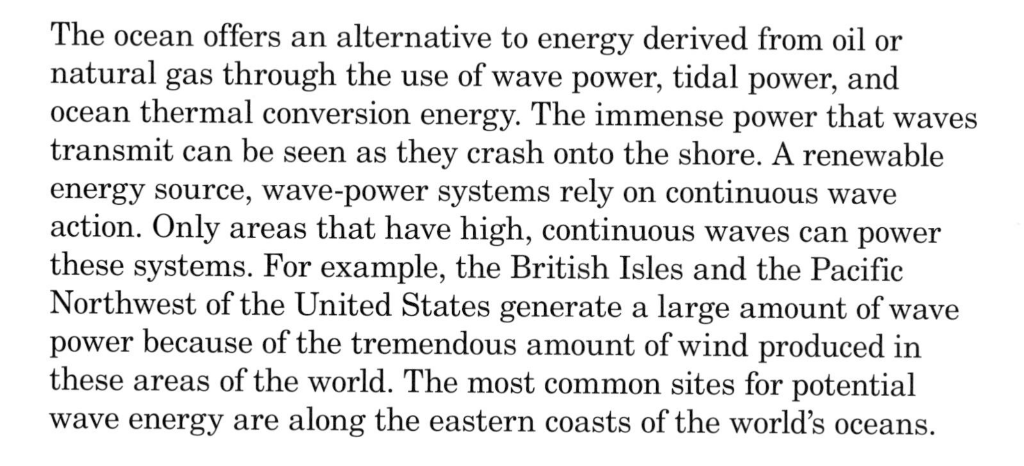

The ocean offers an alternative to energy derived from oil or natural gas through the use of wave power, tidal power, and ocean thermal conversion energy. The immense power that waves transmit can be seen as they crash onto the shore. A renewable energy source, wave-power systems rely on continuous wave action. Only areas that have high, continuous waves can power these systems. For example, the British Isles and the Pacific Northwest of the United States generate a large amount of wave power because of the tremendous amount of wind produced in these areas of the world. The most common sites for potential wave energy are along the eastern coasts of the world's oceans.

Tidal power is another renewable energy source from the ocean. This technology channels water through a narrow passageway at high tide, creating enough force to generate electricity. Systems that employ tidal energy are very similar to dams that produce hydroelectric energy. However, tidal energy, like wave energy, is practical only in certain areas that have a significant tidal range.

Offshore drilling

Energy is also available from the ocean through ocean thermal energy conversion (OTEC). OTEC systems depend on the difference in temperature between deep, cold water and warm surface water. Warm surface water is pumped into a

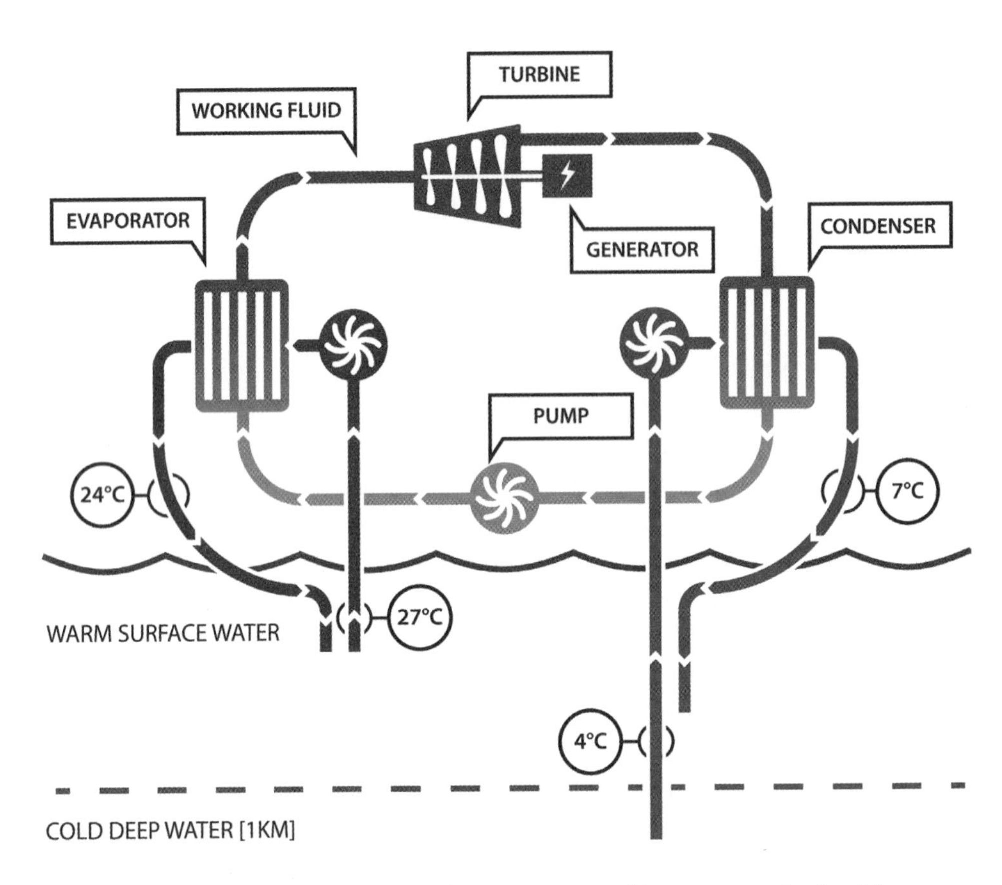

An ocean thermal energy conversion (OTEC) system

heat exchanger. The water's heat causes the ammonia inside the heat exchanger to vaporize. The vaporized ammonia is then compressed in a turbine connected to a generator, which produces electricity. Cold ocean water pumped through another heat exchanger condenses the ammonia vapor into a liquid, which is then reused to repeat the process. OTEC systems can generate electricity day and night all year long.

The ocean has a vast supply of resources. Many resources may still be hidden, yet to be discovered. Some resources have already been put to good use, but others may have been exploited. It is important that all the resources God has provided in His creation be respected. Individuals, communities, and ecosystems all benefit if ocean resources are used properly.

LESSON REVIEW

1. Summarize different ocean resources.
2. Why are people not able to extract more ocean minerals?
3. What kind of climate promotes desalination processes?
4. How is the direct contact membrane distillation process different from the standard distillation process?
5. Why might some people oppose offshore drilling?
6. Name two renewable resources that are alternatives to energy derived from oil or natural gas.

UNIT 5

Meteorology

Chapter 1: *The Atmosphere*
Chapter 2: *Weather*
Chapter 3: *Climate*

Vocabulary

aeroplankton
air mass
anemometer
atmosphere
atmospheric pressure
barometer
CFCs
climate
climate change
cloud
coalescence
conduction
convection
deposition
El Niño
fog
front
greenhouse gas
heat
humidity
ice age
interglacial period
ion
isobar
lightning
microclimate
ozone
plasma
radiation
shelterbelt
solar wind
temperature
thunder
UV
virga

Key Ideas

- Systems, order, and organization
- Evidence, models, and explanation
- Change, constancy, and measurement
- Evolution and equilibrium
- Form and function
- Abilities necessary to do scientific inquiry
- Understandings about scientific inquiry
- Structure of the earth system
- Earth's history
- Earth in the solar system
- Energy in the earth system
- Origin and evolution of the earth system
- Abilities of technological design
- Understandings about science and technology
- Personal health
- Natural hazards
- Risks and benefits
- Science and technology in society
- Personal and community health
- Natural and human induced hazards
- Science and technology in local, national, and global challenges
- Science as a human endeavor
- History of science
- Nature of scientific knowledge
- Historical perspectives

SCRIPTURE

He draws up the drops of water, which distill as rain to the streams; the clouds pour down their moisture and abundant showers fall on mankind.

Job 36:27–28

5.1.1 *Composition of the Atmosphere*

OBJECTIVES

- List the components of the atmosphere and their concentrations.
- Explain the purpose of oxygen, nitrogen, and carbon dioxide.
- Illustrate how the levels of oxygen and nitrogen are maintained.

VOCABULARY

- **aeroplankton** microscopic organisms that float in the atmosphere
- **atmosphere** a mixture of gases that surrounds the earth
- **atmospheric pressure** the pressure exerted by Earth's atmosphere at any given point

Imagine flying thousands of kilometers above the earth. What would you see? The oceans would look dark blue, the continents would look brown and green, and clouds would stretch across the surface of the globe in swirling bands and clusters. The **atmosphere** is a mixture of gases that surrounds the earth and is held in place by gravity.

God wrapped this thin layer of gases around the earth like a protective cocoon to help maintain the living things on Earth. Although the atmosphere reaches hundreds of kilometers above the earth, a large percentage of it is squeezed into the first 40 km. In fact, you travel through the earth's atmosphere whenever you take a step.

If you were to compare the atmosphere near the ground with the atmosphere near its upper limit, you would notice differences in pressure. **Atmospheric pressure** is the pressure exerted by the weight of Earth's atmosphere at any given point on Earth. The atmospheric pressure is greater at lower altitudes than at higher altitudes because the gases in the atmosphere are most highly concentrated at sea level, where they are "packed down" from the weight of the gases above them. The gases thin out with an increase in altitude. People may have a hard time breathing in the mountains because there are fewer air molecules. Almost 90% of the atmosphere's mass lies within 40 km of the earth's surface. The constant motion of the air keeps the atmospheric gases near the earth's surface well mixed. If this were not the case, you would run the risk of walking into a patch of air with no oxygen.

The lower portion of the atmosphere contains about 78% nitrogen, 21% oxygen, and 1% of other trace gases such as carbon dioxide. The lower atmosphere

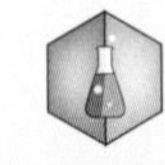

TRY THIS

See the Atmosphere

The atmosphere has mass and takes up space, similar to liquids. This concept can be difficult to believe because the atmosphere cannot be seen and people can walk right through it without any effort. To help you "see" the atmosphere, crumple a paper towel and stuff it into the bottom of a beaker so it cannot fall out. Fill a large pan or tub with water. The sides of the pan need to be taller than the beaker. Invert the beaker and carefully push it straight down to the bottom of the pan. Now, remove the beaker without tilting it. Was any part of the beaker wet? If so, which parts? Why? What happened to the paper towel? Why?

also contains water vapor. Humid air holds up to 4% water vapor; dry air holds less than 1%. Many different kinds of particles and pollution also float around in the atmosphere—dust, mineral particles, soil, ash, smoke, salt crystals from sea spray, carbon monoxide, smog, pollen, fungal spores, small organisms, and insect eggs. Some of the solid particles can float in the atmosphere for months or even years. The small organisms that float in the atmosphere are called **aeroplankton**. The solid particles in the atmosphere are called *atmospheric dust.*

High concentrations of atmospheric dust can be a problem in large cities like Beijing, China.

Most atmospheric gas is nitrogen. Living things need nitrogen. Animals need nitrogen to form amino acids to build proteins. Nitrogen is a key ingredient in chlorophyll, which plants use in photosynthesis. Nitrogen is recycled from the atmosphere to the soil and back into the atmosphere through the nitrogen cycle. Through this cycle, nitrogen-fixing bacteria convert nitrogen in the atmosphere into nitrogen compounds that plants can use. Without these nitrogen-fixing bacteria, life on Earth could not exist. The cycle is completed when nitrogen is

FYI

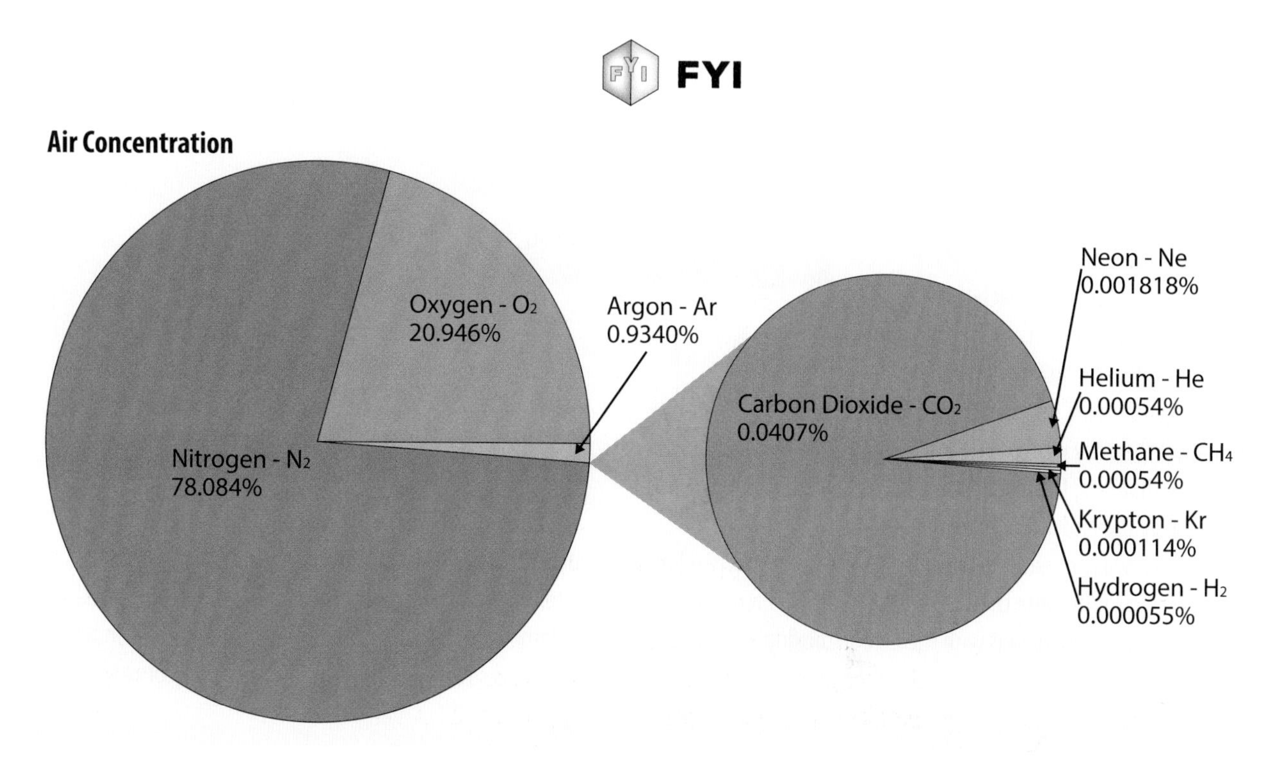

NITROGEN CYCLE

N_2
NITROGEN FIXATION
DENITRIFICATION
AMMONIFICATION
ASSIMILATION
NITRIFICATION
NH_4
NO_2
NO_3
NH_3
Nitrogen fixing bacteria
Nitrifying bacteria
Denitrification bacteria

released back into the atmosphere through the decay of dead animals and the waste products of living animals. Lightning also converts some atmospheric nitrogen into usable nitrogen compounds.

Because nitrogen is nonreactive, it helps maintain the proper concentration of oxygen, the gas most people associate with the atmosphere. Animals, plants, bacteria, and microorganisms need oxygen for respiration, the process that produces energy for life. God designed the atmosphere to maintain a constant 21% concentration of oxygen through the photosynthesis of green plants, algae, and diatoms in spite of forest fires, burning fuels, and the weathering of rocks, which also use oxygen. Both too much or too little oxygen would be disastrous. If

FYI

Biosphere II

In 1987, construction began on Biosphere II in Arizona, USA. On June 16, 1994, a group of eight people entered the 3.14 acre structure to live for two years. The structure was designed to be completely self-sufficient, creating and maintaining all the food and atmosphere necessary for life. Plants and bacteria were placed to maintain oxygen, carbon dioxide, and nitrogen. But after only 6 months, the atmosphere contained a mere 17% oxygen. Something was terribly wrong. Scientists feared that at that rate, the levels would be down to 10% by the end of the two-year project, and that was not enough to support life. Outside oxygen had to be added for the group to continue living in isolation. So, what went wrong? Why were these cycles created by God so difficult to recreate? After the two-year project had ended, scientists concluded that the problem was with the carbon dioxide, not the oxygen. The carbon dioxide was reacting with a compound in the concrete walls. So, there was not enough carbon dioxide for the plants to photosynthesize and maintain sufficient levels of oxygen. The recycling "engines" of Earth are incredibly complex and refined.

the concentration of oxygen were too high, fires would burn more quickly and animal metabolisms would run too fast. If the concentration were too low, life would cease.

Carbon dioxide accounts for only a small percentage of the atmosphere, but it plays an important role in the world. Without carbon dioxide, plants could not photosynthesize, so there would be no oxygen. Carbon dioxide is also important because it traps heat in the atmosphere, warming the earth. A small amount of carbon dioxide is necessary to keep the planet from freezing. Carbon dioxide is a product of combustion processes, such as the burning of fossil fuels.

When people consider valuable resources, they usually think about minerals, fossil fuels, and soil. Some people might describe rivers and lakes swelling with freshwater or the vast oceans teeming with food as resources. Not much thought is given to the atmosphere unless the skies bring heavy rains or hurricane winds. But the atmosphere is a most precious natural resource, and it should be protected.

LESSON REVIEW

1. Why is there more atmospheric pressure at lower altitudes than at higher altitudes?
2. What are the main components of the atmosphere? What is the usual concentration of each component?
3. What else is in the atmosphere besides gases and water vapor?
4. Explain the purpose of oxygen, nitrogen, and carbon dioxide.
5. If living organisms use oxygen and nitrogen, how is it possible that the concentration of each of these gases is maintained at a constant level?

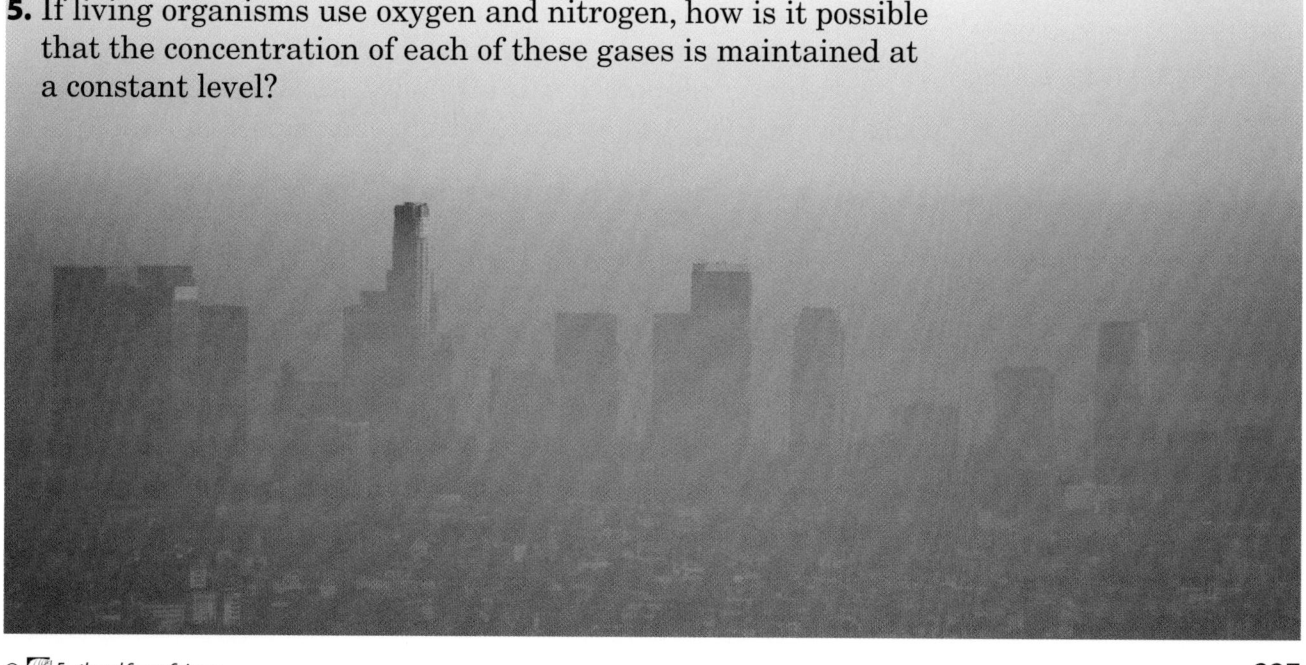

5.1.2 *Layers of the Atmosphere*

OBJECTIVES

- Compare the layers of the atmosphere.
- Identify the benefits of the atmosphere.
- Relate the benefits of the atmosphere to how God sustains life on Earth

VOCABULARY

- **ion** an atom with an electrical charge that has gained or lost one or more electrons

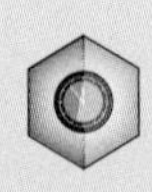

HISTORY

Shell Theory

Greek philosopher Plato believed that the earth was round and that the stars had circular orbits. Contrary to the culture of his time, he believed a divine being created the earth for the good of mankind. Plato's student, Aristotle, rejected the idea of a divine creator. He believed the earth could neither be created nor destroyed; it would last forever. Aristotle hypothesized the spherical earth was surrounded by three shells made of water, air, and fiery matter. Even before the help of modern technology, the evidence of God's design was apparent: the atmosphere had layers.

The atmosphere is divided into two main parts. The lower part of the atmosphere is called *the homosphere* because it is the same throughout (in Greek, *homo* means "same"). The homosphere extends from the surface of the earth upward about 80 km. Even though the components of the homosphere are the same throughout, its temperature varies widely. Above 80 km, air currents no longer mix the atmospheric gases. The upper level of the atmosphere is called *the heterosphere* because the gases there are not mixed, but are separated (in Greek, *hetero* means "different"). Earth's gravity pulls heavier gases, such as oxygen and carbon dioxide, closer to its surface, but in the heterosphere, lighter gases move farther away from the earth and can eventually escape into space.

The homosphere and heterosphere can be further divided according to temperature, composition, and density. The three layers within the homosphere are the troposphere, stratosphere, and mesosphere.

The troposphere is the layer of the atmosphere closest to the earth. All life exists in the troposphere. Its average height is about 12 km. The word *troposphere* comes from the Greek root meaning"change." This name is appropriate because almost all weather happens in the troposphere. Hurricanes, tornadoes, rainstorms, blizzards, hailstorms, monsoons, wind, lightning, thunderstorms, and all other weather patterns occur in the troposphere. Most clouds also form in the troposphere. The changing weather mixes up the gases into a homogeneous, or uniform, solution. The troposphere acts like Earth's air conditioner. The sun heats up the earth's surface, which then heats the air it touches. The warmed air expands and rises, but as it moves higher, the air expands further and cools. Consequently, the temperature within the troposphere drops as the altitude increases.

The boundary between the turbulent troposphere and the next layer is called *the tropopause*. The air temperature remains fairly constant in the tropopause at about –60°C. Gaps in the tropopause form a layered structure. Jet streams, which are ribbons of high-speed winds that occur at altitudes of 6–14 km, form in these gaps. The airline industry benefits from these high-speed winds because flying planes along the jet streams saves fuel and speeds up flight times, bringing travelers to their destinations faster.

The stratosphere is the layer of the atmosphere above the troposphere. It is 12–50 km above the earth. The stratosphere has very little vertical air movement. Jets that fly in the stratosphere take advantage of the calm, thin air and leave white trails of fine, white crystals across the sky called *contrails*. The top of the stratosphere is called *the stratopause*, where the temperature reaches about –15°C. The stratosphere contains the very important ozone layer. The temperature of this layer increases with altitude because ozone molecules absorb incoming solar energy. This energy absorption maintains earth's temperatures and prevents much of the sun's harmful ultraviolet radiation from reaching the earth's surface.

Jet flying through the stratosphere

The layer above the stratosphere is the mesosphere, which is 50–80 km above the earth. With temperatures that can drop to –100°C, the mesosphere is the homosphere's coldest layer. The mesosphere has very few oxygen molecules to absorb heat, which is why it is so cold. The mesosphere is the layer where meteors, or shooting stars, burn up and leave beautiful streaks across the night sky. The upper part of the mesosphere is called *the mesopause*, where the temperature begins to increase again.

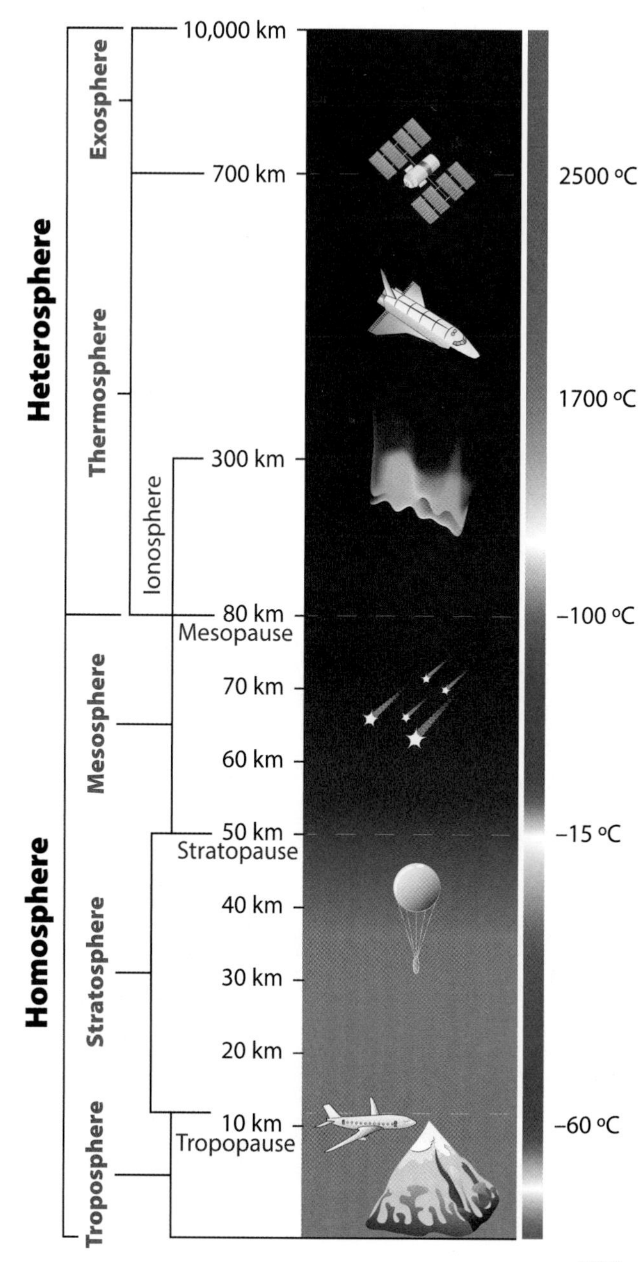

The outer two layers of the atmosphere are part of the heterosphere. Beyond the mesopause is the thermosphere. It reaches more than 227°C at night and steadily rises to 1,700°C during the day, probably because free atoms of oxygen there absorb heat from the sun. However, because there are so few oxygen molecules in the thermosphere, there are not enough of them to provide warmth. If you were in the thermosphere, you would be very cold.

The lower region of the thermosphere, at 80–300 km above the earth, is called *the ionosphere*. Here the air is extremely thin. Ultraviolet radiation from the sun bombards the molecules here, smashing them apart into **ions**, which are electrically charged atoms that have gained or lost one or more electrons. Ions create an electrical layer that

Meteor

reflects radio waves. Short wave radio signals bounce off the ionized air and return to Earth, making it possible to broadcast radio signals beyond the horizon. Also, when the ionized particles collide, beautiful lights are created. In the Northern Hemisphere, they are called *the Aurora Borealis* and in the Southern Hemisphere they are called *the Aurora Australis.*

Finally, the outermost region of the heterosphere is called *the exosphere.* The exosphere is the atmosphere's hottest layer. The few molecules of air that exist in the exosphere have a huge temperature range. During the daytime, temperatures can reach upwards of 2,500°C. However, the nighttime temperature drops to –270°C, which is almost absolute zero, the coldest possible temperature. This final region of the atmosphere continues to thin out and ultimately becomes outer space. Satellites that allow communication through television and other means are located in the exosphere.

LESSON REVIEW

1. What are the differences between the homosphere and the heterosphere?
2. Describe the layers of the heterosphere.
3. Why does the temperature decrease with increasing altitude in the homosphere?
4. Where is the ionosphere located? List two benefits of the ionosphere.
5. Why does the temperature increase in the mesosphere?

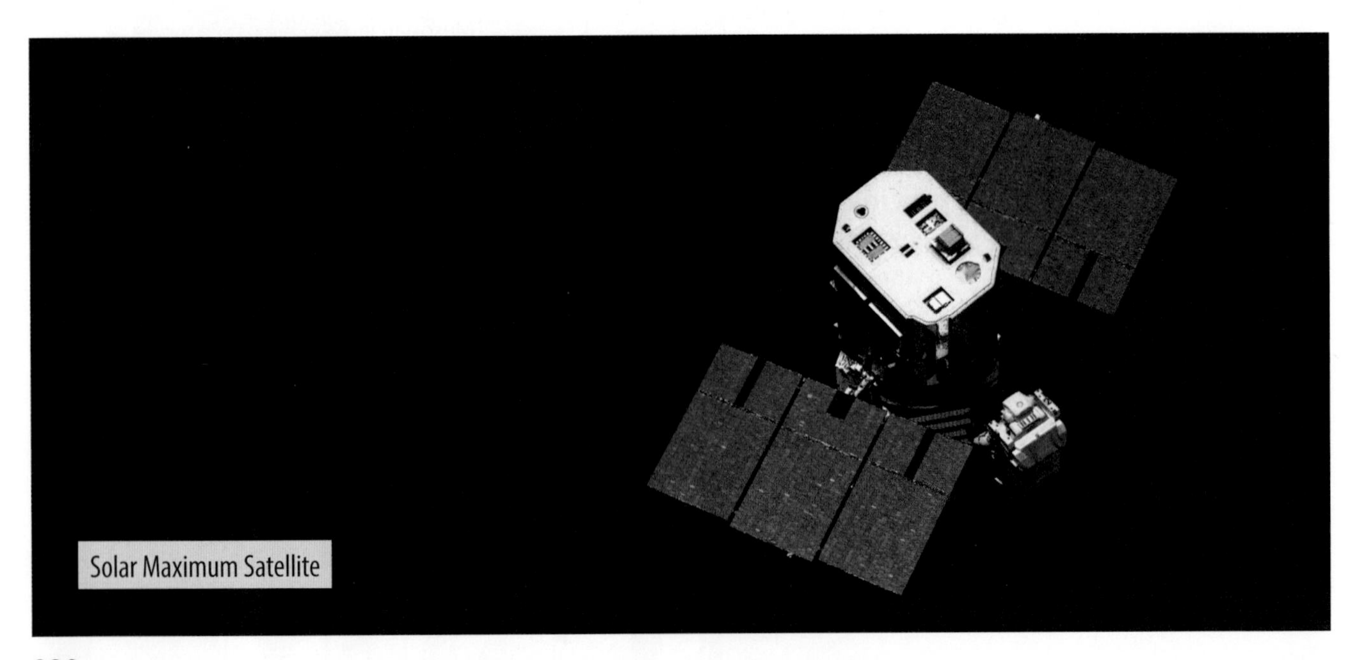
Solar Maximum Satellite

Have you ever played with magnets? It is fun to hold them some distance from an iron object such as a nail and then watch the magnet and the nail spring together. Magnetic forces attract the nail to the magnet. In a similar way, the earth acts like a giant magnet. It has two magnetic poles: the north magnetic pole and the south magnetic pole. Lines of force extend between these poles, which produce a magnetic field around the earth. The area around the earth that is affected by the earth's magnetic field is called *the magnetosphere.*

Generally speaking, scientists believe the motion of the earth's liquid iron core produces electric currents that create the magnetic field surrounding the earth. However, scientists have differing theories on the origin of the electric current: the dynamo theory and the rapid-decay theory.

The dynamo theory supposes the magnetic field is the result of processes that are currently happening. According to this theory, the rotation of the earth and the convection currents in the mantle keep the motion within the outer core going. This motion produces and maintains the electric current necessary to maintain a magnetic field. The details of the theory support the fact that the magnetic field has reversed several times, and it hypothesizes that each reversal has taken place over thousands of years. According to this theory, the strength and intensity of the magnetosphere should remain constant. The dynamo theory does not explain the origin, or creation, of the magnetosphere, however. The dynamo theory assumes that the earth is old.

OBJECTIVES

- Illustrate the structure of the magnetosphere.
- Summarize how solar wind affects the magnetosphere.
- Compare the two theories about the electric current in the core.
- Infer the benefits of the magnetosphere.

VOCABULARY

- **plasma** a superheated gas composed of electrically charged particles
- **solar wind** the continuous flow of plasma from the sun

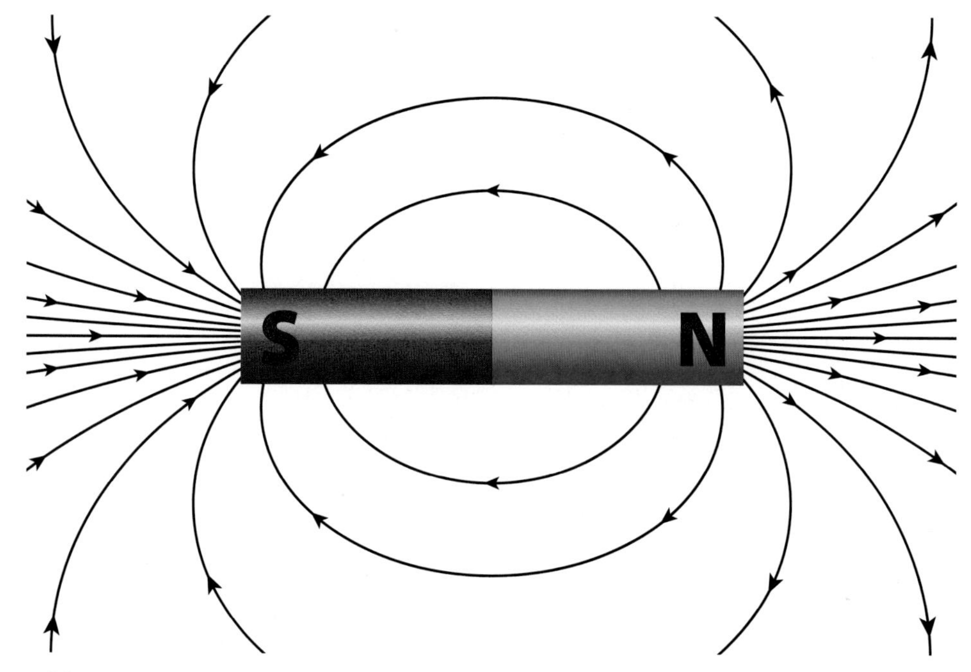

Bar magnet with field lines

Curiosity is a robotic rover exploring Mars to determine if the planet has ever supported life. It has been on Mars since August 2012.

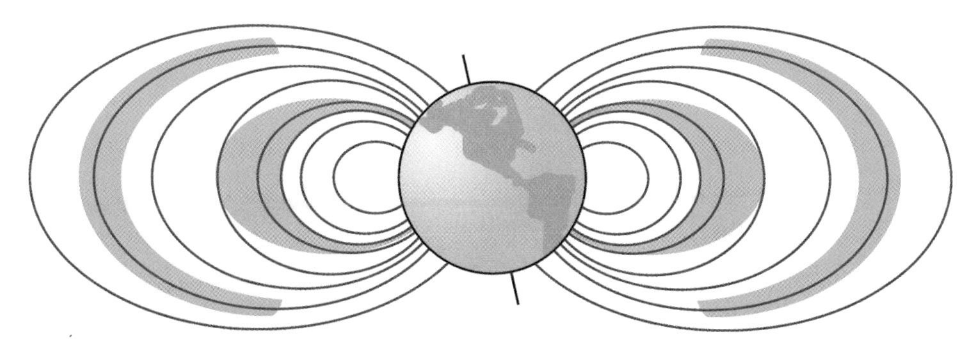

Model of Van Allen radiation belts

The rapid-decay theory assumes the magnetic field is the result of how the earth was created. According to this theory, the process of creation generated the motion necessary to create the electric current that results in the magnetosphere. As the motion of the earth and its core continues, the flow of electricity is resisted and the magnetosphere decays, or becomes weaker. Studies conducted from 1971–2000 indicate that the magnetic field weakened by 1.4%. Evidence of magnetic field reversal exists on every continent, which the rapid-decay theory suggests has happened as the result of catastrophic events such as the Flood. Using the mathematical equations in the rapid-decay theory and projecting backward in time, the earth would be no more than 10,000 years old, which supports young-earth theory.

In science, when making and testing theories with indirect observations and data, scientists take the theory and make

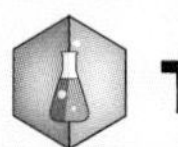

TRY THIS

Deflection Protection

The earth is surrounded by a magnetic field that is invisible but powerful. The solar wind produced by the sun contains particles that are dangerous to human life. As the solar wind approaches the earth, the magnetosphere stops much of it from reaching the surface. Punch a small hole, about 1 cm in diameter, through the center of a 7.5 cm foam ball. Feed 3 m of fine insulated wire through the hole, and form continuous loops of varying sizes around the ball. Make the loops look similar to the magnetic field lines. Allow the ends of the wire to extend about 15 cm from each pole. Remove about 1 cm of insulation from each wire end and use electrical tape to attach the exposed wire ends to a 1.5 volt battery. Place this setup on a large piece of paper and sprinkle iron filings through the loops. What happens to the iron filings? How is this similar to what might happen to solar wind particles as they approach the earth? Then, hold a compass away from the model and note where north is. A compass always points north because it is affected by the magnetosphere. Now place the compass near the model and move it from pole to pole. What happens to the compass? Why?

HISTORY

Van Allen Radiation Belts

In 1958, James Van Allen detected belts of trapped radiation within the magnetosphere. These belts are now known as *the Van Allen radiation belts.* Van Allen had explored the earth's upper atmosphere with balloons that could measure atmospheric radiation levels. Van Allen and his team placed a Geiger counter and an altimeter on Explorer I, America's first spacecraft, to take radiation readings at different heights. During the flight, the Geiger counter began to register thousands of particles passing through the satellite every minute. Scientists learned that space was radioactive. When spacecraft are exposed to fast photons that can penetrate several millimeters of metal for long periods, the electronic circuits and solar cells of spacecraft can deteriorate. Space missions are generally planned to minimize exposure to the most intense regions of the radiation belts.

predictions. The dynamo theory suggests the magnetic field will fluctuate over time, but overall the strength will remain the same. The rapid-decay theory predicts the earth's magnetosphere will decay, or continue to get weaker and weaker, over time. Both theories have been used to predict the magnetic fields for other planets. The dynamo theory predicted Mercury should not have a magnetic field, but it does. It predicted that Mars should have one similar to the earth's, but the magnetic field of Mars is very weak in comparison. The rapid-decay theory predicted the magnetic fields for Neptune and Uranus years before they were actually measured. In those cases, the measurements matched the predictions.

As the earth soars through space, it is bombarded by **solar wind**—the continuous flow of **plasma**, or superheated gases composed of electrically charged particles, from the sun. The earth's magnetic field repels the solar wind, protecting the earth from the wind's harmful effects. The magnetic field of a dipolar magnet is very symmetrical, so it would be reasonable to assume the field around the earth would be symmetrical. But the effect of solar wind creates an area surrounding the earth that is shaped like a comet. The winds on the sun side press against the magnetosphere to compress it. Then it spreads out on the other side of the earth.

Scientists have used the sensitive instruments on satellites to determine that the magnetosphere is filled with various plasmas that distort the magnetic field. Bands of high energy radiation called *Van Allen radiation belts* stretch away from the earth for several thousand kilometers to tens of thousands of kilometers. James Van Allen discovered these belts of radiation in 1958 through the use of radiation detectors called *Geiger counters* on the satellites *Explorer 1* and *Explorer 3*.

Sometimes huge explosions occur on the sun, causing solar flares and plasma to be hurled in all directions. When this happens, solar wind becomes stronger. Gusts of solar particles enter Earth's atmosphere and disturb the earth's magnetic field. This extra disturbance from solar wind is called *a geomagnetic storm*. Geomagnetic storms can disrupt radio signals, create errors in navigation systems, and even cause power surges and blackouts on Earth.

LESSON REVIEW

1. How is the magnetic field generated around the earth?
2. Explain the structure of the magnetosphere.
3. Describe the two theories about the electric current in the earth's core.
4. How does solar wind affect the magnetosphere?
5. Explain how technology was used to discover radiation in the magnetosphere.
6. How does the magnetosphere benefit the earth?

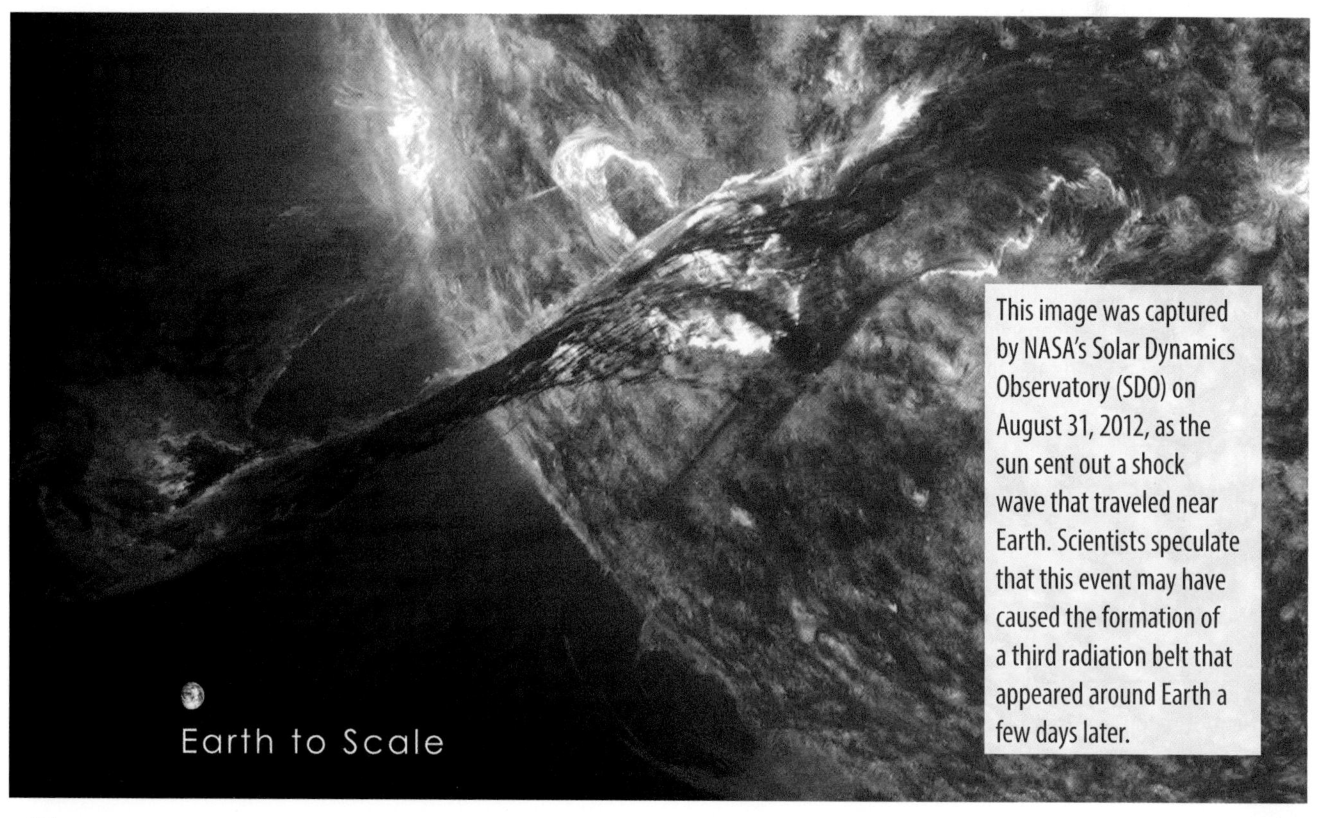

This image was captured by NASA's Solar Dynamics Observatory (SDO) on August 31, 2012, as the sun sent out a shock wave that traveled near Earth. Scientists speculate that this event may have caused the formation of a third radiation belt that appeared around Earth a few days later.

5.1.4 *Ozone Layer*

OBJECTIVES

- Explain the purpose of the ozone layer.
- Compare the oxygen in the ozone to the oxygen used for respiration.
- Theorize the relationship between CFCs and the hole in the ozone.

VOCABULARY

- **CFCs** synthetic compounds consisting of carbon, fluorine, and chlorine
- **ozone** a three-atom form of oxygen gas (O_3) that protects Earth from UV radiation
- **UV** ultraviolet radiation from the sun

On average, the sun is 150 million km from the earth, yet it has enough power to raise Earth's temperature to a sweltering level or to burn your skin badly. Along with heat and light, the sun casts ultraviolet, or **UV** radiation at the earth. Ultraviolet radiation is high-frequency radiation from the sun. Although it is invisible light, it can damage your skin and eyes. You might think that this sounds dangerous—it is. But God provided a filter to protect Earth from most UV radiation. A layer of gas called **ozone** protects all life on Earth from UV radiation. Although the psalmist was not writing about the ozone layer, he did paint a helpful picture of its protection when he said: "In the heavens He has pitched a tent for the sun . . . It rises at one end of the heavens and makes its circuit to the other; nothing is deprived of its warmth" (Psalm 19:4b, 6). The ozone layer acts like a tent for the earth to shield it from harmful UV radiation.

The stratosphere is home to 90% of the ozone in the atmosphere. Although the ozone layer protects living things from most UV radiation, it is only a tiny fraction of the atmosphere. The layer is about 20 km thick and it is not very dense. If all of the ozone molecules in the atmosphere were compressed to 1 atm (atmosphere) of pressure at 0°C, the ozone layer would be only 3 mm thick—about the height of three dimes. Amazingly, God designed this thin layer to sustain His creation.

FYI

UV Index

The World Health Organization has established guidelines for reporting the intensity of UV radiation. The UV index was designed to inform the public about the dangers of UV radiation so people could take precautions when outdoors. The Global Solar UV index was developed in 1995 and it ranges from 1–11. The number 1 indicates the lowest levels of UV and the number 11 indicates the highest levels. When outside, follow the "shadow rule." If your shadow is taller than you are, the UV exposure is probably low. But, if your shadow is shorter than you are, usually around midday, your exposure may be high and necessary precautions should be taken, such as seeking shade to protect skin and eyes. Small amounts of exposure are necessary for the production of vitamin D, but too much can be damaging.

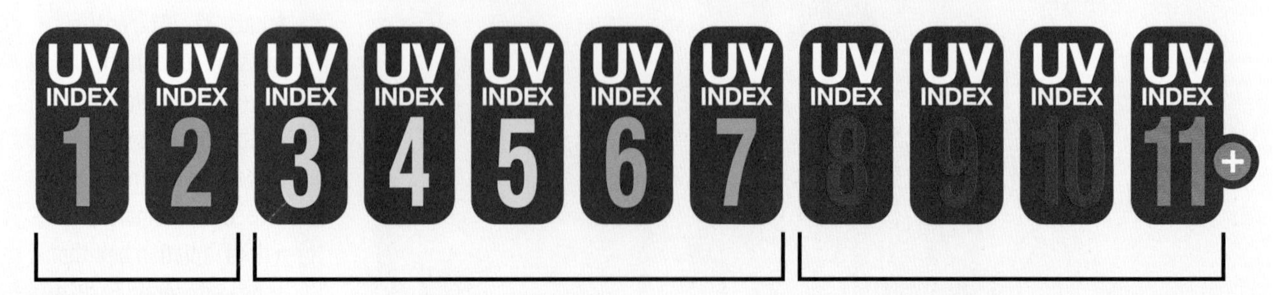

No protection required
You can safely stay outside.

Protection required
Seek shade during midday hours.

Extra protection required
Avoid being outside during midday hours.

Ozone is a toxic and explosive form of oxygen. The oxygen molecules used in respiration contain two oxygen atoms, but ozone molecules contain three. This three-atom structure is unstable and can be easily destroyed by incoming radiation. However, ozone formation also depends on such energy from the sun. Ozone forms when heat splits normal two-atom oxygen molecules into separate, free atoms. When one of these free atoms combines with another two-atom oxygen molecule, it forms an ozone molecule.

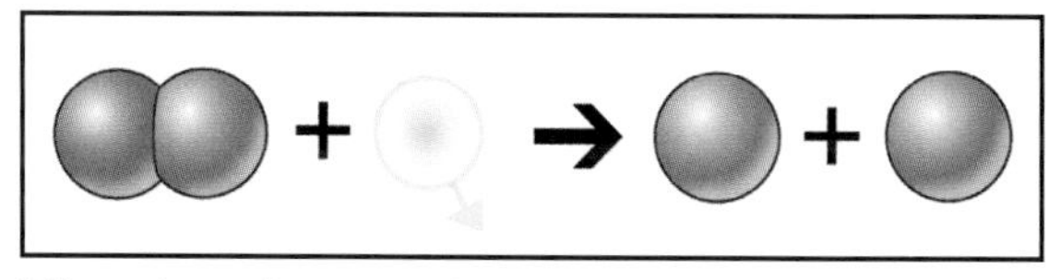

When ultraviolet rays strike oxygen molecules, the molecules split into two oxygen atoms.

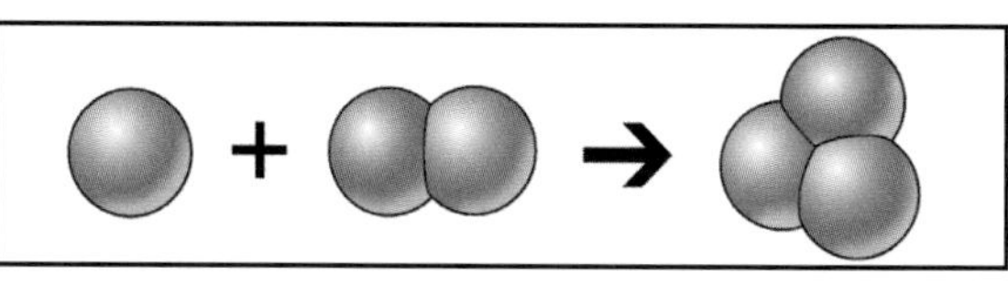

A stray oxygen atom combines with another oxygen molecule to form ozone, which protects the earth form ultraviolet radiation.

German chemist Christian Schönbein discovered and named the ozone layer in 1840. He used the word *ozone* from the Greek for "to smell" because the gas has a strong odor. In 1924, Gordon M. B. Dobson, a lecturer in meteorology at the University of Oxford, was studying meteor trails with a colleague. They observed that the temperature above the troposphere was not constant. Dobson hypothesized the temperature changed because the ozone layer absorbed UV solar radiation, which warmed the air. He designed instruments to test his hypothesis and began studying the ozone

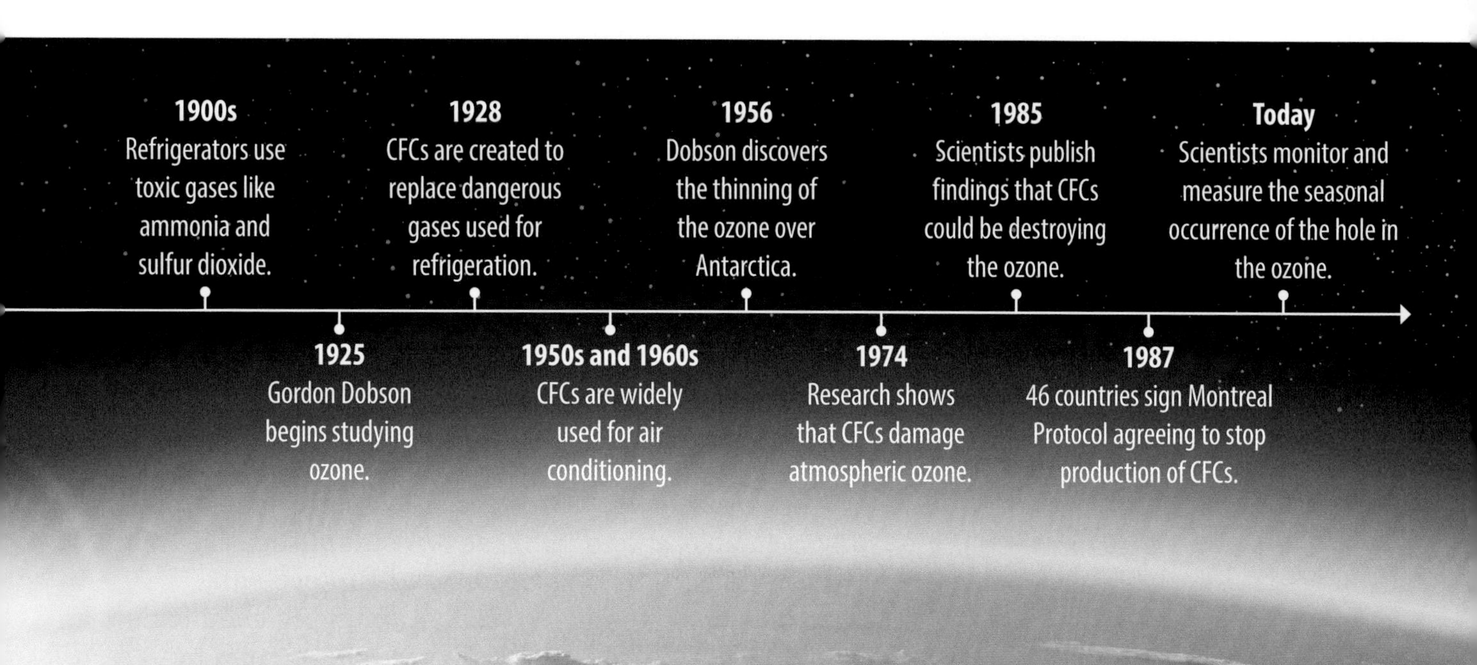
1900s
Refrigerators use toxic gases like ammonia and sulfur dioxide.
1925
Gordon Dobson begins studying ozone.
1928
CFCs are created to replace dangerous gases used for refrigeration.
1950s and 1960s
CFCs are widely used for air conditioning.
1956
Dobson discovers the thinning of the ozone over Antarctica.
1974
Research shows that CFCs damage atmospheric ozone.
1985
Scientists publish findings that CFCs could be destroying the ozone.
1987
46 countries sign Montreal Protocol agreeing to stop production of CFCs.
Today
Scientists monitor and measure the seasonal occurrence of the hole in the ozone.

layer in 1925. By 1956, Dobson had refined his instruments and 44 Dobson spectrometers were distributed throughout the world to measure the level of ozone in the atmosphere at different locations. Soon after, he discovered the yearly variation of ozone at Halley Bay in Antarctica. He found that the ozone layer would thin out annually between the months of August and November, the time of a natural phenomenon called *the polar vortex.*

Meanwhile, after several gas leaks in early refrigerators resulted in fatalities, a search for a less toxic refrigerant began. Chlorofluorocarbons, or **CFCs**, were first synthesized in 1928 as a safe alternative to toxic gases like ammonia and sulfur dioxide that were used as refrigerants. Less than 10 years later, millions of refrigerators were sold with the new, safer refrigerant. CFCs were also widely used for air conditioning in homes, businesses, and cars.

Old refrigerator

During the 1970s, scientists began questioning whether emissions from high-altitude jets or spacecraft would damage the ozone layer. Two chemists, Professor F. Sherwood Rowland and Dr. Mario Molina, showed that CFCs could damage atmospheric ozone. This information, along with decades of data collected over Antarctica, convinced many people that such advances were destroying the ozone layer. Concern about the use of CFCs increased in the 1980s when scientists in the British Antarctic Survey published a paper claiming to have discovered a hole in the ozone. The seasonal thinning of the ozone over Antarctica, first discovered by Gordon Dobson, then became known as *the hole in the ozone*. Although this was not a new discovery, it did appear that the area was thinner than it had been in the past. When the study was published, many people thought that the industrialized world was going to destroy the ozone layer completely. In 1987, as a result of the research, 46 countries signed the Montreal Protocol, an agreement to stop using ozone-damaging chemicals by 1996. The agreement has now been signed by nearly 200 countries.

Has the ban on CFCs decreased the size of the ozone hole? Is it too soon to tell? There are different opinions on whether the ban has affected the size of the seasonal ozone hole. Some scientists believe the ban has helped the ozone hole shrink. Others believe the area's size fluctuations are strictly seasonal and have little to do with CFCs. As in all areas of science, personal bias affects how events are interpreted.

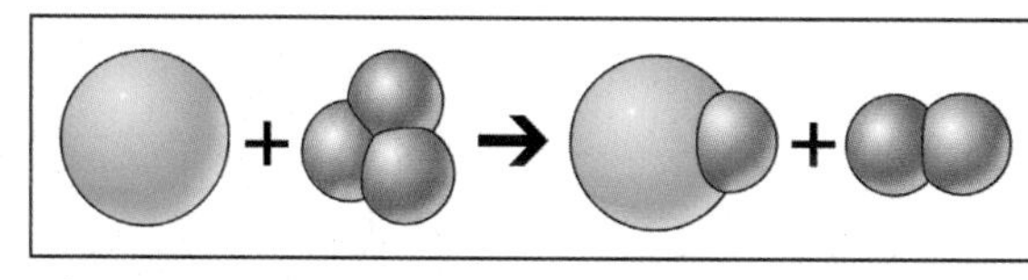

When CFCs are exposed to heat and radiation, chlorine atoms are freed. These atoms then attach to an oxygen atom in ozone, destroying the ozone's filtering ability.

Scientists continue to monitor the ozone layer. In 2016, the thin area over Antarctica reached a record size in spring, but shrank back to a below-average measurement by fall. As scientists continue to study the ozone layer and the seasonal phenomenon of its thinning, more details of God's creation will be discovered and better understood.

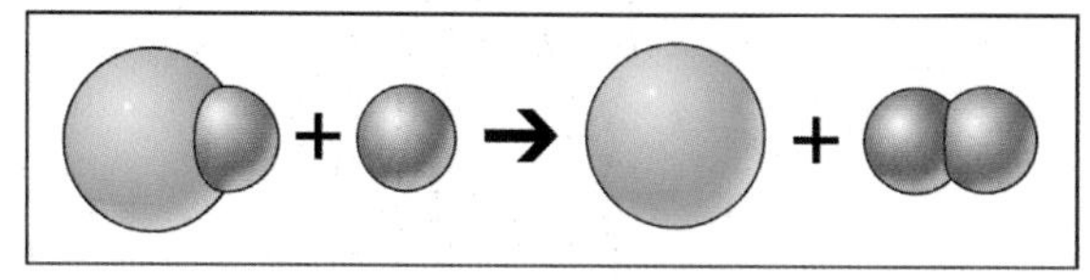

When an oxygen atom of chlorine monoxide combines with a free oxygen atom to form an oxygen molecule, the chlorine atom is released, which destroys another ozone molecule. In this way, the chlorine atoms in CFCs can destroy many ozone molecules.

LESSON REVIEW

1. Where is the ozone layer located in the atmosphere?
2. What is the purpose of the ozone layer?
3. What is UV radiation?
4. How is the oxygen used for respiration different from ozone?
5. Explain the two theories on the hole in the ozone layer.
6. Why were CFCs banned?

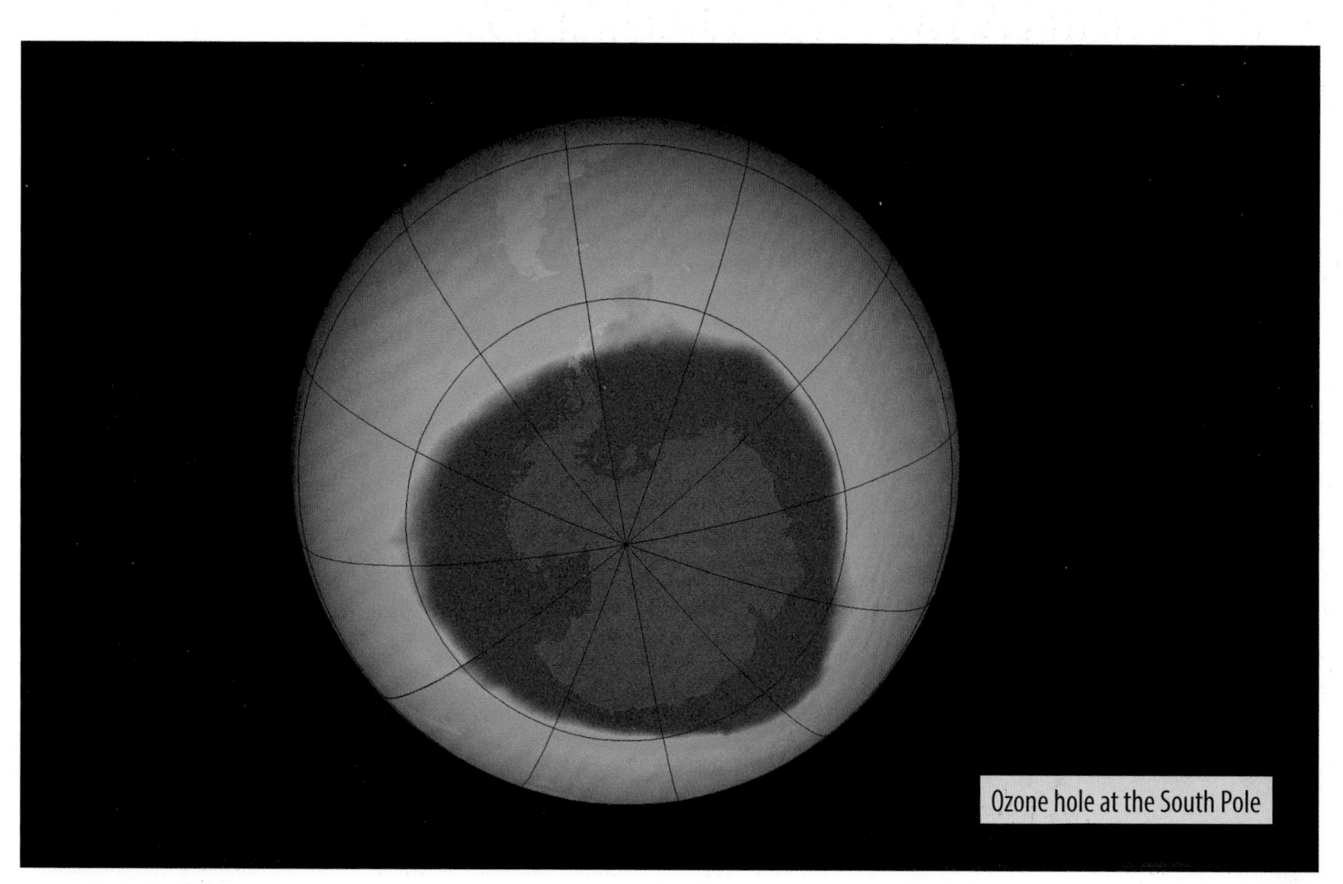
Ozone hole at the South Pole

5.2.1 *Heat Transfer*

OBJECTIVES

- Compare the methods of heat transfer.
- Correlate the earth's seasons to its orbit.
- Infer how a thermometer measures temperature.

VOCABULARY

- **conduction** the transfer of heat from one substance to another substance through direct contact
- **convection** the transfer of heat that occurs in moving fluids, liquids, or gases that is caused by the circulation of currents from one region to another
- **heat** the transfer of energy from one substance to another
- **radiation** the transfer of energy through space by electromagnetic waves
- **temperature** the measure of energy in the molecules of a substance

Weather—the daily variations of temperature, humidity, cloud cover, wind, and precipitation in the atmosphere—influences your life constantly. Your ball game is rained out. A blizzard strikes, so school is cancelled. Your hat gets blown away at the bus stop. The weather helps determine whether you will wear shorts or jeans, whether you will go camping in April or July, or maybe even whether you feel cheerful or grouchy. Some hobbies or interests even depend on the weather. For example, whether you can snow ski or water ski depends on the weather. In some parts of the world, the weather is somewhat consistent. In other areas, the weather seems to change daily.

Although weather might seem unpredictable, the processes that create it are orderly. One piece of the weather puzzle involves heat. The heat on Earth comes from the sun, of course. But have you ever thought about how the sun actually heats the earth? **Heat** is the transfer of energy from one substance to another. God created heat to travel from place to place in an orderly fashion, so it always moves from warmer objects to cooler objects. Heat can travel from one object or location to another in three different ways: radiation, conduction, and convection. Heat from the sun is transferred through space to the earth by **radiation**, which is the transfer of heat through space by electromagnetic waves. When heat radiates from the sun through space, it reaches the air molecules in the earth's atmosphere. This radiated heat then warms the air molecules, which then warm the molecules of other substances they come in contact with.

Soccer players

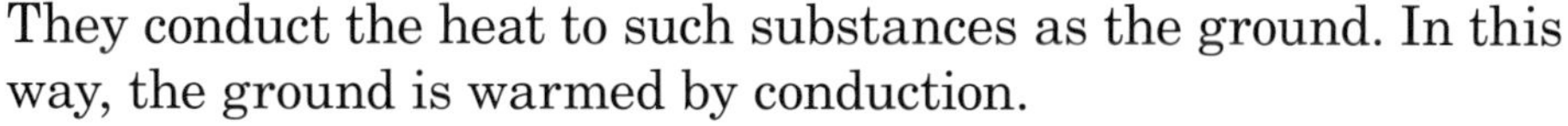
The sun provides radiant heat.

FYI

Gliding On the Currents
Hawks and other birds of prey often sail through the sky without flapping their wings. They glide on the warm convection currents that are rising from the earth. By gliding on these currents as they search for prey, these birds can conserve the energy they would otherwise have to use for flying.

They conduct the heat to such substances as the ground. In this way, the ground is warmed by conduction.

Conduction is the transfer of heat from one substance to another substance through direct contact. When you put an ice pack on your forehead, the heat from your forehead is conducted to the ice pack. In reality, the ice pack cools the forehead because the energy is transferred from your forehead to the ice pack. This heat transfer continues until the ice pack and your forehead are the same temperature. Conduction is why the ice melts and your head feels cooler. A pan on a hot burner is another example of conduction. The pan is very hot because metal conducts heat well. If you placed your hand near the pan, you would feel the radiated warmth as the heat energy from the pan was conducted to your fingers. The heat of the stove burner moves through conduction. When heat radiates from the sun through the atmosphere to the earth's surface, the warmed air comes in contact with the warm ground, and the temperature of the air rises even more. In this way, the earth is heated by conduction.

Heat will be conducted if the girl touches the pan.

Have you ever heard the expression "warm air rises"? This phrase describes **convection**, the

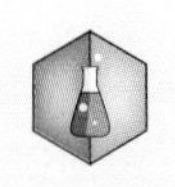

TRY THIS

Convection

Pour hot water into a beaker. Pour an equal amount of cold water into another beaker. Using a triple beam balance, measure the mass of a sample of hot water and compare it with the mass of an equal volume of cold water. Do they have the same mass? Use the definition of convection to explain the results.

transfer of heat that occurs in moving fluids, liquids, or gases that is caused by the circulation of currents from one region to another. The gases in the atmosphere are constantly moving. As warm air near the earth's surface is heated by radiation and conduction, its gases expand and it becomes less dense. Because the warm air is less dense, it rises and the denser cool air sinks. Rising warm air and sinking cool air form convection currents that transfer heat around the world. Most of the weather patterns on Earth can be traced to these convection currents.

In most areas of the world, the amount of heat that reaches the earth varies with the seasons. The quantity of heat that reaches a region and creates seasons depends on the earth's tilt. The earth tilts on its axis at a 23.5° angle in relation to the sun. As the earth rotates around the sun, the part of the earth that is tilted toward the sun experiences summer, and the part of the earth tilted away from the sun experiences winter. During June, July, and August, the earth's axis points the Northern Hemisphere toward the sun. This concentrates the heat, making the ground warm in the summer months for the Northern Hemisphere. As the earth orbits the sun and approaches December, the Northern Hemisphere is angled away from the

Seasons in the Northern Hemisphere

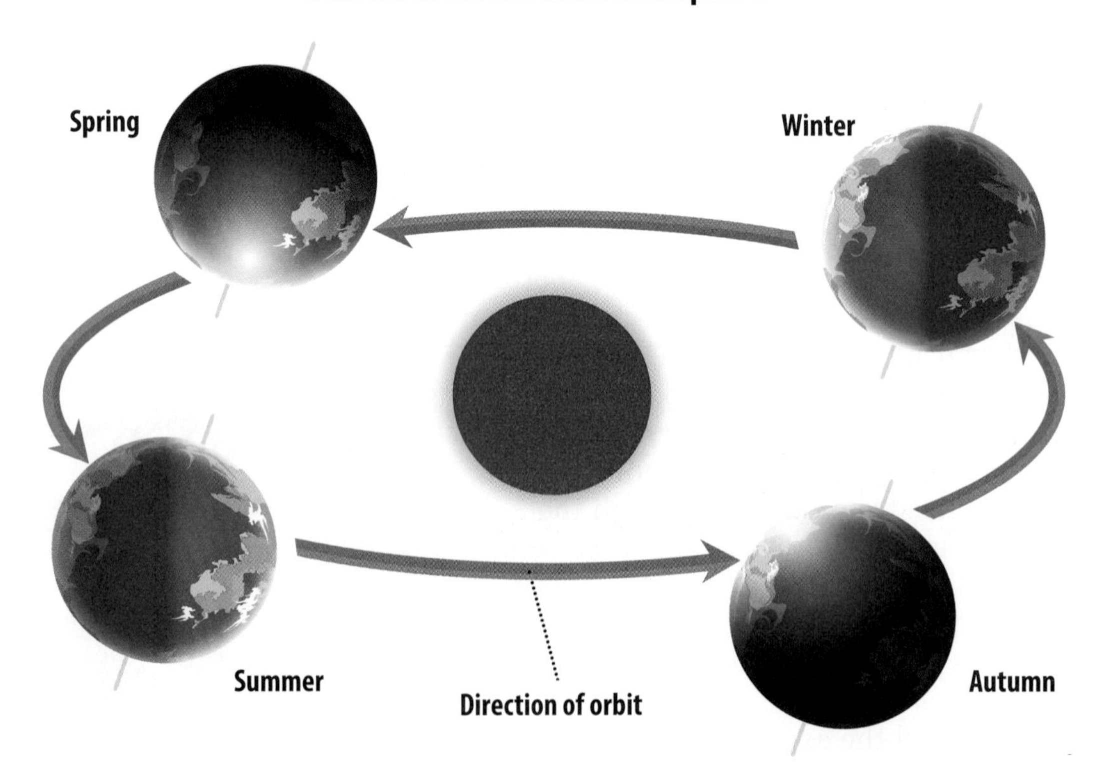

sun, but the Southern Hemisphere is closer. As a result, the Northern Hemisphere has winter as the Southern Hemisphere has summer. Without the tilt, the seasons would not exist because the intensity of the heat from the sun would be more constant year-round.

Temperature is a measure of how much energy is in a substance's molecules. Thermometers are instruments that measure changes in temperature. One common type of thermometer uses a liquid such as mercury or alcohol sealed in a glass tube. The molecules in the thermometer have a certain amount of energy and so does the substance being measured. For example, if you place a thermometer that reads 26°C in water that is 75°C, the energy of the water will be transferred to the thermometer. As this happens, the liquid in the thermometer will rise to read 75°C. In contrast, if you place a thermometer that reads 26°C in water that is 15°C, the thermometer transfers energy to the water, which causes the liquid to go down in the thermometer.

Meteorologists use different types of thermometers such as bimetal and electrical thermometers. A bimetal thermometer has a bar with two strips of different metals. Because different metals expand by varying amounts, the bar bends when it is heated and straightens when it is cooled. Bimetal thermometers work by measuring the angle of the bend, which corresponds to a temperature change. A resistance thermometer has an electric current running through certain materials; the current increases as the temperature increases. Meteorologists use these thermometers because they are faster and more accurate than liquid thermometers.

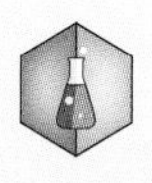

TRY THIS

Make a Thermometer
Use an eyedropper to put three drops of food coloring into a clear, narrow-necked plastic bottle. Add equal amounts of water and isopropyl alcohol to the bottle until it is one-quarter full. Insert a clear straw into the bottle until the bottom of the straw is about 1 cm from the bottom of the bottle. Seal the neck of the bottle with modeling clay so the straw stays in place. Observe your thermometer in the sun and in shade. Watch the water level in the portion of the straw that extends above the bottle. What happens? Why?

LESSON REVIEW

1. What is heat?
2. Compare the three methods by which heat can be transferred.
3. What creates the seasons? Explain.
4. If the Northern Hemisphere is experiencing summer, what season is it in the Southern Hemisphere? Why?
5. How does a liquid thermometer measure temperature?

5.2.2 Air Pressure

OBJECTIVES

- Describe the factors that affect air pressure.
- Compare low-pressure and high-pressure areas.
- Demonstrate how atmospheric pressure relates to weather.
- Explain how a barometer measures atmospheric pressure.

VOCABULARY

- **barometer** an instrument used to measure atmospheric pressure

The weight of the atmosphere presses down on everything on Earth's surface. The pressure exerted by Earth's atmosphere at any given point is called *atmospheric pressure*. Atmospheric pressure varies from place to place on Earth. These differences are caused by Earth's rotation on its axis, solar energy, gravity, and altitude.

The earth's rotation and convection currents move air masses of varying pressures into different regions, which changes the air pressure in other areas. Air masses with different densities create low- and high-pressure areas, which cause Earth's weather patterns. An area where warm air is rising is referred to as *a low-pressure area*. As air rises in low-pressure areas, strong winds develop, and water vapor from warm air condenses to form clouds. Low-pressure systems bring unsettled weather such as cloudy skies, storms, rain showers, or blizzards. An area where cold air is sinking is called *a high-pressure area*. In high-pressure areas, the sinking air prevents the formation of many clouds. Usually, high-pressure systems have clear, sunny skies.

Solar energy heats the atmosphere near the equator more than it heats the air near the poles. This heat energy causes air molecules to move around and spread out. The volume of the air expands, which makes the air less dense. The resulting warm air has a lower atmospheric pressure. Because it is less dense, warm air rises. Cold, dense air has a higher atmospheric pressure than

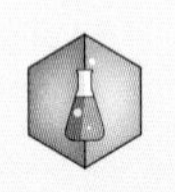

TRY THIS

Caving In

Hot air is less dense than cold air and therefore has lower air pressure. Boil two liters of water. Using a funnel, carefully fill a 2 L bottle with the hot water. To avoid the risk of getting burned, do not hold the bottle when pouring the water. Leave the water in the bottle for two minutes. Pour it out and screw the lid on the bottle immediately. What happened to the bottle? Why?

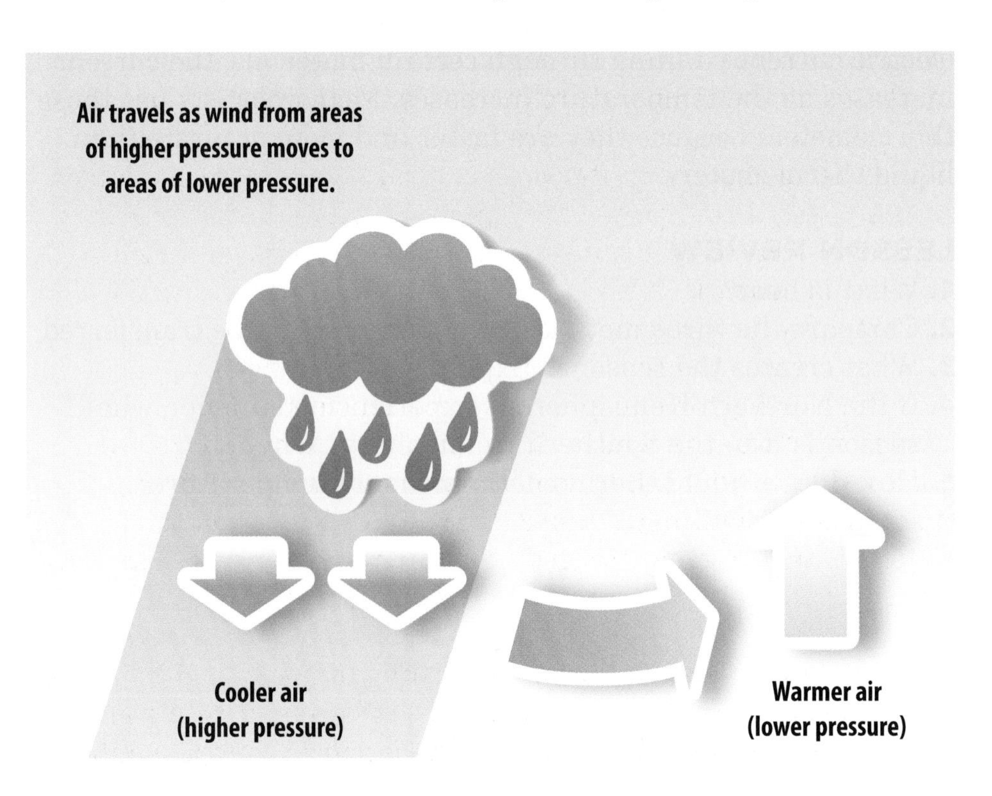
Air travels as wind from areas of higher pressure moves to areas of lower pressure.
Cooler air (higher pressure)
Warmer air (lower pressure)

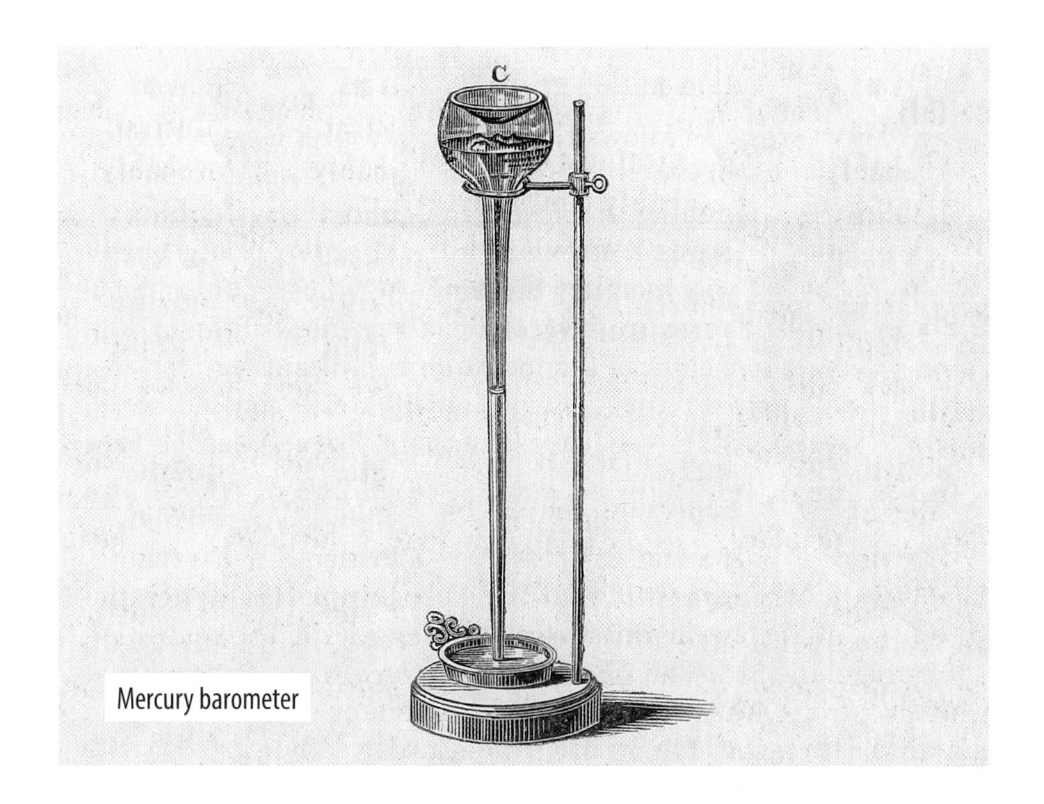

Mercury barometer

warm air. Because cold air is more dense than warm air, cold air sinks beneath warm air. This movement generates convection currents of air.

Gravity is another factor in atmospheric pressure change. Gravity pulls gas molecules to the earth's surface, which compresses 99% of the atmosphere's mass into a height of only 40 km above the earth's surface. The air at sea level is more dense than the air at high altitudes.

Since higher altitudes have less dense air, there is less weight pressing down on objects. This produces a lower atmospheric pressure. Your body is naturally acclimated to the air pressure of its usual surroundings. When you experience a change in altitude, the air pressure around you changes as well, but the pressure inside your body takes time to adjust. For example, your ears may pop when you drive into the mountains or ride a skyscraper's elevator. This sensation happens because the cavities in your body, such as those in your lungs, ears, and sinuses, contain air. Since these areas do not adjust automatically to pressure changes, you may experience ear pain or a headache at times with a change in altitude.

Atmospheric pressure is measured using an instrument called a **barometer**. There are two basic types of barometers. A mercury barometer is a tube filled with liquid mercury that opens into a container of mercury. Rising atmospheric pressure forces the mercury higher in the column; falling pressure allows the mercury to sink lower. A falling barometer indicates that the atmospheric pressure is falling and that a low-pressure system is forming, strengthening, or approaching. One way mercury barometers indicate atmospheric pressure is by the measurement of the height of the mercury in millimeters. For example, a height of 760 mm is considered standard atmospheric pressure. A second type of barometer is the aneroid barometer. The word *aneroid* means "not liquid." An aneroid barometer consists of a metal container from which most of the air has been removed. When the atmospheric pressure rises, the sides of the container bend inward. The sides bulge outward when atmospheric pressure drops. These changes cause a pointer to move along a dial, indicating the change in air pressure.

Aneroid barometer

LESSON REVIEW

1. Explain how the rotation of the earth, solar energy, gravity, and altitude affect air pressure.
2. What effect does the change in altitude have on your body? Why?
3. Explain the difference between a low-pressure area and a high-pressure area.
4. How is atmospheric pressure related to weather?
5. What is a barometer?
6. How does an aneroid barometer work?

FYI

Cave Breathing

Temperature differences create wind as warm air rises and cooler air sinks. A change in temperature also creates a change in atmospheric pressure. Wind Cave in South Dakota is so large that it has its own atmospheric pressure. When the earth's surface pressure increases, air is forced into the cave and its pressure increases as well. When the surface pressure lowers, or the temperature rises, air rushes out of the cave and the atmospheric pressure lowers. This movement of air in and out of the cave makes it appear the cave is breathing, but the air movement is the result of changes in atmospheric pressure.

If you have ever flown a kite at the beach, you know that lake or ocean shores are usually windy, but do you know why? When air is heated, its density decreases. As warm air rises, its air pressure lowers, creating a low-pressure area. Cooler, denser air from a high-pressure area then moves underneath the warm air. Earth's surface absorbs heat from the sun more quickly than a body of water can, so at the beach when the warm air over the land meets the cooler air over the water, it results in wind. Wind is the movement of air under high pressure toward an area of low pressure. There are two types of wind: local winds and global winds. Both types of wind result from atmospheric differences caused by the unequal heating of the atmosphere. Global winds will be discussed in the next lesson.

Sea breezes are local winds that form during the day when cooler air over the water moves in to replace the warmer air that rises up from the land. At night, land temperatures drop more quickly than water temperatures. Air from the cooler land is then drawn toward the warmer air over the water, which forms local winds called *land breezes.*

Local winds are also influenced by the landscape. During the day, mountains heat up more quickly than valleys because the sun's radiation reaches the slopes before it moves down into the valleys. In addition, bare mountain slopes can absorb solar energy better than areas that are covered with plants like in most valleys. The surface of the mountain heats the air around it. The warmer air expands, creating a low-pressure area near the top of the mountain. The low-pressure pulls the cooler air up from the valley, creating a local wind known as *a valley breeze.*

OBJECTIVES

- Summarize the nature of wind.
- Compare the types of local winds in different geographical areas.
- Explain why meteorologists measure wind speed.

VOCABULARY

- **anemometer** an instrument used to measure wind speed

TRY THIS

Wind Speed

Cut a piece of strong string 30 cm long. Glue one end of the string to a table tennis ball. Glue the other end of the string to the center point on the base of a protractor. Hold the protractor upside down and away from your body so the ball can swing freely. The ball should hang straight down to 90°. If it does not, make whatever adjustments are needed. To measure the wind speed, hold the instrument so it points into the wind. Mark the angle where the ball swings. Use the following chart to find out how strong the wind is. Compare your results with those of other students.

Angle	90°	85°	80°	75°	70°	65°	60°	55°	50°	45°	40°	35°
Kph	0	9.3	13.2	16.3	19.0	21.6	24.0	26.6	29.0	31.5	34.4	37.6

Sea and Land Breezes

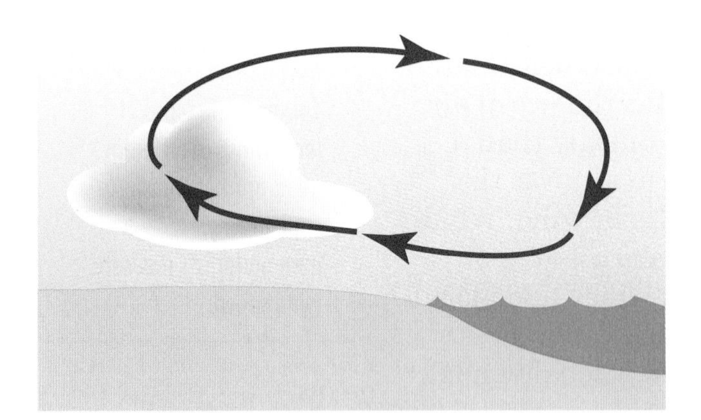

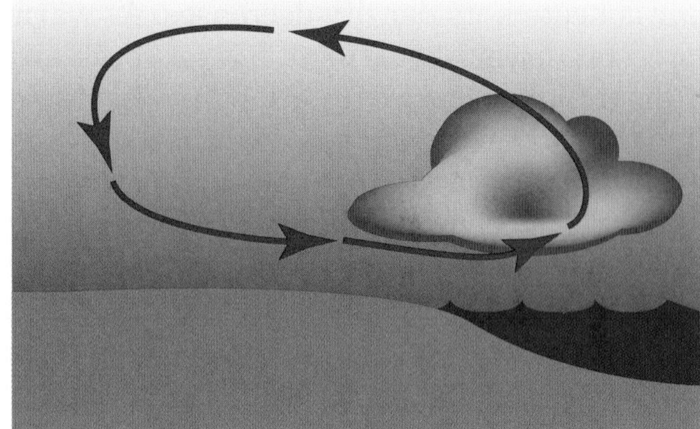

Without thick vegetation to hold in heat, mountains lose heat faster than valleys at night. This heat loss causes the local winds to change direction. *Mountain breezes* are local winds that form at night when cooler, denser mountain air moves down into the valleys. If you have ever camped on a mountain, you know that the temperature drops quickly after the sun sets.

As local winds blow over mountain peaks and sink over the other side, the winds form high-pressure systems. These systems create warm temperatures that can produce intense warm winds. Some examples of local winds that sweep down mountain slopes are the chinook on the east side of the Rocky Mountains, the foehn in Switzerland's alpine valleys, and the zonda in the Argentine Andes. Local winds can also be formed by low-pressure areas that result from the intense heating of inland areas. The sirocco, a hot wind formed in this manner, blows to the Mediterranean Sea from the Sahara Desert, and the khamsin brings hot winds to southern Egypt from the Sahara.

Anemometer

Meteorologists measure wind speed using an instrument called an **anemometer**. An anemometer looks like a weather vane. Small cups, all pointing in the same direction, are attached to spokes, which are connected to a freely rotating shaft. As the wind hits the cups, it turns the shaft. Wind speed is determined by counting the number of rotations that occur in a set time. Meteorologists measure the wind's speed and direction to help graph the movement of high- and low-pressure systems, which helps them predict changing weather patterns.

Valley and Mountain Breezes

LESSON REVIEW

1. Explain what wind is and how it is created.
2. What factors affect local winds?
3. Describe sea breezes and land breezes.
4. What is the difference between mountain and valley breezes?
5. Explain how a chinook wind is formed.
6. Why do meteorologists measure wind speed?

Kite flying at the beach

5.2.4 *Global Winds*

OBJECTIVES

- Identify and explain three global wind patterns.
- Apply the Coriolis effect to global travel.

The unequal heating of the earth's surface forms not only local winds but also large global wind systems. Near the equator, the sun is almost directly overhead most of the year. The direct rays of the sun heat the earth's surface there rapidly and create a low-pressure area. In contrast, regions where the sun's rays strike at a greater angle do not heat up as quickly, which is why temperatures near the equator are warmer than those at the poles.

At the equator, warm air rises and moves toward both the North and South Poles. As it rises and travels away from the equator, the air begins to cool. When these winds, which are called *the trade winds*, reach about 30° latitude, they start sinking. The trade winds then change direction and return to the equator to start the process all over again. The opposite happens at the poles. The high pressure at each pole moves the cold air toward the equator. As the air sinks, it travels near Earth's surface and begins to warm up. As it warms, winds called *polar easterlies* expand and rise. Eventually, at about 60° latitude, they rise to the upper troposphere where they cause a high-pressure area. The air then changes direction and heads back toward the poles.

A third loop of wind is created by the actions of the trade winds and the polar easterlies. Between 30° and 60° latitude, the

Global Wind Patterns

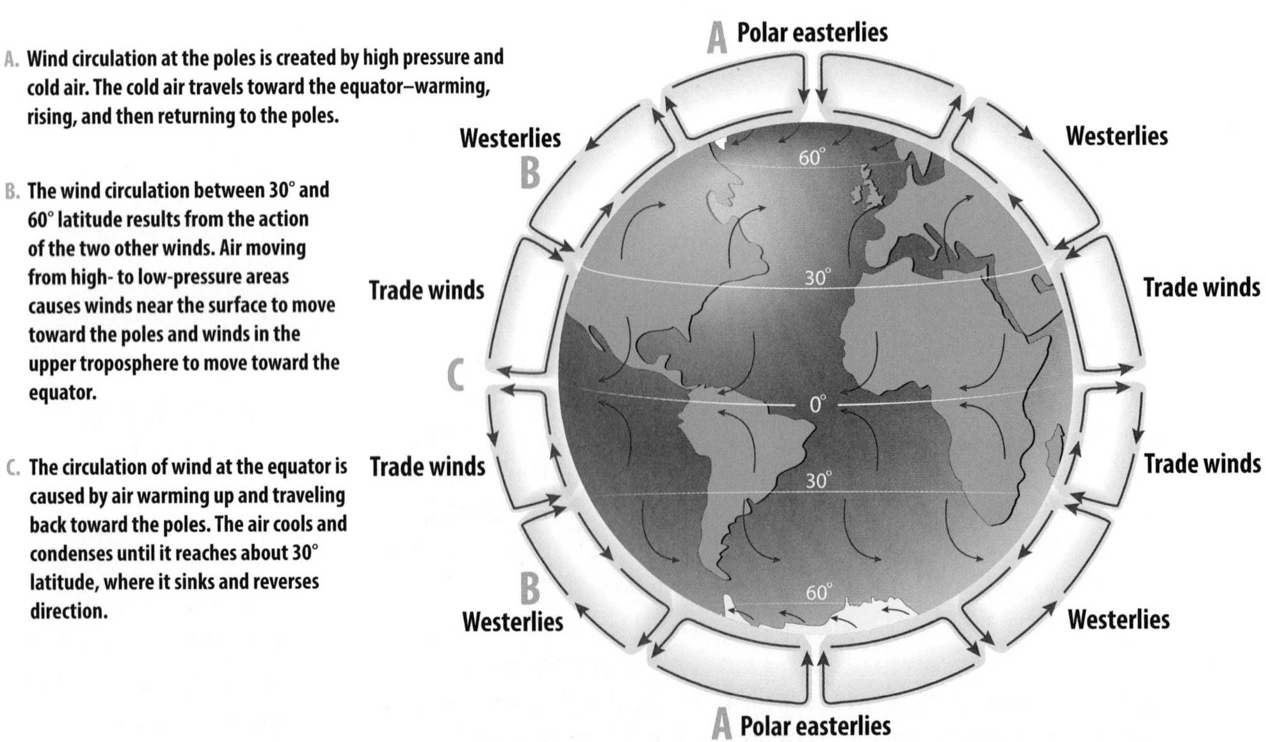

A. Wind circulation at the poles is created by high pressure and cold air. The cold air travels toward the equator–warming, rising, and then returning to the poles.

B. The wind circulation between 30° and 60° latitude results from the action of the two other winds. Air moving from high- to low-pressure areas causes winds near the surface to move toward the poles and winds in the upper troposphere to move toward the equator.

C. The circulation of wind at the equator is caused by air warming up and traveling back toward the poles. The air cools and condenses until it reaches about 30° latitude, where it sinks and reverses direction.

winds blow toward the poles at the surface and toward the equator in the upper troposphere. These winds, called *westerlies*, can be very strong and can cause unstable weather patterns in the middle latitudes.

Hurricanes are steered by global winds.

Weather patterns would not be difficult to predict if you only had to consider global winds. However, the rotation of the earth adds another dimension to the movement of the winds. The latitudes of the earth move at different speeds because Earth is a sphere. The equator is the widest part of the planet, so Earth's circumference is greatest at 0° latitude. The latitudes near the poles, on the other hand, have the smallest circumference. If you plotted points along a line of longitude from the North Pole to the South Pole, the points near the equator would have to travel much faster to make a full circle in 24 hours than the points near the poles.

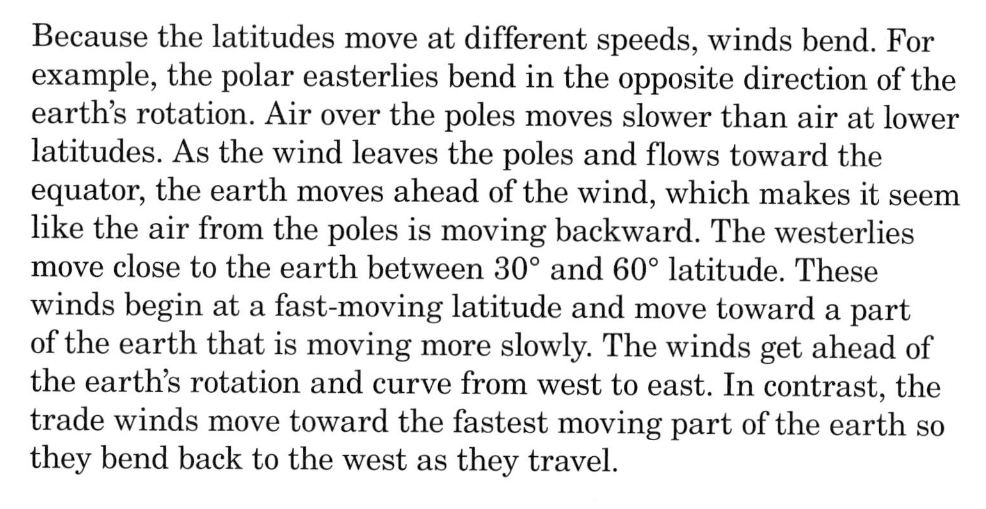

Because the latitudes move at different speeds, winds bend. For example, the polar easterlies bend in the opposite direction of the earth's rotation. Air over the poles moves slower than air at lower latitudes. As the wind leaves the poles and flows toward the equator, the earth moves ahead of the wind, which makes it seem like the air from the poles is moving backward. The westerlies move close to the earth between 30° and 60° latitude. These winds begin at a fast-moving latitude and move toward a part of the earth that is moving more slowly. The winds get ahead of the earth's rotation and curve from west to east. In contrast, the trade winds move toward the fastest moving part of the earth so they bend back to the west as they travel.

FYI

Windy Jargon

Trade winds: These winds occur between the equator and 30° latitude. The trade winds helped ships sail on the trade routes west from Europe to the Americas.

Polar easterlies: These winds originate at the poles and bend from east to west.

Westerlies: These winds originate between 30° and 60° latitude, blow from the west, and bend to the east.

Horse latitudes: At around 30° latitude, the winds become very weak. In the 18th and 19th centuries, sailors on ships that got stranded in this latitude might throw any horses they were carrying overboard to save the drinking water.

The rotation of the earth curves the paths of winds, flying objects, and sea currents that travel through different latitudes because of the Coriolis effect. The Coriolis effect was first described by the French mathematician Gustave-Gaspard Coriolis in the early 19th century. Because of the Coriolis effect, an object that moves in a straight line above the earth's surface and not parallel to the equator appears to curve because the earth is spinning beneath it. Similarly, something that is relatively stationary near the equator will tend to turn because the earth is moving faster than places to the north or south of it. Tropical storms rotate counterclockwise in the Northern Hemisphere and clockwise in the Southern Hemisphere. A common myth is that water in toilet bowls, bathtubs, and sinks rotates counterclockwise in the Northern Hemisphere and

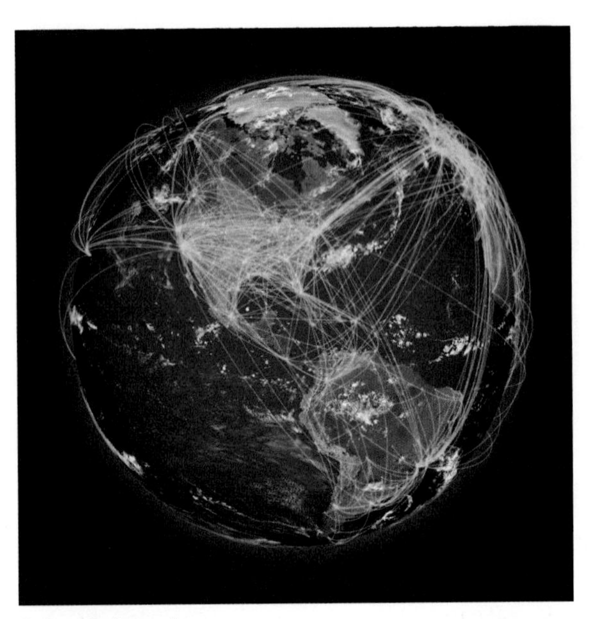
Airline flight paths

clockwise in the Southern Hemisphere as it drains. However, the Coriolis effect is very slight on something as small as water going down a drain. Other rotational forces easily overcome the Coriolis effect in such instances.

Scientists calculating the trajectory of a vehicle launched into space must take the Coriolis effect into account. The Coriolis effect is also considered when airlines determine flight paths. Suppose a commercial jet is scheduled to fly from Norway to Nigeria. If the plane were to fly directly south, it would completely miss Nigeria. Nigeria, which is close to the equator, is on a latitude that is moving much faster than one near Norway. When the plane reached the equator, the earth would have moved to the east and because of the Coriolis effect, the plane's path would bend. Consequently, the plane would end up over the Atlantic Ocean rather than in Nigeria.

LESSON REVIEW

1. Why is the air warmer at the equator than at the poles?
2. Describe the trade winds.
3. Describe the pressure and wind pattern in the polar latitudes.
4. Explain how and where the westerlies form.
5. Other than different air temperatures and pressure areas, what else affects the movement of global winds?
6. An airplane is traveling straight south from the equator to Antarctica. What direction would its path seem to bend? Why?

The Speed of the Earth

Outside on a paved surface, use chalk to draw four large concentric circles. Consider the center circle to be a line of latitude near the North Pole. The largest circle is the equator, and the other circles are lines of latitude in between. Have one person stand on each line of latitude, lining up as though creating a line of longitude. Have each person grasp a long pole to maintain the straight line. Mark the starting point for the line of people. Now, direct the whole line to move once around their circles. The person at the North Pole will dictate the speed. The line of people should stay straight as it moves around its circles and should arrive back at the starting point at the same time. Which person moved the fastest? Which person moved the slowest? Why was there a difference in the speeds? How does this activity relate to the movement of the earth?

Have you ever laid on your back looking at clouds shaped like cars, horses, or faces? What are clouds and how do they form? **Clouds** are visible collections of tiny water droplets or ice crystals in the atmosphere. Tiny particles of dust, ice, salt, and other solids remain suspended in the air for a long time because they are so small. When water vapor condenses on these small particles, the water droplets combine to form clouds. **Fog**, which is condensed water vapor near the ground, forms in a similar way at lower levels. Fog forms when a low-level cloud of warm water vapor passes over a cool area, such as a lake or valley.

Although people have watched clouds for thousands of years, the modern names for the various clouds only came into existence in the 19th century. In 1803, British scientist Luke Howard used Latin terms to classify clouds according to their common shapes. Howard named puffy, white clouds *cumulus clouds*, which means "lumpy." Clouds that stretched out in layers across the sky he called *stratus clouds*, which means "layered." He named thin, feathery clouds *cirrus clouds*, which means "lock of hair." By using Howard's classification system, scientists can combine these names to describe even more specific cloud formations, such as stratocumulus, which are groups of large, puffy clouds that form in lines or waves.

OBJECTIVES

- Describe how a cloud is formed.
- Categorize different cloud types.
- Summarize how clouds affect weather.

VOCABULARY

- **cloud** a visible collection of tiny water droplets or ice crystals in the atmosphere
- **fog** a low-level cloud caused by condensation of warm water vapor as it passes over a cold area
- **virga** a streak of precipitation that evaporates before reaching the ground

Field covered in fog

Cumulus clouds

Stratus clouds

Cirrus clouds

Cumulonimbus clouds

Cirrus and cumulus clouds

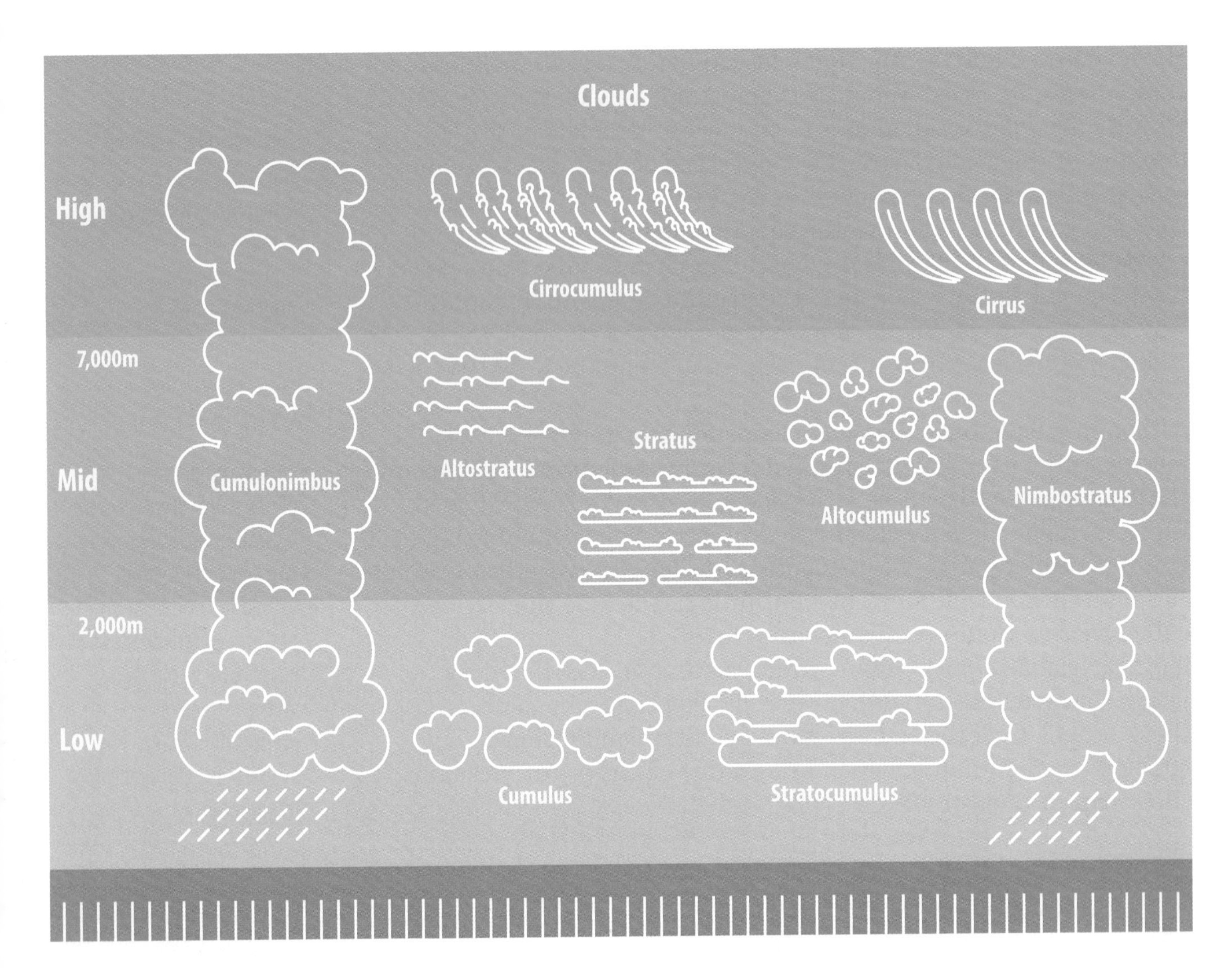

Sometimes prefixes and suffixes are added to specific cloud types to further classify them. For example, *nimbus* means "rain." The prefix *fracto*, which means "fracture," is used to describe clouds that have been blown apart by the wind. The prefix *alto*, which means "high," describes mid-level stratus or cumulus clouds. So a cumulonimbus cloud is a puffy white rain cloud.

Different types of clouds form at varying altitudes. You have probably seen thin, wispy, feathery clouds high in the sky. These high-level clouds are cirrus clouds, and they form above 8,000 m. Cirrus clouds contain ice crystals because the temperatures are 0°C or below at that altitude. The wind blows cirrus clouds into feathery strands. Cirrocumulus clouds, which are found from 3,000 m to 18,000 m depending on the climate, are thin, patchy clouds that form in wavelike patterns. Cirrostratus clouds form at the same altitude as cirrocumulus, but they are widespread, and look like thin veils or wind-blown strands of cotton. These clouds are responsible for the beautiful halos of light that

Rain in the Bible

Clouds can bring rain and refreshment or storms and destruction. Rain appears often in the Bible. In Noah's day, God used the clouds to bring forth great rain and through the rain, judgment: "The floodgates of the heavens were opened. And rain fell on the earth forty days and forty nights" (Genesis 7: 11b–12). During Elijah's time, Israel experienced a severe drought and famine because God withheld the rain until the unfaithful people of Israel acknowledged Him as Lord. Elijah sent his servant to go out to the sea to look for a cloud. He did this seven times until finally, the servant reported, "A cloud as small as a man's hand is rising from the sea." Elijah told King Ahab to hitch up his chariot and get off the mountain before the rains stopped him. "The sky grew black with clouds, the wind rose, a heavy rain started falling and Ahab rode off to Jezreel" (1 Kings 18:44–45).

sometimes form around the sun or the moon when the ice crystals of cirrostratus clouds refract light at certain angles.

The middle layers of clouds are generally stratus and cumulus clouds. These clouds form between 2,000 m and 8,000 m. Altostratus clouds are sheets of gray or blue across the sky. When sunlight pierces through these clouds, it looks like a light

Storm supercell

Relative altitude of cloud formations

shining through frosted glass. In contrast, altocumulus clouds are white or gray patches of puffy clouds that form layers across the sky. When seen through this type of cloud, the sun can form a corona, or a disk, that is pale yellow or blue on the inside and a reddish hue on the outside.

Low-level clouds form below 2,000 m. Cumulus clouds are the familiar white, puffy clouds people sometimes see animal shapes in. They form during the day but disappear at night and are generally signs of fair weather. Gray stratus cloud layers make the sky look heavy and ominous, but they produce only a fine drizzle of rain. Dark gray nimbostratus clouds, however, are true rain clouds that produce light but continuous rain. Stratocumulus clouds are not rain clouds; they are gray, irregular masses that spread out into rolling layers or puffy waves. Cumulonimbus clouds are sometimes called *thunderheads* because these clouds are frequently associated with thunderstorms. High winds often flatten their tops, which can rise to great heights. Cumulonimbus clouds have low bases under which ragged clouds can form. Sometimes cumulonimbus clouds produce **virga**, which is precipitation that evaporates before it reaches the ground. Some cumulonimbus clouds produce violent tornados.

Clouds affect both weather and climate. They carry water inland from the oceans and thereby bring rain and snow to regions far from large bodies of water. Clouds have a cooling effect on the earth because they reflect sunlight. However, they also have a warming effect because they absorb or trap heat, which keeps the earth warm. Both of these features affect regional weather patterns and global temperatures.

LESSON REVIEW

1. Explain how water becomes a cloud.
2. What do the three Latin root words for types of clouds mean?
3. Give the name and meaning of the prefixes and suffixes that can be added to cloud root names.
4. Describe two types each of high-level, mid-level, and low-level clouds.
5. How do clouds affect weather?

On a humid day, the air feels sticky, and you feel sticky too. When it is very humid, it can feel harder to breathe and the heavy, damp air makes you feel hot. The air feels uncomfortably sticky because it has more water vapor than drier air. Humidity makes you feel hot because the extra water vapor prevents your perspiration from evaporating. The evaporation of sweat is what cools the body because the process removes heat energy.

The amount of water vapor in the air is called **humidity**. Humidity increases as more water molecules evaporate into the air. Relative humidity is the amount of water vapor in the air compared with the amount that the air can hold at that particular temperature. For example, if a cubic meter of air is holding 16 grams of water vapor at a temperature with the potential to hold 20 grams of water vapor, then the relative humidity is 80% ($[16 \div 20] \times 100 = 80\%$). The air is holding 80% of what it can hold. Warm air can hold more water vapor than cool air, so humid days tend to be hot days. The higher the relative humidity, the warmer a person feels. All precipitation can be traced back to this water in the air.

The most common forms of precipitation are rain, snow, sleet, and hail. Precipitation falls to the ground for the same reason that any other object falls to the ground—gravity. Rain does not constantly fall from clouds because the size of a cloud droplet is only 0.0001–0.005 cm in diameter; this is so tiny that air currents hold the droplets aloft. In a process known as **coalescence**, cloud droplets join into drops large enough to fall. Once the water is at least 0.5 cm in diameter, it is considered a raindrop. The average raindrop contains a million times more water than the average cloud droplet. Rain may begin as frozen crystals in high, cold clouds or as water vapor in lower, warm clouds.

Sleet forms when precipitation falls through a layer of freezing air. Scientists have differing views on how sleet forms. According to cold cloud theory, it can start as snow, then melt and refreeze. Warm cloud theory suggests it starts as rain, passes through a layer of freezing air, and freezes before it hits the ground. If the rain does not freeze until it lands, it is called *freezing rain*. These raindrops fall through a layer of air that is close to freezing, which lowers the temperature

OBJECTIVES

- Compare relative humidity in warm and cool temperatures.
- Describe the process of cloud droplets becoming precipitation.
- Correlate precipitation types to atmospheric conditions.

VOCABULARY

- **coalescence** the process of coming together
- **deposition** the changing of a gas directly into a solid
- **humidity** the amount of water vapor in the air

Cold Cloud Precipitation

Frozen precipitation melts and reaches the ground as rain.

Frozen precipitation melts in warm air. Rain falls and freezes on cold surfaces as freezing rain.

Frozen precipitation melts in shallow warm air, then refreezes into sleet before reaching the surface.

Snow falls through cold air and reaches the surface.

of the raindrops to within a degree or two of 0°C. When the drops reach the surface, they lose enough energy to freeze on contact.

In contrast, hail is precipitation in the form of ice lumps. Hail forms when convection currents carry rain droplets up to altitudes where they freeze. Hailstones may be carried back up through freezing air several times, which adds layers of ice. Large hailstones can be very destructive, even damaging crops and property. In April 1986, the heaviest hailstone ever recorded, which weighed 1 kg, fell on Bangladesh.

Snow is made of ice particles that fall as small pellets, individual crystals, or a combination of crystals called *snowflakes*. In order for snow to form, the air must be supersaturated with water vapor at a temperature below 0°C. The lower the temperature, the smaller the snowflakes produced. Low temperatures result in small snowflakes because cold air holds less water vapor; there is not as much moisture to form big, fluffy snowflakes. For this reason, snow that falls in very cold temperatures is hard to pack into snowballs. The snowflakes do not have enough moisture to hold together well. Snowflakes become larger as the air becomes warmer.

Freezing rain on branches

Dew forms when the water vapor above the ground cools in the night air and condenses on

TRY THIS

Rain Gauge

Obtain a tall, narrow jar and a large, wide-mouthed jar such as a peanut butter jar. The opening of the large jar should be the same diameter as the jar itself. With a metric ruler and black marker, draw centimeter markings on the large jar. Add water to the large jar to a height of 2.5 cm and pour this water into the tall, narrow jar. Mark this level as *2.5 cm*. Divide the space below this mark into ten 0.25 cm units. Place the jars outside where water will not splash into them or run into them from a roof. Use the large jar to measure heavy rainfall and the tall jar to measure light rainfall.

the ground. The air temperature at which water vapor begins to condense is called *the dew point*. If a dew point below 0°C is reached, frost forms. Frost is caused by **deposition**, which is the changing of a gas directly into a solid. In the case of frost, water vapor becomes ice without first becoming a liquid.

LESSON REVIEW

1. Explain the difference between humidity and relative humidity.
2. What is the relative humidity if the air has 16 grams of water in every cubic meter, but it can hold 17 grams in every cubic meter?
3. Two different locations have a temperature of 36°C. One has a relative humidity of 25% and the other has a relative humidity of 85%. Which location will feel hotter? Why?
4. What has to happen for a cloud droplet to precipitate?
5. Compare the atmospheric conditions that result in rain, sleet, freezing rain, and snow. Describe these types of precipitation.

Close-up of a snowflake

FYI

Rain Records

The greatest recorded annual rainfall is 2,300 cm from August 1860 to July 1861 in Cherrapunji, Meghalaya, India.

The greatest rainfall in 24 hours is 182.5 cm in 1952 in Cilaos, Reunion, in the Indian Ocean.

The greatest average annual rainfall is in Mt. Waialeale, Hawaii, with 1,140 cm each year.

One of the driest places on Earth is the Atacama Desert in Chile, where less than 5 mm of rain falls each year.

5.2.7 Air Masses and Fronts

OBJECTIVES

- Classify air masses.
- Explain how fronts are formed.
- Evaluate a front to determine what weather will result.

VOCABULARY

- **air mass** a large body of air with consistent temperature and humidity
- **front** the boundary between two air masses

When you listen to the weather report online or watch it on TV, the meteorologist might say that a cold air mass is moving down from the Arctic or that a warm air mass will be moving in, bringing a change in the weather. An **air mass** is a large body of air with a consistent temperature and moisture level. Air masses usually cover hundreds or thousands of square kilometers. Because the air mass has a consistent temperature and moisture level, it will tend to stay together as it moves.

Air mass names refer to the regions where they formed. A region's topography influences the moisture level of an air mass. Continental air masses form over land and are characterized by dry air; maritime air masses form over water and are characterized by moist air. The regions' temperature affects the temperature of the air mass. Polar air masses form in the polar regions and tropical air masses form over warm tropical areas. These designations are combined to form four different classifications for air masses that more accurately describe their characteristics. A cold air mass that forms over water is called *a maritime polar* (mP), and a warm air mass that forms over water is called *a maritime tropical* (mT). A cold air mass that forms over land is called *a continental polar* (cP), and a warm air mass that forms over land is called *a continental tropical* (cT). Another type of air mass, called *an arctic air mass* (A), can form over the Arctic in the winter. These air masses are very cold and very dry.

Air masses can change as they travel and encounter different conditions. If they stay over an area for a length of time, the mass can take on the characteristics of that area. For example, a maritime polar can become a continental polar if it stays over land for a length of time. A continental tropical can become a

Air Masses

Air Mass Type	Weather Map Symbol	Source	Characteristics
Arctic	A	Arctic basin	Extremely cold
Maritime Polar	mP	Polar ocean regions	Cold and humid
Maritime Tropical	mT	Tropical ocean regions	Warm and humid
Continental Polar	cP	Polar land regions	Cold and dry
Continental Tropical	cT	Tropical land regions	Warm and dry

Air Masses

maritime tropical if it stays over water for a length of time. How much a mass changes depends on how fast it is moving.

At some point, a moving air mass will encounter another air mass. The boundary between two air masses of different densities and temperatures is called a **front**. Fronts are usually responsible for weather changes. For a front to form, one air mass must overtake another air mass. The type of front that forms is determined by the way the colder air mass is moving.

Cold fronts form when a cold air mass overtakes a warm air mass. The dense, cold air lifts the warm air. If the warm air is moist, cumulus and cumulonimbus clouds form. Cold fronts produce strong but short-lived storms. Sometimes a line of heavy thunderstorms called *a squall line* develops ahead of a high-speed cold front. Slower moving cold fronts produce less cloud cover and precipitation because the cold air lifts the warm air very slowly.

Sometimes fast-moving cold air overtakes a warm air mass that is moving in the same direction and lifts it entirely off the ground. This occurrence is called *an occluded front*. The warm air is completely cut off, or occluded, from the earth's surface and held up in the atmosphere's upper levels. The advancing cold front joins with the cool air mass already beneath the warm air mass. Occluded fronts produce low temperatures, many clouds, and lots of precipitation.

Warm fronts form when a warm air mass overtakes a cold air mass. Being less dense, the warm air rises above the cold air

Cold front

Occluded front

Stationary front

Warm front

and forms a gradual slope that is often marked by clouds. Cirrus clouds condense at the height of the slope, and cirrostratus clouds form in the middle. If the warm air mass is very humid, nimbostratus clouds accumulate at the leading edge of the front, producing heavy rains or snowfall over large areas.

A stationary front forms between two air masses that meet and stall with neither replacing the other. Stationary fronts produce weather that is similar to the weather formed by warm fronts.

LESSON REVIEW

1. What is an air mass?
2. Describe each type of air mass.
3. How is a front formed?
4. Explain the difference between a cold front and a warm front.
5. What type of weather results from an occluded front?

OBJECTIVES

- Identify conditions necessary for a blizzard.
- Model the stages of a thunderstorm and the formation of lightning.
- Compare the nature of a tornado to the nature of a hurricane.

VOCABULARY

- **lightning** the electrical discharge of energy from storm clouds
- **thunder** the sound that results from the rapid heating and expansion of air that accompanies lightning

Have you ever been caught in a violent storm with pelting rain, fingers of lightning flashing all around you, and thunder booming in your ears? If so, you may know how the disciples felt in such a storm out on the lake. In Luke 8:22–25, the disciples woke Jesus, saying, “Master, Master, we’re going to drown!” Jesus got up and rebuked the wind and the raging waters, and the storm subsided. This passage was not written to frighten readers but to comfort them because through Christ His followers can triumph over any circumstance, no matter how scared they are. Few forces on Earth are as powerful and terrifying as storms, which remain a symbol of an untamed nature. Often even with advanced technology, the best option in the face of a violent storm is to pray in faith, warn others, and seek shelter.

The most familiar storms are rainstorms, which often appear along cold fronts. When the warm air is moist and the cold front is moving quickly, cumulonimbus clouds form, producing short but often violent storms. If the humid air is unstable, it is pushed slowly up over a moving cold front; then cumulonimbus clouds may form and bring thunderstorms. Warm fronts can also create heavy rains if advancing, warm, very humid air overtakes a slow moving cold air mass. When that happens, nimbostratus clouds pile up at the base of the front, bringing heavy rains over large areas. Snowstorms form much like rainstorms, but they occur in colder clouds. Severe snowstorms are called *blizzards*. A blizzard is a storm with heavy snowfall, winds above 56 kph for at least three hours, and visibility that is reduced to 0.4 km or less. Blizzards create life-threatening conditions and often cause power outages.

Lightning storm

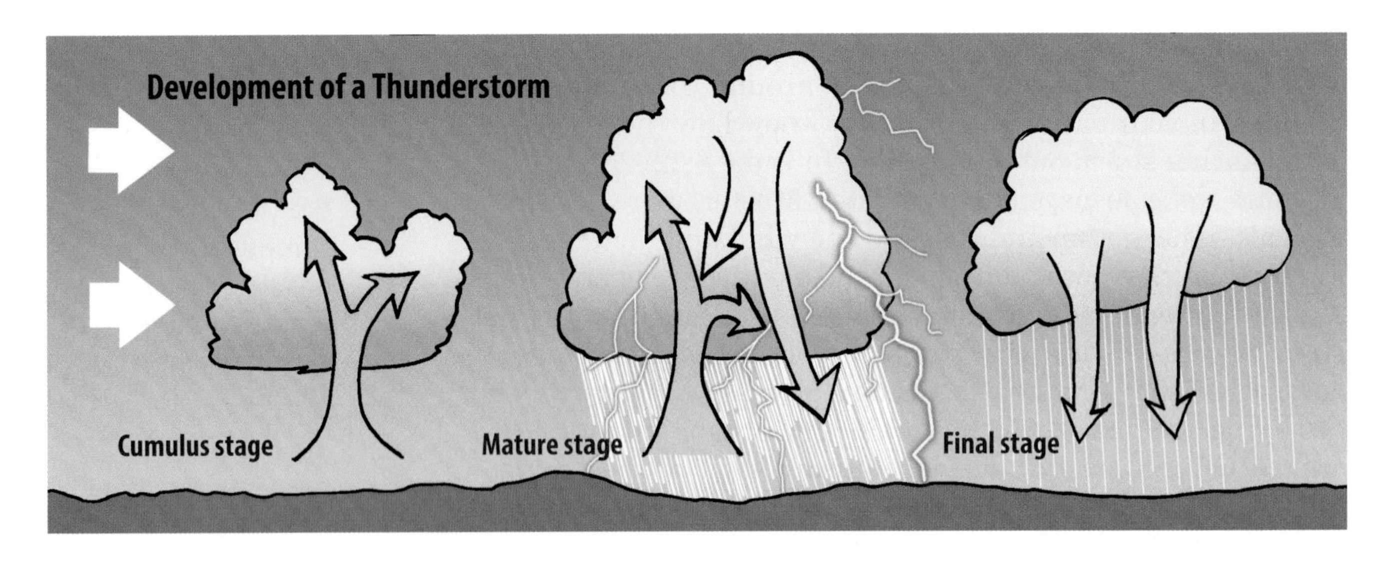

A thunderstorm is a short-lived, intense weather system that produces strong winds, heavy rain or hail, lightning, and thunder. These storms happen most often in the spring and summer in tropical and midlatitude zones. They usually occur late in the afternoon after the ground has become quite warm.

Thunderstorms develop in three stages. During the cumulus stage, warm air that is quite a bit warmer than its surroundings rises from the ground; a cumulus cloud forms as warm humid air rises and condenses into tiny cloud droplets. Very little rain is produced in this stage, but there may be some lightning. During the mature stage, the fully formed cumulonimbus cloud takes on an anvil shape. As it reaches near the tropopause, it is flattened out by overhead winds. The water droplets become too big for the updraft to support and rain begins to fall. Downdrafts can become very gusty. Thunder, lightning, strong rain and sometimes hail fall. During the final stage, the thunderstorm dissipates, or dies out, as it uses up its supply of water vapor.

Cloud to ground lightning formation

Lightning is the electrical discharge of energy from storm clouds. It can heat the air to 30,000°C. It forms during a thunderstorm when positive and negative charges build up within the thundercloud or between the cloud and the earth's surface. First, electrical charges build up in the cloud. The friction of rapidly moving ice crystals or raindrops builds up the electric charges. As they hit each other, electrons are knocked off and charges begin to accumulate. The positive charges collect near the top of the cloud and the negative charges collect near the bottom. The negative charges attract positive charges on the ground. Then, the beginning of a lightning bolt, which is called *a stepped leader*, forms when the negative charges stretch toward the ground. A stepped leader reaches down from the cloud and a positively charged return stroke reaches up from the ground. Finally, when the pressure between the positive and negative charges becomes too high, the charges are released as lightning. As the air heats up from the lightning, the rapid increase in temperature causes the air to expand. The sound that results from the rapid heating and expansion of air is called **thunder**.

Tornado

Thunderstorms can produce violent tornadoes. A tornado is a rotating funnel of air that has a high wind speed and a low central air pressure. Tornadoes are usually attached to the base of a thundercloud. High winds may cause rising warm air to rotate. When this happens, the cloud begins to spin at incredible speeds, forming a tornado. Many funnel clouds gyrate through the troposphere without touching down, but when the spinning section of the cloud reaches down to the earth's surface, the funnel cloud becomes a tornado and it can cause severe damage. Tornadoes can rise and touch down in a random path across the

FYI

Enhanced Fujita Scale

In 1971, Dr. Tetsuya Theodore Fujita created a scale to estimate tornado wind speeds according to damage done by a tornado. The Enhanced Fujita Scale (EF) has replaced the original scale, and it takes more variables into account. The EF scale considers 28 different damage indicators, including building types and trees.

EF Scale	Class	Description	Wind Speed
EF0	weak	Gale	105–137 kph
EF1	weak	Moderate	138–177 kph
EF2	strong	Significant	178–217 kph
EF3	strong	Severe	218–266 kph
EF4	violent	Devastating	267–322 kph
EF5	violent	Incredible	>322 kph

TRY THIS

Tornado in a Bottle

Fill a 2 L bottle about two-thirds full of water. Add a little food coloring. Use a tornado tube connector or electrical tape with a 9.5 mm washer to connect this bottle to another 2 L bottle. Place the two bottles on a table so the filled bottle is on top. Rapidly rotate the bottles in a circle a few times, and then place the bottles on the table. Observe the formation of a funnel-shaped vortex. Notice the shape of the vortex and the flow of the water as it empties. How is this like a real tornado? How is it different from a real tornado?

The hurricane's eye wall pulls up warm air from the ocean's surface. The rising warm air draws in more air from the surface to take its place. The warm air is less dense, so the air pressure drops at the surface, creating an area of low pressure, or the eye. The cold, dense air from above sinks down and warms. As more air rises, more air rushes toward the center, creating the spiraling winds.

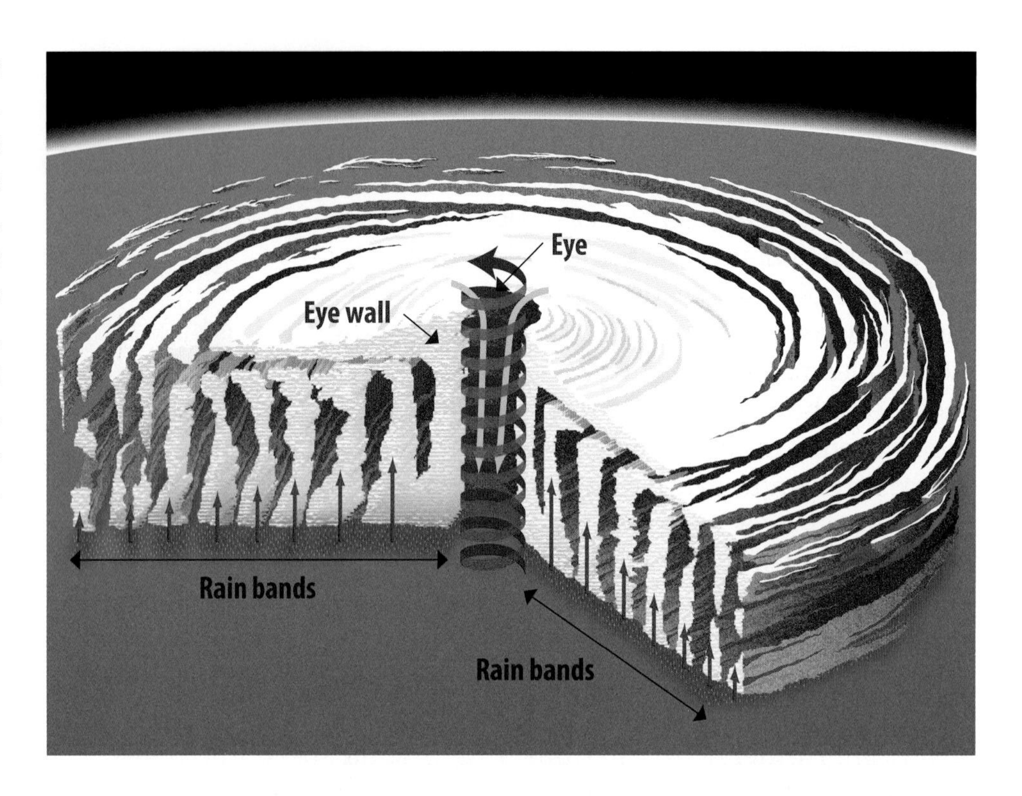

earth. For example, tornadoes can destroy houses on one side of a street without even touching the houses on the other side.

Several warning signs help meteorologists predict that a thunderstorm is spawning a tornado. They watch for strong and persistent rotation in the base of the cloud, or hail and heavy rain followed by dead calm or an intense wind shift. Loud, continuous rumbling and white flashes at ground level can also be signs of a tornado. Another sign that a tornado may form is a low-hanging appendage that looks like a crashing ocean wave reaching toward the ground and rotating.

Another very destructive storm is a hurricane. Hurricanes are large, rotating tropical weather systems with sustained wind speeds from 119 kph to 240 kph. These storms pack more power than hundreds of thunderstorms. A large hurricane holds enough energy to supply the United States with electricity for six months. Unlike tornadoes and short-lived thunderstorms, hurricanes can last for several days.

Hurricanes form over warm ocean waters near the equator. When the moisture in warm, rising air condenses to produce a large amount of energy, a low-pressure area is left above the surface of the water. The high pressure surrounding this low-pressure area moves in to take its place; it will warm up and also rise. As warm air keeps rising, cooler, denser air continues to move in. The warm air is drawn up into a narrow column in the center of the storm, where it releases more energy and sustains the storm's power. The eye of the hurricane remains calm as the winds swirling around it gain more energy. Hurricanes generate their power over open water and continue to grow and move as long as the storm stays over warm waters. The hurricane includes torrents of rain and causes storm surges. A storm surge elevates the surface of the sea, sometimes as much as 6 m above normal, which is a huge hazard for coastal populations.

House damaged by a hurricane

LESSON REVIEW

1. Where do rainstorms usually form? What type of cloud is involved in a thunderstorm?
2. If it has been snowing for five hours and the wind is blowing at 45 kph and visibility is 2 km, is this a blizzard? Why?
3. Describe the three stages of a thunderstorm.
4. Give a detailed description of how lightning forms.
5. What weather conditions can create a tornado?
6. How is a hurricane formed?

CAREER

Hurricane Hunters

Have you ever dreamed of being a pilot, soaring high above the earth? When you think of a pilot, you may picture someone who flies commercial jets carrying people from destination to destination. Or maybe you think of high-speed fighter pilots, who dart between the clouds and wear oxygen masks because they fly so high. However, one group of pilots makes a living by flying into severe weather. NOAA (National Oceanic and Atmospheric Administration) Corps pilots are specially trained to fly into the eyes of hurricanes and into other dangerous storms. The pilots and the scientists onboard the planes are referred to as *hurricane hunters*. Most pilots fly over or around storms, but the skill and expertise of these pilots is needed to carry the meteorologists and electronic engineers directly into the storms to collect data, to understand the storm, and to make better predictions. More accurate forecasts can save lives. During the months outside of hurricane season, the planes are fitted with different equipment and used for other atmospheric research. These specialized pilots fly all over the world in all kinds of weather conditions.

5.2.9 *Forecasting Weather*

> **OBJECTIVES**
> - Identify various weather instruments and the data they collect.
> - Interpret weather map symbols.

> **VOCABULARY**
> - **isobar** a line that connects points of equal atmospheric pressure

If you want to know what kind of weather to expect later in the day, you probably turn on the TV to catch the weather forecast, listen to a weather report on the radio, or check the weather map on the Internet. Before these conveniences were available, people relied on their own observations to predict the coming weather.

Even in Bible times people tried to predict the weather using physical signs without knowing the science behind it. Once when Jesus was speaking to some Pharisees, He said, "When evening comes, you say, 'It will be fair weather, for the sky is red,' and in the morning, 'Today it will be stormy, for the sky is red and overcast.' You know how to interpret the appearance of the sky" (Matthew 16:2–3a). A reddish evening sky is caused by light interacting with dry dust particles, so a red evening sky indicates that dry weather is coming. A gray evening sky means that the atmosphere is heavy with water droplets that will probably fall the next day. If clouds look red in the morning, the sun is rising in clear skies to the east with clouds approaching from the west. This indicates that a storm system to the west is moving your way. Perhaps you have heard the saying "Red sky at night, sailors delight; red sky in morning, sailors take warning." This adage relies on the same principle. People have used observation to predict the weather for thousands of years.

Weather prediction becomes more efficient and accurate with each passing decade. Modern weather forecasting began after

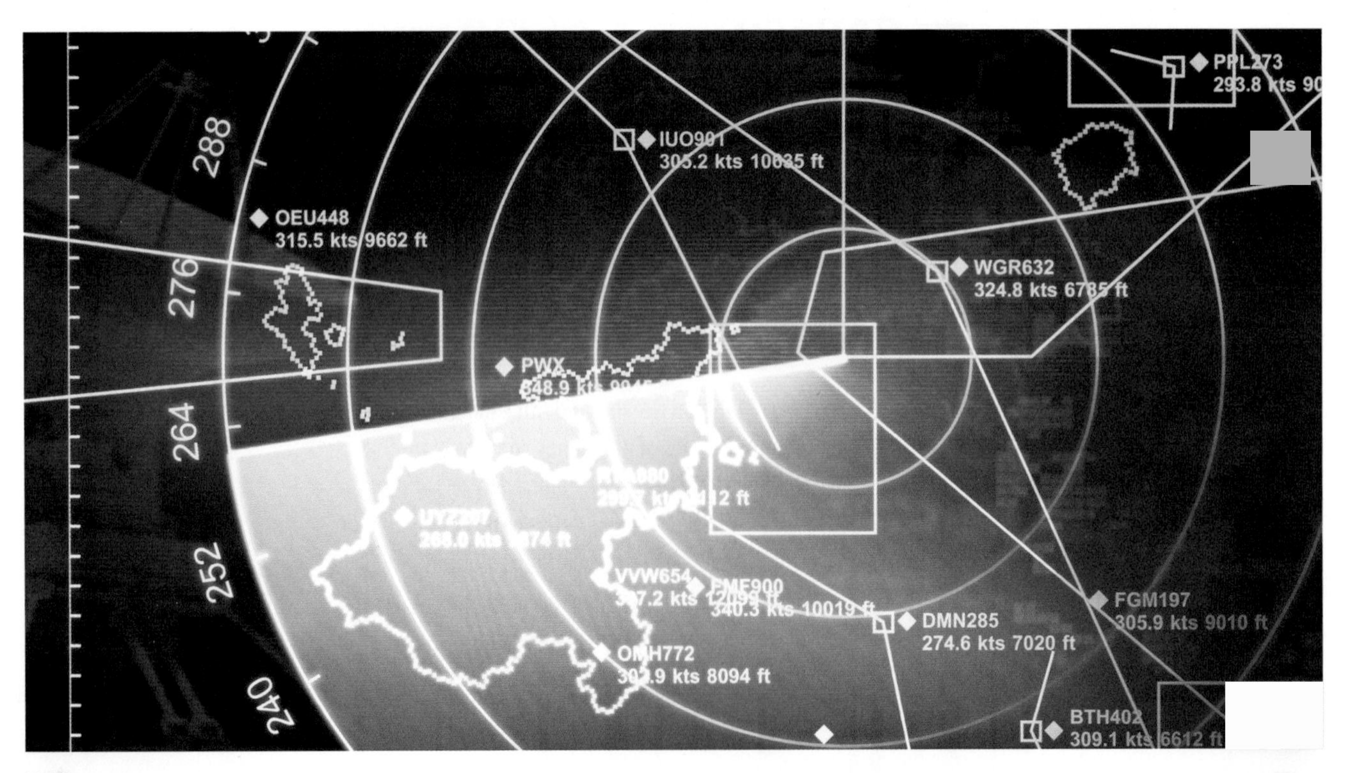

the barometer, which measures atmospheric pressure, and the thermometer, which measures temperature, were invented in the 17th and 18th centuries. The hygrometer, which measures humidity, and the anemometer, which measures wind speed, were also used in early forecasting. Today meteorologists use these and other instruments to help predict the weather. For example, instruments called *radiosondes* measure the temperature, pressure, and humidity at different heights of the atmosphere. Weather balloons calculate wind speed and direction by tracking the position of the radiosondes they carry. Radio transmitters then send the information to a receiver on the ground.

Doppler radar

Radar helps meteorologists track storms. Airplanes have specially designed radar to help pilots avoid storms or turbulent areas. Radar beams are concentrated electric pulses that shoot outward. These pulses are returned when they hit objects such as rain, hail, or even bugs. Radar screens show the location, velocity, shape, and sometimes size of the objects that the radar beams strike. The newest type of radar, Doppler radar, allows meteorologists to track precipitation within a storm and identify areas of rotation, which indicate tornadoes.

Weather satellites are also important weather forecasting tools. The first weather satellite was sent into orbit in 1960. Newer satellites carry instruments that map clouds, measure atmospheric moisture, determine wind speeds, and calculate ocean surface temperatures for the whole world, day and night. Because clouds outline storms, satellite images can show weather patterns across the world.

Computers have also helped more reliably forecast the weather. Accurate weather forecasts require observations from many satellites and other sources. Supercomputers can process thousands of observations from weather stations, aircraft, ships, and satellites from around the world every few hours. Developing technology will have the ability to process quadrillions of calculations every second. This wealth of data will enable computers to create accurate images of current weather conditions around the world.

TV meteorologist

Ocean weather research buoy

However, all this information is useless unless it is organized in a way that people can understand. A weather map is one basic tool for organizing this information. Meteorologists use weather maps when they are forecasting weather. Weather maps were once drawn by hand, but now computers prepare them. Observations from local weather stations and data from aircraft, satellites, radar, Automated Surface Observing Systems (ASOS), and radiosondes are collected, and the information is plotted on surface maps. These maps are constantly updated as new information is collected.

Surface maps use weather symbols to show weather conditions in a particular region. Common weather symbols describe cloud cover, wind speed, wind direction, air masses, and weather fronts. Cold fronts are indicated with arrows pointing in the direction of travel. Warm fronts have semicircles on the side of travel. Stationary fronts show triangles and semicircles on either side of the line, indicating the front is at a standstill. And occluded fronts have triangles and semicircles on the same side of the line as both a cold air mass and a warm air mass are

FYI

Weather Map Symbols

Cloud Cover

- No clouds
- 20%–30% cloud cover
- 50% cloud cover
- 70%–80% cloud cover
- Completely overcast

Cloud Types

- Thick altostratus
- Thin altostratus
- Bands of thin altostratus
- Patches of thin altostratus
- Fair weather stratus
- Partial cirrus cover
- Complete cirrus cover
- Scattered cirrus
- Patches of dense cirrus
- Fair weather cumulus
- Stratocumulus

Fronts & Pressure

- Cold front
- Warm front
- Occluded front
- Stationary front
- H High pressure
- L Low pressure

Wind Speed

- Calm wind
- 5 knots
- 10 knots
- 15 knots
- 20 knots
- 50 knots
- 60 knots

A knot is about 2 kph.

Precipitation

- Rain
- Drizzle
- Showers
- Hail
- Thunderstorms
- Snow
- Fog

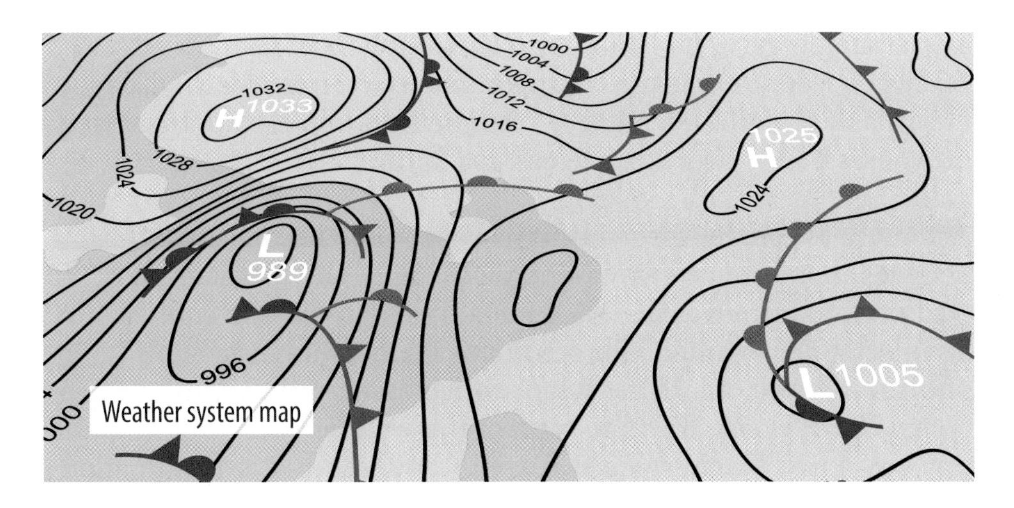

Weather system map

moving in the same direction. Precipitation and storms are also indicated on weather maps. The barometric pressure is shown by lines drawn between areas of equal atmospheric pressure. These lines are called **isobars**. The isobars, which appear on maps as odd-shaped ovals or circles, show areas of high (H) or low (L) pressure. The H or L is placed at the center of a pressure area to indicate where that pressure is the greatest. The decrease in pressure is indicated by isobars that move out from the center.

After meteorologists gather and map all of this data, how accurate are their predictions? Meteorologists make three types of forecasts: short-range forecasts, medium-range forecasts, and extended forecasts. Short-range forecasts predict weather conditions over the next 12–48 hours. They give detailed predictions of temperature, cloud cover, wind speed, and rainfall. Medium-range forecasts cover periods of two to seven days. Predictions beyond seven days are considered extended forecasts. Extended forecasts are limited to predicting general trends in the weather and cannot give specifics. It may never be possible to accurately predict weather far in advance because small changes at the start of weather patterns lead to wide variations at the end.

LESSON REVIEW

1. What instruments were used at the onset of modern weather forecasting? What information do they collect?
2. What information do weather balloons and radiosondes collect?
3. How is radar helpful to pilots?
4. Which type of front has triangles and semicircles on the same side of the line?
5. What are isobars?
6. If an *H* is in the middle of several isobars, what does it mean?

FYI

Weather Forecasting

After the telegraph was invented in 1845, meteorologists were able to more easily share weather information. In 1870, the United States formed a weather forecasting agency as part of the Army Signal Corps. Around 1890, this agency was organized into the Weather Bureau. In 1970, it was renamed the National Weather Service. Canada's weather service began in 1871. Today the service is part of Environment and Climate Change Canada.

Many countries recognize that weather forecasting services are valuable. China employs 50,000 people in its weather service. Because the entire atmosphere is linked, truly efficient weather services require worldwide cooperation. Most countries have recognized this need. The World Meteorological Organization (WMO) is a cooperative effort that has created a global network of technology and information exchange to predict the weather and monitor climate change.

5.2.10 *Controlling Weather*

OBJECTIVES

- Explain how cloud seeding works.
- Summarize the pros and cons of controlling weather.

VOCABULARY

- **shelterbelt** a barrier of trees or shrubs designed to protect crops from wind damage

The struggle between Elijah and the prophets of Baal is one Biblical account of people taking action to change the weather. Elijah asked God to bring fire from heaven and a rainstorm to prove His power over the lifeless god Baal.

Attempts to control the weather can be made because weather behaves in an orderly way. When looking at the methods that God uses to form weather, it is sometimes possible to control its effects. For example, for centuries farmers have grown **shelterbelts** to divert the wind, which can erode soil and destroy crops. But serious efforts to control the weather were not made until recently. During World War II, the thick British fog made safely landing planes very difficult. Winston Churchill initiated the development of a system to clear fog from runways so Allied aircraft could land. The Fog Investigations and Dispersal Operations (FIDO) was formed. FIDO used oil burners near the runways to clear fog from English airfields. The heat from the burners lowered the relative humidity and caused the water droplets to evaporate. This effort saved the lives of many Allied military personnel.

A breakthrough in weather control was made in 1946 when scientists discovered cloud seeding. Seeding clouds can reduce the amount or size of damaging hail, reduce the density of fog, or cause clouds to produce precipitation. In order to form rain droplets, water vapor needs particles, such as dust or salt. Clouds are seeded with crystals of dry ice, or frozen carbon dioxide, to provide particles for rain droplet formation. The tiny crystals attract water molecules, which eventually grow large enough to form rain or snow. Today, silver iodide crystals and calcium

Shelterbelt of trees

WWII aircraft

chloride are also used, depending on the type of clouds. However, scientists warn that chemical cloud seeding can harm the environment.

Cloud seeding has not always turned out well. In 1947, scientists associated with Project Cirrus tried to weaken hurricane winds by seeding the storm clouds. After the first hurricane seeding, the storm changed course, hitting Savannah, Georgia, and causing widespread damage. Weather modification experiments are still conducted today by countries around the world.

Scientists continue to conduct research on other methods of cloud seeding that are less expensive and less harmful to the environment. Jérôme Kasparian, physicist at the University of Geneva, Switzerland, is experimenting with the use of laser beams to create cloud condensation nuclei to encourage the formation of precipitation without adding harmful chemicals into the environment. Laser beams are also easier to control and less costly than chemical seeding procedures. The powerful laser beam bursts remove electrons from molecules in the atmosphere.

FYI

Suitable for Seeding

What makes a cloud suitable for seeding? There are three tests a cloud has to pass in order to qualify. The cloud must be able to sustain a large updraft of moist air. It must be free of ice because the presence of ice means the cloud does not need to be seeded. And the temperature within the cloud needs to be less than 0°C.

Lightning over city

Negev Desert, Israel

TRY THIS

Making Snow

It is your turn to control the weather. Put 5 g of sodium polyacrylate in a cup. Add 55 mL of water to the cup. Watch what happens. The powder has such a high concentration of sodium that it draws the water into the powder. This process is called *osmosis*. Did you really make snow? Could this process be used to make snow? Why?

The newly charged particles then attract polar water molecules, which condense and form water droplets. Laser beams can also be used to direct electric discharges. Researchers have been able to control short distance electrical discharges and even redirect them around objects. This technology eventually may be used to redirect long distance discharges, like cloud to ground lightning.

Many scientists consider the benefits of controlling the path of lightning bolts, reducing the amount and size of hailstones, or bringing rain to areas experiencing drought worth pursuing. Lives could be saved, crops could be protected or watered, water supplies could be increased, and property damage could be reduced. Other scientists argue that controlling the weather is a dangerous attempt to play God that may damage the environment because Earth's systems are delicately balanced. Manipulating weather conditions could change the course of storms or cause flooding in some areas and droughts in others. Controlling the weather could also become political as nations work to provide their citizens with the weather they need at the expense of other countries. Though the outcome is uncertain, both the research and the debate will continue.

LESSON REVIEW

1. How do shelterbelts control the effects of the weather?
2. What weather element was a problem for WWII aircraft in Britain? How was it controlled?
3. Explain the process of cloud seeding.
4. Explain how laser beams may be used to control the weather.
5. What are the benefits and dangers of controlling the weather?

5.3.1 *Climate Factors*

OBJECTIVES

- Differentiate between weather and climate.
- Relate factors that influence climate.

VOCABULARY

- **climate** the weather pattern an area has over a long period of time

What are the long-term weather conditions where you live? Whether you live in Norway or Nepal, Albania or Argentina, you have some idea of what kind of weather to expect in any given month. The weather tends to follow the same general pattern year after year. **Climate** is the weather pattern an area has over a long period of time.

Climate describes many factors, including average monthly precipitation, average high and low daily temperatures, average humidity, cloud cover during different seasons, wind speed, maximum wind gusts, and levels of solar radiation. In general, climate describes the average temperature range and average annual precipitation of a region. However, a study of climate also analyzes extreme fluctuations of these factors over long periods of time.

The climate in a specific area is determined by a combination of many factors. One of the most important factors is latitude, which is the area's distance from the equator. Latitude is measured in degrees. Areas closest to the equator, at a latitude of 0°, receive the most direct sunlight. Annual temperatures do not vary much from place to place in regions near the equator, but there is a wide variation of annual rainfall amounts. As a result, this region of the world is not described as having four seasons. A better way to describe the climate near the equator is by designating alternating wet and dry seasons.

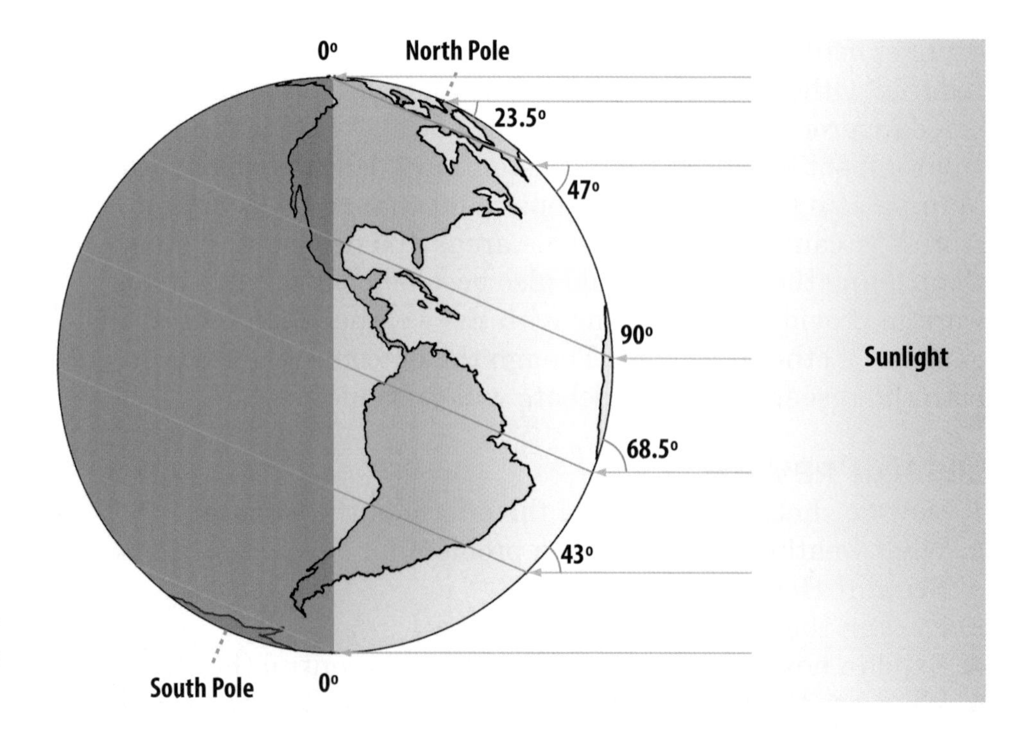

The sun strikes different latitudes at different angles. This illustration shows the sun's angle at the summer solstice.

Given that the earth is tilted on its axis, the sun's rays strike latitudes located closer to the poles at indirect angles. Also, the curvature of the earth forces the sun's rays to spread out over a larger distance. Much less sunlight reaches these latitudes, and the sunlight that does come in contact with the land is often reflected by ice. Indirect sunlight dispersion and energy reflection make these regions of the world relatively cold. The average daily temperatures near the poles are lower than the average daily temperatures near the equator. In these regions, the sun appears for only a few hours in the winter and never sets in the summer. The lowest average temperatures usually occur near the poles at a latitude of 90°, where the angle of the sun is the least direct.

Wind is another factor that affects climate. For example, the doldrums produce warm, low-pressure air that constantly rises and loses moisture. Areas in this latitude subsequently have heavy rains. The wind moving into subtropical areas is usually dry and sinking, so these areas have little precipitation. In middle latitudes, warm air masses collide with cold air masses. These areas have average amounts of precipitation.

The direction of the wind also affects an area's climate. For example, the Sahara—the world's largest desert—is one of the

Sahara Desert

TRY THIS

Changing Times

Design an experiment to show how the climate in an area may change. Include only one climate factor as your variable.

driest places on Earth, even though it is bordered on the west by the Atlantic Ocean. The trade winds that blow across the Sahara dissipate cloud cover. This allows more sunlight to penetrate and heat the surface of the earth. Even with such a large body of water nearby, the winds keep the Sahara very dry.

Topography also influences climate. Elevation and the presence of mountains or large bodies of water have a great impact on climate. Altitude—the height above sea level—is one important factor. When altitude increases, the average temperature decreases. As a general rule, for every 100-meter increase in altitude, the temperature drops 0.65°C. Even at the equator, low temperatures allow high mountain peaks to be covered with snow year-round.

Mountains also change the temperature and humidity levels of passing air masses. This creates different climates between the top of a mountain and nearby valleys. As air carried by wind travels up the windward side of the mountain, it cools with increasing elevation and much of the contained moisture condenses and falls in the form of precipitation. Increased precipitation occurs at the highest elevations. An increase in precipitation means that lush vegetation often grows on the windward side of a mountain. On the other side of the mountain, the leeward side, a rain shadow effect can be observed. The dry air that released most of the moisture content travels down the mountain. As it travels down the leeward side, the air temperature increases and any moisture on the ground is absorbed by the air mass. The result is an arid climate, often a desert. A great example of the rain shadow effect occurs over the Tibetan Plateau where moist air travels over the Himalayan Mountains, releasing all moisture content before reaching the dry plateau.

Rain shadow over the Andes Mountains

Ocean currents that can carry warm or cold water for thousands of kilometers also influence the climate of coastal regions. In general, currents carry warm water from the equator to the poles and bring cold water back toward the tropics. The air above the ocean water either releases or absorbs heat that is then transported over land. Without the circulation of ocean water, regions near the equator would be unbearably hot, and regions near the poles would be even colder. Currents regulate global climate and allow for coastal regions to have minimal temperature fluctuations compared to inland areas. Typically, coastal regions are warmer in the winter and cooler in the summer compared to inland areas at similar latitudes. On the west coast of the United States, cold ocean currents produce cool air, which the wind blows to shore. As a result, California's coastline is cool, even though temperatures a few kilometers inland often reach temperatures above 38°C in the summer.

Ocean currents not only influence temperature, they also affect precipitation. Warm, moist air from warm ocean currents produces more precipitation. The ocean currents near Peru and the northern coast of South America affect rainfall in places as far away as Australia. Ocean currents also influence the development of storms, especially where cold polar air meets moist, warm air. Winter storms can quickly strengthen near the eastern coast of the United States and Canada when polar air masses collide with warmer air from the Gulf Stream.

LESSON REVIEW

1. What is the difference between weather and climate?
2. Why do regions at varying latitudes have different climates?
3. Describe a rain shadow effect.
4. Explain how ocean currents affect the climate of coastal areas.
5. What are five main factors that affect climate?

Compare the leeward and windward sides of the Hawaiian islands.

5.3.2 *Climate Regions*

OBJECTIVES

- Categorize climates according to the Köppen climate classification system.
- Identify the main contributing factors for each climate region.
- Distinguish between climate and microclimate.

VOCABULARY

- **microclimate** the unique climate conditions that exist over small areas of land within larger climate regions

The study of different climates is important and fascinating. To help individuals examine climates more closely, scientists have devised various climate classification systems. It can be difficult to classify climate regions because no two locations have exactly the same climate conditions. Most of the classification systems attempt to group regions that have similar climate patterns and geographic features.

The most widely used classification system was derived by German climatologist Wladimir Köppen in 1900. Köppen grouped climates by measuring and observing average temperature, average precipitation, and natural vegetation patterns on each of the seven continents. His classification system is divided into five main climate regions—tropical, dry, moderate, continental, and polar. Each region has a letter designation of A, B, C, D, or E. The five main regions are further divided into a number of subtypes to include humid subtropical, mediterranean, and continental subarctic.

Tropical climates, region A, can be found at low latitudes on either side of the equator, roughly between 0° latitude and 15° latitude in both the Northern and Southern Hemispheres. Intense, constant sunlight is indicative of this region. As a result, high temperatures occur each month, usually above 18°C, and there are no distinct seasons. The warm air produces

World Map of Köppen–Geiger Climate Classification

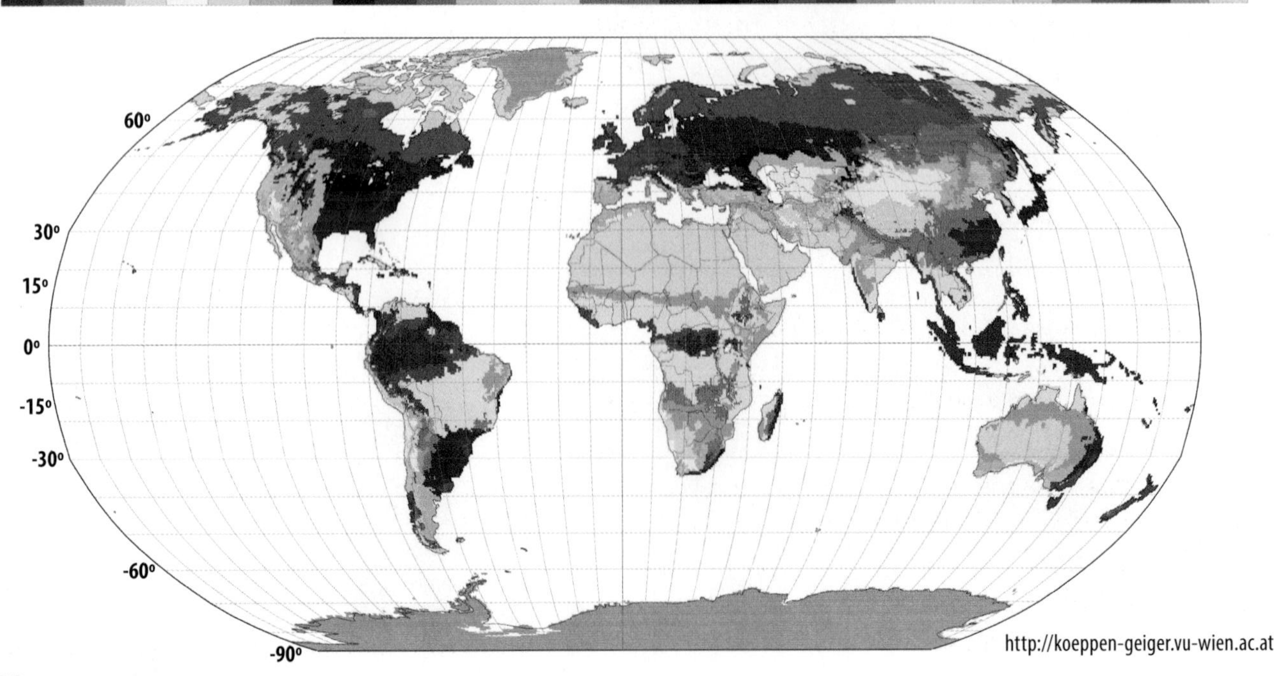

high humidity levels and heavy precipitation. True selva, canopy rain forest, and jungle-like vegetation flourishes in this climate region.

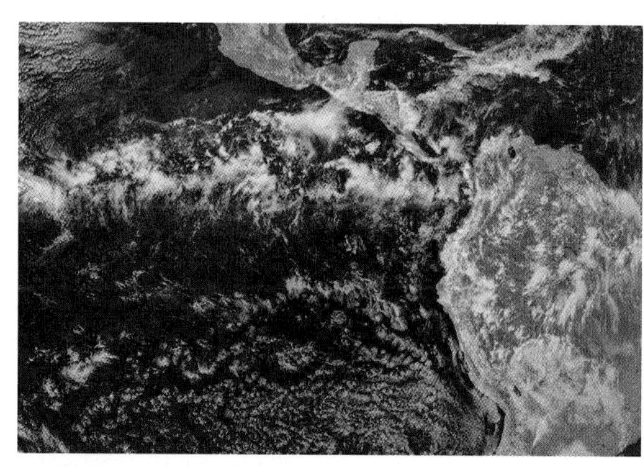
Intertropical convergence zone

Tropical climate conditions are determined mainly by fluctuating trade winds during warm and cool months, the intertropical convergence zone, and the monsoon wind system in eastern Asia. Trade winds persistently blow from east to west toward the Equator. As the winds encounter the coastlines of tropical regions that are often lined with mountain ranges, precipitation occurs. Tropical disturbances, including tropical cyclones, can also be carried in the trade winds that result in excess moisture production. The intertropical convergence zone is a band that wraps around the earth close to the equator. In this zone, trade winds converge and air ascends. Widespread cloud cover, frequent thunderstorms, and heavy rainfall occurs in this zone. As the intertropical convergence zone moves away from a particular area, the active, warm air is replaced by stable, dry air. In some tropical climate subtypes, the effects of alternating monsoon wind systems are noticeable. During the warmer months of the year, warm, moist, maritime tropical air moves in one direction across the land to produce precipitation. The winds change direction during the cooler months of the year, bringing cool, dry air over the land.

There are three tropical climate subtypes. These subtypes include wet equatorial climate, tropical monsoon and trade-wind littoral climate, and tropical wet-dry climate. Rain forests are common in the tropical regions. Most rain forest climates are found in Central Africa, the Amazon Basin, and Southeast Asia. Tropical climates also include savannas, which have very wet, warm months and very dry, cool months.

Dry climates, region B, are classified as arid or semiarid. This region can be found mostly between 50°N and 50°S, mainly in the 15°–30° latitude band in both the Northern and Southern Hemispheres. Low precipitation, great annual precipitation variability, low relative humidity, high evaporation rates, little cloud cover, and intense sunlight are characteristics of dry climates. On average, dry climates receive

B – Dry
Jaisalmer, India

0–25 cm of rainfall each year. However, average values have little meaning because one year 25 cm of rain may fall and in another year there may be no rainfall. Some researchers claim that portions of the Atacama Desert in Chile have never received any rain.

Dry climates are surrounded by dry air that creates high average temperatures. Average monthly temperatures range between 21°C and 32°C. Temperatures vary greatly each day with an increase or decrease of up to 35°C. The highest air temperatures on Earth have been recorded in dry climates. As of 2016, Death Valley, California held the world record for the highest air temperature of 56.7°C. The actual surface temperatures in this area can reach 94°C. There is very little vegetation in dry climates. Vegetation must be hardy and drought-tolerant with thick bark, no leaves, and large water storage capabilities to be able to survive in such harsh conditions. Examples of dry climate vegetation include cacti, Joshua trees, and creosote bushes.

The three dry climate subtypes are tropical and subtropical desert climate, mid-latitude steppe and desert climate, and

Sonoran Desert

tropical and subtropical steppe climate. Tropical and subtropical desert climates are the driest places on Earth. Many of these regions are located far into the interior of continents where moisture-bearing winds are not present. Also, high mountains along the western coasts block the winds, so rain falls on the windward sides of the mountains, leaving the leeward sides dry.

Mediterranean climate

There are exceptions to general dry climate conditions. Exceptions can be found in West Coast desert areas, such as the Sonoran Desert in North America, the Peru Desert in South America, and the Sahara and Namib Deserts in Africa. These deserts are much cooler than would be expected given their latitude. The average monthly temperatures in these areas are 15°C–21°C. Temperature inversions—cool surface air layers located beneath warmer air layers—that are accompanied by low-level clouds and fog are very common.

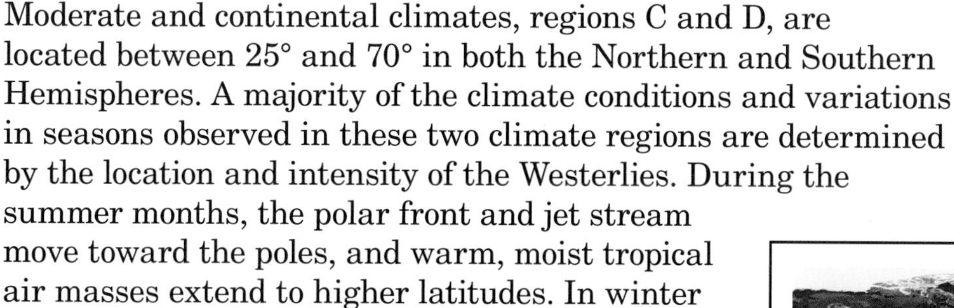

Moderate and continental climates, regions C and D, are located between 25° and 70° in both the Northern and Southern Hemispheres. A majority of the climate conditions and variations in seasons observed in these two climate regions are determined by the location and intensity of the Westerlies. During the summer months, the polar front and jet stream move toward the poles, and warm, moist tropical air masses extend to higher latitudes. In winter months, the wind pattern circles toward the equator, the tropical air masses move back to lower latitudes, and cold polar outbreaks infiltrate these two climates. The majority of vegetation that grows in these regions includes evergreen and deciduous trees, bushes, shrubs, and grasses.

C – Moderate
Joinville, Brazil

Moderate climate subtypes include humid subtropical climates, Mediterranean climates, and marine west coast climates. Climate conditions vary among subtypes. It is common for different moderate climate subtypes to have severe thunderstorms, tropical cyclones, frost, tornadoes, and strong monsoonal wind gusts. Summers can be moderate to hot. Winters are usually mild. The average temperatures vary by subtype. Some subtypes have an average

D – Continental
Khabarovsk, Russia

temperature of 27°C during the summer with a maximum value between 30°C and 38°C. In other subtypes, the temperature rarely exceeds 20°C during the summer. The average temperature during winter months is between 5°C and 13°C. Precipitation also varies from one subtype to another. Many portions of this climate region have evenly distributed precipitation throughout the year. More precipitation is typically produced in the summer. Annual precipitation totals vary from 50 cm to 250 cm of rain and can even reach totals of over 500 cm of rain. A smaller percentage of subtypes have a reduced annual precipitation total, usually 35–90 cm of rain. Areas located far into the interior of the land have even less precipitation and opposite seasonal patterns—dry summers and rainy winters.

The largest annual temperature ranges on Earth occur in continental climates. Inland temperatures can change by 30°C during different seasons. An extreme temperature range occurs in central Siberia where temperatures can increase or decrease by as much as 60°C during different times of the year. Coastal areas have more balanced temperature ranges. Continental climate summers are relatively hot. Some interior regions reach temperatures near 25°C. Winters are cold with average temperatures remaining below freezing for several months. Different subtypes have longer winters than others. It is common to have average temperatures of –40°C to –50°C at higher latitudes.

Annual precipitation totals vary across the humid continental climate subtype and the continental subarctic climate subtype. Precipitation totals for humid continental climates range from 50 cm to 125 cm. Most of the precipitation that falls on continental subarctic climate regions occurs during summer months, and totals are usually less than 50 cm. With extremely low temperatures during the winter months, snow tends to remain on the ground for the majority of the year. Summers are generally short and mild.

Siberia

Weather is subject to change in lower Northern Hemisphere latitudes because the region is located between polar and tropical air masses. These land masses can experience severe thunderstorms, tornadoes, and high winds that can create blizzard conditions. The higher latitudes are dominated by more continental polar air that results in short, clear days with low humidity.

Polar climates, region E, are influenced by arctic and polar air masses at latitudes of 60°–90° in both the Northern and Southern Hemispheres. These regions are significantly cold with average temperatures generally remaining below 10°C. The highest latitudes never have an average monthly temperature

Urban Climate

In metropolitan areas, climate conditions are significantly different from the surrounding rural communities. This is because of the installation of tall buildings and pavement that affect wind flow, precipitation runoff, and the overall energy balance. Asphalt, specifically, absorbs, stores, and redirects more solar energy than vegetation and soil in rural areas. Also, high pollutant concentrations have a considerable impact on temperature, visibility, and precipitation in urban areas. Sometimes, weather patterns can allow for the buildup of pollutants to remain stagnant over a city for days. This creates a temperature inversion where air temperature increases with increasing elevation. Excess pollutants can cause acute stress and even death. Londoners experienced the effects of too much pollution in December 1952 where 3,500 people died from respiratory issues.

The centers of cities are especially warm. They are known as *heat islands*. It is common for the daily minimum temperature in these heat islands to be 6°C to 11°C warmer than surrounding rural areas. At night, the city remains warm because the stored heat radiation is gradually released. The average relative humidity in these areas is usually several percentages lower than their rural counterparts because cities lack the moisture released by plants, and runoff increases without soil absorption. Average wind speeds are 20% to 30% lower than the country because of increased frictional drag between city buildings and low-level wind meetings. Atmosphere particles hovering over cities reduce solar radiation penetration and often cause water vapor to condense in the form of fog. Precipitation has also been estimated to be higher in urban environments.

Temperature inversion over Dubai

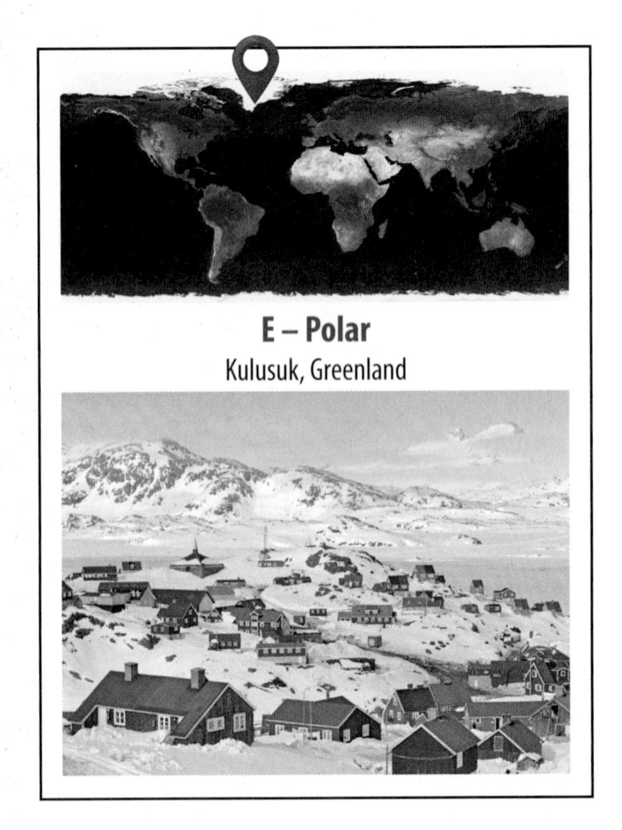

that exceeds 0°C. It is common for polar climates to remain below freezing for nine months of the year. These regions are permanently covered with snow and ice. The cold air does not contain very much moisture, so this region also receives very little precipitation. Interestingly, polar climates receive more precipitation than desert climates.

There are two polar subtypes—tundra climate and snow and ice climate. The Arctic Circle has a tundra climate. Winters are severe in this part of the world, and the short tundra summer temperatures are mild with a daily maximum of 15°C to 18°C. The lowest extreme temperature of –89.2°C was recorded at the Vostok II research station in Antarctica. Lower latitudes in this climate region have few trees and it is covered in lichen, moss, algae, and rocky areas without vegetation. Some grasses and low shrubs can also survive in portions of the polar climate.

There are small climate regions that were not included in the original Köppen classification system. These regions are not easily categorized and account for the highland areas that are scattered throughout the other climate regions. In general,

Antarctica

higher elevations result in a decrease in pressure, temperature, and atmospheric humidity. Highland areas have similar annual temperature ranges and precipitation amounts compared to the surrounding lowlands. They are usually slightly cooler and receive somewhat more precipitation. Sequoias and bristle cone pines thrive in highland climates until they reach the tree line, where trees cease to exist.

Not all climate regions are uniform. Unique climate conditions that exist over small areas of land within larger climate regions are called **microclimates**. A few examples of microclimates include gardens, valleys, and parks. These regions are usually located within a few meters above Earth's surface and are surrounded by vegetation. Microclimate conditions are determined by temperature, wind, humidity, and solar radiation near the ground surface. Changes in topography can create microclimates. Razor-backed mountains on the Hawaiian Islands separate lush rainforests from dry savannas. Large bodies of water, such as oceans and the Great Lakes of North America, moderate the weather conditions on the shore. The temperature contrast between the cold air moving over the Great Lakes and the warmer water temperature in the Great Lakes often causes heavy snow squalls downwind of the Great Lakes. This snowfall is called *lake effect snow*.

Some plant and animal species may have specific living conditions that are well-suited to microclimates. For example, some species of ants rely on specific microclimate conditions to regulate their body temperature. Various microclimates located within close proximity to one another promotes beneficial biodiversity.

LESSON REVIEW

1. What are the three factors that determine a climate region according to Köppen's climate classification system?
2. What climate region has the largest annual temperature ranges?
3. Identify the three contributing factors that determine tropical climates.
4. How does the intertropical convergence zone affect land masses in tropical regions?
5. What is the difference between climate and microclimates?
6. Compare and contrast dry and polar climate regions.

BIBLE CONNECTION

The Negev

Moses described the popular seasonal migrations to the Negev in Genesis 20. For thousands of years, people have traveled with their flocks and herds to the southern region of Israel located between the hill country of Judah to the north and the deserts of Zin, Shur, and Paran to the south. Abraham, Isaac, and Jacob grazed their livestock in the semiarid Negev during the winter and migrated north to Judah, located near Bethel and Shechem, for the summer months. Open, rugged and sparsely populated, the region supports scrub brush but no forests. It has two seasons: a mild winter with periodic rains and a hot, dry summer. Given that less than 200 mm of rain falls annually in the Negev, the area is unsuitable for farming.

5.3.3 *Climate Changes*

OBJECTIVES

- Summarize short-term and long-term climate change.
- Examine theories that attempt to explain what causes ice ages.
- Outline natural processes and human activities that contribute to climate change.

VOCABULARY

- **climate change** any long-term change in Earth's climate
- **El Niño** periodic changes in oceanic and atmospheric conditions in the Pacific Ocean that cause unusually warm surface water
- **greenhouse gases** a portion of atmospheric gas molecules that deflects infrared radiation back to Earth's surface that was initially on a path to escape into space
- **ice age** a period of time when ice collects in high latitudes and moves toward lower latitudes
- **interglacial period** a warm period that occurs between glacial periods when large ice sheets are absent

The weather changes all the time. It can be hot and dry one day and cool and rainy the next. Sometimes the weather may even change within a day. Changes in the weather are obvious. Climate changes are much less noticeable given that they occur over a longer period of time. Although climates change very slowly, they do change. It has been determined that for most of history climate change resulted from natural processes. Today, many scientists have come to the conclusion that human activity is also influencing climate change.

Climate change is the term currently used to describe any long-term change in Earth's climate. Climate change not only refers to the increase in Earth's temperature, but also changes in precipitation and wind patterns. Climatologists attempt to measure climate change using fragmented and indirect evidence such as tree rings, ice cores, and geologic patterns. Most observations and measurements have been collected beginning in the 19th century. Few geologic records exist prior to the late 18th century. Predictions for climate conditions during this period of time are largely hypothetical.

Changes in climate have both short-term and long-term effects. An example of a short-term change occurs as a result of pollutants, ash, or dust in the atmosphere. Air pollutants gather over industrial areas, block sunlight penetration, cool

FYI

Number of Ice Ages

Prior to the 1970s, many old-earth scientists originally thought there have been four ice ages in Earth's past. That belief was rejected and replaced with the idea that there have been thirty or more ice ages. In the past 800,000 years, old-earth scientists speculate that there have been eight ice ages that each lasted 100,000 years. However, these scientists have difficulty explaining any recent ice ages based on the temperature and precipitation rates observed today. Young-earth scientists attempt to reconcile this issue by proposing that only one ice age occurred and that it followed the biblical Flood. A worldwide Flood would have caused major changes in the earth's crust, earth movements, and tremendous volcano activity that would have greatly disturbed the climate. The shroud of volcanic dust and aerosols that would have been produced during this time would have been trapped in the stratosphere for several years following the Flood. That dust could have reflected some of the solar radiation back into space and caused cooler summers.

regions, and cause greater precipitation. Ash and dust from volcanic eruptions can have the same effect as pollutants. Major eruptions have been known to induce freezing climates because the dust and the gases block solar energy from reaching the earth's surface. Volcanic clouds cause temperatures to drop. The greatest volcanic eruption on record happened on the island of Sumbawa in 1815. The following year became known as *the year without a summer.* Parts of Europe and the New England area of the United States experienced heavy snow in June and frost in July and August. In 1991, Mount Pinatubo in the Philippines released a haze of sulfur dioxide gas that spread throughout much of the world. The two summers following the eruption were cooler than usual.

Short-term climate change induced by volcanic plumes of ash and dust

Another short-term climate change, known as **El Niño**, results from periodic changes in oceanic and atmospheric conditions in the Pacific Ocean that cause unusually warm surface water. During El Niño years, easterly trade winds in the Pacific Ocean decrease or change direction, allowing warm water to flow eastward. The shift in wind patterns brings drought to parts of Africa and Australia and extraordinary typhoons to Polynesia. California and the southern portion of the United States usually suffer severe winter storms during El Niño conditions. Canada and other parts of the United States usually experience warmer winters with less precipitation than usual.

Long-term climate change often has more dramatic results. Indirect geologic evidence indicates that during certain periods the earth's climate was much colder than it is now. At times, much of the earth was covered with sheets of ice. An **ice age** is a period of time when ice collects in high latitudes and moves toward lower latitudes. Ice ages have periods of cold and periods of warmth. During cool glacial periods, the sheets of ice advance and cover a larger area. Sea level drops because a large amount of ocean water freezes. **Interglacial periods** are warm periods that occur between glacial periods when large ice sheets are absent. During these times, some of the ice melts and the sea level rises.

Scientists have several theories on why ice ages occur, even though they may disagree on the number of ice ages that have occurred. In the 1920s, Serbian astronomer Milutin Milankovitch linked ice ages to changes in the earth's orbit and

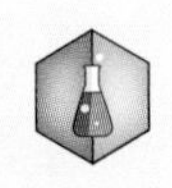

TRY THIS

Ocean CO_2
Fill a jar halfway with cabbage water. Observe the color. This water represents the ocean. Place a straw in the water and gently blow without causing any water to spill out of the jar. Note the color change. How is increased atmospheric carbon dioxide affecting oceans?

the tilt of the earth's axis. According to his theory, the amount of solar radiation that reaches the earth varies with changes in the earth's orbit. Over an estimated cycle of 100,000 years, Earth's orbit becomes less circular and more elliptical. When the orbit is more elliptical, seasons are more severe—summers are hotter and winters are colder. Seasonal extremes occur less during more circular orbits. In addition, over a 41,000-year period, scientists hypothesize that the earth's tilt on its axis varies between 22.1° and 24.5°. The variation in the earth's tilt could affect seasonal differences. Winters would have more precipitation and warmer temperatures. Summers would have less precipitation and cooler temperatures. Snow in high latitudes would not melt in the summer because temperatures would be cooler than average, which could result in increased glacial formation. According to the Milankovitch theory, scientists predict that the next ice age will occur in another 50,000 to 100,000 years.

Some theories attribute climate change to solar activity and the movement of plate tectonics. Observations and measurements have indicated that the sun has been increasing in brightness over time. This is important to understand because the sun contributes heat energy to the earth. An increase in heat energy would lead to an increase in the atmospheric temperature on Earth. Also, sunspots appear and disappear over time. Some scientists relate the reduced sunspot activity from 1645 to 1715 with the theorized Little Ice Age. During the Little Ice Age, Europe and the North Atlantic region felt the greatest

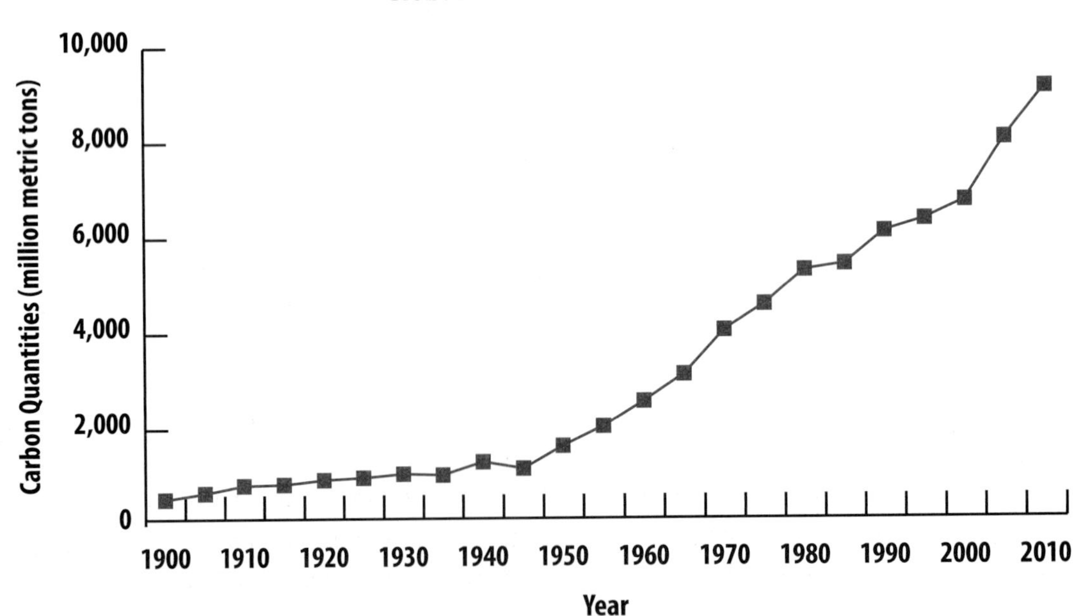

Greenhouse Gases

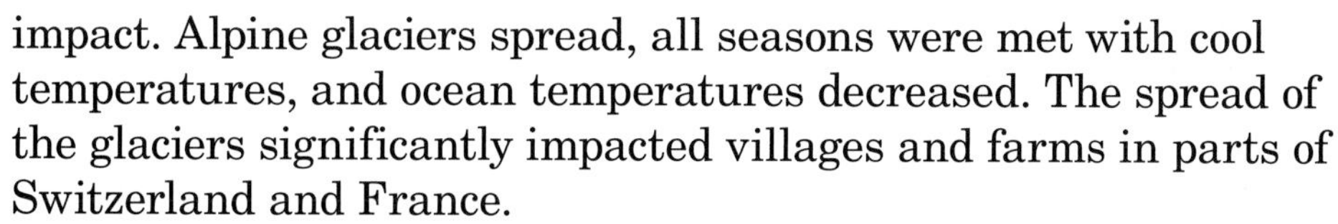
impact. Alpine glaciers spread, all seasons were met with cool temperatures, and ocean temperatures decreased. The spread of the glaciers significantly impacted villages and farms in parts of Switzerland and France.

Scientists also propose that changes in continental uplift derived from the movement of plate tectonics can change global circulation patterns in the oceans and atmosphere. The uplift can also reduce the concentration of carbon dioxide, resulting in a cooler climate. This is because carbon dioxide is a greenhouse gas that helps keeps the earth warm. **Greenhouse gases** are a portion of atmospheric gas molecules that deflect infrared radiation back to Earth's surface that was initially on a path to escape into space. Without greenhouse gases, the average temperature of Earth's surface would be about –18°C. The three most important greenhouse gases are water vapor, carbon dioxide, and methane. Concentrations of these gases fluctuate. During warm climate periods, concentrations are high. Concentrations are low during cool climate periods. Plate tectonics, vegetation, oceans, and wetlands all play a role in changing greenhouse gas concentrations.

In recent years, the earth's temperature has been increasing at a faster rate than previously recorded. Many scientists estimate that the average global temperature has risen 0.8°C since 1980. This may seem like a small number, but slight temperature changes can have big effects on local climates. Different regions

FYI

Climate Change Refugees

The Marshall Islands are a small chain of Pacific Ocean islands. The native people who live there have experienced the devastating effects of climate change. With increasing storm frequency and rising sea levels, the people are at risk of losing their homes. Over the past century, global sea levels rose about 20 cm. In the early 1990s, that rate began to double. It is projected that sea levels could rise up to a meter in the next 100 years. Scientists do not believe that the Marshall Islands will be completely swept away because storms bring ocean sediment and coral reef to the shore that is rebuilding the shoreline. However, a major problem that the people face during these frequent, strong storms is saltwater contaminating crops, freshwater supplies, and groundwater aquifers. One option that many islanders have had to choose is relocation to the continental United States. Climate change may not be noticeable worldwide; but for this group of people, climate change could be the cause of a lost culture.

Solar panels

may experience increased flooding, wildfires, hurricanes, or extreme droughts with minor global temperature changes. These natural disasters may lead to disrupted water supplies, failing crops, widespread starvation, and fluctuating fuel prices.

Climatologists hypothesize that Earth is currently experiencing warming that can be traced back to an increase in carbon dioxide and other greenhouse gases. Fossil fuel combustion and deforestation are primary sources of carbon dioxide released by humans into the atmosphere. In response, the global community has been taking action to reduce greenhouse gas emissions. More energy-efficient methods have been introduced to power and regulate temperature in housing and industrial facilities. Less energy is used and productivity levels remain steady. Alternative energy sources have also been implemented in many countries to include solar, wind, and bioenergy sources. Lowering transportation emission levels is also a high priority in many countries. By limiting deforestation practices and the use of fossil fuels, individuals can reduce the effects of human-induced climate change.

LESSON REVIEW

1. Name and describe one short-term climate change and one long-term climate change.
2. What two Earth attributes did the Milankovitch theory suggest are the causes of ice ages?
3. How do changes in solar activity contribute to climate change?
4. Explain how greenhouse gases affect the earth's atmospheric temperature.
5. What are the two primary sources of carbon dioxide released by humans?

UNIT 6

The Environment

Chapter 1: *Natural Resources*
Chapter 2: *Pollution Solutions*

Vocabulary

biomass
coal
contour farming
cover crop
crop rotation
desertification
fossil fuel
furrow
geothermal energy
incineration
leachate
natural gas
natural resource
nonrenewable resource
nuclear energy
ore
peat
petroleum
quarry
renewable resource
sludge
smog
solar energy
stewardship
strip cropping
terrace farming

Key Ideas

- Systems, order, and organization
- Evidence, models, and explanation
- Change, constancy, and measurement
- Evolution and equilibrium
- Form and function
- Abilities necessary to do scientific inquiry
- Understandings about scientific inquiry
- Structure of the earth system
- Geochemical cycles
- Abilities of technological design
- Understandings about science and technology
- Personal health
- Populations, resources, and environments
- Natural hazards
- Risks and benefits
- Science and technology in society
- Personal and community health
- Population growth
- Natural resources
- Environmental quality
- Natural and human induced hazards
- Science and technology in local, national, and global challenges
- Science as a human endeavor
- Nature of science
- Nature of scientific knowledge
- Historical perspectives

SCRIPTURE

Therefore I tell you, do not worry about your life, what you will eat or drink; or about your body, what you will wear.... But seek first His kingdom and His righteousness, and all these things will be given to you as well.

Matthew 6:25, 33

6.1.1 *Renewable and Nonrenewable Resources*

OBJECTIVES

- Distinguish between renewable and nonrenewable resources.
- Recognize the importance of energy and resource conservation.

VOCABULARY

- **natural resource** any substance, organism, or energy form found in nature that can be used by living things
- **nonrenewable resource** a resource that cannot be replaced once it is used or can only be replaced over an extremely long period of time
- **renewable resource** a resource that is constantly available or that can be replaced in a relatively short period of time through natural processes

God created the earth with everything that is needed for His people to live and thrive. These sustaining materials are called **natural resources**. A natural resource is any substance, organism, or energy form found in nature that can be used by living things. Certain natural resources, such as air and water, are necessary for life. Some natural resources, such as coal and natural gas, make people's lives more convenient and comfortable. Many natural resources provide energy. Natural resources may be found in the atmosphere, oceans, or deep within the earth's crust.

Natural resources are often classified as renewable or nonrenewable. **Renewable resources** are resources that are constantly available or that can be replaced in a relatively short period of time through natural processes. For example, when energy from the sun powers a solar-powered calculator, the energy used is immediately replaced by more energy from the sun. Air, water, and living things are considered *renewable resources*. Renewable resources include energy resources such as solar energy, wind energy, and energy gleaned from the heat inside of the earth. A resource can maintain a renewable status as long as the resource is not completely depleted before it can reproduce or be naturally replaced. For example, trees are a renewable resource. However, if too many trees are cut down before more trees can be produced or replaced, the renewable resource no longer exists.

Nonrenewable resources are resources that cannot be replaced once they are used or can only be replaced over an extremely long period of time. Once these resources have been completely depleted, there will be no more available for people and other organisms. Examples of nonrenewable resources are fossil fuels (coal, oil, and natural gas) and minerals. These substances exist in limited quantities. Fuel alternatives will need to be in place when the fossil fuel stores have been depleted.

Natural, renewable resource

Many people do not know what it is like to live without readily accessible energy sources. When cars run low on gas, more gasoline is usually available. When it is dark, people can quickly turn on the lights. If the outside temperatures are cold, people turn up the heat. Because nonrenewable resources have been available for a long time, most people do not think about how many resources and how much energy are being

CAREER

Conservationist

A conservationist works primarily with landowners and government agencies to develop ways to protect natural resources. These resources include soil and water. Conservationists help develop ways to efficiently utilize land without harming the environment.

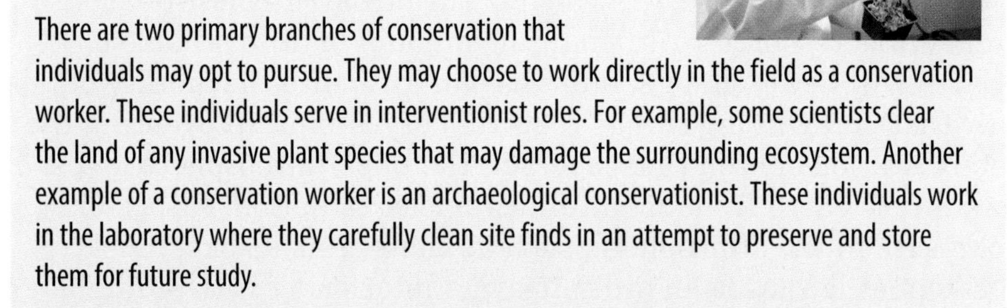

There are two primary branches of conservation that individuals may opt to pursue. They may choose to work directly in the field as a conservation worker. These individuals serve in interventionist roles. For example, some scientists clear the land of any invasive plant species that may damage the surrounding ecosystem. Another example of a conservation worker is an archaeological conservationist. These individuals work in the laboratory where they carefully clean site finds in an attempt to preserve and store them for future study.

The second primary branch of conservation is conservation science. Individuals who pursue this avenue do not get to participate in many hands-on activities. Rather, they focus on theory, conduct research, and develop conservation materials and methods to be used in the field.

consumed. Although energy can never be created or destroyed, nonrenewable energy resources can be completely expended. Likewise, energy can be used wisely or unwisely.

It is important to think carefully about how choices regarding natural resources relate to the well-being of God's creation. Even small choices matter. For example, those who can afford to pay high electric bills should be careful not to waste electricity. Although more gasoline is usually available at the next gas station, making good energy choices, such as walking, biking, or skating whenever possible instead of riding in a car, helps to maintain the delicate resource balance in nature.

The issues related to renewable and nonrenewable resources are not always obvious. Making good energy choices involves some careful thought and a lot of personal responsibility.

LESSON REVIEW

1. What type of resource cannot be replaced once it has been used up?
2. What are the main sources of renewable energy?
3. Fossil fuels are an example of what type of resource?
4. How can individuals help manage renewable resources wisely?

6.1.2 *Air, Water, and Trees*

OBJECTIVES

- Examine the natural processes that renew oxygen, nitrogen, and carbon.
- Discover the implications of an uneven global distribution of water.
- Correlate the value of tree contributions with the need to protect this resource.

Imagine hearing the following scenario on the evening news: *Scientists have calculated that the earth has enough oxygen left to sustain the population for only 29 more years. Please try not to breathe too deeply. And hold your breath a few times a day. If everybody does their part, the air might last for 32 years.* Does this sound like a ridiculous statement? Yes, because air is a renewable resource.

The atmosphere is a mixture of gases that surrounds the earth. These gases comprise air, which is one of Earth's most precious renewable resources. Although the amount of air available on Earth will never change, humans can influence the quality of air that many living things require. For example, preventing the deterioration of ozone gas layers in the upper atmosphere helps shield the earth from harmful ultraviolet radiation. Also, solid particles in the atmosphere, such as those from smoke, must be kept at low levels in order to avoid interfering with sunlight penetration. Toxic materials in the air must also be kept at low levels so that living things do not inhale or absorb them. It is important that the atmosphere maintain the right balance of gases.

Two primary atmospheric gases—oxygen and nitrogen—are important ingredients for the majority of life on Earth. Humans, animals, plants, aerobic bacteria, and most other microorganisms require oxygen for respiration to produce the energy they need to thrive. Oxygen is renewed by green plants, bacteria, algae, and plankton that produce oxygen as a by-product of photosynthesis. As long as green plants and other oxygen-producing organisms are alive, the atmosphere will have a supply of oxygen.

The atmosphere is a renewable resource.

Water is a renewable resource.

A large percentage of the atmosphere is made of nitrogen—a noncombustible gas. Plant and animal cells process nitrogen to make proteins that stabilize cell boundaries. Nitrogen-fixing bacteria pull nitrogen out of the air to make nitrogen compounds. Plants absorb the nitrogen compounds to make amino acids—the building blocks of proteins. Animals ingest the amino acids in plants to manufacture proteins. Lightning also converts atmospheric nitrogen into useful nitrogen compounds. When animals decay, bacteria recycle nitrogen gas back into the atmosphere.

Even though only a small percentage of the atmosphere is made of carbon dioxide, this gas works in conjunction with other greenhouse gases to act like a blanket for the earth. It traps heat and keeps the biosphere warm. Without carbon dioxide and the other greenhouse gases, the earth would be freezing cold.

Similar to nitrogen and water, carbon circulates in various forms through nature. Plants need carbon dioxide in order to carry out photosynthesis. Carbon dioxide is renewed by humans and animals who produce this gas as a by-product of respiration. The burning of fossil fuels adds more carbon dioxide to the air. This extra carbon dioxide traps additional heat and is maybe contributing to an increase in global temperature. God created

TRY THIS

Transpiration

Place a sealable bag over a small, leafy tree branch early in the morning. The branch needs to be in direct sunlight for at least two hours. Secure the opening of the bag around the tree branch with a rubber band or tape to prevent any air from entering the bag. After two hours have elapsed, clip off the branch and gently tap the branch to collect the water in one corner of the bag. Carefully pour the water into a graduated cylinder and record the volume of water that was transpired. Estimate the percentage of tree leaves that are contained in the bag. Calculate how much water the entire tree will transpire in one day. (Should the calculation cover a 24-hour period or only daylight hours?)

an atmosphere that works in harmony with water, land, and Earth's creatures to provide all living things with a healthy environment. The atmosphere is an amazing resource!

Water is another renewable resource. Earth will always hold the same amount of water, although some may be held in combination with other elements. To be a useful resource, water must be available, easily accessible, and of good quality.

There is an uneven global distribution of water. Some regions have plenty of water, others have very little water and must be careful to conserve it. In very dry areas, the water supply may be located entirely underground, having soaked into the ground long ago when the climate was wetter. People would need to tap into the underground aquifers if they wanted access to these water sources. Aquifers recharge at a rate of about one meter per year. If too much water is withdrawn from the aquifer before it can recharge, the water table may drop and create the risk of water sources running dry.

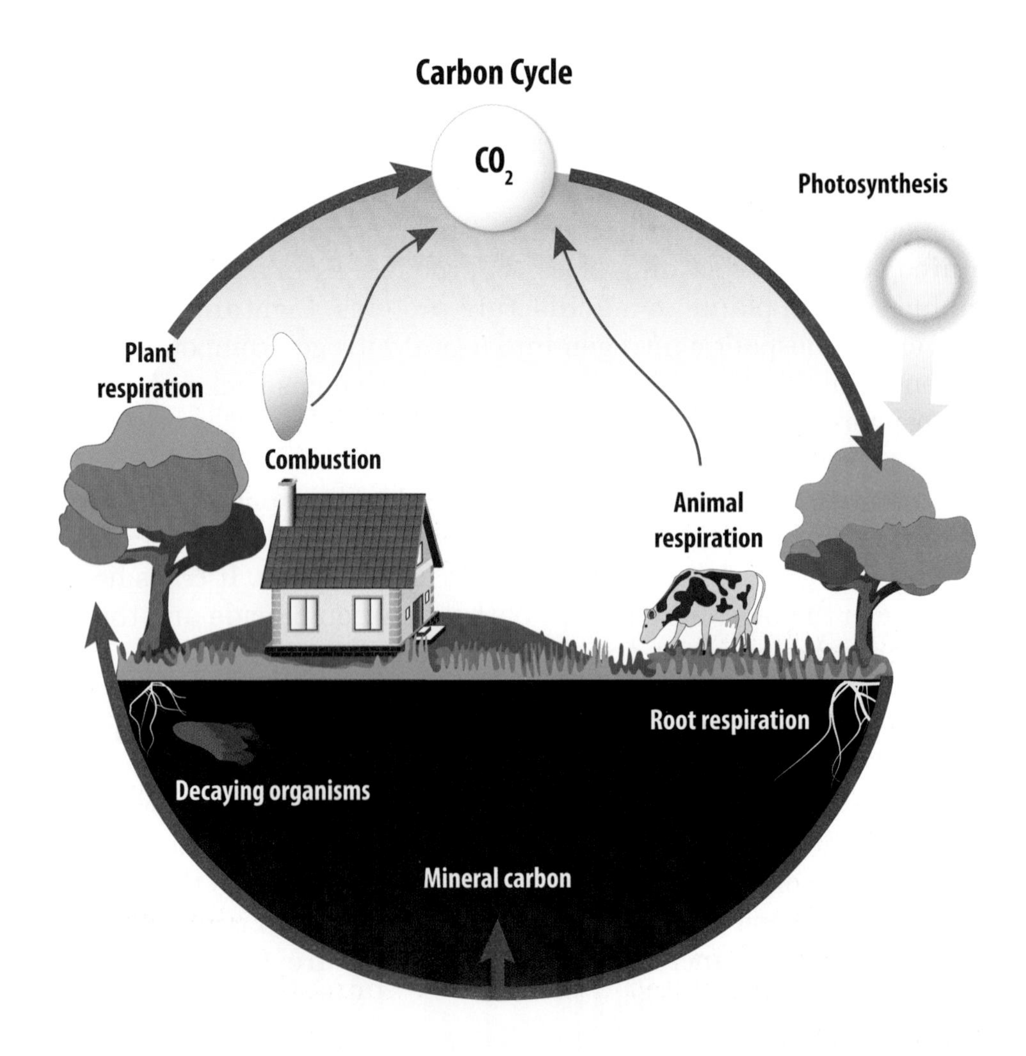

Water supplies also vary from season to season. Many regions of the earth have rainy and dry seasons. Twenty-five countries (mostly in Africa) are experiencing chronic water shortages. This issue compounds with increasing population numbers. Saudi Arabia is one such country that experiences freshwater shortages. It has implemented a process called *desalination* to remove the salt from ocean water to provide drinking water.

Trees are a renewable resource.

Trees are another renewable resource. They replenish the atmosphere's oxygen and contribute to the water cycle through transpiration of water. Trees also shelter a majority of Earth's land species. They supply the material to form paper, and their wood is a valuable building material. In fact, more than 5,000 products come from trees: items from furniture to chewing gum to hair dye.

Trees are renewed through the natural processes of seeding, but this renewal process can be thrown out of balance. A large percentage of Earth's forests have been cut down. With growing global populations, there is an increasing need of tree materials. Developing populations are having to respond to the ever-growing demand, and large land masses are experiencing the effects of deforestation. In many industrialized nations, numerous old-growth forests (trees that are 120–150 years old) have been cut down, and people are now relying on younger or less productive forests.

It is apparent that trees are a valuable resource and that it is very important to conserve them. This includes trying to keep forests in balance—replacing trees that are cut down for paper or wood products, or allowing trees to grow naturally. If trees are carefully managed, they can truly be a renewable resource.

LESSON REVIEW

1. What two primary atmospheric gases are important for most of life on Earth? Why?
2. Why is the carbon cycle important?
3. How are the oxygen, nitrogen, and carbon cycles renewed?
4. What are implications of the uneven global water distribution?
5. What value do trees offer as renewable resources and what threatens the supply of them?
6. How can people protect atmospheric resources?

6.1.3 *Fossil Fuels*

OBJECTIVES

- Summarize the formation of fossil fuels.
- Highlight the properties and uses of fossil fuels.
- Examine the advantages and disadvantages of processing fossil fuels.
- Describe four types of coal.

VOCABULARY

- **coal** a solid fossil fuel formed from decomposed plant remains
- **fossil fuel** a source of energy formed from the buried remains of dead plants and animals
- **natural gas** a mixture of methane and other gases formed from decomposed marine organisms
- **peat** a substance made of partially decayed plant matter
- **petroleum** a liquid fossil fuel formed from microscopic plants, animals, and marine organisms

Did you know that the energy that powers the car or bus that takes you to school originally came from the sun? Gasoline is derived from oil, which is a fossil fuel. **Fossil fuels** are sources of energy formed from the buried remains of dead plants and animals. The process for the formation of fossil fuels is very slow. This is why fossil fuels are nonrenewable resources.

Like the energy that people obtain from food, fossil fuels can be traced back to producers that harness energy from the sun in a process known as *photosynthesis*. This process models the first law of thermodynamics that states that energy cannot be created or destroyed. Plants convert energy from the sun into stored energy. As the plants decay, pressure and heat cause the matter to form layers that are eventually converted into fossil fuels. When the fossil fuels are burned, the thermal energy is released in the form of heat. Therefore, the energy in the natural gas that your furnace burns and the energy in the gasoline that fuels your car ultimately came from the sun!

The three major types of fossil fuels are petroleum, natural gas, and coal. **Petroleum**, a crude oil, is a liquid fossil fuel formed from microscopic plants, animals, and marine organisms. It can be found in underground pools or reservoirs. This oily, flammable mixture is separated into liquid fuels and other products in refineries. The liquid fuels include gasoline, jet fuel, diesel fuel, kerosene, and fuel oil. Other products separated from petroleum include lubricants, waxes, and tars such as asphalt.

Petroleum is a nonrenewable fossil fuel.

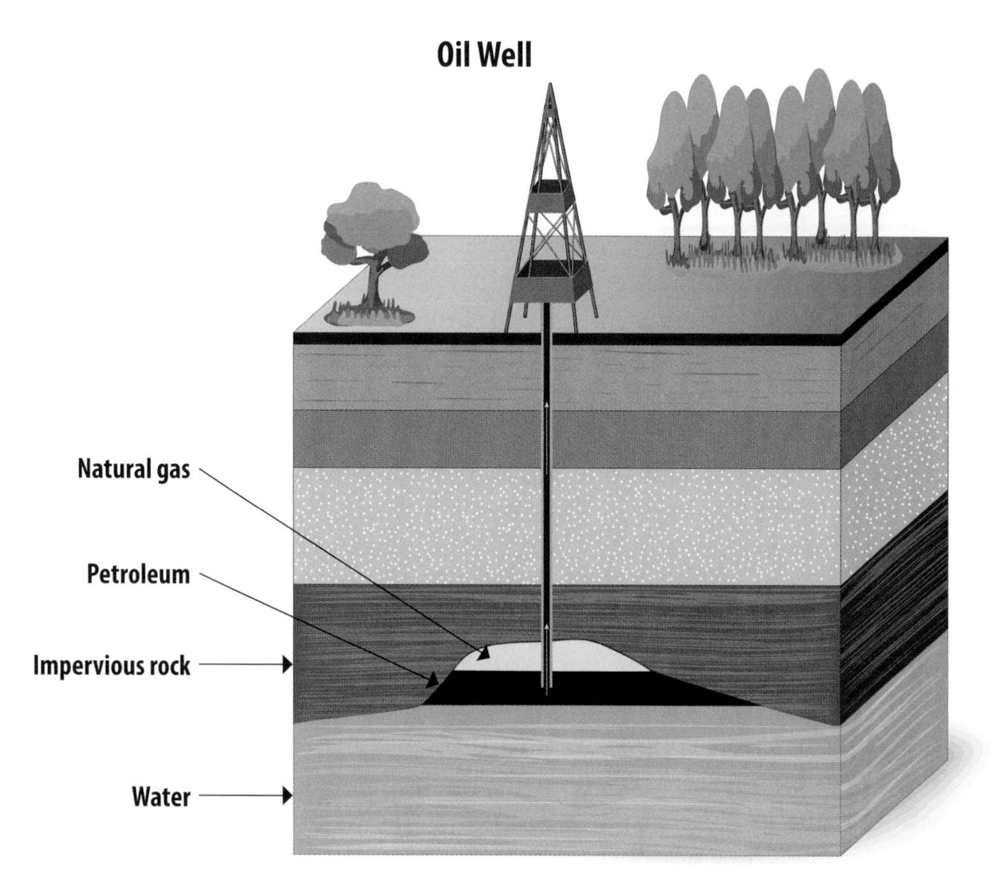

Underground natural gas and petroleum layers

Petroleum meets a large portion of the world's energy needs. Most petroleum is drawn from oil wells, but some petroleum is located near the surface of the earth in the form of oil shale and tar sands. Oil shale is a fine-grained rock containing a solid, waxy mixture of hydrocarbon compounds. Tar sands are layers of sand soaked with thick petroleum.

Some of the world's largest mining projects mine oil from the tar sands in northeastern Alberta, Canada. Clay, sand, and water along with bitumen, a thick black oil, are the components of tar sand. Alberta's tar sands are the world's largest. This form of oil can be mined using two methods. Open-pit mining involves digging huge holes in the earth's surface. Oil miners use heat and diluents (thinning agents) to remove oil from the tar sand. The remaining sand is put back into the open-pit mine, which is reclaimed—brought back to a condition where it can be used for other purposes. The second method involves injecting steam into the tar sand deposit. Oil miners pump out and process the heated oil. This method is useful for deep deposits.

Petroleum is not only an energy resource, it is also a valuable ingredient in many manufactured products. Petroleum is used to

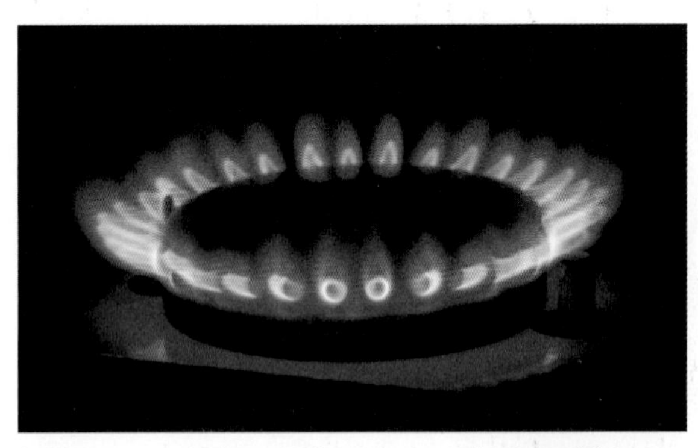

Butane is a natural gas hydrocarbon used in portable stoves, aerosol propellants, refrigerants, and heating fuels.

make products such as plastics, nylon and rayon fabrics, vitamin capsules, and other products.

The reliance on petroleum has advantages and disadvantages. It is an inexpensive, trusted source of energy. High-grade oil and gasoline burn relatively efficiently. Petroleum is convenient to transport and new drilling technologies continue to improve oil production. One disadvantage of burning petroleum is the production of atmospheric pollution, such as smog and carbon dioxide, that contributes to climate change. Another issue is the potential for oil spills that harm the environment.

C_4H_{10}

BUTANE

Natural gas is a mixture of methane and other gases formed from decomposed marine organisms. When these organisms died and sank to the ocean floor, they were covered by layers of sediments and compressed into sedimentary rock. Pressure, heat, and bacterial activity transformed these organic substances into oil and natural gas. Geologists typically find oil and natural gas together. The gas layers usually rise above the oil layers because gas is less dense than oil.

Almost all natural gas provides fuel for heating and for generating electricity. People commonly burn methane to warm houses and cook on gas stoves. Butane and propane are also natural gases. Butane is used in lighters and camp stoves. People burn propane as heating fuel and as cooking fuel for outdoor grills. Some motor vehicles are powered by natural gas. These vehicles produce less pollution than gasoline and diesel vehicles. Natural gas burns cleaner than other fossil fuels and creates less pollution. Natural gas is also plentiful, and it is convenient to transport and use. Burning natural gas does have a drawback—it produces carbon dioxide, a major greenhouse gas. However, it produces less carbon dioxide than petroleum or coal for the same amount of heat energy produced.

Coal mine

Coal, a solid fossil fuel formed from decomposed plant remains, was the first fossil fuel to be used by humans. Prior to this time, wood was the primary source of fuel throughout the world. Coal mining in Europe dates back to at least the 13th century. This fossil fuel was once the leading energy source for home heating in the United States and Canada. Many power plants still use coal to generate steam needed to produce electrical energy in power plants.

The formation of coal can be traced to wetlands such as swamps, bogs, and moors. **Peat** is a substance made of partially decayed plant matter. Over time, heat and pressure turn the peat into coal. There are four types of coal that contain various types and amounts of carbon and other impurities. Each type produces a different amount of heat energy. When placed under tremendous pressure from overhead rock layers, peat is transformed into lignite. Lignite is a soft coal with a woody texture. It is very moist and crumbles when exposed to air. Subbituminous coal forms when lignite is placed under pressure. This type of coal is less moist and has more carbon than lignite. The application of both pressure and heat to lignite produces bituminous coal. The majority of coal is bituminous coal, which has less moisture and more carbon than subbituminous coal. It also has a high sulfur content. When bituminous coal is burned, sulfur dioxide is released into the atmosphere. Sulfur dioxide is a serious form of air pollution that causes a variety of lung diseases. When sulfur dioxide mixes with the water in the atmosphere, acid rain precipitates. Bituminous coal under extreme pressure forms anthracite coal, the highest ranked coal and hardest form of coal. Anthracite coal contains the highest energy content.

Burning coal has both advantages and disadvantages. Coal is the most abundant fossil fuel, is relatively inexpensive to produce, and is easy to transport. Devices called *scrubber systems* work like a shower to dissolve sulfur oxides before they are released into the atmosphere. This process helps to reduce pollution. However, these systems do not reduce all pollution. Burning coal produces more carbon dioxide per unit of heat energy than burning either petroleum or natural gas. Coal mines can also pollute the land, and strip-mining coal out of the ground can harm a region's environment.

LESSON REVIEW

1. Describe how petroleum and natural gas are formed.
2. Contrast the properties and uses of the three major fossil fuels.
3. Examine the advantages and disadvantages of processing fossil fuels.
4. Name four types of coal and explain how they are formed.

FYI

Rapid Fossil Fuel Formation

Young-earth scientists do not agree with old-earth scientific evidence that supports the idea that fossil fuels require millions of years to form. Rather, their geologic data suggests fossil fuels can form rapidly. If given the proper anaerobic conditions, fossil fuels can be created within a few hours. So, where did today's fossil fuels come from? There are two explanations. One states that God created fossil fuels during the week of creation. Those fuel reserves were located deep in the earth. When the Flood occurred, the shifting of tectonic plates forced the reservoirs to crack open, and fuel permeated the upper layers of the earth's crust. The other young-earth explanation addresses additional fossil fuel quantities. An enormous amount of vegetation was buried very quickly during the Flood. The vegetation became the coal that can be observed today. Each of these schools of thought more closely adheres to the idea that the earth is less than 10,000 years old.

6.1.4 *Rocks and Minerals*

OBJECTIVES

- Relate the properties of minerals with their uses.
- Compare mining and quarrying.
- Indicate issues associated with mining.

VOCABULARY

- **ore** a naturally occurring mineral from which a useful metal or mineral is recovered
- **quarry** a location where rocks are removed from the ground

Historically, people have utilized minerals in various aspects of daily living. Ancient people valued salt for its taste and as a food preservative. They used metals in tools and vessels. Gold, silver, and other minerals represented currency. Eventually, coins were stamped from these valuable metals. Rare gemstones were prized for their durability and beauty.

A mineral is a natural, inorganic solid found in the earth's crust. Many modern conveniences and necessities would not be possible without minerals. Water pipes, electric wires, toothpaste, soap, refrigerators, bowls, glasses, spoons, vitamins, clock radios, and doorknobs are manufactured with minerals. Almost everything that cannot be grown is a mineral or comes from a mineral.

Metals are extremely useful minerals. Metals are good conductors of heat and electricity. This means that they allow heat and electricity to easily pass through them. Because they are able to conduct electricity, copper and other metals are fashioned into electric wires. A variety of metals is used to make pots and pans, which efficiently conduct heat to cook food. Metals also have high melting points that prevent them from melting under ordinary temperatures.

Press molding machines demonstrate the malleability of aluminum.

Two other properties belonging to metals are malleability and ductility. Malleability is a substance's ability to be flattened into thin sheets by hammering or by the application of intense pressure. Aluminum is a malleable metal commonly rolled into kitchen foil. For thousands of years, people have hammered gold, silver, and copper into jewelry, tools, and weapons. Today, people use malleable metals to make steel girders, iron fences, and countless other products. Ductility is a substance's ability to be drawn or pulled into the form of a wire. Gold and copper are highly ductile metals. An ounce of gold can be drawn into a wire more than 1.6 km long. Copper wires have been used for decades for telephone lines although now landlines have become less popular. Malleability and ductility make it possible for metals to be shaped into many useful forms.

Some metals are found in nature not bound to other elements. However, many metallic and some nonmetallic minerals form ores. An **ore** is a naturally occurring mineral from which a useful metal or mineral is recovered. Ores are often found in veins—ore-filled fissures. The veins vary in thickness from 1 cm to over 100 m. Some veins are deep within the ground. Others lie close to the earth's surface. Veins of ore at Earth's surface are exposed to weathering. They are often redeposited in gravel or sand. To be useful, the metals must be extracted from their ores. This is done with various methods that depend on the type of ore. Possible methods involve separating metal from ore by use of magnets or electricity, or by crushing and separating.

Ductile metal fences keep livestock secure.

The process of removing useful minerals from the ground is called *mining*. Mining minerals from the ground has a greater impact on the land than quarrying because valuable minerals must be separated from unusable ones. Metals must be separated from their ores. This type of mining operation leaves large amounts of waste. Dumping the rubble back into the hole is not an easy solution. Before they are mined, rocks and minerals are tightly compressed. However, once they are broken and processed, spaces are created between fragments, increasing the volume. Wet residues are kept in ponds. The ponds where the wet wastes are kept may break, releasing toxic chemicals into rivers, lakes, or oceans. Dry waste rock is stored in piles. If the discarded mineral fragments are exposed to water, they release acids and toxic metal compounds into the ground. Dry rubble can blow around as dust. Large, unstable piles of rubble may also create landslides.

Some minerals, such as gold and silver, must be processed with toxic chemicals after they are removed from the ground. The chemicals used for processing, such as potassium cyanide, can pollute nearby soil and streams. Today, the disposal of wastes is carefully regulated to ensure that damage is reduced.

Alloys, which are made of two or more metals or a metal and a nonmetal, are some of today's most important industrial materials. Alloys are often preferred over pure metals given that alloys are usually much stronger and harder than the individual metal components. Around 3,000 BC, the first alloy—bronze—was discovered. Bronze, an alloy of copper and tin, was so much

Iron ore

harder than copper that it transformed civilization, ushering in the Bronze Age. About 3,000 years ago, iron metallurgy was discovered. This began the Iron Age.

Today, people benefit from hundreds of alloys made from numerous metallic elements. Many alloys are formulated to resist corrosion and have low melting points. Iron-aluminum alloys are magnetic. Copper alloys have desirable thermal and electrical properties. Some alloys are very strong even at high temperatures, and others are unusually resistant to wear.

Metals are not the only useful minerals. Many nonmetallic minerals are also useful. The "lead" in your pencils is not lead but a mixture of clay and the mineral graphite. Feldspar is used to make glass, porcelain, and tableware. Garnet and emery are adhered to paper to make sandpaper. Barite is a mineral rich in barium, which supplies the bright green color in flares and fireworks. The mineral talc is used as a filler in cosmetics, paint, and plastics. Calcite is the primary mineral in limestone and marble. Muscovite has many uses in the electrical industry. Quartz is used to make ceramics, industrial cleaners, and laboratory equipment. Sulfur is used to make paper, rubber, and fertilizers. It is also used to preserve dried fruits. Fluorite is used in the process of smelting iron.

Minerals are not only practical, many are beautiful as well. Throughout history, people have fashioned precious gemstones and metals into jewelry and other decorations. Talc is used to make porcelain paper. Native Americans have used turquoise to make jewelry for centuries. Precious gemstones such as diamond, sapphire, and emerald, and semiprecious stones such as peridot, aquamarine, amethyst, citrine, and onyx are cut and polished as gemstones.

Rocks, which are composed of one or more minerals, are also valuable resources. Limestone, an important building stone, is the main component in cement, glass, and soil conditioners. Sand and gravel are ingredients of concrete and asphalt. Sandstone is an important building stone and it can be made into glass and other products. Clay

The Golden Gate Bridge is made of steel, an iron-carbon alloy.

Rock quarry

and shale are materials mixed in cement, bricks, ceramics, and tiles. Gypsum provides strength to wallboard and is a stiffening agent in bakery products.

Quarries are locations where rocks are removed from the ground. Many old, abandoned quarries are still visible as holes, but many countries are now requiring mining companies to restore the sites to a usable status. Although quarries can leave holes and strip vegetation, they do not poison the land. Plants eventually grow again on the site. Abandoned quarry sites typically cannot be reworked into farming land, but they can eventually support interesting ecosystems.

LESSON REVIEW

1. The minerals used in pots and pans exhibit what physical properties?
2. Why do malleable and ductile physical properties help make minerals useful?
3. Where are rocks removed from the ground?
4. How does quarrying differ from mining?
5. How can individuals reduce the environmental impact associated with mining?

6.1.5 *Land*

OBJECTIVES

- Explain three processes that cause land deterioration.
- Identify ways that people can prevent land deterioration.

VOCABULARY

- **desertification** the making of new deserts by degrading land that used to be healthy and productive

There have been numerous inventions over the past few centuries that have changed people's lives. For example, it may be hard to imagine what life would be like without indoor plumbing, cars, computers, plastic, television, refrigerators, glass windows, sewing machines, aluminum cans, or cell phones. About 11,000 years ago, an invention changed the course of history. That invention was farming.

Farming and agriculture originated in the Middle East. Individuals who lived in the area known as *the Fertile Crescent* began clearing native vegetation in order to cultivate selective crops. Agriculture also began around the same time in East Asia with the domestication of millet and rice. Farming spread throughout the region of the Tigris and Euphrates Rivers more than 6,000 years ago, and soon people could raise enough food to support cities. Beginning 2,000 years later, agriculture spread throughout Europe. People in Central America began to grow grain more than 5,000 years ago. The developments in food production transformed the land and changed the world.

Land is a renewable resource. Although people cannot make more land, if properly managed, land can be renewed for further use. This renewal requires care, because improper treatment can cause land to become useless. Today, it is more important than ever not to let this happen. The world's population is growing quickly, in part, because many people have been blessed with better health care and more efficient food production. At the same time, however, the amount of farmland per person is shrinking. Expanding deserts and exponential population growth

Wheat field farming

HISTORY

Presidential Protection

"We have become great because of the lavish use of our resources. But the time has come to inquire seriously what will happen when our forests are gone, when the coal, the iron, the oil, and the gas are exhausted, when the soils have still further impoverished and washed into the streams, polluting the rivers, denuding the fields and obstructing navigation."
– Theodore Roosevelt

Theodore Roosevelt, 26th president of the United States, was a great proponent of conservation. When he became president in 1901, Roosevelt created the United States Forest Service to protect wildlife and preserve public lands. The intent was to conserve forests for continued use and utilize natural resources to ensure their sustainability. He established 150 national forests, 51 federal bird reserves, 4 national game preserves, 5 national parks, and 18 national monuments by issuing the American Antiquities Act. During his presidency, Theodore Roosevelt protected approximately 230 million acres of public land. Today, there is a national wildlife refuge in every state.

are destroying farmland. Because less land is now available to raise food, people should make good use of the land they have to ensure that everyone has enough to eat.

People in the United States and Europe do not feel the pinch of decreasing farmland as much as people who live in developing countries. About 80% of the world's people live in developing countries. Many of these countries are located in tropical regions where poverty, unequal land distribution, and growing populations are forcing the people to destroy rain forests and convert the land into cropland and pasture. Tropical forests, which make up half of the earth's forested land, have more plants and animals than any other ecosystem. Most of the nutrients are in the upper canopy of the trees, making the soil thin and poor. When rain forests are cut down for logging and agricultural purposes, the species-rich forest disappears and heavy rains wash away the topsoil. This makes the land fertile for only two or three growing seasons. Poor farmers must then clear more forests. The deforestation also puts the land at risk for floods and landslides. For example, in recent years, forests above the city of Ormoc in the Philippines were logged. The rains from a

Desertification by overgrazing

Salinization

1991 typhoon caused a mudslide in the unforested area that killed 7,000 people.

One solution to the tropical deforestation problem is to encourage people who live in and near these forests to find ways to utilize rain forest resources instead of chopping down vegetation. Tropical plants offer countless foods and medicines. People who do not live in these forests can help prevent deforestation by using recycled items, reducing use of palm oil, and supporting conservation organizations.

Another land use issue is **desertification**, the making of new deserts by degrading land that used to be healthy and productive. The degradation of land may be influenced by human activities such as letting livestock overgraze the land and cutting down forests to collect fuel. About 25% of the world's people live in dry areas. Most of the people in these areas make their living by raising livestock. If the livestock overgraze the dry land, the land turns into a desert. This activity along with other degradation processes converts 12 million hectares of land into deserts every year. Planting native vegetation in the affected areas can prevent desertification. The vegetation anchors soil and retains water. Other ways of preventing desertification include improving irrigation methods, rotating crops, rotating grazing patterns, and terracing (creating multiple steplike levels of flat ground on hillsides).

Salinization, the process in which water-soluble salts accumulate in soil, is another process that can ruin land. This process can happen in two ways. Salts occur naturally in soil. If the water that evaporates from the soil is not replenished, the concentration of salt increases. Too much salt is toxic to plants. Such land may have to be abandoned. This type of salinization occurs in arid and semiarid regions such as the plains and prairies. Salinization may also be caused by irrigation. If the water drawn from rivers or underground reservoirs has a high salt content, it will increase the salinity of that irrigated land over time.

Wetlands are another important land resource. A **wetland** is an area of land where the water level is near or above the soil surface for all or most of the year. Wetlands are important habitats and nurseries for waterfowl, fish, and invertebrates. They filter pollution and help prevent flooding by soaking up excess water. Until recently, few people understood the value of wetlands. As a result, many wetlands were drained for farmland or converted into development areas.

Today, fewer wetlands are being destroyed. Some are being restored, and new wetlands are being created. A few groups of people worry that restoring wetlands creates a breeding ground for mosquitoes. However, mosquitoes are rarely a problem in properly restored wetlands. This is because the birds that wetlands attract eat the mosquitoes.

You can see that land resources are valuable. As people learn more about the design of the earth and how it works together as a whole, they can make better decisions about land use. It is important that everyone has enough room to live and enough food to eat. If cared for properly, the beauty of God's creation can be enjoyed by many future generations.

LESSON REVIEW

1. What factors contribute to the destruction and deterioration of farmland?
2. Why is land considered a renewable resource?
3. Explain why rain forest deforestation is a growing problem.
4. Why do desertification and salinization occur?
5. What can individuals do to prevent land deterioration?

Wetlands are an important natural resource.

6.1.6 *Soil*

OBJECTIVES

- Analyze and explain why soil erosion occurs.
- Investigate methods that help prevent soil erosion.

VOCABULARY

- **contour farming** the plowing of furrows around a hill perpendicular to its slope to reduce erosion
- **cover crop** the fast-growing vegetation planted on bare farmland to prevent erosion
- **crop rotation** the successive planting of different crops to prevent erosion and to improve fertility
- **furrow** a ditch in farmland
- **strip cropping** the planting of alternating bands of crops and cover vegetation in a planned rotation of equal widths
- **terrace farming** the construction of steplike ridges built into the slope of the land

Have you ever closely examined soil? Without soil, most creatures living on land would not last very long. Soil is a very precious gift. God designed soil to be a source of nutrients for living things—even those that live in the water.

Soil is formed over a long period of time by the interaction of living and nonliving things. Rain, wind, sleet, and ice break rocks apart through weathering. The process of erosion transports these rock particles to other places. The resulting rock particles are an important part of soil. Nutrients are added to soil by bacteria, decomposing plants, and animals. The formation of soil is an extremely slow process. Soil is formed at a rate of about 10 mm every 100 to 400 years.

Although the process of erosion naturally forms soil, problems arise when erosion speeds up so much that the topsoil washes or blows away faster than it can be replaced. Erosion may speed up as a result of human activity. Soil's ability to be renewed depends on human use.

For example, trees and other plants prevent erosion because their roots hold soil in place. When hills and other land surfaces are deforested, the topsoil is exposed to water and wind. The topsoil can then be washed or blown away. Leaving farmland bare allows wind and running water to speed up erosion. Plowing **furrows**—ditches in farmland—down sloped land allows water to move quickly over soil, forming gullies. A gully is a narrow ditch cut in the earth by runoff. This process, known as *gully*

Cover crop

erosion, wears away land quickly and can make the area useless for farming.

Contour farming

Soil erosion happens in two steps. First, soil particles become detached from topsoil layers. Then, these particles are carried away from the land. Reducing soil erosion must address both of these steps. When land is not being used to grow crops, cover vegetation should be planted. A **cover crop** is fast-growing vegetation planted on bare farmland to prevent erosion. These crops also help to increase nutrients in the soil and provide organic matter. When rain falls on vegetation or wind blows across plant-covered ground, soil particles are less likely to detach from topsoil.

Another method farmers often employ is the planting of grains after the fall harvest to prevent erosion during the winter. Alternating strips of crops and grass can also help by reducing the amount of bare land exposed to erosion. Corn may be planted in bands next to alfalfa, which is an excellent cover crop. The cover crop greatly reduces soil erosion. The planting of alternating bands of crops and cover vegetation in a planned rotation that are of equal widths is called **strip cropping**.

Combining strip cropping with contour plowing can reduce erosion by 75%. **Contour farming** is the plowing of furrows around a hill perpendicular to its slope to reduce erosion. Because the furrows are at right angles to the slope, lower furrows trap the soil eroded from higher furrows. If furrows

BIBLE CONNECTION

The Sabbath Year

In Leviticus 25, God commanded Moses to provide instructions to the Israelites regarding the use of their land. The Israelites may not have rotated their crops or introduced terrace farming, but they did give their fields a year of rest. God said, "For six years sow your fields, and for six years prune your vineyards and gather their crops. But in the seventh year the land is to have a year of Sabbath rest, a Sabbath to the Lord" (Leviticus 25:3–4a). The purpose of resting the land was to invigorate the land for future production. The Israelites learned that they did not need to worry during this year, because the Lord always provided.

FYI

Farmers Using Global Positioning Systems

Global positioning systems are no longer just for providing travel directions. Farmers around the world are participating in "precision farming" or "site-specific farming" with the aid of GPS and geographic information systems (GIS). They use these systems to map fields, plan farms, sample soils, guide tractors, measure variable rate applications, scout crops, and map yields. GPS is especially useful when farmers attempt to work in low visibility conditions such as dust, rain, fog, or darkness. Specifically, farmers employ GPS to help them more precisely apply pesticides, fertilizers, and herbicides. This practice ensures the farmer has better control over the dispersion of specific chemicals, and they no longer have to use human "flaggers" to guide aircraft sprayers. As the crop dusters fly over the field, chemicals are applied only to certain areas. This reduces the amount of chemicals needed and minimizes chemical drift. Overall, GPS has helped farmers reduce expenses, increase their production yields, and become more environmentally friendly.

were plowed parallel to the slope, water would run down through them, carrying away precious topsoil.

Terrace farming is often used to prevent erosion on steeper slopes. **Terrace farming** is the construction of steplike ridges that are built into the slope of the land. The terraces help keep water from flowing downhill. Short, level steps allow heavy rains to soak into the soil rather than run off and cause erosion. Bench terracing converts the land into a series of level strips like a staircase. This method requires extensive planning, but it is very effective. Countries that experience severe erosion hazards and require flood irrigation methods benefit from bench terracing.

Crop rotation is another soil conservation method. **Crop rotation** is the successive planting of different crops to prevent erosion and to improve fertility. Some crops, such as corn, expose the soil to erosion. Cover crops, such as alfalfa, do not. Farmers may choose to plant corn one year and alfalfa the next. The small gullies formed during the corn years are filled in with soil during the alfalfa years. Some crops, such as soybeans, replenish important nutrients like nitrogen to the soil that were depleted by previous crops such as corn.

A recent method of farming is called *no-till farming*. Rather than plowing the land, the farmer leaves the stubble from the previous year's crop on the surface and plants the new crop using special planters that do not greatly disturb the soil. The stubble prevents wind and water erosion and helps trap snow for additional moisture.

Soil erosion is an ever present issue. Scientists continue to investigate methods to prevent it. Can you think of other ways to prevent soil erosion?

LESSON REVIEW

1. Why does soil erosion occur?
2. Describe the two steps of soil erosion.
3. Why would a farmer choose to plant cover crops in strips between rows of crops?
4. What type of land benefits most from terrace farming?
5. What method involves the successive planting of different crops to prevent erosion and improve soil fertility?
6. Name the two techniques farmers combine to reduce erosion by 75%. How does the combination reduce erosion?

Terrace farming

6.1.7 *Alternative Energy Sources*

OBJECTIVES

- Examine ways people harness alternative energy sources.
- Summarize uses of alternative energy sources.
- Compare the benefits and drawbacks of using alternative energy sources.

VOCABULARY

- **biomass** organic matter that contains stored energy and is used to produce fuel
- **geothermal energy** the energy collected from heat trapped in the earth's crust
- **nuclear energy** the energy that comes from changes in the nuclei of atoms of radioactive elements
- **solar energy** the radiation from the sun that causes chemical reactions, generates electricity, and produces heat

God wove enough energy resources into the design of the solar system to provide all of the energy people would ever need. Communities have already begun to tap into some of this energy. Fossil fuels have been a tremendous blessing over the past years. However, they are nonrenewable resources, so people need to find other ways to heat homes, power vehicles, and run factories.

Consider the sun's energy. Think about how hot the sun feels when you are sitting on a beach in the middle of the summer, or the scorching temperatures the sun produces in deserts. **Solar energy** is radiation from the sun that causes chemical reactions, generates electricity, and produces heat. The earth receives more energy from the sun each year than the combined energy total contained in all of the known fossil fuel reserves. In fact, every year the sun emits enough radiation to supply the earth with 15,000 times more energy than the world consumes. This makes solar energy a good energy choice.

Solar energy can be captured and used in many ways. Simple forms of direct solar energy collection include the positioning of windows in a house to absorb the maximum amount of sunlight and hanging clothes outside to dry. Technology has helped people capture solar energy more efficiently. Sunlight can be changed directly into electrical energy by using solar cells. Solar cells have been made out of layers of silicon and metal, solar inks, solar dyes, and conductive plastics. When sunlight enters the cells, electrons flow across the layers, creating an electric current. One solar cell produces a very small amount of electrical energy. For example, it takes a few solar cells to power a calculator or a watch. Thousands of solar cells are needed to provide enough electrical energy for a house or a business. A building that uses solar energy typically has large panels

BIOGRAPHY

Mária Telkes

Mária Telkes, a Hungarian-born American physical chemist and biophysicist, designed the first solar-powered heating system to be used in the home. In 1948, the world's first home heating system was constructed in Dover, Massachusetts that used solar collectors and Glauber's salts to store heat. Telkes also created a solar distiller during World War II that separated salt from seawater, creating water that was safe to drink.

mounted on the roof to provide the electrical energy. Solar panels consist of many solar cells wired together.

Solar cells are quiet and reliable. They do not have any moving parts and do not require fuel to produce electric power, and they can last for many years without maintenance. The use of solar cells does not create any pollution, and solar energy is free. Why, then, do so few people harness solar energy this way? One reason is cost. Although solar energy is free, solar cells are expensive to make. Fortunately, the cost of solar power has been decreasing, and many believe that solar power will become more cost effective compared to other sources of energy.

Solar energy can also be captured by using unglazed solar collectors. Unglazed solar collectors consist of boxes covered with a dark metal or plastic that absorbs solar energy. The energy is transferred to a fluid in the collector. The fluid is then pumped through tubes that run through pipes. This action raises the temperature of the fluid. In warm, sunny regions, many people have solar water heaters. Even if an individual does not live in a warm and sunny climate, solar energy can be harnessed in any climate. Solar collectors can also be used to generate electricity.

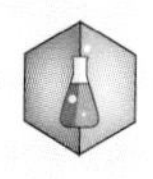

TRY THIS

Solar Energy Conversion

Tape a band of black construction paper around one beaker. Fill it and one other beaker with 100 mL of room temperature water. Cover both beakers with plastic wrap. Poke a small hole in the plastic wrap of both beakers and insert a thermometer into each beaker. Record the initial temperatures. Place both beakers on a windowsill in direct sunlight for 20 minutes. Record the final temperatures. Why was there a noticeable temperature difference between the water samples in the two beakers?

Solar Panel

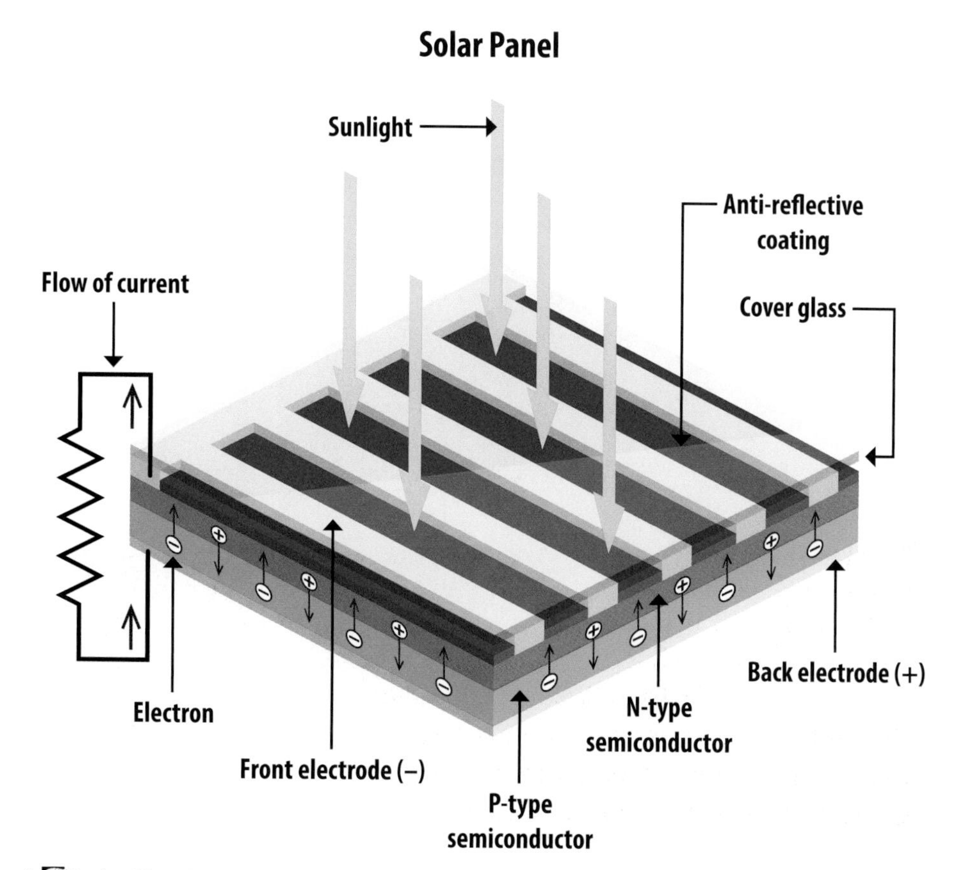

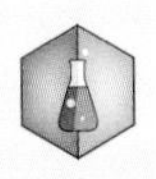

TRY THIS

Turbines

Tape cardboard strips to a cork or insert metal or plastic fins into slits on the cork that were cut using a single-edge blade. Insert pushpins into the two ends of the cork to act as axles. Fashion a U-shaped holder using craft sticks. Allow water to flow underneath the turbine. What other renewable resources could move the turbine?

Another alternative energy source is wind power. A substantial percentage of the solar energy reaching Earth is converted into wind energy through convection currents that develop as a result of temperature differences. Wind power can be used to generate electricity. The wind spins the blades on a wind turbine that is connected to a hub that is mounted on a turning shaft. The shaft travels through a gear transmission box, which increases the turning speed. A generator converts the mechanical energy into electrical energy. Wind power is very inexpensive in areas where strong winds blow. In Denmark, 42% of the population's energy consumption is generated by wind turbines. A drawback of wind power is that not all regions receive enough wind to make good use of wind power. Wind turbines are also noisy. Some people are concerned about the amount of space taken up by wind turbines and the threat they may pose to flying bats and birds.

Imagine obtaining energy to run your vehicle or heat your home from plants. **Biomass** is derived from organic matter, such as crops or waste products, that contains stored energy and is used to produce fuel. This energy ultimately comes from the sun. Plants use energy from the sun during photosynthesis to make food, and animals obtain this energy by eating plants. You have used biomass energy if you have ever burned wood or paper. Food

Wind power

is also biomass. About 90% of energy consumption in developing countries comes from burning wood or charcoal. Many people also burn dried animal dung. Other sources of biomass include yard clippings, crop waste, and sawdust or bark from lumber mills. Using biomass not only helps conserve fossil fuels, it also helps reduce greenhouse gas and other air pollutant emissions and saves space in sanitary landfills.

Biomass power plant with wood chip fuel storage

New ways of using biomass are now being discovered. Biogas—methane from manure and organic waste—is an energy source in some developing countries such as portions of India and China. Another way to use biomass is through a process called *fermentation*, which converts sugars and starch into alcohol. This alcohol can be separated and burned as a fuel or mixed with gasoline to produce gasohol. One bushel of processed corn can produce about 9.5 liters of ethanol. It would take more than 90% of the land in the United States to make fuel that its citizens use in their cars. Although biomass is renewable, it requires a tremendous amount of land that could be used to grow food for people.

Certain bacteria can act on biomass to make methane gas, which is then converted into methanol. Both ethanol and methanol are now being blended with gasoline to reduce pollution levels, and biomass has the potential to be converted into gases that are burned to produce electricity.

Another alternative energy source is known as **geothermal energy**—energy collected from heat trapped in the earth's crust. In some regions, the rainwater that penetrates the ground comes in close proximity to magma. The energy from the magma heats the groundwater and turns it into steam. The water can reach temperatures of more than 150°C—much hotter than boiling water. This steam and hot water escape through geysers or wells. Sometimes engineers use the steam to turn turbines to generate electrical energy. They also pump hot water through pipes that travel to buildings to produce heat. A place called *The Geysers* in California generates enough electricity to power a city the size of San Francisco.

If you have ever visited Niagara Falls or some other large waterfall, you have seen how much energy falling water holds. Hydroelectric power is electricity produced from the conversion of potential energy in falling or fast-flowing water to mechanical

Geothermal power plant in Kenya

energy. A dam built across a river holds back the water, which is then directed past the turbines of a generator to produce electricity. Hydroelectricity is the world's most widely used renewable resource. It supplies nearly 16% of the world's electric power. This type of power is well suited for hilly countries that receive high amounts of rainfall. Dams, however, disrupt the migratory paths of salmon and steelhead. Dams also lower water quality and cause erosion problems.

Another alternative energy source is **nuclear energy**—energy that comes from the changes in the nuclei of atoms of radioactive elements such as uranium. Usually nuclear energy is produced through a process called *fission*, in which the nuclei of radioactive atoms are split and a tremendous amount of energy is released. Nuclear power plants use radioactive atoms as fuel. The energy released by fission produces steam to run electric generators. Nuclear reactors are also used to propel ships, submarines, and spacecraft.

Although the production of nuclear power does not produce the same kinds of pollution compared to the burning of fossil fuels, it does produce dangerous wastes. These radioactive wastes must

Nuclear power plant

be removed from the power plant and stored until they are no longer radioactive. The deactivation of radioactive waste can extend for thousands of years.

Nuclear fuel rods

Nuclear power plants generate a lot of heat. In response, large amounts of water are required to cool power plants. If the cooling system fails, the plant can overheat and the reactor could melt. The meltdown would allow a large amount of radiation to escape into the environment. This happened in Chernobyl, Ukraine, in 1986 and in Fukushima, Japan, in 2011.

Nuclear power plants are more expensive to build than fossil fuel facilities. However, nuclear power is relatively inexpensive to maintain. As more fossil fuels are depleted, nuclear energy will probably become a common choice. Uranium, the fuel used in nuclear power plants, is also relatively inexpensive compared to coal and other fossil fuels. Scientists estimate that a pellet of uranium that has a mass of several grams can produce as much energy as 564 L of oil or 807 kg of coal. Uranium is a nonrenewable resource, but many speculate that uranium supplies will last longer than oil supplies. This projection is subject to change with new data observations.

Nuclear energy can also be produced through a process known as *fusion*—the joining of two or more nuclei with small masses into a nucleus with a larger mass. Very high temperatures are required for this reaction to occur. As a result, fusion reactions are limited to laboratory experiments and are currently not useful as an energy source.

LESSON REVIEW

1. Describe how solar cells work. Why do consumers value solar cells?
2. How can wind generate power?
3. What concerns do some individuals have regarding wind turbines?
4. Explain how individuals harness geothermal energy.
5. Name some benefits associated with the use of biomass.
6. Describe the nuclear reaction that is most commonly used today to harness nuclear energy.

6.2.1 *Land Pollution*

OBJECTIVES

- Compare the different types of land pollution.
- Evaluate the different types of waste disposal.

VOCABULARY

- **incineration** the burning of solid waste materials
- **leachate** a solution formed when pollutants from sanitary landfills are dissolved in rainwater and seep into the groundwater
- **sludge** the solid waste leftovers from sewage treatment

Taking out the trash probably is not your favorite chore—moving heavy bags of smelly garbage outside is nobody's idea of fun. Sometimes the bag leaks, and your hands get grimy and slimy. Soon after you carry one bag out of the house, another one fills up. It is a dirty, continual job. Have you ever thought about where all of this garbage goes? When you throw things away, they do not disappear. The trash is just moving from one place to another. Trash pollutes the land.

A pollutant is a substance or condition in the air, soil, or water that harms living things. Pollutants can be solid wastes including those from industrial and agricultural sources; household wastes such as glass, paper, rubber, plastic, and textiles; scraps from butchered animals and food; and **sludge**, which is solid waste leftovers from sewage treatment.

Solid wastes often end up in sanitary landfills, large holes in the ground in which wastes are compacted and covered with soil. Sanitary landfills are designed to store wastes from living areas in a way that protects human health and the environment. The holes are lined with plastic, clay, or other materials, which are intended to keep leachate from leaking into the soil. **Leachate** is a solution formed when pollutants from sanitary landfills are dissolved in rainwater and seep into the groundwater. The wastes in sanitary landfills are compacted into the smallest space possible and covered with soil about once a day. It takes a long time for waste in sanitary landfills to decay. For example, paper can take 60 years to decay, and many plastics and synthetic materials take several hundred years. Because the materials used to line sanitary landfills seal out most oxygen and moisture, both of which speed decomposition, even substances that usually decay quickly do not do so in landfills.

Taking out the trash

Although sanitary landfills are a common method of waste disposal, they present problems. The linings often leak, allowing leachate into the soil before the wastes completely break down. When the wastes in a sanitary landfill do begin to decompose, methane gas is often produced. Methane gas burns easily, sometimes fueling underground fires in sanitary landfills. Some sanitary landfills have even exploded from this gas. Landfill developers sometimes place pipes in

the landfills to safely remove methane gas, after which it is sold as a fuel.

The biggest problem with using sanitary landfills is finding the space for them; besides, nobody wants to live next to a landfill. Sanitary landfills, then, are not a perfect solution to the problem of solid wastes; they take up land space and sometimes leak leachate into the groundwater.

An alternative to sanitary landfills is **incineration**, the burning of solid waste materials. This reduces the volume and weight of trash, but it does not destroy many hazardous chemicals. Special incinerators can burn garbage more safely and heat water, turning it into steam that generates electricity or heats buildings.

Hazardous wastes are another type of pollutant. Factories often pollute the land and water with hazardous wastes, which are products that can cause serious health problems or even death. For example, factories that produce fuels generate hazardous wastes as by-products. If these wastes are not stored properly, they can seep into the soil and pollute the land. The best solution, of course, is for factories to reduce the amount of hazardous wastes that they produce. Another solution is treating these

FYI

Garbage Slide

In July of 2000 in Payatas Estate in Quezon City, Philippines, at an open dumpsite, a landslide occurred that killed at least 140 people. The mountain of garbage was nearly 7 stories high before it failed. The landslide dropped 15 m of trash on nearby homes, burying 350 people in tons of garbage.

2013 Municipal Solid Waste in the United States

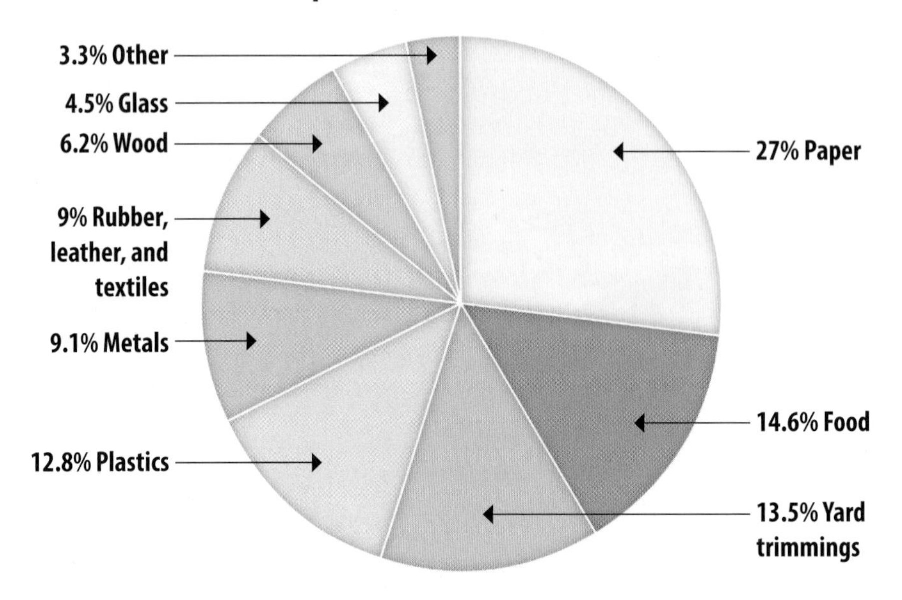

wastes with chemicals so they are no longer toxic, but this process is very expensive. Individual households also generate hazardous wastes because of what is discarded as trash. Such products include batteries, drain cleaners, lighter fluid, nail polish remover, and paint. Many people do not know that these wastes should not be thrown away like regular garbage, since they can seriously contaminate the soil. You should always check the packaging for instructions on how to recycle or properly dispose of these items and their containers.

Fuel processing plants, hospitals, research facilities, and nuclear power plants produce waste material called *radioactive waste*.

The Superfund

In 1896, William Love began digging a canal to connect Lake Erie and Lake Ontario in the United States. The canal was never completed. In the 1920s, the area became a chemical dumping site. Unknown chemicals were buried at the site for decades. Later the site was filled in, and the chemical company gave it to the city of Niagara Falls, New York, so a school and houses could be built on the site. By 1977, chemicals were detected leaking from the site, and many people living on the site were suffering from serious health problems. People were evacuated and the buildings were torn down. The government spent hundreds of millions of dollars to clean up the site and to relocate the people who lived there. Because of the problems discovered at Love Canal, the Superfund, a program to clean up the most contaminated hazardous waste sites in the United States, was started in 1980. More hazardous sites are identified each year.

These pollutants include used fuel rods from nuclear reactors. Such wastes can remain dangerous for thousands of years and were once sealed in steel-lined underground tanks. The waste containers may eventually leak and pollute the nearby land and water, so researchers are searching for alternative disposal methods, including burying them in salt mines or in deep ocean beds.

The best way to manage waste is not to create it in the first place. Many industries are working on methods to reduce toxic substances. Some industries are also recycling toxic materials into harmless products. Individuals can decrease toxic wastes by using less toxic pesticides and preservatives. And everyone can help manage land pollution by paying attention to what is used and by recycling whenever possible.

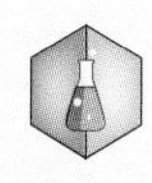

TRY THIS

Waste Not

Before you eat lunch, weigh or calculate the mass of your lunch containers and food. After lunch, weigh or calculate the mass of the containers, packaging, and food scraps. Classify these items according to those that are reusable, such as your lunch container; recyclable; organic, such as apple cores; and garbage that you must throw away. How much of the total mass did you actually eat? How much of the mass can be recycled or composted? How much actually has to be thrown away?

LESSON REVIEW

1. What is a pollutant? What are the different types of land pollution?
2. Describe how a sanitary landfill prevents land pollution.
3. What problems are associated with sanitary landfills?
4. What are the benefits of incineration?
5. Why are researchers exploring new methods of radioactive waste disposal?
6. What is the best way to manage waste?

Chemical waste storage facility

6.2.2 Air Pollution

OBJECTIVES

- Identify causes of air pollution.
- Describe the effects of air pollution.

VOCABULARY

- **smog** a dense, brownish haze formed when hydrocarbons and nitrogen oxides react in the presence of sunlight

It has happened to everyone at one time or another. The sun shines Monday through Friday. You eagerly look forward to the weekend, planning a ball game or a hike or a picnic or a day at the beach. But when Saturday comes, rain drenches your plans. You grumble that it seems to rain more on weekends than during the week. And you know what? It does!

Researchers have found that in some areas, Saturdays have an average of 22% more precipitation than Mondays. This is not a coincidence. It happens because of air pollution. Weather data dating back to 1946 seems to indicate that the air pollution from vehicles driven by people on their way to and from work during the week enhances weekend storms. All raindrops form around particles, and the particles from air pollution can build up until they seed the clouds and cause rain. Weekly pollution levels often match the weekly precipitation levels, peaking on Saturday and dipping by Monday.

Harmful gases and tiny solid and liquid particles contaminate the air. Such particles, called *particulate matter*, are tiny bits of matter that float around in the atmosphere. They include certain kinds of smoke, such as diesel smoke and wood smoke; acids, such as nitrates and sulfates; allergens, like pollen and mold spores; dust; and fine ash. Your nose hairs, mucus, and breathing tubes catch larger particles, but smaller particles can reach your lungs and irritate your respiratory system. In some people, this irritation triggers asthma attacks. Particulates also cover plants and trees, blocking out the sunlight they need for photosynthesis.

Rained-out sporting event

Industrial Revolution

Do you think of air pollution as a recent problem? It is not. In ancient times, smoke from burning wood and trash caused air pollution in cities, but the problem of air pollution was small compared with what it is now. The Industrial Revolution changed England. In the late 18th century, people were leaving their farms to work in factories. The smoke and soot from these factories caused large-scale air pollution. At that point people did not realize that air pollution had serious consequences.

Air pollution worsened during the first half of the 20th century, but people did not pay much attention to the problem until 1952. In London that year, a temperature inversion contributed to smog that killed 4,000 people in four days and hospitalized thousands more. It was called *the Killer Fog*. The particles from this extreme smog entered people's lungs and caused dangerous complications.

Much air pollution comes from the industrial burning of fossil fuels and the burning of fossil fuels in motor vehicles. Here is how this happens. Gasoline contains carbon-based compounds called *hydrocarbons*. Although most gasoline is burned in the vehicle's engine, some is not; so hydrocarbons are released into the air. During the burning process, some nitrogen oxides are also produced from the combination of nitrogen and oxygen at high temperatures. The hydrocarbons, together with the nitrogen oxides, react in the presence of sunlight to form a dense, brownish haze called **smog**. Chemicals in smog irritate the eyes and cause breathing problems, especially for people with asthma or other respiratory ailments.

Smog can build up over cities because of a phenomenon called *temperature inversion*. A temperature inversion occurs when cool air near the earth's surface is trapped under a layer of warm air. Usually cool air is heated by the earth's surface and it rises, taking air pollutants with it; but during a temperature inversion, the warmer layer of air acts like a lid, trapping the pollutants and the cool air near the surface of the earth.

Air pollutants can also cause acid rain. Acid rain is the result of sulfur dioxides and nitrogen oxides reacting in the atmosphere with water and returning to Earth as precipitation. Acid rain contaminates forests and pollutes water and land.

Industrial smoke stacks polluting the air

Hot summer day pollution

Because of weather patterns, acid rain often falls many kilometers away from the source of the air pollution.

Another form of air pollution is ozone pollution. Do not confuse ozone pollution with the ozone layer in the upper atmosphere, which shields the earth from harmful ultraviolet radiation. Ozone is a reactive gas made of three oxygen atoms (O_3). It forms when hydrocarbons react with a group of air pollutants called *oxides of nitrogen*. Hydrocarbons are emitted not only by motor vehicles but also by dry cleaning solutions and many other sources. Heat and sunlight speed ozone formation, so ozone pollution is heaviest in the summer. Perhaps you have heard ozone warnings on the news in the summer. People are encouraged not to drive unnecessarily, mow the lawn, or fill up the gas tank because these things all contribute to the formation of ozone. Breathing ozone can trigger breathing problems, especially for those with asthma or other lung ailments. Ozone adversely affects certain types of vegetation as well.

Sometimes the air indoors can be just as polluted as the air outdoors. Indoor air pollution is a problem inside houses and

Ozone pollution is heaviest in the summer.

office buildings. One reason for this is that modern buildings are well insulated for energy efficiency. This means that there are not any small cracks or spaces through which the indoor air pollution can escape, so it stays trapped inside. Natural gas burned in cooking stoves or space heaters produces nitrogen dioxide and carbon monoxide, and wood burned in fireplaces adds particulates to these gases. Synthetic fibers from carpeting, foam insulation in furniture, particle board, and wall coverings are other sources of indoor air pollution. This is because some of these materials release gases such as formaldehyde. Office buildings with office equipment, carpeting, and poor ventilation usually have high indoor air pollution. Commercial products such as furniture polishes, cleaning agents, and glues also add to indoor air pollution. Smoking can be a major cause of indoor air pollution; that is why smoking is now banned in many public places.

Laws such as the United States' Clean Air Act of 1970 helped define acceptable air quality levels. These laws have encouraged industries and individuals to find new technologies and use energy sources that produce less pollution. New knowledge and a good use of God's gifts can help solve the problem. Hydrogen powered cars may offer cleaner alternatives for the future. Solar power, wind power, and fusion are other possible energy sources that could provide energy without causing pollution. More efficient industrial processes, smaller cars, smaller houses, turning off extra lights, and walking or riding public transportation could reduce the amount of fossil fuels burned. This decreases air pollution. Most cities now have air quality indexes that rate daily air pollution on a numerical scale and report it along with weather forecasts. This is a way of informing people, especially people with respiratory problems, about the risks of air pollution from day to day.

LESSON REVIEW

1. How does air pollution cause rain?
2. What problems result from air pollution?
3. What type of pollution is caused by burning fossil fuels? Why is it bad?
4. Why are temperature inversions a problem?
5. Why is ozone a problem mostly during the summer?
6. List three indoor air pollutants. What causes these types of pollution?

FYI

Smoking

Smoking is a major form of air pollution. Every year more than 480,000 people in the U.S. die from the effects of smoking. About one in every five deaths in the United States and Canada is the result of smoking. Tobacco accounts for 33% of all cancer deaths and 87% of lung cancer deaths.

Why are cigarettes so harmful? Cigarettes contain 4,000 different chemicals. They include acetone (nail polish remover), ammonia (toilet cleaner), arsenic (rat poison), formaldehyde (a fluid used to preserve bodies), hexamine (barbecue lighter), hydrogen cyanide (gas chamber poison), methane (swamp gas), methanol (rocket fuel), nicotine (insecticide), and toluene (industrial solvent).

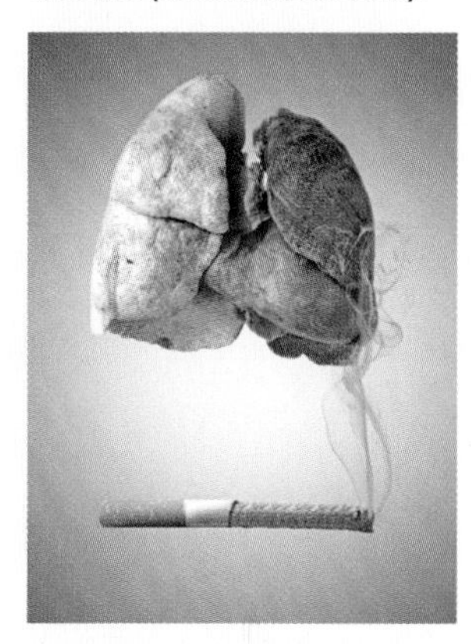

6.2.3 *Water Pollution*

OBJECTIVES

- Compare types of water pollution.
- Identify different types of natural water purification.

Have you ever been really, really thirsty? Maybe you were on a long bike ride and drained your water bottle halfway through the ride. Maybe you forgot to stop at the drinking fountain before you ran laps in physical education class. Or maybe you spent a summer day at the beach and remembered too late how quickly the hot sun dries you out. At times like these, nothing looks better than a glass of refreshing, clear water.

Water is a precious gift from God. As the population grows and agriculture and industry require more water, freshwater is becoming less available. Some regions have plenty of water; other regions are dry.

Water all over the world is being polluted. Acid rain pollutes groundwater and bodies of water such as streams, rivers, and lakes. When the acidity of such a body of water is increased, the organisms that live there can get sick or die. Oil can also pollute the water. Offshore oil wells that drill the oil in ocean beds can have accidents and spill oil into the water. When oil tankers are damaged, oil can leak into the water. For example, on March 24, 1989, the oil tanker *Exxon Valdez* struck Bligh Reef in Prince William Sound, Alaska, spilling more than 42 million liters of oil. The spill harmed or killed migratory shore birds and waterfowl; sea otters; and other species such as porpoises, sea lions, and whales. A larger oil spill occurred in April 2010 when an offshore oil rig exploded in the Gulf of Mexico, which spilled more than 635 million liters of oil. Oil spills are difficult to clean because they spread quickly. Oil companies contain the spill by floating

Clean drinking water

Controlled burn following the Deepwater Horizon Drilling platform oil spill

barriers, called *booms*, and skimming oil from the surface of the water or absorbing it with certain materials. Chemicals can also be used to break down the oil. And because some bacteria consume oil, scientists are exploring the possibility of using bacteria to clean up oil spills. As bad as oil spills are, daily operations of oil tankers leak more oil overall than oil spills do.

The United States and Canada depend heavily on groundwater for drinking water and crop irrigation. Groundwater is easily polluted. One liter of motor oil dumped into a drain can pollute almost a million liters of groundwater. Anything dumped on or into the ground including pesticides, fertilizers, factory wastes, chemicals, oil, and radioactive wastes will eventually find its way into groundwater and pollute it.

Water can also be "polluted" by temperature changes. Power plants use water to cool steam in the turbines. After the water is used, it is released into rivers, lakes, or bays. But it is much warmer than when it went into the plant. Many fish and animals are not created for warmer water, and the temperature increase can kill them. This type of pollution is called *thermal pollution*.

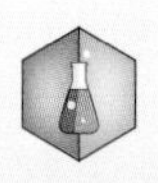

TRY THIS

Dilution Solution

In the past it was common to add clean water to polluted water to dilute the pollution down to safe levels. Do you think this was a good idea? Try it. Pour 300 mL of water into a clean beaker, and then add three drops of food coloring to represent pollution that has moved into groundwater. Pour 150 mL of the polluted water into a second beaker, and then add 150 mL of clean water to the second beaker to represent clean freshwater entering the groundwater. Pour 150 mL of the now-polluted water from the second beaker into a third beaker. Pour 150 mL of clean water into the third beaker to represent more clean freshwater entering the groundwater. Pour 150 mL of the now-polluted water from the third beaker into a fourth beaker. Add 150 mL of clean water to the fourth beaker. Is the water in the fourth beaker cleaner? Why?

Cooling ponds and cooling towers are used to combat the high temperatures.

Sewage and agricultural runoff can pollute water in different ways. For example, disease-causing microorganisms can contaminate the water, making it dangerous for people and animals to drink. Polluted water can also cause cholera and dysentery. The bacteria that break down the organic waste in water use up the oxygen in the water, which may lead to the suffocation of fish and other creatures. And extra nutrients in the water that come from sewage, fertilizers, or pesticides can encourage excessive algae growth. When algae die, the decomposition uses a great amount of oxygen, depriving the rest of the ecosystem.

Solids can also pollute water. Soil from deforested slopes or construction sites washes into bodies of water, interrupting the flow of streams, clogging fish gills, and even smothering coral reefs. Tons of plastic wastes such as bags, soda can rings, and fishing gear are discarded in the oceans each year. Such wastes can choke or strangle fish, sea turtles, sea mammals, and sea birds.

But God wove natural water purification systems into His creation. Biologists have begun to recognize the importance of these natural methods. In fact, they are not only utilizing these methods to do their work naturally but are also developing technologies to duplicate them. For example, land conservationists are planting forests and enlarging wetlands as buffer zones around farms; these ecosystems cleanse water of excess nutrients produced by agriculture. The natural water purification systems can work in several ways.

Quenching the Fire

Ohio's Cuyahoga River flows through the cities of Akron and Cleveland, a densely populated and industrialized area, and empties into Lake Erie. In 1969, the Cuyahoga River became a symbol of water pollution when oil slicks on the river's surface caught fire. The horror of a burning river led to several pollution control actions including the passage of the Clean Water Act in 1972 and the Great Lakes Water Quality Agreement, and the creation of state and federal Environmental Protection Agencies. New laws have greatly improved the river's water quality, and today the Cuyahoga River is experiencing a rebirth. Even very polluted water can be refreshed!

Evaporation. When water evaporates, the impurities remain behind. The purified water returns to its liquid state through condensation so living things can use it.

Bacterial action. Certain bacteria convert organic waste products into simple compounds that do not harm the environment. Huge numbers of decomposing bacteria live in wetlands rich in decaying plant materials. When farm runoff is diverted into large wetlands, these bacteria break down the excess nutrients so algae do not grow too quickly.

Filtration. Gravel and sand act as filters. When water seeps through gravel and sand, suspended particles are filtered out.

God has created marvelous cleaning cycles to purify the water, but it takes a long time for groundwater to cleanse itself. To enjoy the gift of clean water in the future, changes must be made in the way water is used today. What changes can you make to help reduce water pollution?

LESSON REVIEW

1. List ways that oil can get into water sources.
2. Why is an oil spill a problem?
3. What is thermal pollution? What causes it and how can it be remedied?
4. What causes an excess of algae? Why is it a problem?
5. How are sea animals affected by solid waste?
6. Describe the natural water purification processes.

FYI

Bioremediation
Scientists are tapping into the resources of God's creation to clean up soil and groundwater. Bioremediation uses specific bacteria to clean up contaminated groundwater and soil. These bacteria can be added to soil or groundwater to digest certain contaminants and then change them into small amounts of water and harmless gases. The conditions in the soil or water must be right for the bacteria to grow. If the conditions are not conducive to bacterial growth, the soil can be removed, cleaned, and then put back in its original location. Groundwater can also be removed if necessary and then pumped back to the ground, discharged to surface water, or sent to a wastewater treatment system.

6.2.4 *Stewardship*

OBJECTIVES

- Explain why it is important to be a good steward.
- Infer methods of good stewardship.

VOCABULARY

- **stewardship** the attentive management of something entrusted to one's care

Have you ever been disgusted by the sight of someone tossing trash from a car window; cigarette butts littering the sidewalk; or plastic containers floating down a river? People can recognize pollution when they see it, and most know enough not to litter or to dump paint thinner down the drain. It is easy to avoid doing these things, but there are many decisions to make about how to keep God's creation healthy.

Imagine the earth as God created it. Beautiful ecosystems, clean resources, wild places, and amazing creatures decorated the earth. People depend on a healthy, clean biosphere, so it is important to be good stewards of the earth. For the Christian, the importance of **stewardship** runs even deeper. God created a beautifully balanced atmosphere and biosphere and He sustains it by the natural processes He set in place. It is the job of His people to manage and care for that creation.

In the same way God provides for and sustains the world, people should also sustain the earth because they were created to reflect God. It is the privilege of all people to enjoy the fruitfulness of creation, and it is the responsibility of everyone to maintain it, to steward what has been entrusted to all. "The Lord God took the man and put him in the Garden of Eden to work it and take care of it" (Genesis 2:15). When pollution is reduced and resources are maintained, the healthy creation can continue to praise Him—the animals, plants, mountains, streams, stars, and of course, people.

Littered waterway

The idea of stewardship is biblical, but the execution demands both a group effort and individual efforts. Society has done a better job with stewardship in recent decades. Believe it or not, littering used to be acceptable, but now society frowns on littering. Today people do not litter nearly as much, and many organized groups participate in cleanup projects. As a result, the land is much more litter-free than it used to be.

Picking up litter

New technology has been created to improve recycling processes and use cleaner fuel. Solar energy, for example, does not produce as much pollution as burning fossil fuels. Scrubber systems in coal-burning plants work like showers to reduce pollution. Pollution devices in smokestacks and cars are also reducing pollution.

Industries and individuals can also care for creation. One way to do this is to conserve water. Because heating water often requires the burning of fossil fuels, cutting back on hot water reduces air pollution. Industries can reduce water usage by replacing water-cooled equipment with air-cooled equipment; installing automatic shut-off nozzles; and using specialized water brooms instead of hoses to clean floors or other hard surfaces. Taking shorter showers, for example, will conserve water. Turning off the water while brushing teeth also helps.

Another way to be a good steward is to imitate how God sustains His creation. Ecosystems recycle important gases, water, and nutrients through the oxygen cycle, nitrogen cycle, carbon cycle, and water cycle so they can be used over again. Image bearers should follow the example of God in whose image they are made. Conserving and recycling finished products, conserving energy, reducing the demand for fossil fuels, and decreasing pollution levels are means of honoring God.

You can be a better steward by sharing rides, using public transportation, and combining errands. You can walk or bike whenever possible instead of taking the car.

Conserving the environment will help maintain a livable atmosphere for many generations to come. Christians should take the lead in preserving God's wondrous creation and the delicately natural systems He uses to sustain the world. He said, "For every animal of the forest is Mine, and the cattle on

TRY THIS

Reduce

Prepackaged foods generate waste in excess packaging. Collect all packaging waste from your household for a week. Weigh it. The following week, collect all packaging waste again, but use less prepackaged food and pack lunches in reusable containers. Weigh it and compare the weight to the first week. By how much were you able to reduce the waste? If you continued to do this for a whole year, how much waste could you reduce? How much waste would be reduced if everyone in the class did this for a whole year? Do you think there is value in reducing waste? Why?

Recycling

FYI

Solar Bike Path

In November of 2014, the town of Krommenie, Netherlands, built a section of bike path using solar panels. The path collects solar energy to power the city and provides a safe bike path for commuters. The use of the solar road can reduce the use of fossil fuels and the formation of pollution. New technology often comes with a high price but is necessary to move forward. At a cost of $3.7 million, SolaRoad developed and installed a 70 meter stretch of solar panel pathway. After 6 months of use, it generated 3,000 kilowatt hours (kWh), enough energy to power one household. With energy costs at about $2/kWh, the money spent on the solar panel road could have powered 173 households. Although the cost of research and development seems high, pursuing alternate forms of renewable energy is good stewardship. This example demonstrates reduction in fossil fuel use as more commuters are riding bikes on a safe bike path and less coal is burned to generate electricity.

a thousand hills" (Psalm 50:10). Every natural resource belongs to God. Praise Him for His provision and honor Him with your stewardship.

LESSON REVIEW

1. What is stewardship?
2. How does God recycle?
3. Why should you be a good steward?
4. How can you be a good steward?
5. Who benefits from wise stewardship?

Solar energy reduces pollution.

UNIT 7

Astronomy

Chapter 1: *Solar System*
Chapter 2: *Planets*
Chapter 3: *Sun, Earth, and Moon*

Vocabulary

annular eclipse
aperture
aphelion
apogee
asteroid
astronomical unit
aurora
chromosphere
comet
convective zone
corona
crater
dwarf planet
eclipse
electromagnetic radiation
electromagnetic spectrum
ellipse
equinox
friction
full moon
gas giant
geocentric
heliocentric
Kuiper belt
lunar calendar
lunar eclipse
lunar regolith
mare
meteor
meteorite
meteoroid
nebula
new moon
penumbra
perigee
perihelion
phase
photosphere
planet
prominence
radiative zone
reflecting telescope
refracting telescope
rille
solar calendar
solar eclipse
solstice
terrestrial planet
umbra
waning moon
waxing moon

Key Ideas

- Systems, order, and organization
- Evidence, models, and explanation
- Change, constancy, and measurement
- Evolution and equilibrium
- Form and function
- Abilities necessary to do scientific inquiry
- Understandings about scientific inquiry
- Earth in the solar system
- Origin and evolution of the earth system
- Abilities of technological design
- Understandings about science and technology
- Natural hazards
- Science and technology in society
- Science as a human endeavor
- Nature of science
- Historical perspectives

SCRIPTURE

The heavens declare the glory of God; the skies proclaim the work of His hands.

Psalm 19:1

7.1.1 *History of Astronomy*

OBJECTIVES

- Chronologically order significant contributions to the history of astronomy.
- Evaluate the significance of major contributions to the study of astronomy.
- Determine the effect of technology on people's understanding of the universe.

VOCABULARY

- **geocentric** centered on or around Earth
- **heliocentric** centered on or around the sun

Even before modern science, people used observations as a means to understand the orderly nature of creation. For example, even in ancient times people knew about five of the planets: Mercury, Venus, Mars, Jupiter, and Saturn. How could the early astronomers distinguish planets from stars? Unlike stars, planets change position in the sky. (The Greek word for *planet* means "wanderer.") People observed planets temporarily joining star patterns before moving to other parts of the sky. These observations alerted them to the existence of these five faraway bodies.

The ancient Greeks were the first to try to explain why the celestial bodies move as they do. Eudoxus (c. 395–c. 337 BC) suggested that the stars and planets appear to move over time because they were attached to a transparent sphere rotating on a separate axis. More than a century later, the famous Greek philosopher and scientist Aristotle (384–322 BC) published his belief that eclipses showed that Earth is a sphere. He said that Earth does not move and that the other celestial bodies move in perfect circles around Earth. Approximately 100 years after Aristotle published his theories, Eratosthenes (276–195 BC) mathematically proved that Earth is a sphere by using geometry. Eratosthenes calculated Earth's circumference using the lengths of the midsummer shadows at Syrene (now Aswan) and Alexandria, along with the distance between the two cities.

Aristotle

Astrolabe

Sailors navigated by using astrolabes to measure the angle between the horizon and stars. You can create your own astrolabe. Obtain a plastic protractor with a hole in the center of the straight part. Cut a 25 cm length of string and tie a large knot in one end. Thread the string through the protractor's hole. Tie a small weight, such as a washer, to the string's free end. Tape a drinking straw along the flat edge of the protractor; make sure the straw extends past the edges of the protractor by several centimeters. Cut a 10 cm × 10 cm square of card stock and punch a hole in it just big enough for the straw to pass through the hole. Slide the card stock over the straw until the card stock touches the protractor. Hold the protractor so the curved side is down and look through the straw at the top of a tall object, such as a tree. Pinch the string against the protractor and write down the number where the string crosses the protractor. Subtract this number from 90 to obtain the object's elevation in degrees.

In 140 AD, the Greek astronomer Ptolemy (100–170 AD) wrote the *Almagest*. Ptolemy's book was the first successful attempt to explain how all the observations of planetary movements fit into a single system. In this work, Ptolemy described a universe in which the sun, moon, and planets revolve around Earth. He even tried to explain why some planets seem to move backward at times. Ptolemy thought that each planet moved in a type of orbit called *an epicycle*, meaning each planet moved in small circles as they orbited Earth in one large circle. The word **geocentric** describes the view that Earth is the center of the universe. This belief influenced scientific thought until the 16th century.

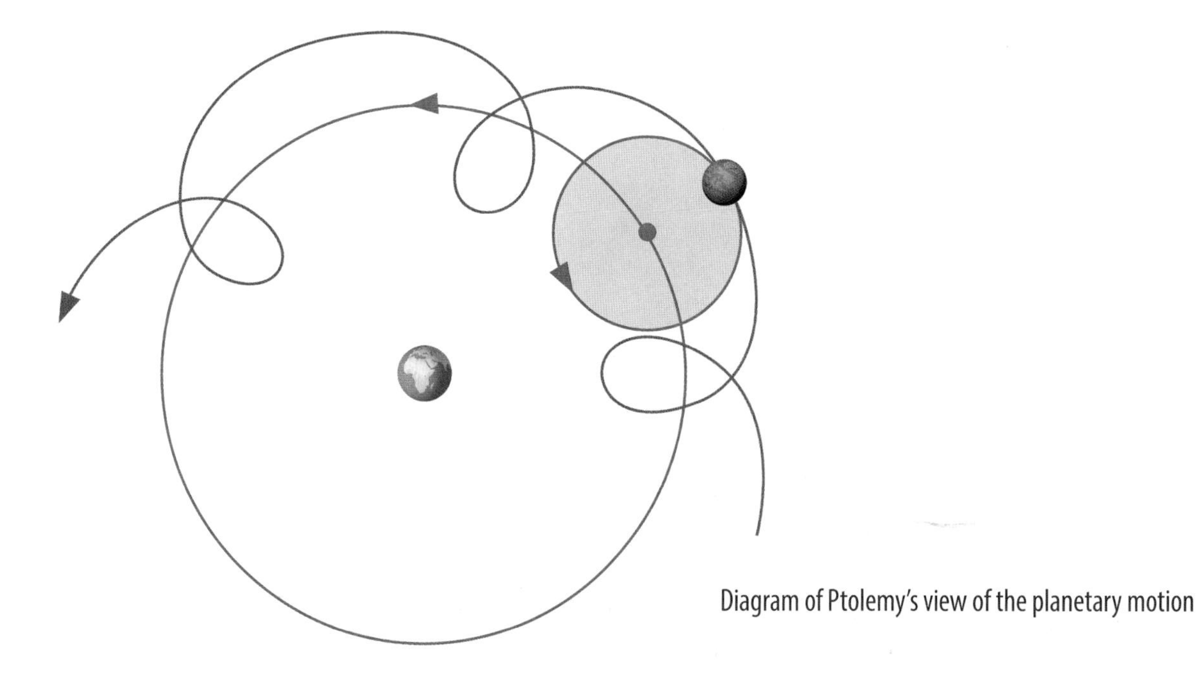

Diagram of Ptolemy's view of the planetary motion

BIBLE CONNECTION

Tell Me the Dream

"In the second year of his reign, Nebuchadnezzar had dreams; his mind was troubled and he could not sleep. So the king summoned the magicians, enchanters, sorcerers, and astrologers to tell him what he had dreamed. When they came in and stood before the king, he said to them, 'I have had a dream that troubles me and I want to know what it means.... Tell me the dream, and I will know that you can interpret it for me.' The astrologers answered the king, 'There is no one on earth who can do what the king asks!' " (Daniel 2:1–3, 9b–10a).

The ancient Babylonians did not distinguish between astrology and astronomy as people do now; the astrologers in Nebuchadnezzar's court were also astronomers. Astrology is the false belief that the movement of the various bodies in the solar system can influence human life. Astronomy is the scientific study of matter beyond Earth's atmosphere. Although these men predicted the movements of the planets, their interpretations of what their false gods meant through the movements was guesswork. Only God could reveal Nebuchadnezzar's dream.

When the Greek and Roman civilizations faded, the knowledge that they had accumulated was not lost. The Arabs built on the Greeks' knowledge of astronomy. Many bright stars have Arabic names. For example, the name *Betelgeuse* (the bright orange star in the constellation Orion) is Arabic in origin. The Arabs perfected an instrument called *an astrolabe* to determine the altitude of the sun and stars and to create accurate charts of their apparent movements. They also invented algebra, which used the works of the Greeks and Indians, and they introduced the number system that includes the number zero. These systems enabled the precise calculation of astronomical distances and movements.

Until the 1500s, Western civilizations were still using Ptolemy's system. But Polish astronomer Nicolaus Copernicus (1473–1543) decided that there must be a simpler system. In place of Ptolemy's geocentric view of complex epicycles, Copernicus proposed that the sun was the center of the solar system. The word **heliocentric** describes this view. The heliocentric view of the universe easily explains the movements of the planets and even explains why some planets appear to move backward at times. In his book

Arabic astrolabe

HISTORY

Music of the Spheres

You may know Pythagoras as the person who developed the Pythagorean Theorem, which is $a^2 + b^2 = c^2$. He also suggested the idea of the "Music of the Spheres." Pythagoras believed that the universe was made of 10 spheres nested inside each other. These spheres were named for objects they were thought to carry: Counter-Earth, Earth, Moon, Sun, Mercury, Venus, Mars, Jupiter, Saturn, and Fixed Stars. Pythagoras also believed that these vast objects produced a tone as they sailed along their courses, much like the whistle of a ball spun on a string. He thought that if a person could hear them, these spinning spheres would be in beautiful harmony, because he thought that the distances between the planets must correspond to the harmonic ratios between musical notes.

Nicolaus Copernicus

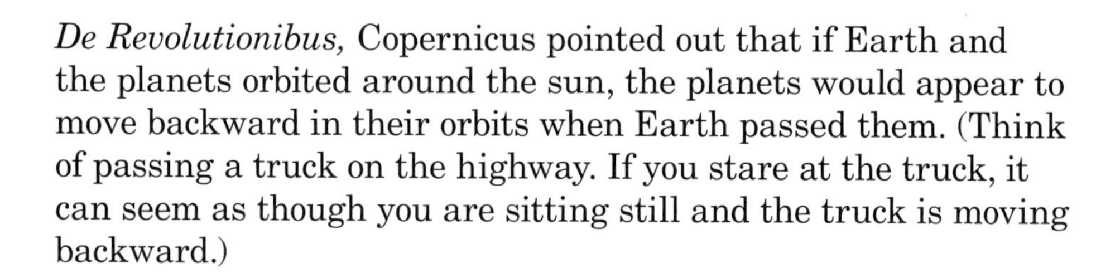

De Revolutionibus, Copernicus pointed out that if Earth and the planets orbited around the sun, the planets would appear to move backward in their orbits when Earth passed them. (Think of passing a truck on the highway. If you stare at the truck, it can seem as though you are sitting still and the truck is moving backward.)

Johannes Kepler

Copernicus's work was expanded by German mathematician and astronomer Johannes Kepler (1571–1630). Kepler benefitted from the work of Danish nobleman Tycho Brahe (1546–1601), who created and updated precise tables of the planets' motion and improved astronomical instruments. As Kepler studied Brahe's data in light of the heliocentric view, he discovered certain laws of planetary motion. For example, planets travel in elliptical orbits with the sun as one of two focus points of those orbits. Kepler's laws have been an important foundation to the study of the solar system. They have helped chart the orbits of planets, the moon, and spacecraft. Although Kepler explained the laws that govern the motion of planets, he could not explain what caused the planets to move.

Galileo Galilei

In the early 17th century, Galileo Galilei (1564–1642) improved the telescope and used it for astronomy. His observations supported the heliocentric view. For example, he observed that Venus does not revolve around Earth. Galileo also made new discoveries about the universe, including the discovery of four of Jupiter's moons. The existence of these moons disproved the idea that only Earth could attract celestial bodies into orbit.

Sir Isaac Newton (1642–1727) identified why the planets orbit the sun and why the moon orbits Earth. Newton suggested that

Sir Isaac Newton

celestial bodies keep their orbits through a force called *gravity*. He went on to mathematically describe the motions of the planets in terms of their mass, momentum, and force. Newton's laws are still applied today as scientists launch spacecraft throughout the solar system. Newton's work tied together the knowledge gathered by Copernicus, Brahe, Kepler, Galileo, and many others.

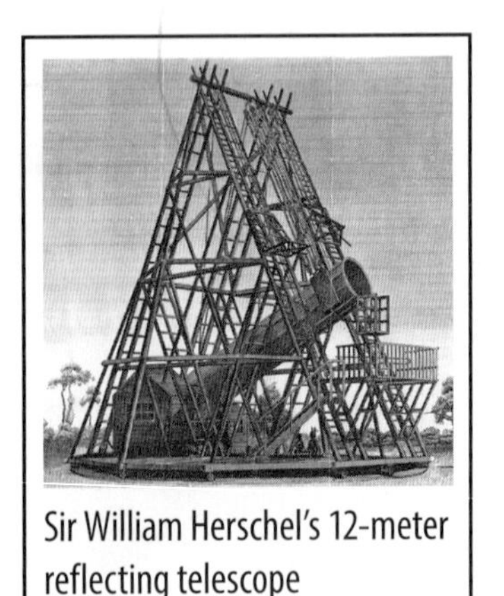
Sir William Herschel's 12-meter reflecting telescope

German astronomer Sir William Herschel (1738–1822), the astronomer who discovered Uranus, was famous for building large, powerful telescopes. Some of the objects that Herschel studied were fuzzy patches of light, which others thought were some sort of luminous fluid called *nebulae*. Herschel's telescopes enabled him to see that a few of these nebulae were actually clusters of stars. However, he was not able to build a telescope strong enough to verify that all the nebulae were star clusters. Herschel called these clusters *island universes* of stars.

As stronger telescopes were built, scientists learned more. In the 1920s, American astronomer Edwin Hubble (1889–1953), discovered that Herschel's island universes are galaxies outside the Milky Way galaxy. Until that time, the Milky Way was all anybody knew about the universe. Most people assumed that even Herschel's island universes were still part of the star system. Hubble not only discovered that the universe is

Galaxy NGC 1309 is 100 million light-years from Earth.

HISTORY

A Changing Understanding

Galileo's use of the telescope gave him a unique view into the solar system and convinced him of the validity of Copernicus's theory that the Earth moved around the sun. Other scientists disputed his finding because they did not have access to this new technology and because the idea of a heliocentric solar system went against the accepted scientific views of the day. When church leaders disputed Galileo's findings, they echoed the opinions of leading scientists, who were reluctant to trust such revolutionary data from one source. Heliotropism was not heretical; it had been used by Pope Gregory XIII to revise the calendar although it was still considered unproven. Ultimately it was not Galileo's scientific findings that got him sentenced to house arrest by the Church; it was his attacks on the biblical arguments against Copernicus's theory and on the Pope. Politics rather than science got Galileo into trouble. In 1992, the Roman Catholic Church officially cleared Galileo's name.

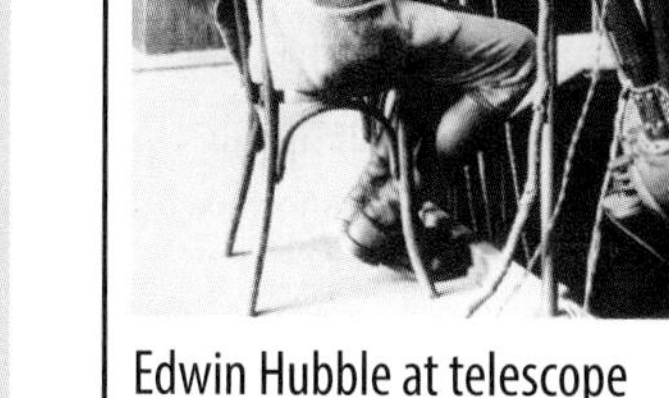

Edwin Hubble at telescope

wider than the galaxy, but he discovered that the universe is expanding. This discovery has become an important part of discussions about the physical beginning of the universe.

Today, advanced telescopes, supercomputers, and spacecraft continue to expand people's knowledge of the universe. But even as new discoveries answer some questions, other discoveries lead to more questions. Many wonders of God's universe wait to be explained and explored.

LESSON REVIEW

1. Starting with Copernicus and ending with Newton, list the scientists who made significant contributions to developing the heliocentric view of the universe and identify each person's contribution.
2. What was significant about Ptolemy's explanation of the universe?
3. Explain the importance of the Arabian contributions to astronomy.
4. In what way did Eratosthenes's calculation of Earth's circumference affect people's understanding about Earth?
5. Explain one way in which the technology of the telescope affected people's understanding of the universe.

7.1.2 *Calendars*

OBJECTIVES

- Determine the usefulness of the sun in measuring time during a day and during a year.
- Summarize the development of the Gregorian calendar.
- Evaluate the benefits of lunar and solar calendars.

VOCABULARY

- **lunar calendar** a calendar that uses the phases of the moon
- **solar calendar** a calendar that uses the amount of time Earth takes to orbit the sun

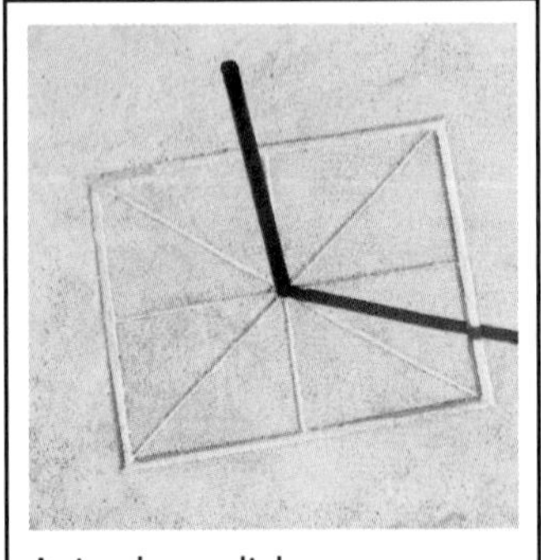
A simple sundial

Ancient people did not fully understand the movements of celestial bodies in the solar system or why the patterns of the stars in the sky changed. However, they did notice the patterns and cycles, and they kept records of the orderly patterns of God's creation. By using their records, they tracked the passage of time and seasons.

Before the invention of mechanical clocks, a simple and common device was used to track time. This device, the sundial, uses a vertical piece to cast a shadow on a horizontal surface. As the sun moves across the sky above the sundial, the sundial's shadow moves. A sundial enabled people to divide daylight time into smaller units. In this way, people could organize their days by time. For example, in one of Jesus's parables in Matthew 20, laborers expected to be paid according to the amount of time they worked.

On a larger scale, keeping track of the sun's movement across the stars helped early farmers determine the best times of year to plant and harvest different crops. Such records led to the creation of calendars. A calendar is a system for organizing time. Different civilizations developed various calendars according to their observations of the sky. It takes Earth a year to revolve once around the sun. The moon takes about a month to revolve around Earth. And in one day, the Earth spins one time on its axis. Most nations now use a calendar in which one year has 365 or 366 days. Each of the 12 months has 28–31 days. However, early calendars were different.

A complex sundial

Astronomers in ancient Babylon (what is now Iraq) tracked the positions of the planets and the moon as early as 700 BC. Their studies resulted in a calendar with 12 months; each month began with a new moon. A calendar that uses the phases of the moon is called a **lunar calendar**. The Babylonians also had a number system based on the number 60. The concept is similar to the metric system, which uses 10. The idea of a 60-second minute and a 60-minute hour came from the Babylonian number system.

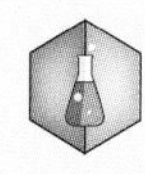

TRY THIS

Cast a Shadow

On a sunny day, fix an upright meterstick outdoors. Track the shadow at regular intervals throughout the day. Graph the data. How can shadows help people keep track of time? What can shadows demonstrate about Earth's relationship to the sun? Could shadows help people keep track of time throughout the year as well as time throughout the day?

The most widely used calendar today is called *the Gregorian calendar*. It is known as a **solar calendar** because it uses the amount of time Earth takes to orbit the sun. However, the Gregorian calendar had its roots in the lunar calendars of ancient Rome. In fact, most ancient calendars were lunar calendars. The Gregorian calendar calculated 355 days in a year. Since the calendar had about 11 fewer days than a true solar year, the calendar dates would shift through the seasons. For example, over time spring would shift from March to October. To keep the calendar in line with the seasons, extra months were added. The system eventually proved to be confusing and ineffective. Julius Caesar consulted astronomer Sosigenes of Alexandria to reform the calendar. They created the Julian calendar after calculating that each year has 365.25 days. Days were added to the year 46 BC to return the seasons to their original positions in the year. An extra day was added every four years to keep the seasons in place according to the calendar. A year in which an extra day, February 29th, is added to the calendar is called *a leap year.*

Julius Caesar

The Julian calendar was not quite accurate. In the mid-1500s, Pope Gregory XIII turned to astronomers for the solution. They determined that there are actually 365.242 days in a year. The Pope dropped 10 days from the year 1582 to bring the calendar back into line with the seasons. To keep the Gregorian calendar accurate, he restricted leap years to years that are divisible by 4, but century years are only leap years if they are evenly divisible by 400. For example, the year 2000 was a leap year, but the year 2100 will not be. This adjustment brought the average year length closer to 365.242 days. Later, years evenly divisible by 4,000 were declared not to be leap years. These adjustments will keep the Gregorian calendar accurate for another 20,000 years.

Pope Gregory XIII

The Gregorian calendar is not the only calendar in use around the world. In some cultures, the Gregorian calendar is used for business purposes, but a lunar calendar is used to determine certain holidays and religious observances. For example, India

FYI

The Jewish Calendar
The Jewish calendar uses the cycles of the moon. The names of the months in the Jewish calendar are Babylonian; they were adopted during the Babylonian exile. The Jewish calendar starts with the creation of Adam.

On the Jewish calendar
- Abraham was born in 1948.
- The Israelites' exodus from Egypt was in 2448.
- Jesus was born about 3754–3756.
- Columbus came to America in 5252.

HISTORY

Accurate Clocks
For thousands of years, people have observed the sky and devised ways to mark the movements of the sun and the moon. For example, an arrangement of stones found at Nabta in southern Egypt are arranged to line up with the sun on the longest day of the year. The stone arrangement is estimated to be 6,000–7,000 years old. Stonehenge, built near Salisbury, England, around 2000 BC, lines up with the sun on the longest and shortest days of the year.

Stonehenge

The Maya, who lived in Mexico and Central America, developed advanced systems of mathematics and astronomy. They had a number system that included the number 0, and they designed buildings so that at set times the sun would shine through precise openings in walls or would cast shadows in predetermined places. The Maya also developed a complex calendar that included an accurate solar year.

Temple of Kukulcan, Chichen Itza, Mexico

BIBLE CONNECTION

The King's Birthday
In the 6th century, a scholar designed the current system of dating from the birth of Jesus. AD means "anno Domini," which is Latin for "in the year of our Lord." BC means "before Christ." There is no year 0 between BC and AD; the calendar transitions from 1 BC directly to 1 AD. Today many scholars believe that Christ was born several years before 1 AD.

and most Muslim nations use the Gregorian calendar for civil purposes. In India, religious observances are determined according to the ancient Hindu lunar calendar that includes adjustments to keep its months aligned with the seasons. Muslims follow a purely lunar calendar established by the Koran for religious observances. Because this calendar does not make any adjustments for the solar year, Muslim religious days do not always occur in the same season. Israel officially uses a lunar calendar that includes an extra month at precise intervals to keep it aligned with the seasons.

LESSON REVIEW

1. Why do you think sundials were more common than solar calendars in ancient times?
2. Summarize the important people and events in the development of the Gregorian calendar.
3. What benefits are associated with a lunar calendar?
4. What benefits are associated with a solar calendar?
5. Why might some cultures use both a solar and a lunar calendar? Use an example to support your answer.

OBJECTIVES

- Evaluate the usefulness of refracting and reflecting telescopes.
- Summarize the key problems and solutions for accurate Earth-based observations of celestial bodies.

VOCABULARY

- **aperture** an opening through which light passes
- **reflecting telescope** a telescope that uses a series of mirrors to magnify objects
- **refracting telescope** a telescope that uses a series of lenses to magnify objects

For thousands of years, people observed the universe by looking up at the sky without any instruments to aid them. Astronomers studied the stars, made charts, and used their observations to try to understand the universe. In the early 1600s, Dutch spectacle makers invented an instrument that could make distant objects appear closer, which was the foundation of the telescope.

Around 1609, Galileo built his own telescope and used it to study the heavens. The telescope widened scientists' view of the universe. Even early telescopes revealed thousands of faint stars never before seen. Today there are many kinds of telescopes that continue to expand the view of the vast universe and help people appreciate God's creative power.

An optical telescope enlarges images of faraway objects that give off or reflect visible light. A telescope that uses a series of lenses to magnify objects is called a **refracting telescope**. The largest lens is called *the objective lens*, and it collects and focuses light. The objective lens is also called the **aperture**, which is the opening through which light passes. Larger apertures permit more light to enter the telescope, which increases the number of objects that can be seen. The second lens, called *the eyepiece*, magnifies the image produced by the objective lens. Different eyepieces produce different magnifications, but at a certain point increased magnification only makes the image look blurry, similar to the way an image on a computer screen becomes blurry if you zoom in too far. The objective lens limits the usefulness of a refracting telescope. If the lens is too large, it sags

Refracting Telescope

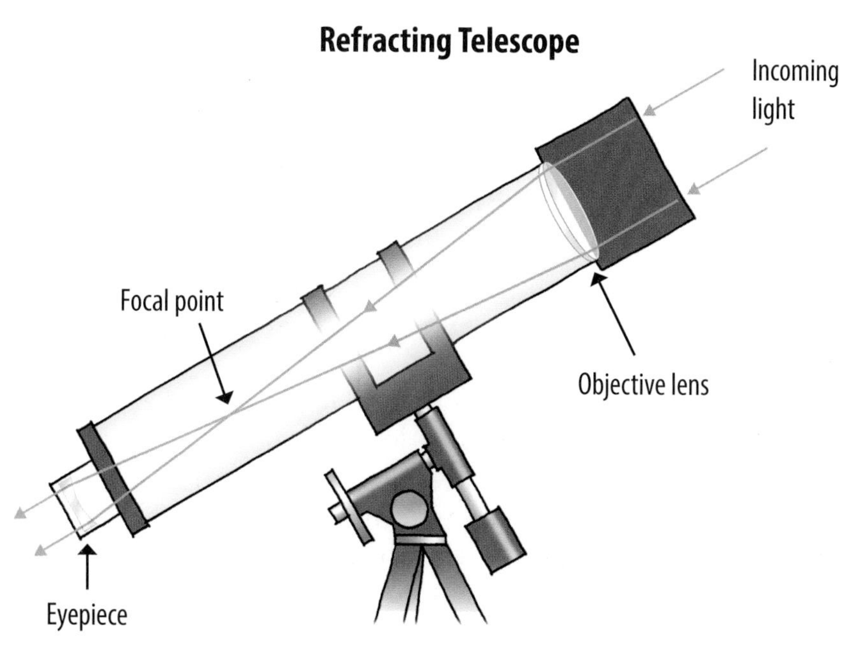

TRY THIS

Reflecting Telescope

On a clear night, place a concave mirror, such as a shaving or makeup mirror, on a table near a window to reflect the moon or stars. Position the mirror at an angle to the window so you can see the reflected light against the window. Place a flat mirror between the concave mirror and the window so you can see the reflection in the flat mirror. Adjust the position and angle of both mirrors until you can see a clear image. Use a convex lens, such as a hand lens, to examine the reflection that appears in the flat mirror. Try magnifying the image further by using more mirrors. What advantages or disadvantages would your reflecting telescope have compared with a homemade refracting telescope?

under its own weight and distorts the image. Another problem with refracting telescopes is that lenses do not consistently bend different colors of light across their entire surfaces. This inconsistency causes colors and objects to appear distorted around the edges of the images, which is called *chromatic aberration*. However, this problem can be fixed by using a series of different types of lenses made of different materials.

A **reflecting telescope** uses a series of mirrors to magnify objects. Light entering the telescope is reflected off a large, curved mirror to a focal point above the mirror. A second mirror may be used to reflect this light to an eyepiece. Because these telescopes' mirrors can be very large, they can collect more light than refracting telescopes. Reflecting telescopes can produce images of stars that are very far away. The mirrors do not focus colors differently as lenses do, so all of the colors of the magnified object are in focus at the same time. Some very large reflecting telescopes have several mirrors that work together to collect light and deliver it to the same focus. For example, each of the twin telescopes at the W. M. Keck Observatory in Hawaii have 36 hexagonal mirrors that work together. Each of these telescopes stands 10 m tall!

Buildings called *observatories* house large optical telescopes, regardless of their type. Observatories protect the telescopes and provide a more comfortable place to work for people using

Reflecting Telescope

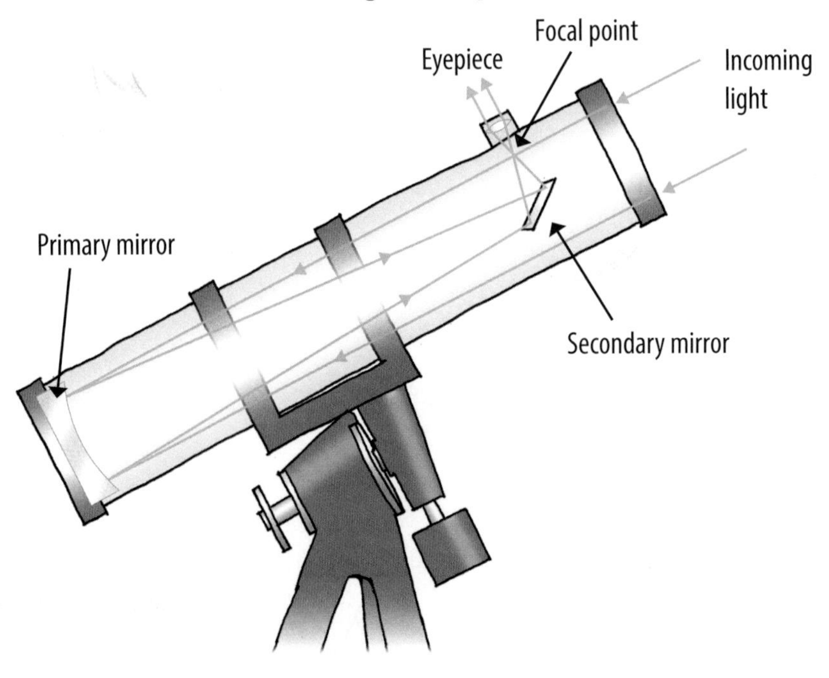

FYI

Twinkle, Twinkle, Little Planet

Why do stars twinkle but planets do not? Planets are closer to Earth than stars are. Stars are so far away that even through a telescope they look like pinpoints of light; through a telescope, planets look like disks of light. The light from the pinpoint of a star seems to shimmer as it comes through the atmosphere, but the different disturbances from across the disk of a planet cancel each other out. So planets seem to shine with a steady light.

the telescopes. Even with a large telescope, observing celestial objects faces several challenges. Light pollution from cities can brighten the sky, limiting the view of distant light objects. In addition, the atmosphere affects what can be seen. Water vapor, heat, and wind change the atmosphere's composition and change how light passes through it. Light bends whenever it passes through a different substance, and the degree and number of times it bends affects how well an object can be seen. Observatories are often built on mountaintops to minimize these problems.

The idea of having an observatory in space was first suggested in the 1940s. Scientists wanted to place telescopes above Earth's atmosphere in order to get the clearest images possible. In the 1970s, the European Space Agency (ESA) and the National Aeronautics and Space Administration (NASA) began building

W. M. Keck Observatory

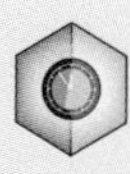

HISTORY

Astronomic Photos

Cameras offer a great benefit to astronomy. The use of photography provides a permanent record, and a camera can gather light over long periods so fainter objects can be observed. The moon was photographed as early as 1840, and the sun was photographed in 1845. The stars were first photographed in 1850.

FYI

Buyer Beware
The more light that a telescope collects, the brighter and more detailed an object will appear. The amount of light a telescope collects depends on its aperture. A telescope's aperture is the diameter of the objective lens or mirror. The larger a telescope's aperture, the more light it can gather and the more detail you can see. During ideal viewing conditions, a refracting telescope's useful magnification is limited to the size of its aperture in millimeters multiplied by 2. However, atmospheric conditions often reduce the useful magnification. In other words, no matter what the advertised magnification, a refracting telescope with a 50 mm aperture is capable of producing clear images only up to 100x magnification.

Hubble Space Telescope above Earth

the Hubble Space Telescope, which today orbits about 600 km above Earth's surface. This telescope features several different instruments that take pictures and record data from light in multiple wavelengths. Hubble has produced images of objects farther away than many telescopes on Earth can detect, and it has done so with greater resolution. Hubble has made many wondrous discoveries possible. Scientists have been able to see stars like the sun at the end of their life cycles, star explosions, and the building blocks of planets forming around young stars in the constellation Orion. Hubble instruments have monitored weather conditions on Mars and enabled greater study of black holes. The Hubble Space Telescope has revealed volcanoes erupting on Io, one of Jupiter's moons, and permitted scientists to witness the Shoemaker-Levy 9 comet breaking apart and crashing into Jupiter as well.

LESSON REVIEW

1. What is the basic difference between refracting and reflecting telescopes?
2. If you were building an optical telescope today, which type of telescope would you build? Why?
3. Why are mountaintops popular locations for observatories?
4. What advantage does the Hubble Space Telescope have over telescopes located on Earth?

Objects such as stars and galaxies emit different types of radiation, most of which are not visible light. To learn more about the universe, scientists study a form of wave energy called **electromagnetic radiation**, which has both electrical and magnetic properties. Each type of electromagnetic radiation represents a different wavelength, just as the different colors of light have different wavelengths. The **electromagnetic spectrum** is the entire wavelength range of electromagnetic radiation. Earth's atmosphere blocks most electromagnetic radiation, but it lets in visible light, radio waves, infrared light (which is sensed as heat), and some ultraviolet light. Visible light is a very tiny part of the electromagnetic spectrum.

Astronomers can detect different types of radiation by using various instruments both inside and outside the atmosphere, but a different type of telescope is needed to examine each type of radiation. These telescopes are called *nonoptical telescopes*, and they are very different from telescopes with lenses and mirrors. Some nonoptical telescopes are huge bowls set in the earth; others are launched into space. Nonoptical telescopes allow scientists to study light from wavelengths that do not include visible light. Because they do not use visible light like optical telescopes, nonoptical telescopes can be used both day and night.

A common type of electromagnetic radiation known as *radio waves* is used for communication on Earth. In 1932, American radio engineer Karl Jansky discovered radio waves coming from

OBJECTIVES

- Identify the radiation used and the purposes for nonoptical telescopes.
- Explain why the study of the universe is not limited to what people can see.
- Summarize the path that data follows from a space telescope to an archive facility.

VOCABULARY

- **electromagnetic radiation** a form of wave energy that has both electrical and magnetic properties
- **electromagnetic spectrum** the entire wavelength range of electromagnetic radiation

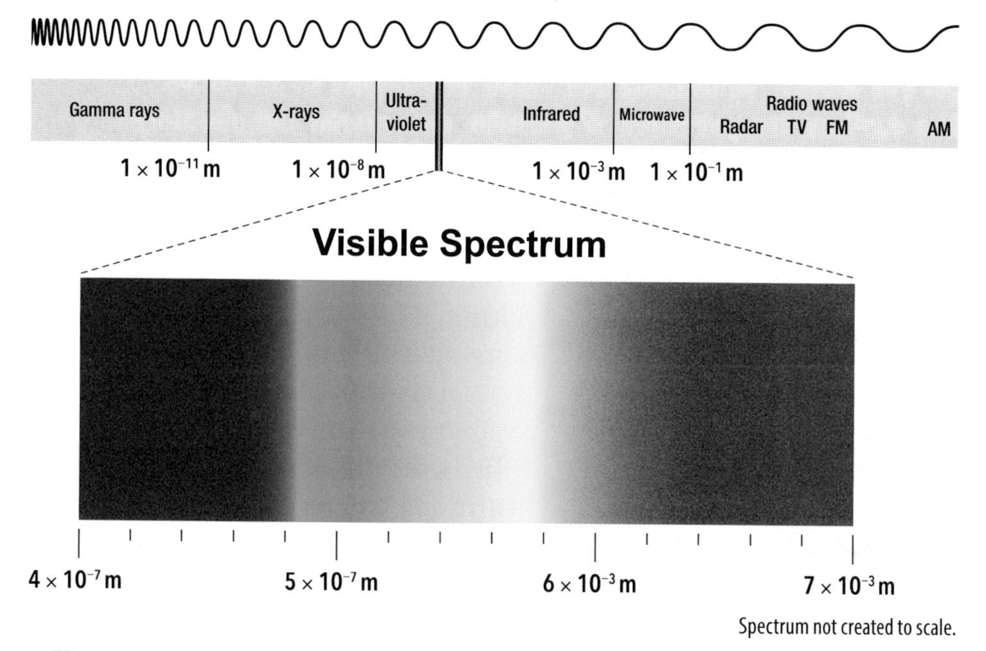

Spectrum not created to scale.

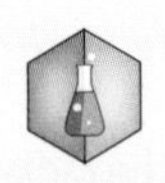

TRY THIS

Detect the Infrared

A liquid crystal sheet includes a material similar to the infrared detectors in telescopes and mapping devices. Place one hand into cold water until your hand feels quite cold. Dry your hand and then place two fingers from each hand on a liquid crystal sheet. Observe the images and how they change. Experiment with putting objects of different temperatures on the liquid crystal sheet. How might an infrared detector help scientists learn about stars or about volcanoes on other moons and planets? Is the liquid crystal detector sheet as sensitive in the sunlight?

The Karl G. Jansky Very Large Array radio telescope in New Mexico, United States

the Milky Way. Radio astronomy was developed in the 1940s to pick up these waves. Radio telescopes do not all look alike. Many of them are very large in order to capture the small amount of radio radiation from space objects that reaches Earth. Since radio wavelengths can measure up to 10 m, telescopes that focus on the longer wavelengths have receiving dishes that look like bowl-shaped metal nets. This type of structure reduces the weight of the receivers and the effect of gravity on its shapes. Some radio telescopes are built as enormous bowls set into the ground with a receiving device hung above them. In order to aim this type of telescope, the receiver is moved to collect different signals reflecting from the bowl. Radio telescopes may be linked together to work as one giant telescope. For example, the 27 radio telescopes of the Karl G. Jansky Very Large Array in New Mexico can be spread out to work as a single receiver that is 36 km across. Scientists use radio telescopes to measure the surface temperature of planets, determine the chemical components of celestial bodies, and identify distant stars and galaxies.

The type of electromagnetic radiation that people sense as heat is known as *infrared radiation.* Infrared astronomy actually began with Sir William Herschel in 1800, but extensive infrared exploration of the universe did not begin until the 1960s. Infrared telescopes are often placed on mountaintops where they are above most of the water vapor in the atmosphere, which absorbs infrared light. In 1983, NASA and two

The Spitzer Space Telescope views radiation in the infrared spectrum.

European partner agencies launched the Infrared Astronomical Satellite into space. This infrared telescope detected heat from stars being born. It also found cooling stars that optical telescopes could not find, and it provided evidence that stars other than the sun have planets. Since then, other infrared telescopes have advanced and improved on the observations made by earlier telescopes. Newer infrared telescopes can detect temperature differences on the surface of planets or determine the gases that make up a planet's atmosphere.

The type of electromagnetic radiation that causes suntans is called *ultraviolet radiation*. Earth's ozone layer blocks out most ultraviolet light, so ultraviolet telescopes must be placed at very high elevations or in space. By the 1940s, scientists were launching rockets with ultraviolet detectors on board. Scientists study ultraviolet radiation to learn about star formation and chemicals in the sun and stars. They also study the way different gases respond to ultraviolet light. This research helps them learn about the gases and the objects the gases are associated with.

Earth's atmosphere blocks most X-rays and gamma rays, which are two more types of electromagnetic radiation. Therefore, X-ray and gamma-ray telescopes are usually placed in space. The Chandra X-Ray Observatory, launched in 1999, studies black

The Galaxy Evolution Explorer views radiation in the ultraviolet spectrum.

FYI

Cosmic Explosions

Gamma-ray bursts are flashes of gamma rays that occur in space. If you could see gamma rays, you would see that one of these bursts would briefly outshine all other sources of gamma rays. Astronomers believe that these gamma-ray bursts indicate the creation of a phenomenon called *a black hole*, which is an extreme gravity field that prevents even light from escaping from it. The length of a gamma-ray burst could indicate how a black hole was formed. A long burst of gamma rays likely comes from a supernova core that collapsed to form a black hole. However, a gamma-ray burst is not emitted by every supernova. Long gamma-ray bursts last between two and several hundred seconds. A short burst of gamma rays is thought to be caused either by two neutron stars colliding and forming a black hole or by a neutron star being sucked into a black hole and creating a bigger black hole. Short gamma-ray bursts last less than two seconds.

FYI

James Webb Space Telescope

In the late 1990s, before the Hubble Space Telescope (HST) was 10 years old, NASA and other international agencies began building the James Webb Space Telescope (JWST) as the HST's successor. The earliest launch date was determined to be sometime in 2018. The JWST's foldable mirror has a 6.4-meter diameter, which is seven times larger than the one on the HST. Eighteen beryllium segments covered in a thin layer of gold comprise the mirror. To protect the telescope from thermal radiation, the agencies designed a five-layer, collapsible sun shield that measures 150 m^2. Both the mirror and the sun shield's design include the capability to expand once the telescope has traveled its 30-day journey into space. The JWST will reside approximately 1.5 million km away from Earth, on its dark side, and use infrared to record things such as young galaxies and the birth of stars. Future peopled spacecraft will have access to the telescope by way of an external, side-mounted docking ring.

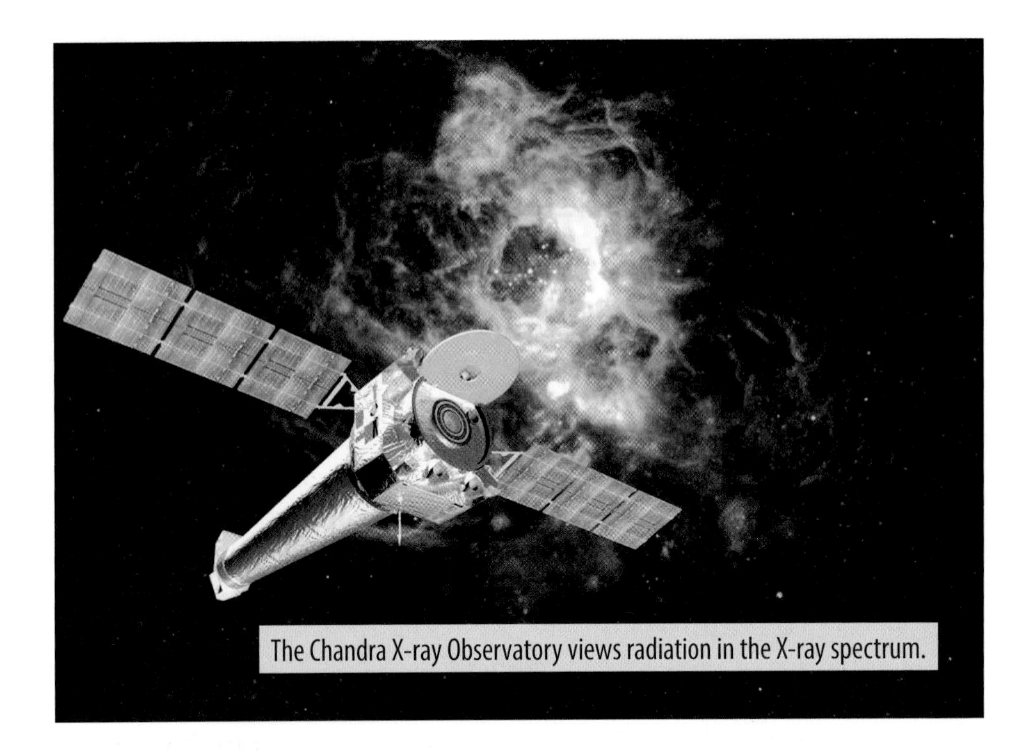

The Chandra X-ray Observatory views radiation in the X-ray spectrum.

holes, star and galaxy life cycles, and exploding stars called *supernovas*. Scientists have discovered X-rays coming from all over the universe. This discovery suggests there may be a great number of radiation sources in the universe that have yet to be identified.

Cosmic gamma rays were discovered accidentally in the 1960s. Artificial satellites designed to detect the gamma rays produced by atomic bomb tests on Earth detected gamma rays beyond Earth's atmosphere. Gamma rays have a very short wavelength, so they can only be detected indirectly. They collide with electrons as they pass through detecting devices, and the collision creates charged particles that can be detected. Gamma-ray telescopes are used to explore black holes, supernovas, and small, dense stars called *pulsars* that give off regular pulses of radio waves, X-rays, or gamma waves.

What happens to all of the data collected by space-based telescopes? Telescopes continuously collect three types of data that are stored on memory chips: system function data, direction, and observation. The data can be sent to Earth in several different ways. In rare cases, the data is transmitted to Earth as soon as it comes in, which is called *real time data*. Most often, however, data is sent to Earth at predetermined times through a satellite relay system or a ground-based antenna system. In the satellite relay system, the telescope sends its data to another satellite, which in turn relays the data to a facility on the ground. With a ground-based antenna system, the data is transmitted directly from the telescope to a receiving facility on the ground. The receiving station then sends the data on to a processing center.

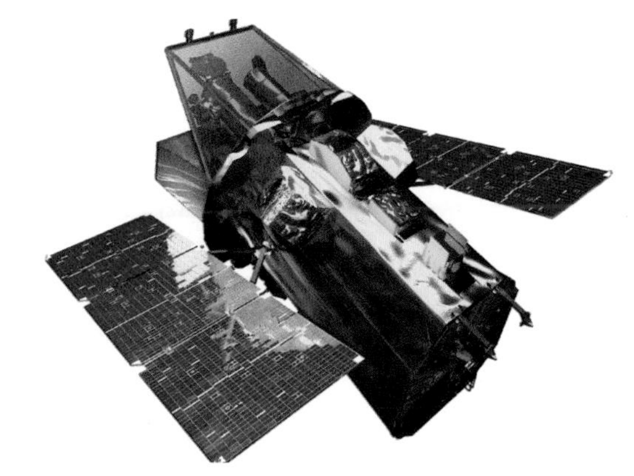

The Swift gamma-ray burst detecting satellite views radiation in the gamma-ray spectrum.

Once the data is at the processing center, it has to be organized. The telescope records and time stamps all its data in groups of bits, called *data packets*. (A bit is a single piece of computer information.) Each of a telescope's systems sends packets of information about how well the telescope was functioning, where the telescope was pointed, or what it saw. A scientist must be able to review all three types of data at the same time to know how good the data is. The job of the data processing center is to take the separate packets and arrange them so a scientist can use them. Data from telescopes in space is eventually made available for anyone to use. To allow multiple systems to understand the data from any telescope without needing a unique program to decode it, a format called *Flexible Image Transport Standard* (*FITS*) was developed.

Finally, the data is stored in an archive facility. At first, only the scientists who requested the data are permitted to use it. This phase is called *the proprietary phase*, and it lasts about a year. After the proprietary phase ends, the data is made available to anyone in what is called *the public phase*. Typically, the data is then made available through the Internet.

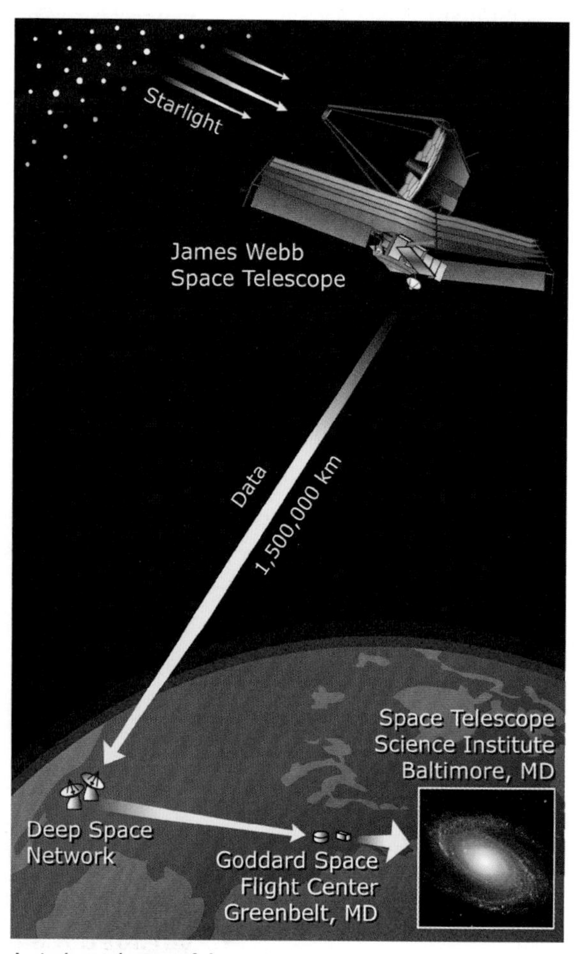

Artist's rendering of the projected data path from the James Webb Space Telescope to an archive facility

LESSON REVIEW

1. What types of electromagnetic radiation can reach Earth?
2. Identify one purpose for each type of nonoptical telescope.
3. Why are optical telescopes not sufficient tools for thoroughly studying the universe?
4. Summarize the path data follows from a space telescope to an archive facility.

7.1.5 Solar System

OBJECTIVES

- Distinguish among the major celestial bodies in the solar system.
- Compare two prominent views of the creation of the solar system.

VOCABULARY

- **asteroid** a rocky object that orbits the sun
- **dwarf planet** a spherical object that orbits the sun but is not large enough to move other objects from its orbit
- **gas giant** a large, gaseous planet of the outer solar system
- **nebula** a vast, moving interstellar cloud of gas and dust
- **planet** a spherical object that orbits the sun and has removed other objects from its orbit
- **terrestrial planet** a small, dense, rocky planet of the inner solar system

Exploring the universe begins with Earth's solar system. At the center of the solar system is the sun. Depending on a person's understanding of the solar system, up to five types of celestial bodies orbit the sun. All scientists agree that planets, asteroids, and comets orbit the sun. Many scientists acknowledge a class of planets called *dwarf planets*. Some scientists believe that an additional group of objects, called *the Oort cloud*, exists at the outermost reaches of the solar system.

According to the International Astronomical Union (IAU), a **planet** has three important attributes. First, it orbits the sun; second, its own gravity shaped it into a sphere; and third, its size and gravity are great enough to have cleared its own path around the sun by attracting any smaller objects in its orbit. Eight objects in the solar system qualify as planets. These planets are generally divided into two groups known as *terrestrial planets* and *gas giants*. A **terrestrial planet** is a small, dense, rocky planet with few or no moons that orbits close enough to the sun to receive its warmth. Extending out from the sun, the terrestrial planets are Mercury, Venus, Earth, and Mars. A **gas giant** is a large, gaseous planet with a very low density and many moons that orbits too far from the sun to receive significant warmth. From closest to farthest from the sun, the gas giants are Jupiter, Saturn, Uranus, and Neptune.

In 2006, the IAU created the new category of *dwarf planet* for certain solar system objects. A **dwarf planet** has four attributes.

Earth's solar system: the sun, Mercury, Venus, Earth, Mars, the asteroid belt, Jupiter, Saturn, Uranus, Neptune

Meteor shower

Like planets, a dwarf planet orbits the sun and its own gravity shaped it into a sphere. But unlike a true planet, a dwarf planet has not cleared its own path around the sun. And unlike similar celestial bodies, a dwarf planet does not orbit around any celestial body except the sun. Currently known dwarf planets are made almost entirely of rock and ice, but this is not a necessary condition for being classified as a dwarf planet. Pluto was once considered a planet, but it is now classified as a dwarf planet because it has not cleared its own path around the sun. Other dwarf planets in the solar system include Ceres and Eris.

An **asteroid** is a rocky object that can be a variety of sizes and that orbits the sun. Most asteroids are located between the orbits of Mars and Jupiter in what is called *the astroid belt.* Similar to asteroids are large objects composed mostly of ice, which are called *comets.* Each comet has its own orbit around the sun. Smaller objects that are thought to have broken off asteroids or comets are called *meteoroids.* When a meteoroid enters Earth's atmosphere, it is called a *meteor.* If a meteoroid strikes Earth's surface, then it is called a *meteorite.*

The Oort cloud is a theoretical sphere of icy bodies surrounding the solar system. Some scientists believe that comets may begin in the Oort cloud. However, other scientists do not believe that the Oort cloud exists at all.

How exactly did God create the solar system? According to young-earth theory, which states that God created the universe out of nothing in six literal days, Earth was created first as a featureless planet covered by water and surrounded by darkness. The first day was established with the creation of light and regular intervals of light and dark on Earth. On the second day, God created the atmosphere. On the third day, God created dry land and bodies of water along with all plants, and on the fourth day, God separated the light into the sun, moon, and stars. God finished His creation in two more days by creating all creatures for the water and air on the fifth day and all land creatures and humans on the sixth day. According to this view, God made all things in an instant. Therefore, there is no need to explain how atoms may have bonded to form various things such as the sun

Comet

or planets. In addition, since God created the solar system in an instant, there is no need to explain why each object exists where it does because God simply put each one where He wanted them.

In contrast, other Christians believe God created the solar system over a long period of time. This old-earth theory assumes that God initially created particles out of nothing, but then allowed the particles to interact and form the universe over billions of years. Many old-earth scientists believe that dust and gas in space gathered together in a vast, moving cloud between the stars called a **nebula**. (*Nebula* is the Latin word for "cloud.") The nebula from which the solar system is thought to have formed is called *the solar nebula*. Scientists theorize the solar nebula would have been mostly hydrogen and helium with some heavier elements and that it collapsed when an increasing number of particles was drawn together by gravity. As the nebula collapsed, the dust and gas were pulled toward the nebula's center to create a sphere. Then, as gravity pulled more material into the sphere, the density of the sphere increased and its gravity became more powerful. The sphere's increasing density had two effects. First, the temperature at the sphere's core rose. Second, the sphere's rate of rotation increased as material was pulled into it. You can visualize this effect by picturing a spinning ice skater who pulls her arms in to increase the rate of her spin. However, as the nebula spun faster, some of its particles moved away from its center. Think of a person spinning a ball on the end of a string. The faster the person's hand spins the string, the more the ball tries to pull away from the person's hand. In a similar way, if the nebula spun fast enough, then some of the material on its perimeter would spread out from the sphere to form a disk around a central bulge.

Nebula

Once the middle of the solar nebula contained sufficient mass and heat, a process called *nuclear fusion* would have begun. Nuclear fusion would have created so much pressure at the solar nebula's center that the inward force of gravity would be balanced. When this happened, the gases would have stopped collapsing, and the sun would have formed.

According to old-earth theory, the sun's temperature eventually dropped to a level where planets could form in the disc surrounding it. Because the temperatures of materials in the disk would vary depending on their distance from the sun, the materials would have condensed at different locations within the disk. Silicates would have formed close to the sun. Hydrogen, helium, and water would have formed farther away from the sun where temperatures were lower. This theory explains why the four planets closest to the sun are made of mostly rocky material, such as silicates, and why the four planets farthest from the sun are gaseous. These condensed materials eventually formed the planets at various distances from the sun.

The planets are thought to have begun as tiny particles in the disk that collided and stuck together, forming pockets of dense materials called *planetesimals*. The colliding planetesimals then slowly grew from tiny specks into larger bodies that continued

FYI

Supporting Observations

Both young-earth and old-earth scientists claim that observations support their models for the beginning of the solar system. Many young-earth theorists point to inconsistencies within the solar system and suggest that these point to a supernatural creation in which God placed things exactly where He wanted them within a very short period of time. Some of the inconsistencies they point to include the relatively slow rotation of the sun, the presence of comets with observable orbits that have not yet disintegrated, and the existence of very large planets in other solar systems that are much closer to their stars than the old-earth theory claims is possible. Old-earth theorists point out that the Hubble Space Telescope shows details about other nebulae in the universe that appear to have stars forming within them. They also use mathematics to show that the laws of physics explain why the planets' orbits lie nearly in a plane with the sun at the center, why planets move around the sun in the same direction, and why most planets spin in the same direction with most of their axes pointing nearly perpendicular to their orbital plane.

Thor's Helmet nebula

Credit: ESO/B. Bailleul

growing by attracting the dust and debris in their path. As the planetesimals grew larger, their collisions would have became more violent. These more violent collisions might explain phenomena such as Venus's slow and backward rotation and Earth's moon. Small planetesimals that did not crash into planets may have been thrown to the outer edge of the solar system by the gravity of the larger planets. According to this theory, asteroids and comets are larger planetesimals that neither adhered to a planet nor moved beyond the planets. Solar radiation then blew away whatever gas and dust that did not adhere to the planets or condense to form asteroids and comets.

In contrast, other scientists do not believe the God of the Bible was involved in the creation of the solar system. Some may believe that is was the god of another faith who created the solar system. Others who do not believe in God's existence theorize that the solar system came into being by chance through the random interaction of gases, particles, and gravity following the creation of the universe through what is called *the Big Bang.*

However, God's creation of the solar system displays His craftsmanship. Like a potter with clay, He shaped trillions of tons of matter into a fiery ball of gas and billions of planets, moons, asteroids, comets, and meteors. And into this harmonious handiwork He carefully designed and set into place a dwelling place for His people.

LESSON REVIEW

1. What are the five major types of celestial bodies in the solar system?
2. Why is Pluto classified as a dwarf planet?
3. What do the terrestrial planets have in common?
4. In what order were the sun and Earth created according to both the young-earth theory and the old-earth theory?
5. According to both the young-earth and the old-earth theories, what did God create out of nothing?
6. Identify one observation that young-earth scientists claim supports their theory of how the solar system was created and one observation that old-earth scientists claim supports their theory of how the solar system was formed.

How close do you have to get to a campfire before you become too hot? If you fill a tub with hot water, is it still hot 15 minutes later? If you had to depend on a woodstove to keep you warm in the winter, would you spend a lot of time away from the stove or stay in that room most of the time?

Most hot things do not radiate heat very far, and they do not stay hot very long. But the sun is very hot. You can be burned by the sun even on Earth, which is separated from the sun by nearly 150 million km of cold space. The sun is actually a rather typical star, but it supplies all the energy needed to make all life on Earth possible. The sun is a fiery ball of hot gases glowing with incredible amounts of energy and giving off amazing amounts of heat.

Looking at the sun from Earth gives you no idea how big it really is. It is enormous! Its diameter is approximately 1,391,400 km (about 109 times Earth's diameter), and its volume is nearly 1,300,000 times the volume of Earth. The sun seems to rise in the east and set in the west, but that is because of Earth's rotation. Like the planets, however, the sun does spin.

The sun seems to have a distinct border, but when you look at it through mist or fog you can see that it is a gas sphere with no definite boundary. The sun, in fact, has layers.

The core of the sun is its center, where the sun's energy is produced. Here, nuclear fusion produces heat and light. The

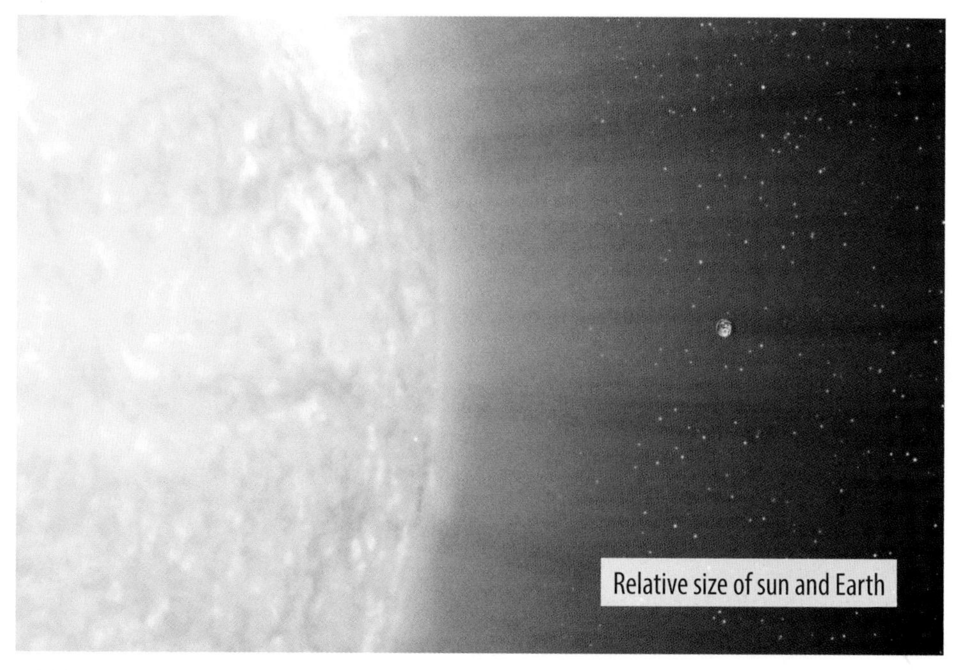
Relative size of sun and Earth

OBJECTIVES

- Model the structure of the sun.
- Describe the sun's physical properties.

VOCABULARY

- **aurora** a band of colored or white light in the atmosphere caused by charged particles from the sun interacting with Earth's upper atmosphere
- **chromosphere** the first layer of the sun's atmosphere
- **convective zone** the zone on the sun where convection currents bring energy to the sun's surface and take gas back into the sun
- **corona** the outer layer of the sun's atmosphere
- **photosphere** the sun's surface, which radiates visible light
- **prominence** a fiery burst of gas from the sun that rises thousands of kilometers into space
- **radiative zone** the zone on the sun where energy from the sun's core moves toward the sun's surface

FYI

Look Away

The sun is about 400,000 times brighter than the moon when it is full. Your eyes are not harmed by looking at the moon, but instinct makes you look away from the dazzling sun, and for good reason. God created people with instincts to keep them safe from the permanent blindness that would result from gazing at the sun, even for a short time. Never look directly at the sun or a solar eclipse with the naked eye, binoculars, or a telescope.

core is about 15 million degrees Celsius. The dense region of the sun next to the core is the **radiative zone**, which moves energy from the sun's core toward the sun's surface. This cyclical process takes about 170,000 years. From the radiative zone, the sun's energy passes through the **convective zone** where convection currents bring energy to the sun's surface and take gas back into the sun. If you could see this process as it happens, the zone would appear to be boiling. The sun's energy finally escapes to spread throughout the solar system when it reaches the photosphere. The **photosphere** is the sun's surface, which radiates visible light.

Like Earth, the sun has an atmosphere. The first layer of the sun's atmosphere is the **chromosphere**, a layer of reddish-pink gas. You can see the chromosphere only when a total eclipse blocks the bright light of the photosphere from view. The outer layer of the sun's atmosphere is the **corona**, which extends millions of kilometers into space. The corona is pale white and can only be seen during a total solar eclipse. The corona has an extremely high temperature, but its density is very low, nearly a vacuum, so it does not release as much heat as the other layers.

Why is the sun so hot? God uses the universe's lightest element, hydrogen, to produce the sun's energy. How does this work? At

Layers of the Sun

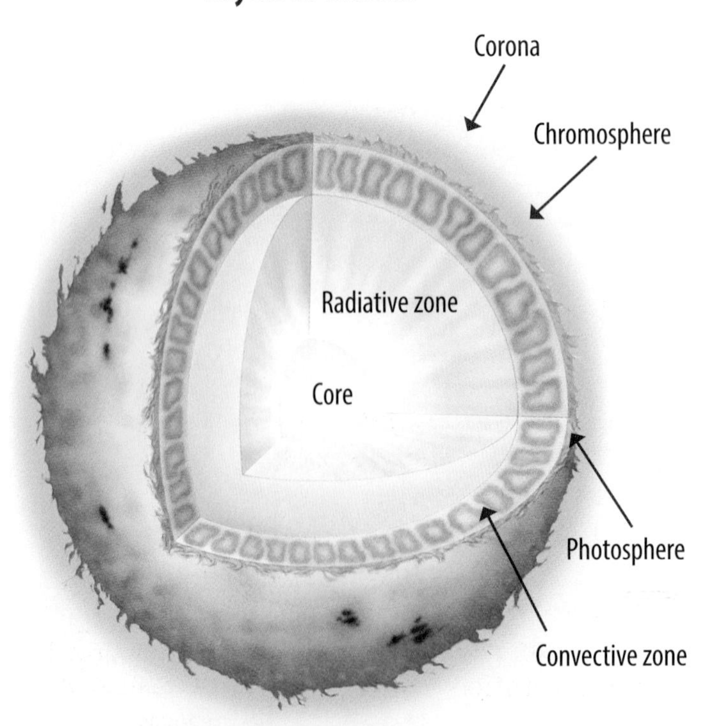

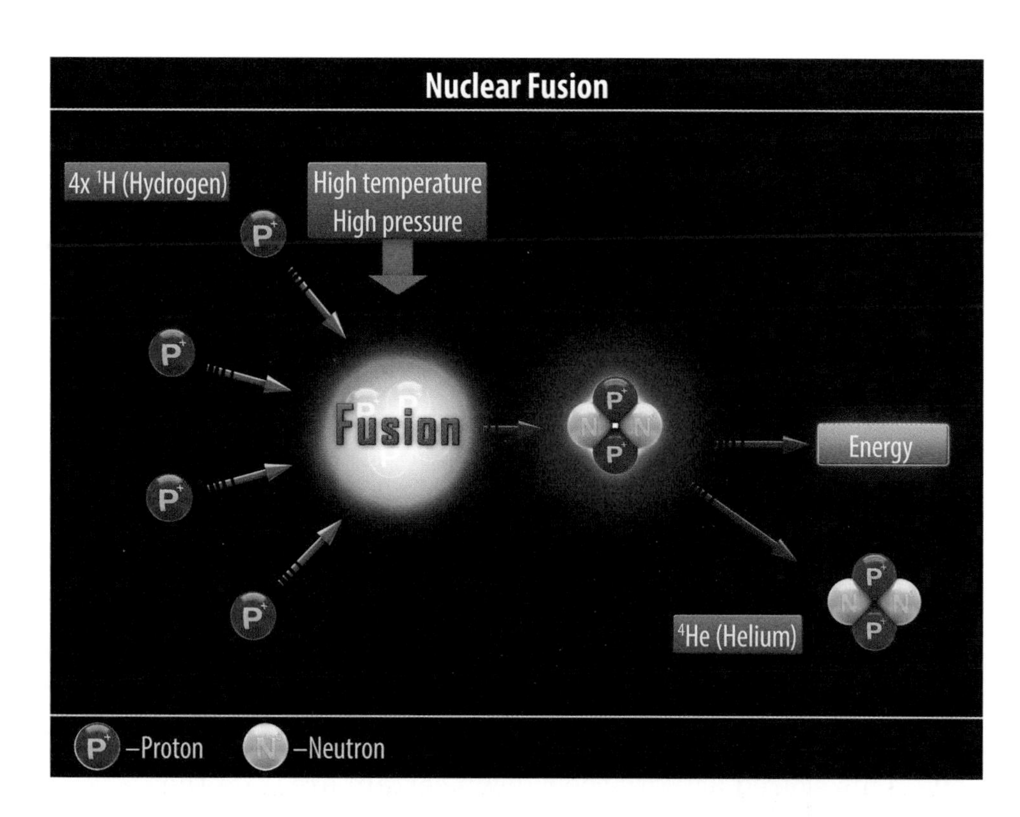

FYI

Sunny Ingredients

By mass, the sun contains about 70.6% hydrogen, 27.4% helium, and 2% heavier elements, such as iron, carbon, and silicon. Almost every known chemical element has been detected in the sun. All of these materials exist in the sun as gases.

the beginning of the 20th century, Albert Einstein recognized that matter and energy are interchangeable. This relationship is described in his famous formula $E = mc^2$, in which E is energy, m is mass, and c is the speed of light. The equation explains that because light travels so quickly, even a small amount of matter can produce a large amount of energy. This concept helps explain a very powerful source of energy called *nuclear fusion*, which is the production of energy by joining two light atomic nuclei to form a single, heavier nucleus. Hydrogen propels the nuclear fusion process deep in the sun's core. The fusion process continuously converts hydrogen into helium. This process releases energy that keeps the sun from collapsing and sends light into the depths of space. The sun has enough hydrogen to continue making light for about 10 billion more years.

Astronomers have discovered that the sun's surface is in constant motion and activity. About 2,400 years ago, Chinese astronomers first observed dark spots on the sun. These darker regions on the sun's photosphere are called *sunspots*. Sunspots look dark because they are cooler than the surrounding regions. How do sunspots form? The sun's rotation and the

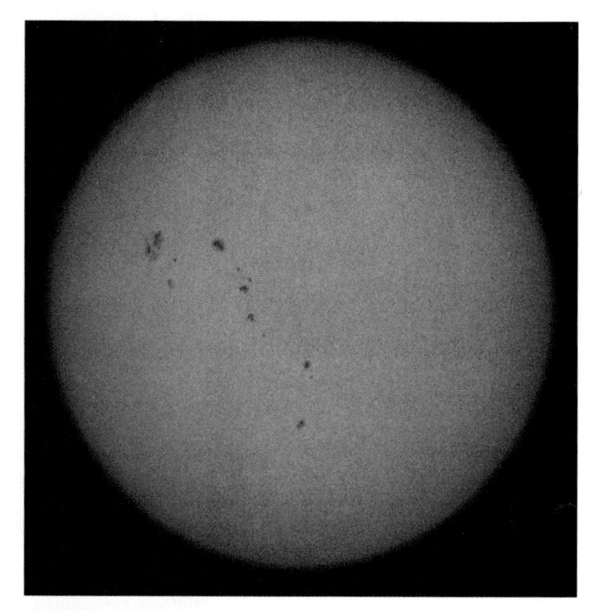

Sunspots

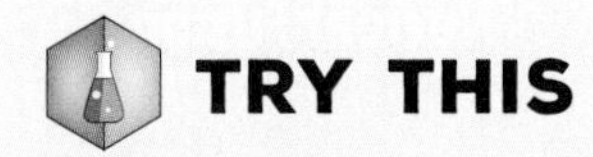

Sunspot Observation

Fasten a small refracting telescope to a tripod; the telescope's objective lens should measure less than 50 mm in diameter. Trace the objective lens on the middle of a sheet of thin cardboard and cut out the circle. Insert the objective lens end of the telescope through the hole and fasten the cardboard as close to the objective lens as possible. Without looking at the sun, point the telescope at the sun. Attach a piece of bright white paper to a clipboard or hardcover book and hold it behind the telescope's eyepiece. Slowly move the paper closer or farther from the eyepiece until a clear image of the sun appears. Trace the image of the sun and the position of any sunspots and label the image with the date and time of day. Repeat the experiment several days later at the same time and note any changes in the sunspots. Do not leave the telescope pointing at the sun for long periods of time or the lenses may become damaged.

circulation of gases inside the sun produce magnetic fields. These magnetic fields slow down the activity in the sun's convection zone. This slowed activity cools down certain areas on the photosphere, creating darker spots. Sunspots undergo 11-year cycles because of the regular changes in the sun's polarity.

The activity on the sun's surface also causes **prominences**, which are fiery bursts of gas from the sun that rise hundreds of thousands of kilometers into space. The shapes and paths

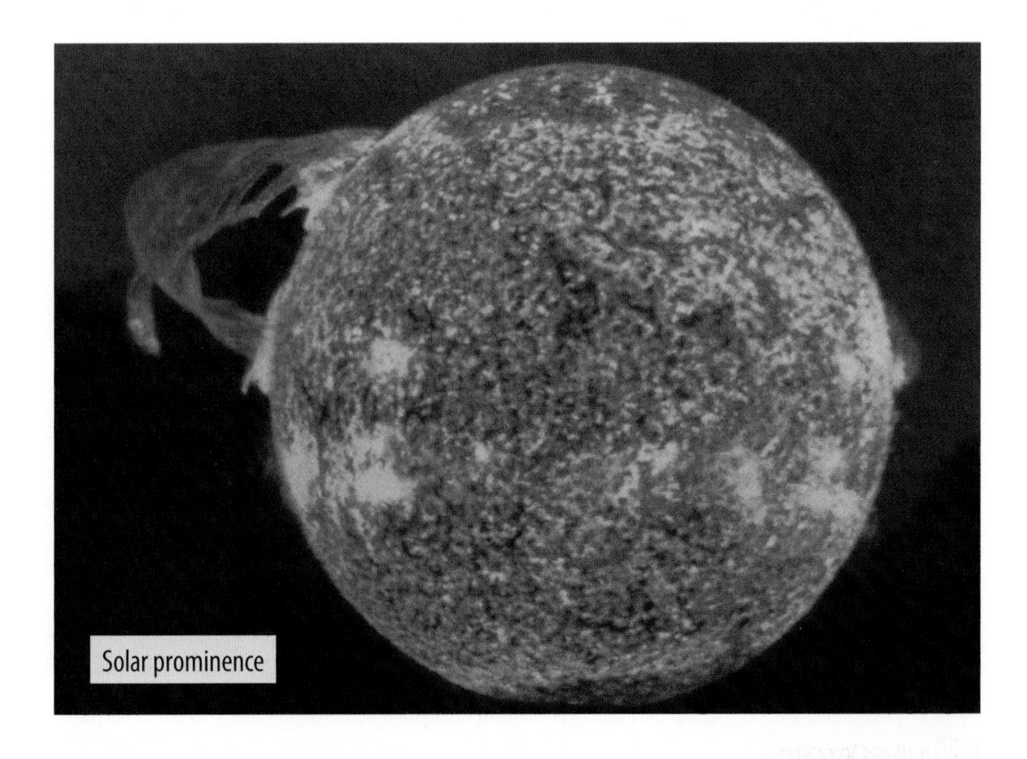

Solar prominence

Aurora

of prominences are determined by the same kinds of magnetic fields that create sunspots.

Violent disturbances on the sun's surface caused by explosions of magnetic energy are called *solar flares.* These explosions send out tremendous bursts of radiation and particles. Solar flares strengthen the flow of charged particles from the sun's corona, which is called *the solar wind.* Gusts of solar particles cause disturbances in Earth's magnetosphere, which works with the other layers of the atmosphere to protect Earth from most of the sun's radiation. An increased disturbance from the solar wind is called *a geomagnetic storm.* These storms can be strong enough to disrupt communication devices and power grids.

Charged particles from the solar wind also create **auroras**, which are bands of colored or white light in the atmosphere caused by charged particles from the sun interacting with Earth's upper atmosphere. In the Northern Hemisphere, auroras are called *the Northern Lights*, and in the Southern Hemisphere they are called *the Southern Lights.*

LESSON REVIEW

1. What is the source of the sun's energy?
2. Describe the different layers of the sun and of the sun's atmosphere.
3. List and describe several solar activities.
4. How do disturbances on the sun affect Earth?

FYI

The Ozone Layer

The sun radiates X-rays, ultraviolet light, and gamma radiation into space. These three forms of radiation are deadly to living things, but God wove a filter system into the atmosphere to prevent harmful amounts from reaching Earth. The ozone layer in Earth's stratosphere keeps most of the sun's ultraviolet radiation from reaching Earth's surface. In recent years, however, the ozone layer has thinned in some areas, increasing the importance of using preventative measures to reduce the risk of skin diseases such as cancer. Such preventative measures include using sunblock, wearing protective clothing, and reducing the amount of time unprotected skin is exposed to the sun.

7.2.1 *Planetary Motion*

OBJECTIVES

- Model the two ways a planet moves as it travels around the sun.
- Summarize Kepler's laws of planetary motion.
- Explain the role of gravity in planetary orbits.

VOCABULARY

- **aphelion** the point in a planet's orbit when it is farthest from the sun
- **astronomical unit** the average distance between Earth and the sun
- **ellipse** a closed curve along which the sum of the distances between two fixed points is always the same
- **perihelion** the point in a planet's orbit when it is closest to the sun

Around the sun are the planets, which move in orderly ways. All planets rotate, or spin, around an imaginary line called *an axis*. Mercury is the only planet with an axis that is perpendicular to its orbital path. Most of the planets' axes are tilted, and Uranus appears to lie on its side because its axis is tilted so far. As a planet rotates, only half of it faces the sun at any given time. The half that faces the sun experiences daylight while the other half of the planet is in darkness. Because all planets rotate, all have day and night just as Earth does. The time that it takes a planet to rotate on its axis is called its *period of rotation*. Earth's period of rotation is about 24 hours. In contrast, Jupiter's period of rotation is 10 hours, and Venus's period of rotation is 5,832 hours, or 243 Earth days. Most planets rotate counterclockwise. However, Venus and Uranus have a retrograde, or backward, rotation, and they rotate clockwise. On these planets, the sun seems to rise in the west and set in the east.

Planets also travel around the sun in a path called *an orbit*. All planets orbit the sun in the same direction. The time that it takes a planet to orbit the sun is called its *period of revolution*. The period of revolution is a planet's year. For example, Earth's period of revolution is very nearly 365 days, 6 hours, and 9 minutes.

German astronomer Johannes Kepler described three laws that describe the motion of planets. Kepler's first law states that planets move around the sun not in circles but in elongated ovals called *ellipses*. An **ellipse** is a closed curve along which the sum of the distances between two fixed points (each called *a focus*, plural *foci*) is always the same. In a planet's orbit, the sun is

Rotation and Revolution

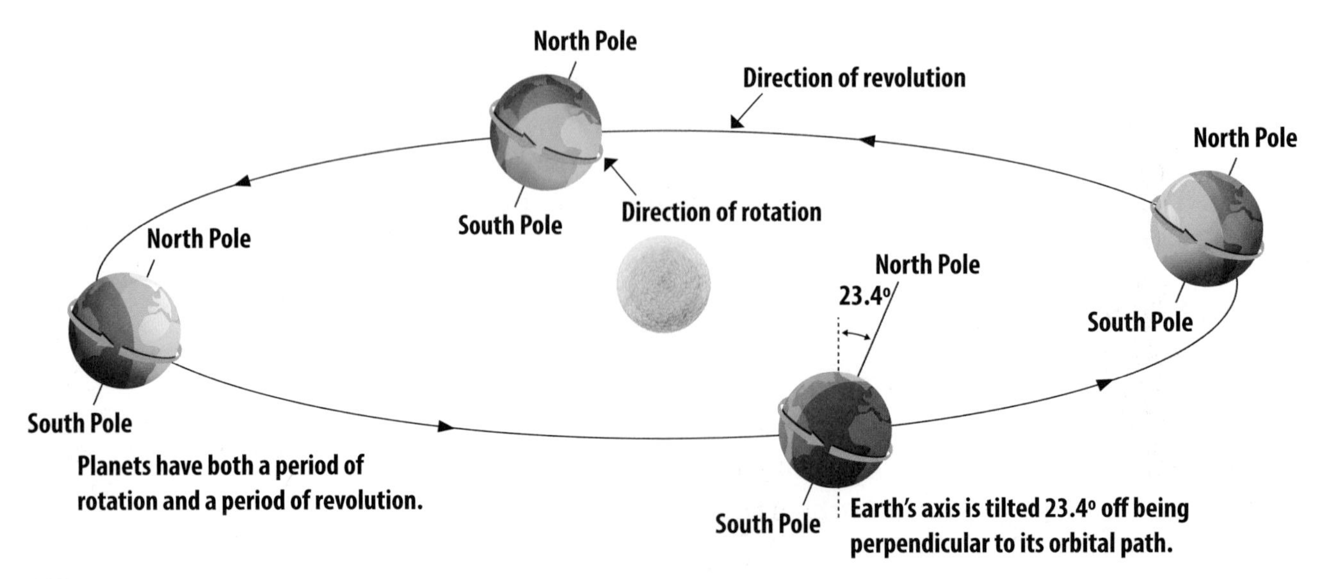

Planets have both a period of rotation and a period of revolution.

Earth's axis is tilted 23.4° off being perpendicular to its orbital path.

one focus, and an invisible point in space is the other focus. The sun, therefore, is off-center in the ellipse, and a planet's distance from the sun varies as it moves through its orbit. The maximum diameter of an ellipse is called *the major axis*, and half of the major axis is known as *the semimajor axis*. The semimajor axis is a planet's average distance from the sun. For example, the semimajor axis of Earth's orbit is about 149,600,000 km. This average distance between Earth and the sun is called an **astronomical unit** (AU). Other planets' distances from the sun are usually measured using this unit. The planet Mercury is 0.387 AU from the sun, so its distance is 0.387 AU × 149,597,871 km = 57,894,376 km.

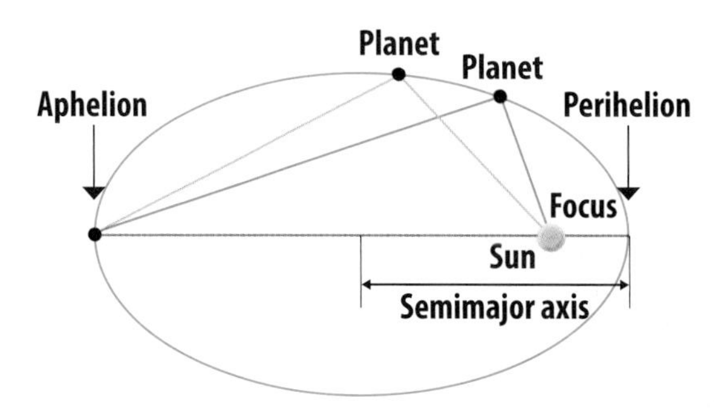

A planet's elliptical orbit

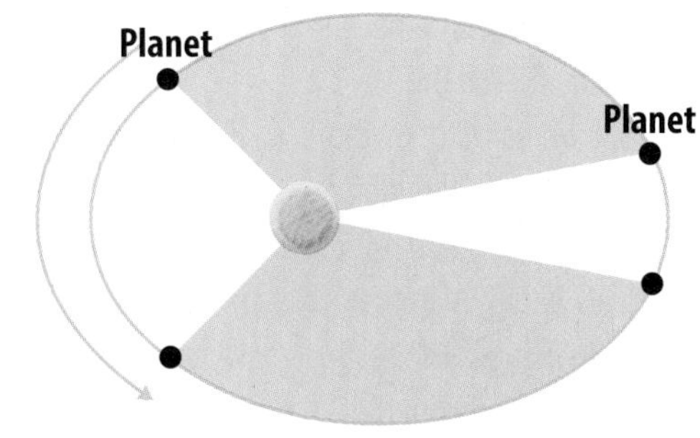

Planets cover equal areas in equal amounts of time.

Kepler's second law of planetary motion states that planets move faster when they are closer to the sun than they do when they are farther from the sun. The point in a planet's orbit when it is closest to the sun is its **perihelion**. The point when a planet is farthest from the sun in its orbit is known as its **aphelion**. Because a planet's speed changes in relation to its distance from the sun, the area it covers during any set amount of time will be the same no matter where the planet is in its orbit. Imagine an elastic string connecting a planet to the sun. When the planet is far from the sun, the string will cover a long, narrow space, and when the planet is close to the sun, the string will cover a short, wide space. The calculation of each space's area during the same amount of time will be equal, however.

Kepler's third law states that the time a planet takes to orbit the sun once is directly related to its distance from the sun. If you know the time it takes a planet to orbit the sun, you can determine the distance from the planet to the sun using $P^2 = a^3$. The semimajor axis is measured in astronomical units (a), and the period of revolution is expressed in years (P). For example, Saturn takes approximately 29 years to orbit the sun.

$$P^2 = a^3, \quad (29 \text{ years})^2 = 841, \quad a^3 = 841$$

$$a = \sqrt[3]{841} = 9.44 \text{ AU}$$

So Saturn is 9.44 AU from the sun, which is more than nine times the distance from Earth to the sun.

FYI

Top Speed

Distances outside the solar system—between stars, for example—are measured in light-years. Distances within the solar system can be measured in light-minutes and light-hours. Light travels about 300,000 km per second in space. If you could move that fast, you would travel around Earth 7.5 times in one second. Light travels nearly 18,000,000 km in one minute. This distance is called *a light-minute.* It takes light from the sun 8.3 minutes to reach Earth. The distance from Earth to the sun is 8.3 light-minutes.

TRY THIS

Foucault Pendulum

In 1851, Jean-Bernard-Léon Foucault suspended a pendulum from the center of the inner dome of a building in Paris. The long wire attached to the pendulum allowed the device an unrestricted swing in any direction. Although the pendulum seemed to change its path during the day, it was actually the earth beneath the pendulum that was moving. The device was called *a Foucault pendulum.*

Tie a small weight to a string. Tie the other end of the string to the clamp on a ring stand. Hang the pendulum over a turntable or a lazy Susan. Put a small piece of masking tape on one side of the turntable. The center of the turntable represents the North Pole. Swing the pendulum and slowly turn the turntable. What direction does the pendulum appear to swing in relation to the tape? Infer what kind of movement causes a real Foucault pendulum to change directions.

The third law also explains that a distant planet takes more time to orbit the sun than a planet near the sun. For example, Mercury is the closest planet to the sun, and its orbit takes 88 Earth days. In contrast, Neptune's year is about 165 Earth years.

Kepler described the planets' orbits, but he never figured out why they behave as they do. Nearly 70 years later, Sir Isaac Newton answered that question by describing gravity. Newton deduced that an attraction existed between all objects. Masses of all sizes are attracted to each other. Furthermore, the strength of an object's attractive force depends on its mass. Newton reasoned that small objects fall to Earth because Earth and the objects are attracted to each other by the force of gravity. According to Newton's law of universal gravitation, the force of gravity is described by the product of the objects' masses divided by the square of the distance between them. The equation looks like this:

$$\frac{\text{Object 1 mass} \times \text{Object 2 mass}}{(\text{distance between objects})^2}$$

This principle means that if two objects that are next to each other are moved 3 times as far apart, then the gravitational attraction between them would be 9 times weaker ($3^2 = 9$). If the objects are moved 100 times farther apart, the gravitational attraction would be 10,000 times less ($100^2 = 10,000$).

Gravity pulls the moon toward Earth, and it pulls Earth toward the sun. However, the moon does not crash into Earth, and Earth does not collide with the sun because of centrifugal force. For example, imagine a person twirling a ball on a string. The ball's attempt to move away from the person is centrifugal force. As long as the person holds the string, however, the ball will orbit the person's hand. Earth's centrifugal force keeps the planet from being drawn into the sun by the sun's strong gravity. In this example, the string acts like gravity. If the string was cut, the ball would fly off in a straight line. The planets would behave in the same way without gravity pulling them toward the sun.

LESSON REVIEW

1. Describe the two ways that planets move.
2. Summarize Kepler's laws of planetary motion.
3. What keeps the sun's gravity from pulling Earth into the sun?
4. What keeps Earth from traveling in a straight line away from the sun?

All the planets follow the same laws of motion, yet the planets themselves are different. Planets in the solar system are divided into inner and outer planets separated by the asteroid belt. The orbits of the inner planets are more closely spaced together than the orbits of the outer planets. The inner planets are also known as *terrestrial planets* because they are all relatively dense, rocky planets. The inner planets are Mercury, Venus, Earth, and Mars.

OBJECTIVES

- Distinguish among the solar system's inner planets.
- Describe the features of Earth that make life possible.
- Evaluate the inner planets' abilities to sustain life.

VOCABULARY

- **crater** a large circular indentation on a planet's surface

Mercury is the closest planet to the sun. Because it orbits so close to the sun, it never strays far from the sun in Earth's sky. Visible for only a brief time before sunrise or after sunset, it looks like a bright star shining just above the horizon. In fact, Mercury is so close to the sun that the sun would appear more than three times larger from Mercury than it appears from Earth.

Mercury is smaller than Earth, and the force of gravity is reduced. Because gravity is weaker on less massive planets, people would weigh less on Mercury than on Earth. When combined with the sun's fierce heat, Mercury's low gravity contributes to its lack of an atmosphere.

Mercury is the solar system's fastest planet. Its year, or period of revolution, is 88 Earth days. If it did not move fast, the planet would fall into the sun. Although Mercury revolves very quickly, it rotates very slowly. It rotates only three times for every two revolutions it makes around the sun. Mercury has a sunrise only every 175 Earth days because of its slow rotation and fast revolution.

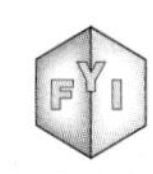

FYI

Mercury

Distance from the sun
57,909,227 km

Period of rotation
58 days, 16 hours

Period of revolution
88 days

Diameter
4,879 km

Density (water = 1)
5.43 g/cm^3

Surface temperature
–173°C to 427°C

Surface gravity
38% of Earth's

Mercury's lack of atmosphere and long period of rotation allow the daytime side of the planet to reach a temperature of more than 400°C. On the nighttime side, temperatures can drop below –170°C. Consequently, Mercury is one of the solar system's hottest and coldest planets.

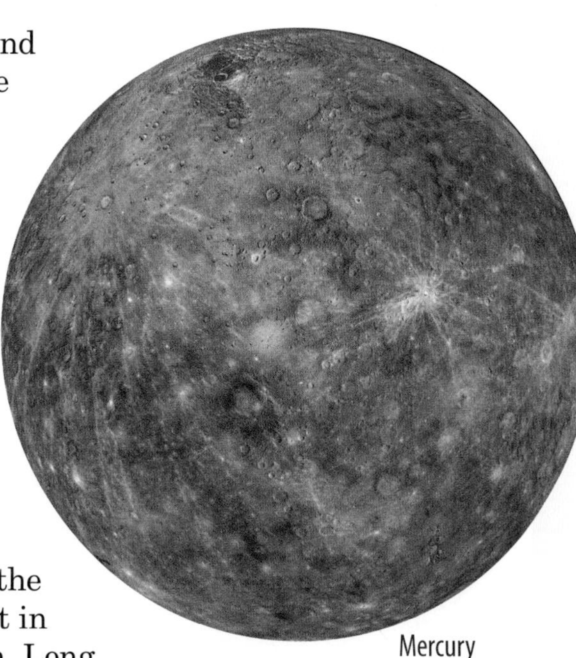

Mercury

It is hard to observe Mercury from Earth because it is so close to the sun. People did not know very much about it until the spacecraft *Mariner 10* flew by it in 1975 and sent back information. Long,

FYI

First Star I See Tonight

Although Venus is a planet, many people mistake it for a bright star. Venus is often called *the Morning Star* or *the Evening Star* because it is often the first light to appear in the sky and the last one remaining in the morning. If you know where to look, and Venus is especially bright in the sky, it can even be seen in full daylight.

FYI

Venus

Distance from the sun
108,209,475 km

Period of rotation
243 days (retrograde)

Period of revolution
224 days, 17 hours

Diameter
12,104 km

Density (water = 1)
5.24 g/cm^3

Surface temperature
464°C

Surface gravity
91% of Earth's

steep cliffs and vast plains stretch across Mercury. The planet's surface is pocked with craters from material striking the planet. A **crater** is a large circular indentation on a planet's surface. Mercury may have small ice caps at its poles. The sun does not melt these ice caps because they lie inside deep craters that are always in shadow.

Venus, the second planet from the sun, comes closer to Earth than any other planet. Dense clouds reflect more than 75% of the sunlight that strikes the atmosphere of Venus. In contrast, Earth's atmosphere only reflects 30% of the sunlight that strikes it. Because its atmosphere is highly reflective, Venus appears very bright. In fact, the planet is often visible before the stars appear in the evening or after the stars fade in the morning.

Venus's diameter, mass, and density are similar to Earth's, which is why it is often called *Earth's twin*. People once thought that Earth and Venus might share other similarities as well, but spacecraft have landed on Venus and sent back photographs revealing how different the planets are. Venus's atmosphere is mostly carbon dioxide, and it has thick clouds of sulfuric acid. The pressure of the planet's atmosphere is 90 times greater than the pressure of Earth's atmosphere, which is enough to squash a person.

Although Venus is farther from the sun than Mercury, it is much hotter than Mercury. Venus's heavy atmosphere traps heat and produces a greenhouse effect. Therefore, the dark side of the planet stays almost as hot as the light side. Venus's temperature rises above 460°C, which makes it the hottest planet in the solar system.

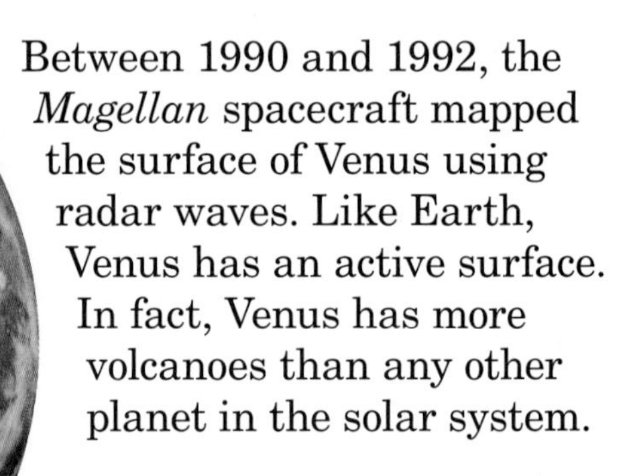

Venus

Between 1990 and 1992, the *Magellan* spacecraft mapped the surface of Venus using radar waves. Like Earth, Venus has an active surface. In fact, Venus has more volcanoes than any other planet in the solar system.

Venus also has a retrograde (backward) rotation, so the sun rises in the west and sets in the east. Its period of rotation is 243 Earth days, and its period of revolution is almost 225 Earth days. If people could be born on Venus, some of them could celebrate two birthdays between one sunrise and the next!

The third planet from the sun is Earth. From space, Earth looks like a blue marble. Swirls of clouds blanket the brown and blue of Earth. As far as scientists know, Earth is the only planet that can support life. The idea that God placed Earth at just the right distance from the sun and specifically designed Earth's systems to support life is called *the anthropic principle*. Earth's distance from the sun ensures that Earth receives the right amount of light and warmth to sustain its biosphere. Earth's atmosphere is perfectly composed to support life, and it is thick enough to deflect or burn up most meteorites. At the same time, the atmosphere is thin enough to keep everything beneath it from being crushed. Earth is the only planet in the solar system with an atmosphere containing the oxygen necessary for life. In addition, gravity on Earth is balanced. If it were stronger or weaker, both living organisms and the atmosphere would not function properly. If even one of these or many other important factors were different, then Earth could not support life. God filled Earth with life and uses these qualities to sustain it.

FYI

It Is Just a Phase

From Earth, Venus appears to have phases, just like the moon. The crescent phases are visible with binoculars. When Venus is nearest to Earth, it appears as a crescent. When it is farthest from Earth, Venus would appear to be round, but it is not visible from Earth because the sun is in the way.

Mars, sometimes known as *the Red Planet*, was studied for years by telescope before spacecraft contributed significantly more information. *Viking 1* and *Viking 2* landed on the surface of Mars and sent back detailed photographs. The *Viking* spacecraft also scooped up and analyzed the soil, which is coated in iron oxide (rust) and accounts for the planet's red color. In 2012, *Curiosity* landed on Mars and conducted more studies of its soil and rocks.

Mars is similar to Earth in several ways. Mars is tilted on its axis slightly more than Earth, which gives it seasons similar to Earth. Mars also has wind and weather patterns. The wind can be strong enough to create dust storms that erode Mars's surface and turn its atmosphere dark pink.

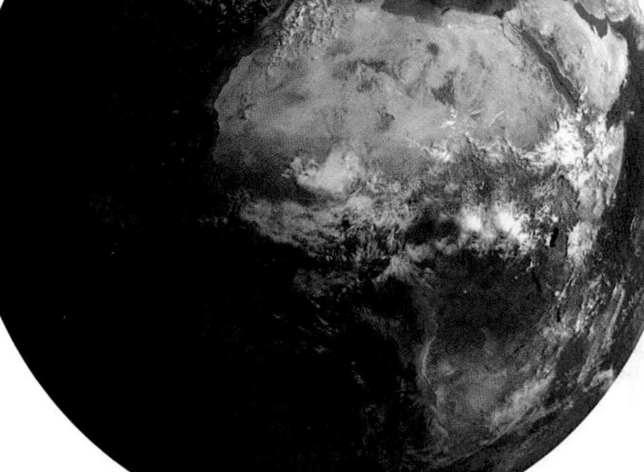

Earth and moon

FYI

Earth

Distance from the sun
149,596,262 km

Period of rotation
23 hours, 56 minutes

Period of revolution
365 days, 6 hours

Diameter
12,756 km

Density (water = 1)
5.52 g/cm^3

Surface temperature
−88°C to 58°C

Surface gravity
100% of Earth's

FYI

Mars

Distance from the sun
227,943,824 km

Period of rotation
24 hours, 37 minutes

Period of revolution
1 year, 322 days

Diameter
6,779 km

Density (water = 1)
3.93 g/cm^3

Surface temperature
–153°C to 20°C

Surface gravity
38% of Earth's

FYI

No Pressure

Water boils at 100°C, right? Yes, as long as the water is at sea level on Earth's surface. The boiling point of water depends on atmospheric pressure. Water boils at a lower temperature on top of a high mountain because the atmospheric pressure is less at high altitudes. The atmospheric pressure on Mars is too low for liquid water to exist. If ice does happen to melt, it almost instantly evaporates.

Mars

Like Earth, the surface of Mars displays large craters, deep canyons, and inactive volcanoes. Mars has several regions marked by former volcanic activity. The Tharsis Montes region is the largest, and it stretches 4,000 km across Mars. It contains Olympus Mons, the largest mountain in the solar system at 25 km tall and 624 km wide. This shield volcano is similar to Hawaii's Mauna Loa. Scientists believe that because Mars's crust does not move around like Earth's crust, volcanoes there build up in the same spots instead of forming in chains.

Mars even has water, but what instruments can detect is all frozen. Mars has two polar icecaps containing frozen water and frozen carbon dioxide. Scientists believe that additional water may be frozen beneath the soil. Mars has features that look like dry riverbeds, which indicates that liquid water existed on Mars in the past. The past presence of liquid water suggests that Mars was once a warmer place. Liquid water cannot collect in observable amounts on Mars because the atmosphere is mainly carbon dioxide, and it is about 100 times thinner than Earth's atmosphere. The thin atmosphere does not trap heat on the planet's surface. Also, the sun does not warm Mars as much as it does Earth because Mars is farther from the sun. Therefore,

System Error

On December 11, 1998, the multimillion dollar space probe *Mars Climate Orbiter* was launched. About nine months later, on September 23, 1999, it reached Mars and was lost. The orbiter mistakenly steered to within 57 km of the Martian surface, and atmospheric friction burned it up. How could a mistake like this happen? Some of the directional commands to the spacecraft were sent in English units rather than the metric units the spacecraft was programmed for. The spacecraft interpreted the digits as metric and entered the Mars atmosphere incorrectly.

temperatures on Mars remain very cold, ranging between –153°C and 20°C, which would keep water frozen most of the time. Whenever ice does melt on Mars, it boils away quickly because the atmospheric pressure on the planet is so low that water boils at only 10°C.

Deimos

Mars has two very small moons, Phobos and Deimos. On average, Phobos is only about 22 km wide, and Deimos is only about 14 km wide. The moons' small size suggests that they may have been asteroids that were captured by Mars's gravity.

Phobos

LESSON REVIEW

1. Which of the inner planets, other than Earth, is most suitable for life? Why?
2. Which of the inner planets has the fastest period of rotation? What benefit does this provide?
3. Which of the inner planets has the most dense atmosphere? Is this atmosphere conducive to life? Why?
4. Describe two unique features of Earth that make life possible.
5. Which inner planet, other than Earth, is confirmed to have water?

FYI

What is a Day?
Earth's period of rotation is not exactly 24 hours. This statement may be confusing because a day is measured in 24 hours. A day is the time between two successive passages of the sun over a location on Earth, such as from noon to noon in Cairo, Egypt. The length of a solar day varies slightly during the course of a year, but it averages approximately 24 hours. A day is assigned exactly 24 hours for purposes of time measurement. Astronomers measure days as Earth's rotation relative to the fixed stars, which is called *a sidereal day*.

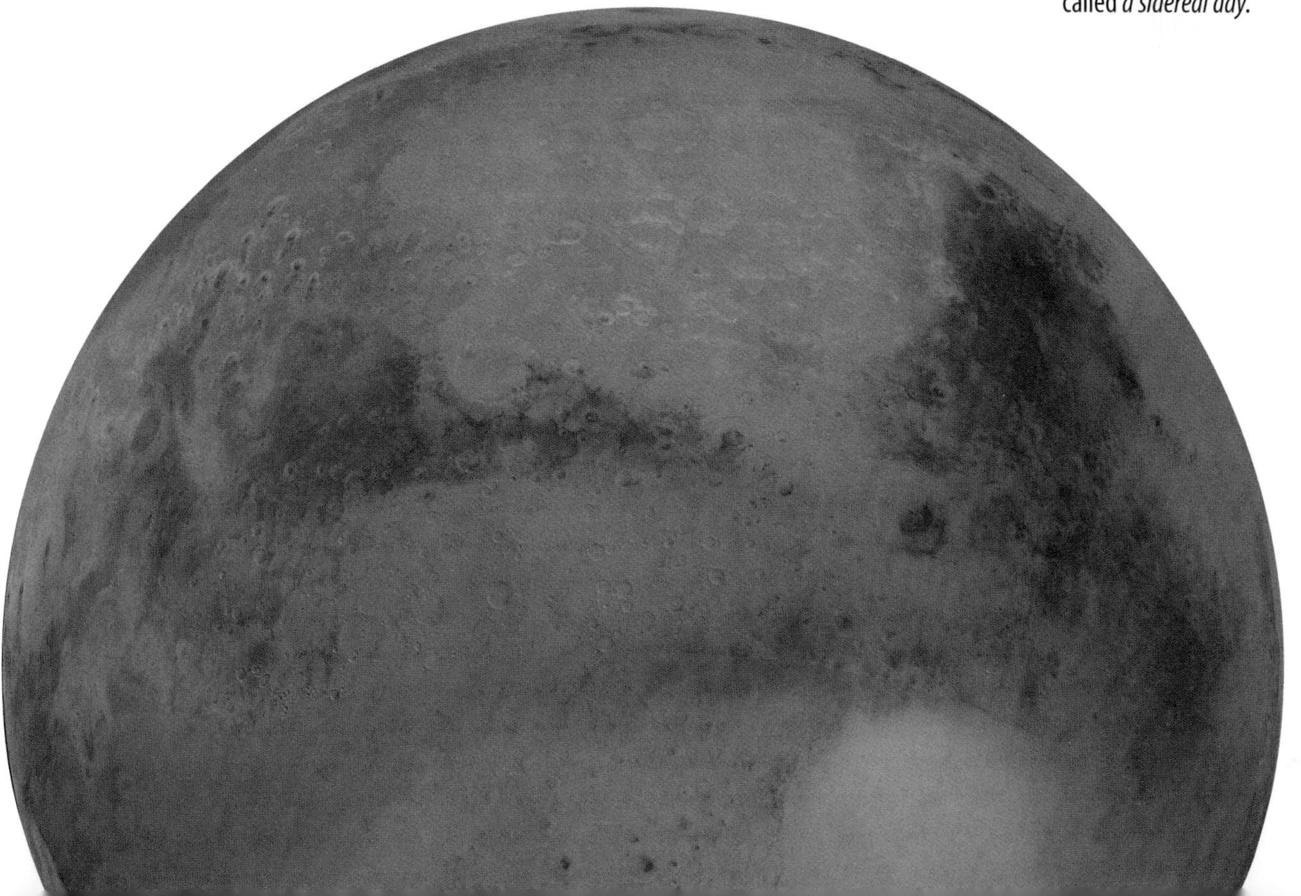

Mars

7.2.3 *Outer Planets*

OBJECTIVES

- Identify the solar system's outer planets.
- Describe the distinguishing features of the outer planets' largest moons.
- Generalize characteristics common to the gas giants.
- Evaluate Pluto's official status as a dwarf planet.

VOCABULARY

- **Kuiper belt** the region of the solar system outside Neptune's orbit

Beyond Mars lies the asteroid belt, which will be discussed in the next lesson. The planets beyond the asteroid belt are called *the outer planets.* These planets are very different from the inner planets both in size and in composition. All of the outer planets are also known as *gas giants* because they are significantly larger than the inner planets and have no known solid surfaces. The gas giants include Jupiter, Saturn, Uranus, and Neptune.

Jupiter is the solar system's largest and most colorful planet. It is a true giant! More than 1,300 Earths could fit inside Jupiter. However, Jupiter's mass is only that of about 318 Earths because it has a relatively low density. Jupiter has a very short day of only 9 hours and 55 minutes. Because this gaseous planet rotates so quickly, it bulges at the equator and flattens at the poles.

Like the sun, Jupiter is primarily hydrogen and helium. Jupiter sends more heat into space than it receives from the sun, but how this heat is generated is unknown. The outer part of Jupiter's atmosphere is composed primarily of colored bands of methane and ammonia. The planet's thick cloud cover exerts enough pressure on the planet to change Jupiter's hydrogen into a liquid. As pressure increases closer to Jupiter's core, the liquid hydrogen acts like a metal. This liquid metallic layer creates a magnetic field called *the magnetosphere*, which stretches for millions of kilometers beyond Jupiter.

FYI

Jupiter

Distance from the sun
778,340,821 km

Period of rotation
9 hours, 55 minutes

Period of revolution
11 years, 318 days

Diameter
116,464 km

Density (water = 1)
1.33 g/cm^3

Temperature
−148°C

Gravity
236% of Earth's

Jupiter's clouds are very active and stormy. A hurricane-like storm was first observed on Jupiter through a telescope. Over the years, this storm has changed color, grown, shrunk, and even disappeared several times. Some scientists question whether only one storm has been observed or whether different storms are appearing and disappearing. The storm as it can currently be seen is known as *the Great Red Spot*. It has been measured at over three times the size of Earth.

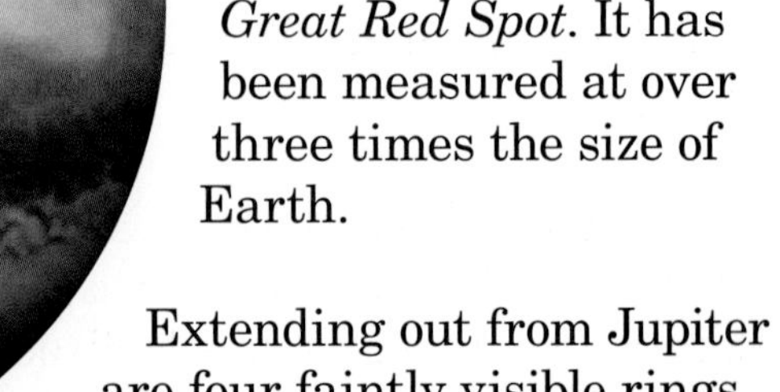

Jupiter

Extending out from Jupiter are four faintly visible rings. Fifty-three confirmed moons orbit Jupiter among its rings, and another 14 objects appear to be moons of Jupiter as well. Galileo discovered Jupiter's four largest moons in 1610. These moons are known as *the Galilean satellites.* Io, the closest to Jupiter of the Galilean satellites, has a high sulfur content and is covered with active volcanoes. Its blotchy orange, red, and yellow appearance reminded one scientist of a pepperoni pizza. In contrast, Europa, an ice-covered moon, has a bright and extremely smooth surface. Ganymede, Jupiter's largest moon, is the largest moon in the entire solar system. It is even larger than Mercury. Half water and half ice, Ganymede seems to have cracks that scientists believe resulted from upheavals similar to earthquakes. Callisto is the solar system's most heavily cratered object.

TRY THIS

Jupiter's Spot

Using a spoon, mix 250 mL of white glue and 1 L of water in a bowl. Place two drops of red food coloring and two drops of yellow food coloring on the mixture to represent Jupiter's atmosphere. Take turns blowing on the surface of the mixture through a straw. Experiment with blowing across the middle of the bowl and along the side of the bowl. What happened?

Saturn is the second largest planet in the solar system. It has about 755 times the volume and 95 times the mass of Earth. Saturn can be seen without a telescope, but it is less dense than water, which means that if Saturn was placed in enough water, it would float. Saturn is like Jupiter because it is mostly hydrogen and helium with lesser amounts of methane and ammonia, it gives off more heat than it receives from the sun, and it spins very rapidly.

Although all of the gas giants have rings, Saturn's rings are the most famous. Galileo first discovered the presence of rings around Saturn. Later astronomers determined that the rings are composed of little bits of ice and ice-covered matter in orbit around the planet. Saturn has at least seven major rings, which are made up of thousands of thin rings. The rings start about 6,700 km from the top of Saturn's clouds and extend approximately 420,000 km from Saturn (more than twice the diameter of Saturn itself). They can be as thin as 100 m. The icy particles that make up the rings range in size from a grain of sand to over a kilometer across. These magnificent rings actually contain very little material. If the material was compressed into a sphere, the sphere's diameter would be only about 400 km across.

FYI

Saturn

Distance from the sun
1,426,666,422 km

Period of rotation
10 hours, 39 minutes

Period of revolution
29 years, 160 days

Diameter
120,536 km

Density (water = 1)
0.69 g/cm^3

Temperature
–178°C

Gravity
92% of Earth's

Like Jupiter, Saturn has at least 53 moons. The moon Phoebe travels east to west in a retrograde direction, but the others travel west to east in a direct rotation. Titan, Saturn's largest moon, is the only moon in the solar system known

Saturn

FYI

Uranus

Distance from the sun
2,870,658,186 km

Period of rotation
17 hours, 14 minutes
(retrograde)

Period of revolution
84 years, 26 days

Diameter
50,724 km

Density (water = 1)
1.27 g/cm^3

Temperature
–216°C

Gravity
89% of Earth's

to have a thick atmosphere. Titan glows orange and has methane clouds and methane deposits on its mountaintops that resemble the snow on Earth's mountains.

English astronomer William Herschel identified Uranus as a planet in 1781. Before that time, people thought Uranus was a star. Its classification as a planet doubled the size of the known solar system because Uranus is almost twice as far from the sun as its neighbor Saturn. Uranus, the smallest of the gas giants, is a blue-green planet with outer layers made primarily of hydrogen, helium, and methane. Uranus's clouds have faint bands that are invisible to the naked eye.

Uranus

Like Venus, Uranus has a retrograde rotation. Uranus is unique in that its axis is tilted about 90°, so it appears to be on its side. For part of the Uranus year, one pole points toward the sun and the other is dark. At the other end of its orbit, this position is reversed. Some astronomers theorize that early in its history Uranus may have been struck by a massive object that tipped it.

Uranus has 27 known moons. Dark, narrow rings of large particles also orbit the planet. The first five faint rings were discovered in 1977 when Uranus eclipsed a star. Later, eight more rings were discovered.

The planet Neptune cannot be seen without a telescope. Even with large telescopes, its features are not clear. Scientists suspected that Neptune existed before they discovered it, however. Scientists studying Uranus found that it does not follow an expected orbit. Astronomers concluded that the gravity of another object beyond Uranus must be pulling on it. They calculated the size and position of an object that would affect Uranus this way. Looking where their calculations pointed, they discovered Neptune in 1846.

Little was known about Neptune until *Voyager 2* flew by it in 1989. It is now known that Neptune and Uranus have about the same size, mass, temperature, and composition. At the time of the *Voyager 2* mission, Neptune had a dark spot similar to Jupiter's Great Red Spot that changed over time. In 2016, the Hubble Space Telescope confirmed that such spots were vortexes in Neptune's atmosphere. Like the interiors of Saturn and Jupiter, Neptune's interior layers release heat into its outer layers. Some astronomers think that the released heat causes Neptune's warm gases to rise as its cool gases sink. They believe the circulating gases cause wind patterns that create the belts of observable thick clouds.

Neptune is a blue planet. Scientists believe it has a small core about the mass of Earth that contains hydrogen, helium, water, and some rocky material, but no solid surface. One of Neptune's more unique features is its wind. Neptune has the solar system's fastest wind. Some air currents travel nearly 2,000 kph, which is much faster than the speed of sound on Earth.

Voyager 2 also revealed that Neptune has four thin, faint rings composed of dust particles of various sizes. In some places, material has clumped together for unknown reasons. Also orbiting Neptune are 13 confirmed moons, and one object that is thought to be a fourteenth moon. Neptune's largest moon is Triton. It is the only one that orbits Neptune in a retrograde direction. Because of this, some scientists think that Triton may not be an original moon of Neptune but that it may be another object that Neptune's gravity captured. Geysers on Triton expel an icy substance more than 8 km into its atmosphere.

In 1930, a new solar system object was discovered. The small, icy body was named *Pluto*. Although this object was nothing like the gas giants, astronomers classified it as a planet. In 1978, a moon, Charon, was discovered orbiting Pluto. Charon is approximately half the size of Pluto. Four additional moons have been discovered in orbit around Pluto since 2005. However, in 2006, the International Astronomical Union decided to classify Pluto as a dwarf planet because it has not cleared its own path around the sun. This decision was controversial among astronomers and the general public. The change in Pluto's classification does not change the solar system itself; the change only affects the way people talk about it.

Many astronomers now categorize Pluto as a Kuiper belt object (KBO). The **Kuiper belt** is a broad, flat ring of relatively small, icy objects orbiting the sun beyond Neptune. Pluto may be the largest example of a KBO.

Neptune

FYI

Neptune

Distance from the sun
4,498,396,441 km

Period of rotation
16 hours, 7 minutes

Period of revolution
163 years, 307 days

Diameter
49,244 km

Density (water = 1)
1.64 g/cm^3

Temperature
–214°C

Gravity
112% of Earth's

Major Moons of the Solar System Scaled to Earth's Moon

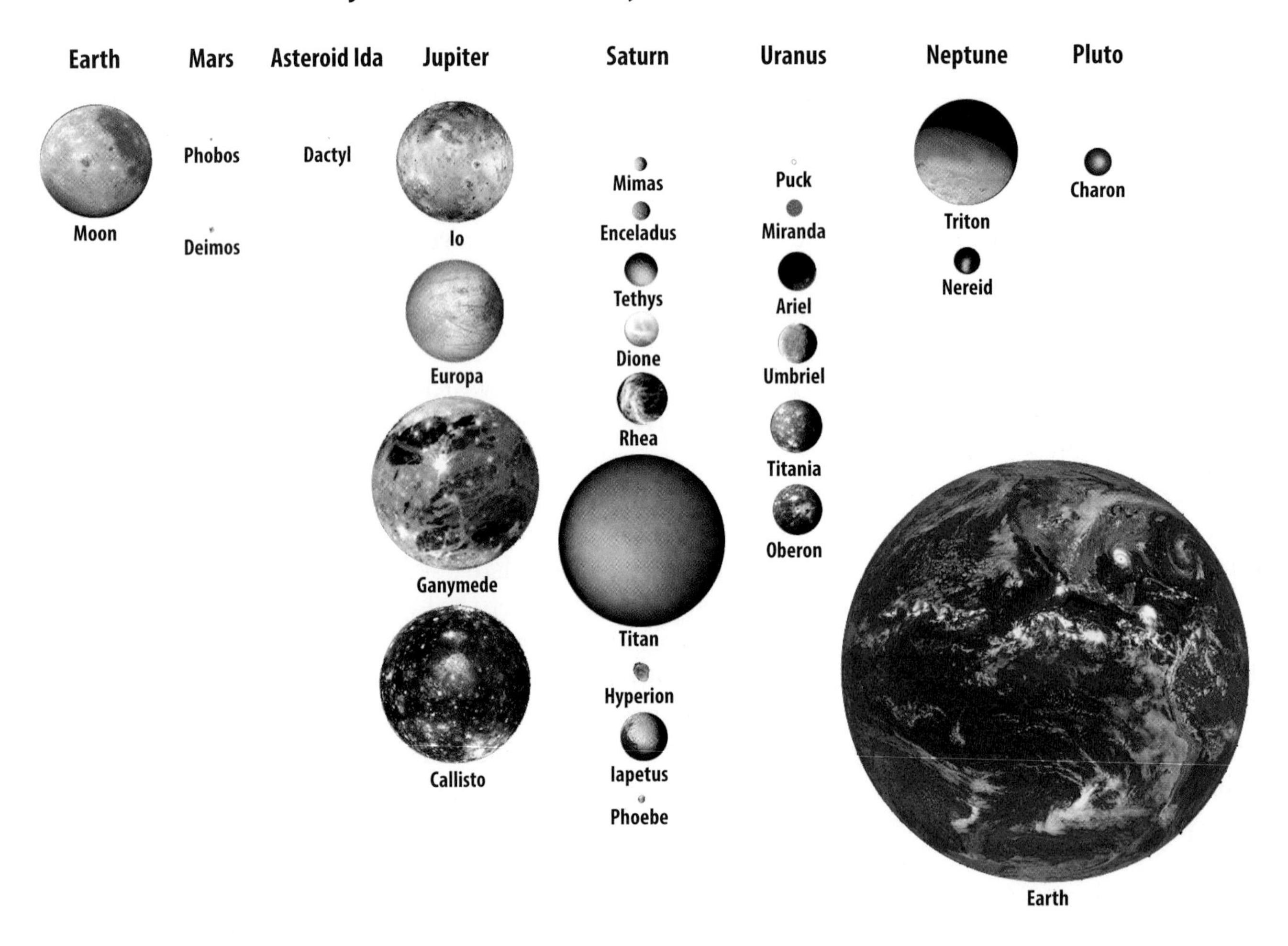

LESSON REVIEW

1. What sets Jupiter apart from all the other planets?
2. Identify one distinguishing feature of each of Jupiter's four Galilean satellites.
3. What characteristics are common to the gas giants?
4. Which outer planets are thought to have internal heat sources?
5. What two elements are present in great quantities in all the gas giants?
6. How is Pluto different from the gas giants?

Pluto and its distant moon, Charon

The major planets are not the only objects that revolve around the sun. Smaller bodies such as comets, asteroids, and meteoroids also orbit the sun. A **comet** is a frozen chunk of ice, dust, and rock that gives off tails of dust and charged particles as it passes near the sun during its orbit. Although the orbits of most planets are nearly circular, the orbits of comets are very elliptical. Astronomers often describe comets as *dirty snowballs*. The *snow* part is frozen water and gases; the *dirt* part is rocks and dust. The solid center of a comet, called *the nucleus*, is typically about 10 km in diameter, but it can be larger or smaller.

When a comet passes close to the sun, solar radiation heats the ice, changing it directly from a solid to a gas in a process called *sublimation*. This process releases the dust and rock trapped in the ice. The gas and dust create a halo, called *a coma*, around the comet. As it approaches the sun, the comet changes from a cold, dark object into one so bright that people can see it from Earth.

A comet forms two tails as its gas sublimates. One tail is made of dust, and the other is made of charged particles called *ions*. Because the solar wind radiates away from the sun, it causes a comet's ion tail to point away from the sun. A comet's dust tail tends to follow the comet's orbit around the sun and does not always point away from the sun. When a comet is close to the sun, its tails can extend millions of kilometers through space. The dust tail leaves behind pebble-sized debris that other celestial bodies, such as Earth, encounter on a regular basis during their orbits.

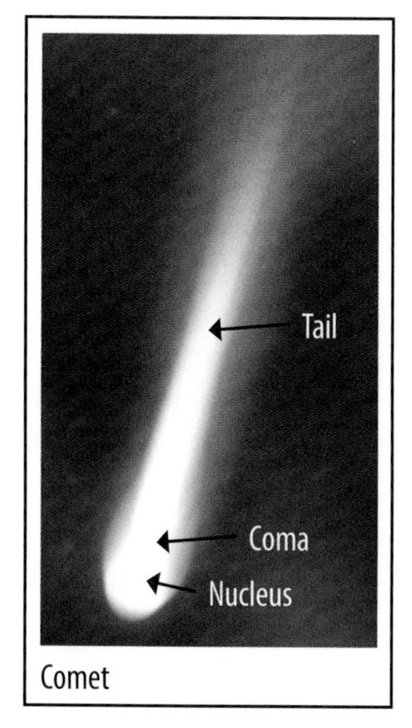

Comet

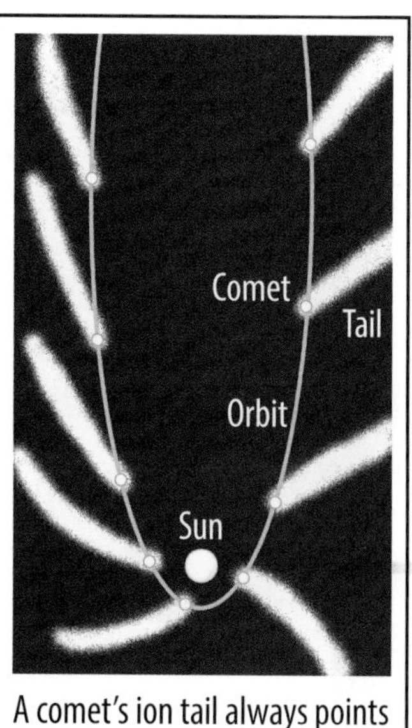

A comet's ion tail always points away from the sun.

OBJECTIVES

- Explain why a comet changes during its orbit.
- Explain the effect of atmospheric friction on a falling body.
- Determine when an object should be classified as a meteoroid, meteor, and meteorite.
- Distinguish among comets, asteroids, and meteoroids.

VOCABULARY

- **comet** a frozen chunk of ice, dust, and rock that orbits the sun
- **friction** the force that resists motion between two surfaces that are in contact with each other
- **meteor** a meteoroid that enters the earth's atmosphere and burns up
- **meteorite** a meteoroid that enters Earth's atmosphere and strikes the ground
- **meteoroid** a rock fragment from an asteroid or comet

FYI

New Comets

Scientists continue to discover new comets, many of which can be seen only with the use of a telescope. As comets first become visible, they look like a blob of light; they brighten and grow a tail as they approach the sun. New comets are named after the people and spacecraft they are discovered by. For example, the Shoemaker-Levy 9 comet, discovered in 1993, was discovered by Carolyn Shoemaker, Eugene Shoemaker, and David Levy, who realized that the comet was going to collide with Jupiter. This unusual comet had been captured by Jupiter's gravity and broken into 21 distinct pieces. Over a period of seven days, these pieces impacted Jupiter one at a time. One of the flares from these explosions shot about 3,000 km above Jupiter's clouds. Another piece of the comet created a temporary dark spot on Jupiter that was larger than Earth.

HISTORY

No Omen

Comets have long been objects of superstition. In fact, the word *disaster* comes from the Latin words *dis*, meaning "negation" and *astrum*, meaning "star." Combined, these words mean "bad star." Cultures around the world believed that comets signaled some form of disaster. Comets were considered evil omens that appeared right before wars, famines, floods, or other disasters. For example, many English citizens believed that Halley's Comet caused the Black Death. Some people today still believe that comets signal disaster.

Although it had been proposed that comets were heavenly bodies like the planets as early as the 1st century, it was not proved until the 16th century by Tycho Brahe. Today people can easily predict the appearance of known comets, and comets are largely understood as part of an orderly creation rather than as bad omens.

Comets appear to originate in the outer solar system. Some astronomers believe they are leftovers from the process of planet formation. If this theory is true, then each comet is a sample of the early solar system, and learning about comets can help scientists piece together the chemical and physical aspects of the solar system's history. Many scientists believe that a sphere of icy bodies called *the Oort cloud* surrounds the solar system and that comets with long periods of revolution come from that region. If the Oort cloud exists, then it probably lies 40,000–50,000 AU from the sun. Comets with relatively short periods of revolution originate in the Kuiper belt. Movies and television programs often show comets zooming across the sky. However, because comets are so far away from Earth, they actually appear to move very slowly in comparison to the stars.

Other small orbiting bodies are known as **asteroids**. Most asteroids are irregularly shaped bodies of various sizes that are pitted with craters from colliding with other space debris. Most asteroids are located in the region between Mars and Jupiter known as *the asteroid belt*. Through a telescope, asteroids look like stars; the word *asteroid* means "starlike."

Composite photo of asteroids Lutetia, Gaspra, and Ida

Some astronomers think that asteroids are leftover material from the solar system's creation. One theory regarding

BIOGRAPHY

Maria Mitchell
Astronomer Maria Mitchell (1818–1889) was the first person in America to discover a comet. She discovered the comet in 1847 when she looked through a telescope and saw a new star above the North Star. When she observed the same object the next night, she noticed that it had moved, and she realized that it must be a comet. Her discovery was eventually submitted to the king of Denmark, who had offered a gold medal to anyone who discovered a comet seen only through a telescope. Mitchell received the prize, and the comet was named *Miss Mitchell's Comet.*

Mitchell was granted several other honors for her discovery. In 1848, she was the first woman to be elected as a member of the American Academy of Arts and Sciences. In 1849, she became a computer (someone who uses math to determine information) for the American Ephemeris and Nautical Almanac. She was elected a member of the American Association for the Advancement of Science in 1850. Mitchell visited Europe in the late 1850s and met several distinguished astronomers. When she returned home, she received a large telescope purchased by women who wanted to support the first woman astronomer in the United States.

Mitchell was chosen as professor of astronomy and director of the college observatory at Vassar College in New York in 1865. As part of her work, she was one of the first to photograph sunspots on a daily basis. She also studied a variety of other objects in space, including comets and the satellites of Jupiter and Saturn. Among her achievements is her assistance in establishing the American Association for the Advancement of Women in 1873.

Mitchell retired from Vassar in 1888 and died in 1889, but her work continued to be recognized after her death. In 1905, she was added to the Hall of Fame of Great Americans at New York University, which is now at Bronx Community College. She was named a member of the National Women's Hall of Fame in Seneca Falls, New York, in 1995. Mitchell never lost her sense of wonder at the universe. She once said, "Do not look at stars as bright spots only—try to take in the vastness of the universe."

their formation is that a planet between Jupiter and Mars broke apart, leaving the belt of asteroids. Another theory is that Jupiter's gravity prevented these asteroids from forming a major planet. Asteroids range in size from Ceres, the largest known asteroid at about 1,000 km long, to as small as pebbles. Scientists believe smaller asteroids are debris from larger asteroid collisions.

An asteroid's color depends on the minerals and chemical compounds it contains. Asteroids have a variety of compositions and colors that tend to relate to their place in the asteroid belt. For example, the outermost asteroids in the asteroid belt are

FYI

Meteorite Records
Meteor Crater in Arizona is approximately 1,200 m across and 180 m deep. Scientists calculate the meteorite that formed this crater fell at a speed of over 64,000 kph. The violent impact with Earth's surface destroyed the meteorite. The largest piece found at the site is only 640 kg.

TRY THIS

Turn Up the Heat
Fill a bucket half full with water. Slowly move the broad side of a spatula through the water. How much resistance do you feel? Move the spatula's broad side quickly through the water. How much resistance do you feel? Move the spatula's edge through the water slowly, then quickly. How much resistance do you feel at each speed? How is resistance related to friction? Use your observations to explain why a meteoroid experiences more friction than an aircraft or a skydiver as they pass through the atmosphere.

HISTORY

Halley's Comet

Astronomers once thought that comets moved in straight paths. The work of Edmund Halley proved this theory was wrong. Halley's most famous discovery was the comet named in his honor. Halley noticed a pattern in comet appearances and theorized that what was thought to be different comets were actually all the same one. He successfully calculated that this comet, last seen in 1682, would reappear in 1758. In fact, records indicate that this comet was first sighted by Chinese astronomers in 240 BC, and it has maintained its orbit ever since. It was last seen in 1986 and is expected to appear again in 2061. Astronomers believe that Halley's Comet is an ordinary comet. Potato-shaped and only 15 km long and 8 km wide, the comet's surface is darker than coal. Halley's comet rotates approximately once every 52 hours.

reddish-brown to black, asteroids in the middle tend to be gray, and asteroids in the innermost belt are typically light gray.

The asteroids in the asteroid belt are not tightly packed together. In fact, a person would have difficulty even finding an asteroid in the middle of the main belt because asteroids are approximately 965,000 km apart. If clumped together, all of the material in the asteroid belt would form an object about 1,500 km in diameter.

A third type of smaller orbiting bodies is meteoroids. A **meteoroid** is a small metal or rocky object that is thought to have broken off an asteroid or a comet. Meteoroids move at high speeds. When a meteoroid enters Earth's atmosphere, it experiences friction. **Friction** is the force that resists motion between two surfaces that are in contact with each other. As a meteoroid enters Earth's atmosphere, it forces its way through innumerable gas molecules. The friction between the meteoroid and the gas molecules produces heat and light. As a meteoroid passes through the atmosphere, it burns up and is called a **meteor**. A meteor is also commonly known as *a shooting star*. Most meteoroids travel at such high speeds that if they pass near Earth, the heat from friction burns them up completely as they travel through the atmosphere. Meteors are best seen away from city lights.

When many meteors appear to be coming from the same direction within a short period of time, the event is called *a meteor shower*. These occur when Earth passes through the dusty debris left behind by a comet. For example, when Earth passes through a comet's tail, Earth's gravity can pull in thousands of meteoroids, which then streak across the night sky as meteors in a spectacular display. All of the meteors in a meteor shower appear from the same point in the sky, which is called *the radiant*. Particular meteor showers are named after the constellation of stars behind the radiant. Leonid meteor showers appear in the Leo constellation, for example, and the Perseids originate at Perseus. Of course, the meteors are not really located near the constellations; it just looks as though the radiant of the shower originates in the star group.

Meteoroids that enter Earth's atmosphere and strike the ground are called **meteorites**. When they strike land, large meteorites create craters. Meteor Crater in Arizona in the United States is thought to have formed this way several thousand years ago. Some scientists believe that an earlier meteorite, which left a crater in Mexico's Yucatán Peninsula, caused the extinction

Unlikely Target

Although scientists find all asteroids interesting, some scientists are particularly fascinated with asteroids that could hit Earth. If an asteroid measuring 1 km or more hit Earth, it could potentially cause global environmental disasters. However, it is very unlikely that an asteroid will ever collide with Earth. Genesis 8:22 states that as long as Earth remains, day and night will continue. Scientists have calculated asteroid orbits several hundred years into the future, and their work does not indicate any large asteroids on a collision course with Earth.

Meteor shower

of most animal life on Earth, including the dinosaurs. It is likely that the dust from the collision would have blocked the sunlight on Earth for months, changing the climate. Young-earth scientists hold that the changes on Earth after the Flood led to the extinction of the dinosaurs. The moon and Mars are covered with meteorite craters, yet such craters are rare on Earth. On February 15, 2013, a meteorite caused widespread destruction and injury when it hit Chelyabinsk, Russia. Earth's atmosphere prevents most meteoroids from striking the ground as meteorites. In addition, oceans cover more than 70% of Earth's surface, so it is very rare for meteorites to fall on land.

LESSON REVIEW

1. Compare how comets look when they are near the sun to how they look when they are far from the sun.
2. Why does a meteor appear as a bright streak in Earth's atmosphere?
3. What is the term for a rock that comes from space and lands on the earth?
4. What is the difference between a comet and an asteroid?
5. How is a meteoroid related to comets and asteroids?

Meteor Crater in Arizona, United States

7.3.1 *Structure of the Moon*

OBJECTIVES

- Compare properties of the moon and Earth.
- Simulate the creation of lunar regolith and craters.
- Identify features on the moon's surface.

VOCABULARY

- **lunar regolith** a loose layer of rock and dust on the surface of the moon
- **mare** a flat, lowland plain on the moon's surface filled with hardened lava
- **rille** a channel on the moon's surface

TRY THIS

Moon Gravity

To determine how high you can jump, hold a sticky note and face a blank wall. Then jump as high as you can and place the sticky note on the wall. Use a meterstick to measure the sticky note's height above the floor. Then weigh an object of your choosing. Calculate how high you could jump with it and how much the object would weigh on the moon. How would these differences affect you?

A natural or artificial body that orbits a larger astronomical body is called *a satellite*. The moon is Earth's only natural satellite. Occasionally, it is called by its Latin name, *luna*, which is more commonly used to talk about the moon's features, such as its lunar surface.

The moon is a planned part of the heavens, declaring God's glory along with the rest of creation. God created the moon with a purpose in mind. It is a light for the night (Genesis 1:16–18). The moon's phases help mark the passage of time, and the moon generates the ocean's tides. However, the moon is very different from Earth.

What is the moon like? The moon's diameter is 27.25% of Earth's diameter. Its mass is only about 1% of Earth's. Part of the reason the moon has such a low mass is because it has a relatively small core. The moon has a weaker gravitational pull because it has less mass. If you threw a ball on the moon, it would fall six times more slowly than it would fall on Earth. You could lift six times more mass and jump six times higher on the moon than on Earth. You would also weigh one-sixth as much. The spacesuit and life support system that the astronauts used on the moon weighed about 113 kg on Earth. However, these did not

Earthrise from the moon

weigh down the astronauts, because they weighed only about 18 kg on the moon.

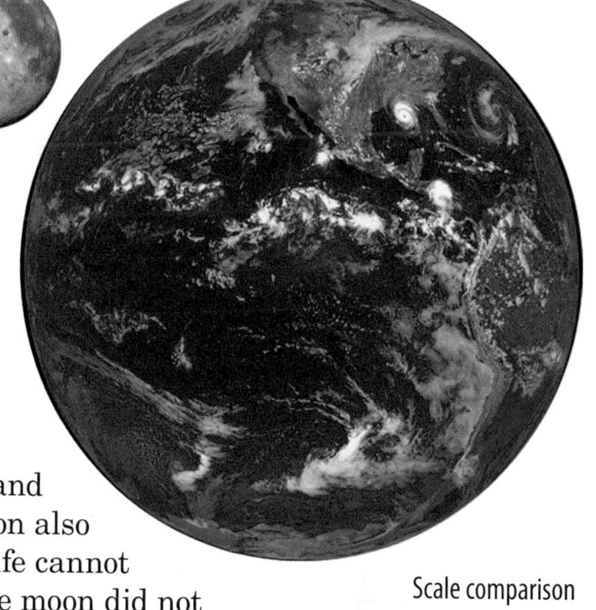

Scale comparison of Earth and the moon

The astronauts who walked on the moon discovered that the weak gravity affected their walking. They bounced a little with each step, causing their stride to be extra long. Such weak gravity can attract only an extremely thin atmosphere to the lunar surface. Because of its lack of atmosphere, the moon has no weather. It has no clouds, no rain, and no wind. Earth's atmosphere traps heat to regulate the temperature, but the moon experiences wide daily temperature swings. It is very hot during the day and very cold at night. Without an atmosphere, the moon also lacks oxygen and liquid water, which means that life cannot exist on the moon. The astronauts who explored the moon did not even find any evidence of bacterial life.

Like Earth, the moon consists of layers. The top layer of the moon is its crust, which is its thinnest layer. Underneath the crust is the mantle. The innermost layer is a small iron core. Earth's large magnetic core gives the planet a magnetic field,

Clementine, a small spacecraft launched in 1994, found indirect evidence of ice in the Tycho Crater at the moon's southern pole.

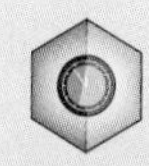

HISTORY

First Footprint

"The surface is fine and powdery. I can kick it up loosely with my toe.... I can see the footprints of my boots and the treads in the fine sandy particles." —Neil Armstrong

On July 20, 1969, Neil Armstrong left the first footprint on the moon.

FYI

Moon

Period of rotation
27 days, 8 hours

Period of revolution
27 days, 8 hours

Diameter
3,476 km

Density (water = 1)
3.34 g/cm^3

Surface temperature
–153°C to 107°C

Surface gravity
16.5% of Earth's

TRY THIS

Make a List

Think about the differences between the moon and Earth. Explain whether each of the following items would be useful on the moon:

1. Portable radio
2. Flashlight
3. Matches
4. Down jacket
5. Umbrella
6. Kite
7. Swimming suit
8. Suntan lotion
9. Compass
10. Seeds to plant

which is what makes compasses point north. The magnetic field on the moon, however, is almost nonexistent; it is 10,000 times weaker than Earth's.

Until *Apollo 11* landed on the moon in 1969, scientists had only theorized what the surface of the moon was like. But as they suspected, the surface was covered with **lunar regolith**, a loose layer of rock and dust. Regolith consists of tiny rock fragments that scientists believe were broken up by the impact of many meteorites. Only the largest meteorites could reach Earth's surface without being completely burned up by atmospheric friction, but on the moon, meteorites can strike the moon's surface at over 48,000 kph. Such an impact pulverizes both the

This thin rock sample from the moon was brought back to Earth by the Apollo 12 mission. The picture was taken using a microscope with a special light to show the different colors and textures of the minerals.

Craters and a rille on the moon

meteorite and the moon's surface, creating dust. Most lunar regolith particles are the size of silt or sand, but some are the size of pebbles.

The Apollo missions to the moon gathered huge amounts of data for scientists on Earth to sift through. Scientists have analyzed 380 kg of moon rock and soil samples, along with photographs and other data sent back to Earth from space instruments. Scientists now know that the moon is made mostly of silicates and oxides that are similar to those found on Earth.

The moon's plains show signs of faulting. Seismic instruments set up by astronauts have registered tremors on the moon's surface called *moonquakes*. Along with rock and soil samples, this data helps scientists form theories about what the inside of the moon is like, what the moon used to be like, and what it might be like in the future.

Without wind or rain to cause weathering on the moon, its surface stays the same. Most changes that do occur on the moon's surface are a result of rock or metal meteorite strikes that form craters of various sizes. Especially large impacts produced features such as the Mare Imbrium, or the Sea of Showers.

TRY THIS

Impact Craters
Line a box with a trash bag and add about 8 cm of flour. Dust the flour surface with powdered paint. Drop marbles one at a time to bombard the surface. Sketch each crater that forms. Drop objects of various sizes from different heights and angles. Sketch the craters. How would the craters change if the marbles or other objects broke on impact?

The moon has dark and light regions. People once thought that the dark regions were seas; these are still called by their Latin name, *mar* meaning "sea." But the moon has no liquid water. A **mare** (pronounced "mah'-ray") is a flat, lowland plain containing hardened lava. Many of the maria (plural for mare) formed when large meteorites created vast impact craters. Lava then welled up and flowed into these craters.

Channels called **rilles** run across the moon. Some rilles wind across the moon's surface. These rilles were formed by the flow of magma on the maria. Other rilles are fairly straight; scientists are not sure how they formed.

The dark areas on the moon are maria, and the light areas are highlands.

The light areas on the moon that are visible from Earth are the rough, pockmarked highlands. Some of the highlands are covered by a type of lava associated with explosive volcanic eruptions. The highlands are all peppered with craters and covered in a layer of broken rock from meteorites.

LESSON REVIEW

1. Compare the properties of the moon to those of Earth.
2. Why are oxygen and liquid water not found on the moon?
3. What do scientists believe formed the moon's craters and regolith?
4. Is it likely that the footprints left on the moon by astronauts are still there? Why?
5. What are the large, lowland parts of the moon called?
6. What covers most of the maria and some of the moon's highlands?

FYI

Many Moons

Even though people talk about Earth's moon as though it were the only one, God created the solar system with more than 173 moons. Some of their diameters can be measured in tens of meters. Others are bigger than the smallest planets. Ganymede, one of Jupiter's moons, is larger than Mercury. The solar system's moons represent the variety in God's creation.

TRY THIS

Mapping the Moon

You can look at the moon on a clear night and identify its features. Impact craters are most visible during or near the first or last quarter phases when the moon looks like a filled semicircle. When the moon is near first or last quarter, draw the visible portion of the moon on a large circle. Include any features that you can see with the unaided eye. Then look at the moon through binoculars or a small telescope and complete the drawing. Consult a labeled map of the moon and identify the more prominent features.

diagnosing

Just as most planets orbit the sun in an elliptical orbit, the moon travels around Earth in an elliptical path, not a circular one. The moon's distance from Earth varies depending on where it is in orbit. Scientists can bounce a laser beam from Earth to a reflector on the moon and back to Earth again to determine the distance of the moon from Earth within 3 cm. The point in the orbit of the moon at which it is farthest from Earth is its **apogee**; the point at which it is closest to Earth is its **perigee**. The closest perigee distance averages about 356,500 km, and the average apogee distance is about 406,700 km.

The moon also rotates on its axis. The moon's period of rotation and period of revolution around Earth are both about 27.3 days. Because of this, people on Earth only see one side of the moon, which is called *the near side*. Although it is not evident from Earth, the far side of the moon from Earth does receive sunlight. During a new moon, in fact, the far side is completely lit up. Because of the speed of the moon's orbit and rotation, the moon passes over the same place on Earth every 24 hours and 50 minutes. The extra 50 minutes keep the moon from appearing above the horizon at the same time each night.

OBJECTIVES

- Explain why only one side of the moon can be viewed from Earth.
- Identify and define the different phases of the moon.
- Simulate the moon's orbit of Earth as Earth orbits the sun.

VOCABULARY

- **apogee** the point in the moon's orbit at which it is farthest from Earth
- **full moon** the phase when the entire near side of the moon is illuminated
- **new moon** the phase when the moon is directly between Earth and the sun
- **perigee** the point in the moon's orbit at which it is closest to Earth
- **phase** each different shape of the moon made visible by reflected sunlight
- **waning moon** the phase after the full moon and before the new moon, when its appearance is shrinking
- **waxing moon** the phase after the new moon and before the full moon, when its appearance is growing

Phases of the Moon Seen from Earth

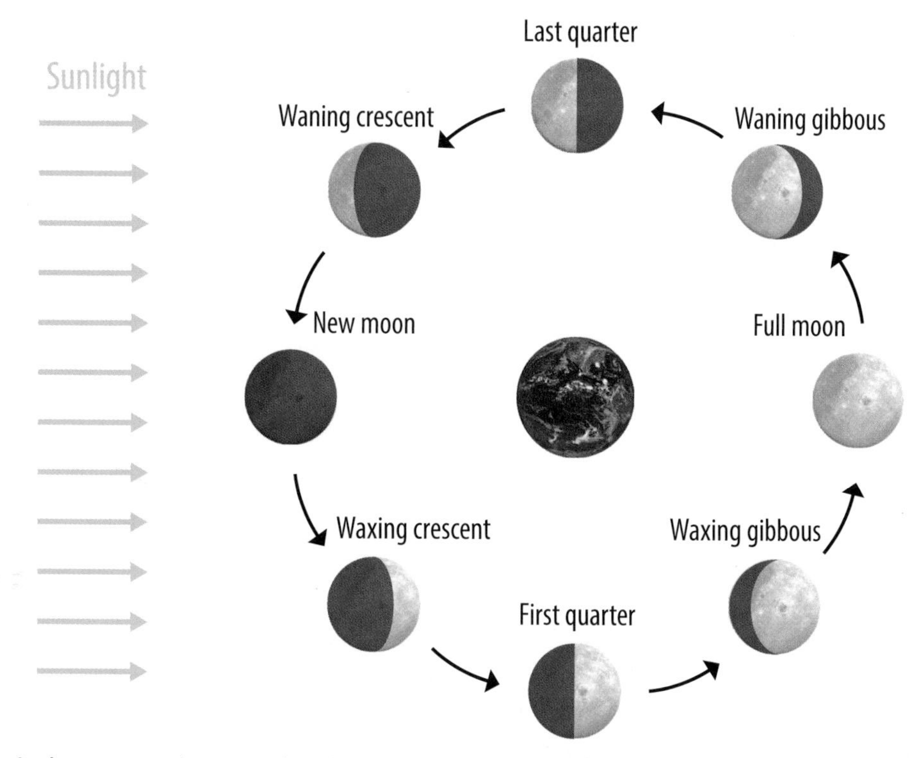

As the moon revolves around Earth, the amount of sunlight on the moon's side that faces Earth changes. This change in sunlight results in different moon phases.

TRY THIS

Moonrise
Observe the rising of the moon every night for one week. Record the time that the moon comes up each night. Sketch or describe any changes you notice in the moon's appearance.

FYI

Celebrate
The Jewish celebration of Passover and the Christian celebration of Easter both follow a full moon. Check this year's calendar to determine how close each celebration is to the full moon.

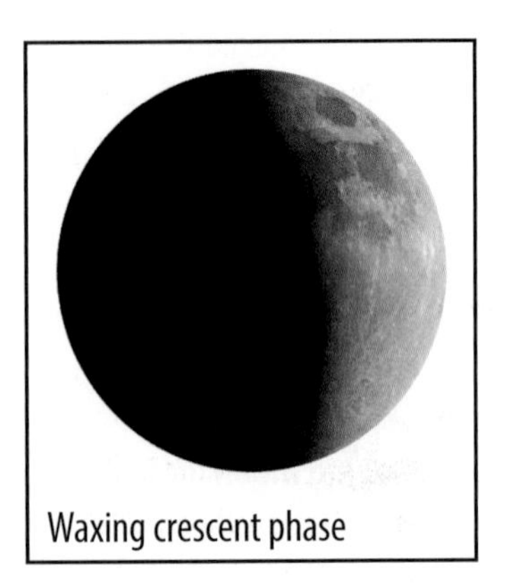
Waxing crescent phase

The moon is the second-brightest object in the sky. Before artificial lights were invented, people depended on moonlight to see at night. A full moon in particular can light up the night. For centuries, farmers have worked in their fields at night during the full moon at the autumnal equinox. That is why the full moon closest to the equinox in September is called *a harvest moon*.

The moon does not always appear to be the same shape. Sometimes it appears as a glowing disk. Sometimes it looks like a filled semicircle, and sometimes it looks like a tiny sliver. At other times, the moon is not even visible, even on a clear night. What accounts for these changing shapes? Although half of the moon is always lit by the sun, people cannot always see the full disk. How much of each side people see depends on the relative positions of the sun, moon, and Earth. Each different shape of the moon made visible by reflected sunlight is called a **phase**. A full cycle of phases takes 29.5 days even though it only takes 27.3 days for the moon to orbit the earth. Because Earth is moving, the moon travels a longer distance to catch up with Earth and finish its phase cycle.

The **new moon** is the phase in which the moon is directly between Earth and the sun. During this phase, the moon cannot

BIOGRAPHY

Buzz Aldrin
One of the first American astronauts to walk on the moon, Buzz Aldrin was accepted at the US Military Academy at West Point, where he studied mechanical engineering. As a pilot in the US Air Force, and he flew 66 combat missions in Korea and was awarded the Distinguished Flying Cross. After earning his PhD in Astronautics from MIT, he was selected as an astronaut by NASA in 1963. The first astronaut with a doctorate, he devised docking and rendezvous techniques for spacecraft that are still used today. He also developed underwater training techniques for astronauts to prepare them for spacewalks. Aldrin saw space exploration as more than science, saying, "There are many of us in the NASA program who trust that what we are doing is part of God's eternal plan for man." On July 20, 1969, Buzz Aldrin joined Neil Armstrong on the lunar surface, becoming the first humans to walk on the moon. Aldrin received the Presidential Medal of Freedom after returning to Earth, and he was awarded the Congressional Gold Medal with his Apollo 11 crewmates in 2011. He has devoted his life to encouraging students' interest in space exploration. In 2015, Aldrin founded the Buzz Aldrin Space Institute at Florida Technical University to continue his quest for a permanent settlement on Mars.

be seen because all of its light reflects away from Earth. As the moon orbits Earth, it moves away from being in line with the sun and Earth. This movement allows people to see some of the sun's light reflecting off the moon's near side. Eventually, the moon moves until Earth is between it and the sun at which time people see the **full moon**, which is the phase when the entire near side of the moon is illuminated.

After the new moon and before the full moon, when the moon's appearance is growing, is a **waxing moon**. When a sliver of the moon becomes visible, the moon is said to be in its *waxing crescent phase*. As the moon eventually moves through one-quarter of its total orbit around Earth, it looks like a filled semicircle of light. The phase after the new moon when the moon appears as this filled semicircle of light is called *the first-quarter phase*. As the moon continues on its orbit, the visible part becomes larger than a semicircle. This stage is called *the waxing gibbous phase*. This term comes from the Latin word *gibbus*, which means "hunchback."

The full moon marks the halfway point of the moon's orbit around Earth. Once past the full moon, the lighted portion of the moon steadily decreases. The moon after the full moon and before the new moon, when its appearance is shrinking, is called a **waning moon**. The stage in which the moon appears to be shrinking but still appears larger than a semicircle is called *the waning gibbous phase*.

When the moon has completed three-quarters of its orbit, it once again becomes a semicircle of light. The phase after the full moon when the moon appears as a semicircle of light is called *the last-quarter phase*. From here, the lighted portion appears to shrink down to a sliver, called *the waning crescent phase*. After this stage, the moon moves between Earth and the sun to become a new moon and begin another revolution around Earth.

LESSON REVIEW

1. Why do people always see the same side of the moon?
2. Why does the moon have phases?
3. Which phase is the moon in if it is getting bigger and appears more than half-full?
4. How much of the moon can people see when the moon is directly between Earth and the sun?

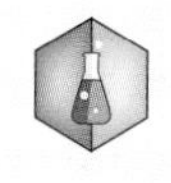

TRY THIS

Phases

Demonstrate the phases of the moon using a ball to represent the moon and a bright lamp to represent the sun. Since people see the moon from Earth, your head will represent Earth. At about what angles are the sun, Earth, and the moon lined up during the new moon, first-quarter phase, full moon, and last-quarter phase?

FYI

Feeling Blue

The phrase "once in a blue moon" refers to something that rarely happens. A couple of different interpretations for blue moon exist, but both pertain to full moons. The modern interpretation of the phrase is that a blue moon is the second full moon in one month. In contrast, the earlier interpretation is that a blue moon is the third full moon when there are four full moons in a season. Since neither event happens very often, the expression means the same regardless of how *blue moon* is interpreted.

7.3.3 Eclipses

OBJECTIVES

- Label the parts of a solar and a lunar eclipse.
- Distinguish among different types of eclipses.
- Model a solar and a lunar eclipse.

VOCABULARY

- **annular eclipse** a solar eclipse during which the outer ring of the sun is visible around the moon
- **eclipse** the casting of one celestial body's shadow on the surface of another celestial body
- **lunar eclipse** an event that occurs when Earth passes directly between the sun and the moon, causing Earth's shadow to block the sun's light from the moon
- **penumbra** an area of partially blocked light surrounding the complete shadow
- **solar eclipse** an event that occurs when the moon passes directly between the sun and Earth, causing the moon's shadow to block the sun's light from a portion of Earth
- **umbra** the dark, central portion of a shadow that completely blocks the sun's light

The sun sheds light in all directions. Celestial bodies such as moons and planets are lit up on the side that faces the sun. These celestial bodies cast long shadows on their opposite sides. An **eclipse** is the casting of one celestial body's shadow on the surface of another celestial body. When the second body becomes completely covered by the shadow, it seems to disappear. This phenomenon is similar to watching someone on an evening walk step from a well-lit street into a building's shadow.

A **solar eclipse** is the casting of the moon's shadow on the Earth's surface. This event occurs when the moon passes between the sun and Earth and part of the moon's shadow falls on Earth. Shadows cast by Earth and the moon have two parts. The **umbra** is the dark, central portion of a shadow that completely blocks the sun's light. Surrounding the umbra is the **penumbra**, an area of partially blocked light surrounding the complete shadow.

The umbra of the moon's shadow falls on a very small region. People within the umbra experience a total solar eclipse in which the moon blocks out all sunlight. Because the umbra is so small, total solar eclipses for a given area are rare. Earth's rotation causes the moon's shadow to move quickly, so a total solar eclipse rarely lasts more than seven minutes at any one place. During a total solar eclipse, the sky becomes so dark that only stars and planets can be seen, and the temperature may drop 10° or more. Around the dark shadow of the moon, the sun's corona glows with a pearly luster. In contrast, the penumbra of the moon's shadow creates a partial solar eclipse. During a partial solar eclipse, the sky only dims and sunlight may take on a slightly different hue.

Solar Eclipse

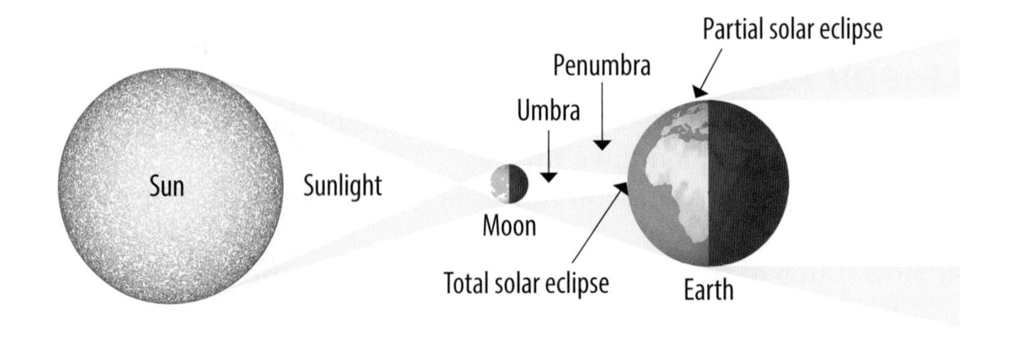

The new moon passes between the sun and Earth during a solar eclipse.

Eclipses: Historical Markers

Since God created the sun, moon, and Earth to interact in an orderly manner, historians can determine exactly when eclipses occurred in the past. Therefore, the dates for historic events that took place around the time of an eclipse can be established. Often events were recorded as happening a certain number of days, months, or years after an eclipse. By comparing these events with actual eclipses that happened near that time and place, historians can determine when the event, such as a battle or the crowning of a king, took place. For example, a Chinese text from the 4th century BC recorded that during a battle, "the sun rose at night" and later the sun "rose" from behind the moon, which is a description of a solar eclipse. Historians have calculated that both the eclipse and the battle occurred on September 24, 1912 BC. Just as it is possible to calculate when past eclipses occurred, astronomers also can forecast when they will happen in the future.

Total solar eclipse

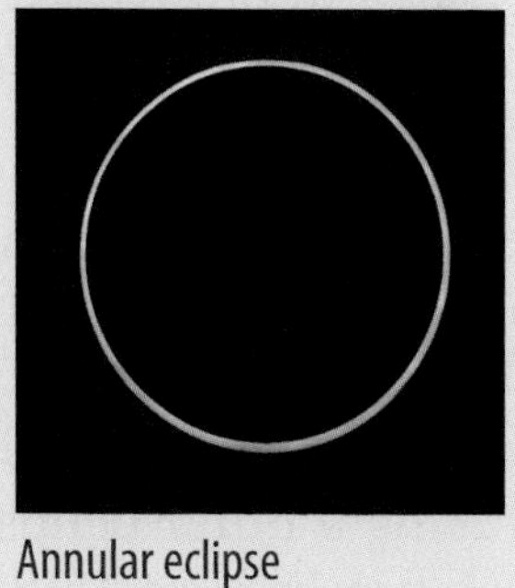

Annular eclipse

FYI

Eclipse Eye Safety

Do not ever look directly at the sun during any type of eclipse! Even as the sun appears to darken, its radiation can still cause blindness. Instead of directly watching a solar eclipse, use a pinhole card to project the indirect image of the sun onto another card.

If the moon's umbra is too far away to reach Earth, a total solar eclipse is not possible. In order for a total solar eclipse to occur, Earth usually has to be near the point in its orbit when it is closest to the sun, the perihelion. However, when Earth is at its farthest point from the sun—the aphelion—an annular eclipse can occur. During an **annular eclipse**, the outer ring of the sun is visible around the moon. The moon does not completely block

Lunar Eclipse

Earth passes between the sun and the full moon during a lunar eclipse.

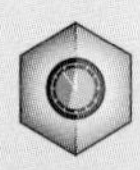

HISTORY

Stop Fighting

Predicted by the Greek astronomer Thales, one of the most famous eclipses in ancient times (calculated to have occurred on May 28, 585 BC) ended a five-year war between two Middle Eastern armies. The historian Herodotus recorded that the Lydians and the Medes were engaged in battle when "the day turned to night" during a solar eclipse. The eclipse persuaded both armies to make peace.

TRY THIS

Figure Out Earth's Shape

Although various people throughout history believed that Earth was flat, Greek scientist and philosopher Aristotle (384–322 BC) used his observations of eclipses to support the argument that Earth is a sphere.

Obtain a paper circle cutout, a tennis ball, and various small objects of different shapes, such as wooden blocks or pens. Hold each object in front of a lamp so its shadow falls on the circle of white paper. Rotate the object in different directions. Record the shapes cast by the shadows. Which objects always make a circular shadow? What shapes do the shadows of the circular paper cutout make?

the sun during an annular eclipse. Instead, a beautiful, bright ring of light around the edge of the moon's shadow is visible.

A **lunar eclipse** is the casting of Earth's shadow on the moon. During a lunar eclipse, Earth's shadow moves across the lighted moon. A lunar eclipse only happens during a full moon. Although the moon loses its direct light from the sun during an eclipse, it does not get completely dark. Sunlight bends as it passes through Earth's atmosphere, causing the moon's color to range from gray to a copper color. Lunar eclipses can last for several hours because Earth's shadow is much larger than the moon's shadow.

When the moon orbits completely into Earth's umbra, a total lunar eclipse occurs. A partial lunar eclipse happens when only a portion of the moon passes through Earth's umbra. Another form of lunar eclipse, called *a penumbral eclipse*, occurs when the moon is shadowed by only the Earth's penumbra. During a penumbral eclipse, the moon becomes only slightly darker because the sun's light is not completely blocked.

Although there are more solar eclipses than lunar eclipses each year, most people see more lunar eclipses. During solar eclipses, the moon's shadow covers a small portion of Earth, which means that solar eclipses are visible only along a

Sunlight bends as it passes through Earth's atmosphere during a full lunar eclipse.

Create an Eclipse

Darken the room. Use a small bouncy ball to represent the moon, a tennis ball to represent Earth, and a flashlight to represent the sun. Manipulate these objects to create the conditions necessary for observers on Earth to experience a partial solar eclipse and a total solar eclipse. Describe or sketch these conditions. What phase must the moon be in for a solar eclipse? Why?

Next, manipulate the sun, moon, and Earth to create a lunar eclipse. What phase must the moon be in for a lunar eclipse? Why? Describe or sketch the conditions necessary for a total lunar eclipse and a partial lunar eclipse.

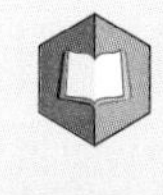

BIBLE CONNECTION

Miraculous Darkness

Solar eclipses occur only during a new moon. Some people believe that the darkness that covered Earth during Jesus's crucifixion was caused by a solar eclipse. However, Jesus was crucified during Passover, which always occurs during a full moon.

narrow path. In contrast, lunar eclipses are visible to everyone on the dark half of Earth because Earth's shadow can completely cover the moon.

Why are eclipses not more common? The moon passes through the plane of Earth's orbit at least twice a year. However, the sun, Earth, and moon have to be aligned for an eclipse to form. A solar eclipse happens if the moon crosses Earth's orbital plane when the moon is between the sun and Earth. A lunar eclipse occurs if the moon crosses Earth's orbital plane when Earth is between the sun and the moon. Usually the sun, the moon, and Earth are not directly lined up when the moon's orbit crosses Earth's, so no eclipse occurs.

LESSON REVIEW

1. Distinguish between an umbra and a penumbra and identify the types of eclipses each produces.
2. Why do lunar eclipses last longer than solar eclipses?
3. What is the difference between an annular solar eclipse and a partial solar eclipse?
4. How are the sun, moon, and Earth arranged in both a solar eclipse and a lunar eclipse?

Stages of a lunar eclipse

7.3.4 Seasons

OBJECTIVES

- Model the way in which Earth's tilt and revolution around the sun cause different seasons.
- Identify Earth's primary lines of latitude.
- Differentiate between a solstice and an equinox.

VOCABULARY

- **equinox** a point in Earth's orbit at which the sun crosses Earth's equator, causing the hours of day and night to be nearly equal everywhere on Earth
- **solstice** one of the two days of the year in which the sun's most direct rays reach farthest north or farthest south

You cannot feel Earth's movement directly, but you can observe its effects. For example, as part of Earth's rotation you can see the sun rising in the east, crossing the sky during daylight hours, and setting in the west. One half of Earth is always bathed in sunlight, and one half is always under the cover of darkness.

You can also see the effects of Earth's revolution around the sun. On January 3, the Earth is at its perihelion. At this point, it is about 147 million km from the sun. Earth's aphelion occurs on July 5, when Earth is more than 152 million km away from the sun. But Earth's distance from the sun is not responsible for seasons. If this were the case, July 5 would be in a cold season not only in the Southern Hemisphere but also in the Northern Hemisphere.

The changing seasons are caused by Earth's tilt as it orbits around the sun. Earth is tilted about 23.4° on its axis. During part of the year, the North Pole is tipped toward the sun. During the other part of the year, the South Pole is tipped toward the sun. When the South Pole is exposed to the sun, the Southern Hemisphere enjoys longer daylight hours and warmer temperatures. The angle of the sun's rays hitting the ground in that hemisphere is more direct and intense. At the same time, the Northern Hemisphere receives less daylight because its pole is facing away from the sun. The angle of the sun's rays striking the Northern Hemisphere decreases. When the sun's rays spread

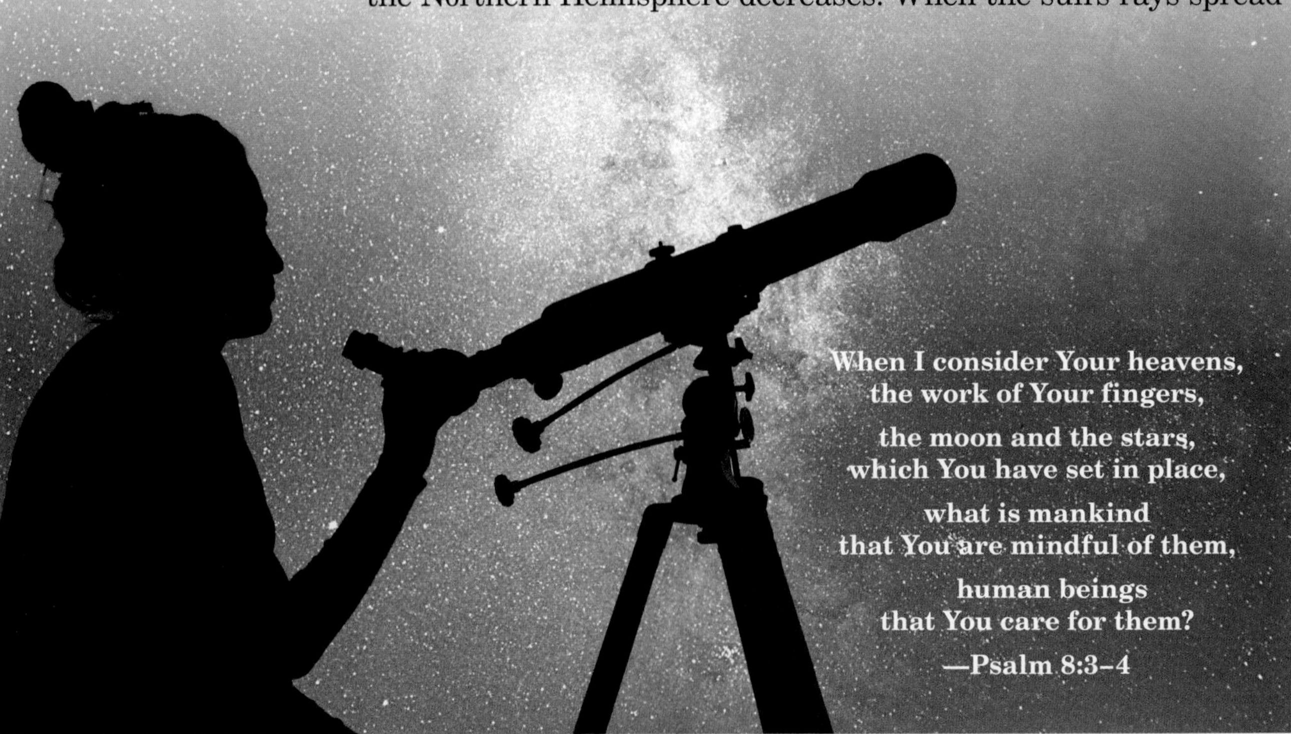
When I consider Your heavens,
the work of Your fingers,
the moon and the stars,
which You have set in place,
what is mankind
that You are mindful of them,
human beings
that You care for them?
—Psalm 8:3–4

Summer Solstice (June 21 or 22)

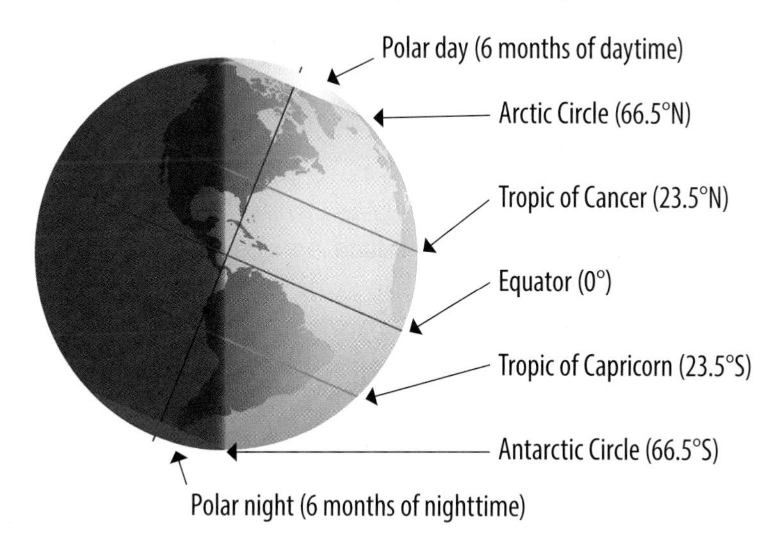

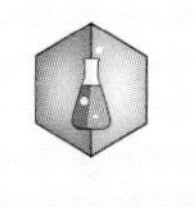

TRY THIS

Change the Seasons
Which feels hotter, the sun's rays at noon or the sun's rays as it is close to setting? Why? Using a globe, a light, and a thermometer, design an experiment to compare the amount of heat shed by direct rays of light with that given off by slanted rays of light.

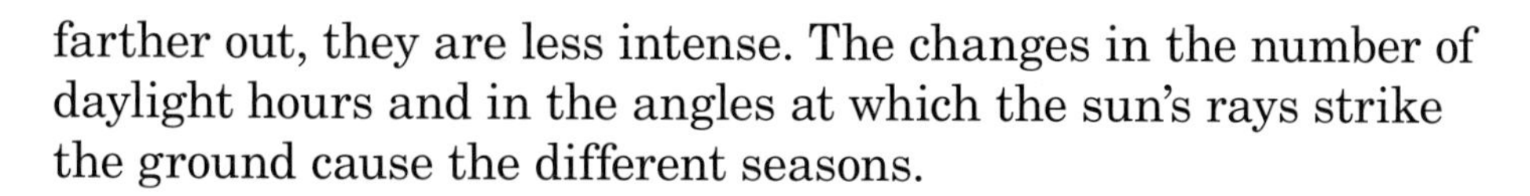

farther out, they are less intense. The changes in the number of daylight hours and in the angles at which the sun's rays strike the ground cause the different seasons.

A **solstice**, which means *sun stop*, is one of the two days of the year in which the sun's most direct rays reach the farthest north or the farthest south. On June 21 or 22, the North Pole tilts more directly toward the sun than it does at any other time of the year, and the sun's rays strike Earth at a 90° angle along the Tropic of Cancer. This day, known as *the June solstice*, marks the beginning of summer in the Northern Hemisphere and the beginning of winter in the Southern Hemisphere. On the June solstice, the Northern Hemisphere receives the maximum

Solstices and Equinoxes

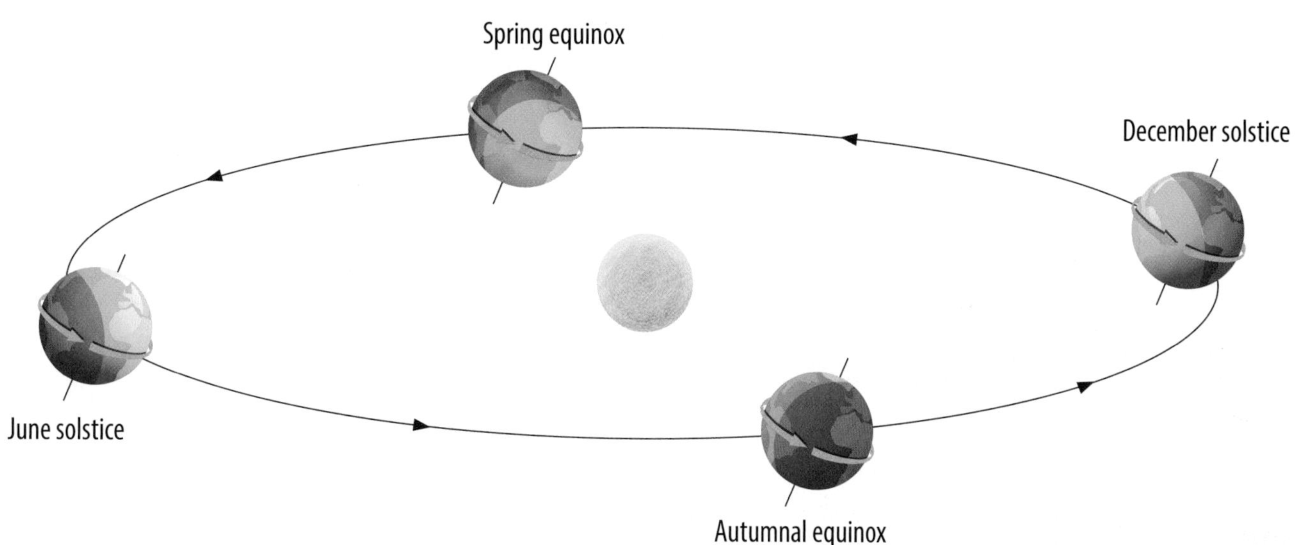

CHALLENGE

Dr. Martin Luther King, Jr.
Dr. Martin Luther King, Jr., had the following to say about science and faith: "Science investigates; religion interprets. Science gives man knowledge which is power; religion gives man wisdom which is control. Science deals mainly with facts; religion deals mainly with values. The two are not rivals. They are complementary. Science keeps religion from sinking into the valley of crippling irrationalism and paralyzing obscurantism. Religion prevents science from falling into the marsh of obsolete materialism and moral nihilism." Do you agree? Why?

number of daylight hours, and the Southern Hemisphere receives the minimum number of daylight hours. At this time, the sun stays above the horizon for 24 hours north of the Arctic Circle, but it does not rise south of the Antarctic Circle.

On December 21 or 22, the sun's rays strike at a 90° angle along the Tropic of Capricorn. This day is called *the December solstice*. On this day, the North Pole is tilted away from the sun, but the South Pole is inclined toward the sun. During the December solstice, the daylight hours and intensity in the hemispheres are reversed from the June solstice, so it is winter in the Northern Hemisphere and summer in the Southern Hemisphere.

Earth also experiences two equinoxes. The word *equinox* means "equal night." An **equinox** is a point in Earth's orbit at which the sun crosses Earth's equator, which causes the hours of day and night to be nearly equal everywhere on Earth. The equinoxes happen on March 20 or 21 and again on September 22 or 23. During each equinox, the sun's rays strike the equator at a 90° angle. The March equinox is called *the spring* or *vernal equinox* and the September equinox is known as *the autumnal equinox* in the Northern Hemisphere. Because the seasons in the Southern Hemisphere are the reverse of those in the Northern Hemisphere, the terms are reversed there as well.

LESSON REVIEW

1. How much does Earth's distance from the sun affect temperatures on Earth?
2. Explain what causes Earth's seasons.
3. Which line of latitude does the sun strike at a 90° angle at the beginning of summer in the Northern Hemisphere? At the beginning of winter?
4. What is the difference between an equinox and a solstice?

UNIT 8

The Great Expanse

Chapter 1: *Stars and the Universe*
Chapter 2: *Space Exploration*

Vocabulary

absolute magnitude
apparent magnitude
binary star system
black hole
Doppler effect
galaxy
galaxy cluster
inertia
light-year
neutron star
parallax
payload
propellant
pulsar
rocket
satellite
space probe
space station
spin-off
star cluster
supernova
thrust

Key Ideas

- Systems, order, and organization
- Evidence, models, and explanation
- Change, constancy, and measurement
- Evolution and equilibrium
- Form and function
- Abilities necessary to do scientific inquiry
- Understandings about scientific inquiry
- Origin and evolution of the universe
- Abilities of technological design
- Understandings about science and technology
- Science and technology in society
- Science as a human endeavor
- Nature of science
- History of science
- Nature of scientific knowledge
- Historical perspectives

SCRIPTURE

Lift up your eyes and look to the heavens: Who created all these? He who brings out the starry host one by one and calls forth each of them by name. Because of His great power and mighty strength, not one of them is missing.

Isaiah 40:26

8.1.1 *Stars*

OBJECTIVES

- Relate the color of stars to the stars' temperature and composition.
- Compare continuous, emission line, and absorption line spectra.
- Explain the different ways scientists classify stars.

VOCABULARY

- **absolute magnitude** the brightness of a star measured by an observer who is a standard 32.6 light-years away
- **apparent magnitude** the brightness of an object as observed from Earth
- **light-year** the distance light travels in a vacuum in one year, approximately 9.46 x 10^{12} km
- **parallax** the apparent shift in an object's direction when viewed from two geographically distant locations

Stars are enormous balls of hot gases—primarily hydrogen and helium. They also contain varying amounts of heavy elements: carbon, nitrogen, oxygen, and magnesium. Stars are fueled by nuclear fusion, which occurs when two light nuclei join together to form a single heavy nucleus. A large amount of energy is released during such fusion reactions. The energy that heats the star originates primarily in the core before escaping into space as radiation.

Have you ever wondered how scientists know such details about stars that are trillions of kilometers from Earth? Actually, much of the information about stars can be found by studying the light they emit. For example, a star's color can indicate how hot it is. When you look at a fire, you see that flames are a variety of colors. Bluish flames are hotter than yellow flames, and red flames are the coolest. In the same way, the color of a star can provide clues to the star's temperature. When you look at the stars, it is hard to distinguish star colors because the cones in your eyes that help you perceive colors do not work well in low light. However, on a clear night, you may notice that although many stars appear white, some appear blue or red.

A star's color not only indicates its temperature but also its elemental components. Identifying the elements present in a star involves separating the different colors in its starlight. Think about a rainbow. When you see a rainbow, you are seeing white light split into many colors. The color separation happens because raindrops act as prisms. The array of colors produced when white light passes through a prism is called *a spectrum.* The main colors in a spectrum are red, orange, yellow, green, blue, indigo, and violet. A hot solid object, such as the wire inside an incandescent light bulb, gives off all the colors necessary to produce white light. This range of color is called *a continuous spectrum.*

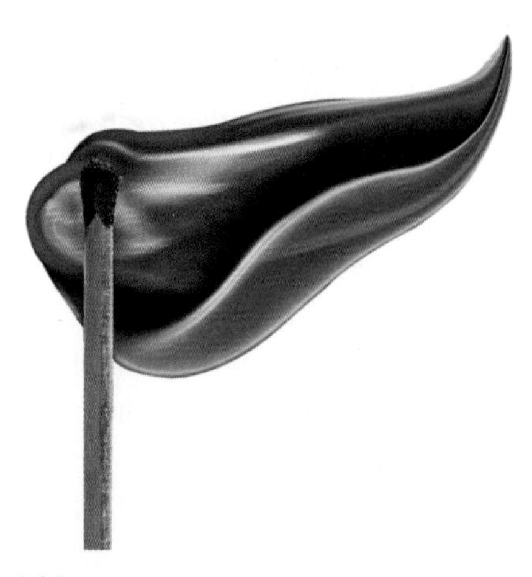

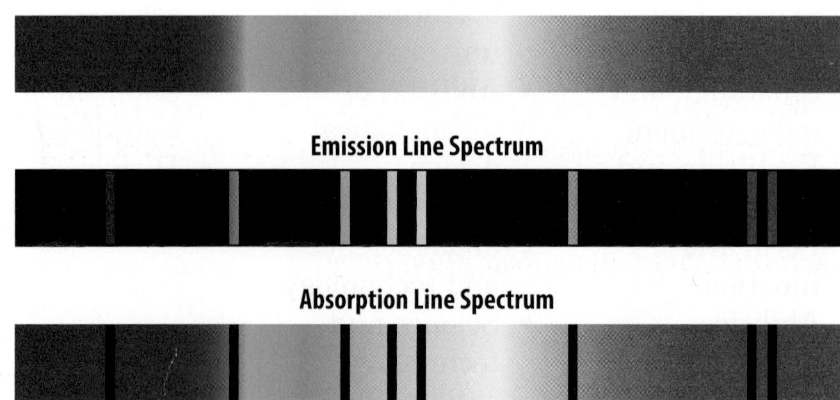

Magellanic Cloud colors indicate varying degrees of heat.

Just as a prism or a raindrop spreads the continuous spectrum into many colors to form a rainbow, an instrument called *a spectrograph* splits starlight into all its colors. However, the light spectrum emitted by a star is not a continuous spectrum. When electrons in the star's atoms are excited during combustion, they quickly "jump" to a higher energy level and then promptly return to their initial lower energy level. This activity releases a photon of light. If the light is split with a spectrograph, only a few colors appear. These colors form what are known as *emission lines.* The light produced by each element in a star has a unique set of emission lines, which helps scientists identify the elements that comprise each star.

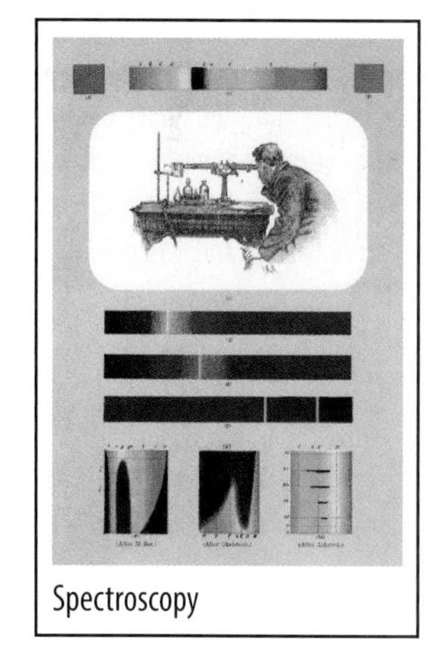
Spectroscopy

Another type of spectrum is produced when white light passes through the cold gas of an element. When that happens, the gas blocks some of the light's colors. If the light is passed through a spectrograph, the spectrum would include a series of black lines where an element's colors were blocked by the gas. The absent colors are the ones emitted when the element is heated. These black lines are called *absorption lines.*

Starlight shows absorption lines because the gases in a star's atmosphere are cooler than the gases on the surface or interior

BIOGRAPHY

Annie Jump Cannon

Annie Jump Cannon was born on December 11, 1863, in Dover, Delaware. She attended Wellesley College where she studied physics and astronomy, and she later studied at Harvard Observatory. Annie was the first woman to receive an honorary doctorate from the University of Oxford. Annie was left almost completely deaf after a bout of scarlet fever. She is best known for her invention of the unique star classification system that assigned classes O, B, A, F, G, K, and M to stars according to their spectra, which is still used today. Over the course of Annie's career, she discovered hundreds of variable stars and classified hundreds of thousands of others. Known for being very diligent, enthusiastic, and patient, Annie was the first woman elected to an officer position in the American Astronomical Society. In her honor, the society created the Annie Jump Cannon Award, which is given to female astronomers who are distinguished in their field.

of a star. The cooler atmospheric gases absorb some of the star's light. This absorption removes certain colors of light from the continuous spectrum of the star—the same colors that the star would emit if it were heated. Because stars are created from a mixture of elements, all of the different absorption lines for these elements appear together in a star's spectrum.

In the 1880s, scientists began to classify stars according to their spectra. This original classification system attempted to measure the strength of element absorption lines, but this method proved unreliable. Stars were then classified according to temperature and designated in order of decreasing warmth by one of the following letters: O, B, A, F, G, K, M, R, N, and S. In this system, classifications O and B are the bluest and hottest, and M through S are the reddest and coolest. However, even the coolest stars are fiery infernos with temperatures that reach 2,700°C. The

Spectral Class	Temperature (K)	Size and Color
O	41,000	
B	31,000	
A	9,500	
F	7,240	
G	5,920	
K	5,300	
M	3,850	

sun has a surface temperature of about 6,000°C. Hotter stars have surfaces between 10,000°C and 25,000°C. The hottest stars' temperatures reach between 25,000°C and 50,000°C on their surfaces. The inside of a star is much hotter than its surface. For example, astronomers think that the temperature inside the sun is 15 million °C.

Polaris is the final star in the handle of the Little Dipper.

Stars have also been classified by brightness. Some ancient astronomers called the brightest stars *first-magnitude stars* and the faintest stars *sixth-magnitude stars*. When telescopes became available, stars that astronomers could not see before became visible; the sixth-magnitude stars did not look so dim anymore. Later, scientists began classifying stars using a system of magnitudes. They adjusted the temperature classification system that they were already using and assigned positive values to dimmer stars and negative values to brighter stars. Modern astronomers use a combination of temperature and luminosity.

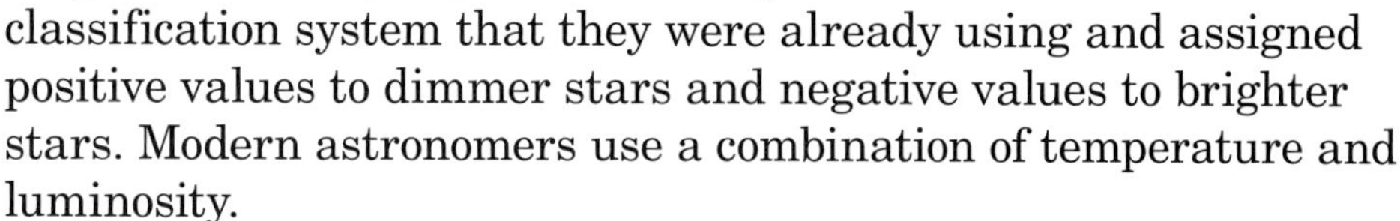

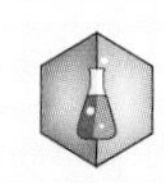

TRY THIS

Make a Spectroscope

Cut a circle of black paper with a diameter larger than the opening of one end of a cardboard tube. Secure the piece of paper to the end of the cardboard tube with tape or a rubber band. Cut a long slit in the middle of the piece of paper. Hold a piece of diffraction grating over the open end of the cardboard tube. Look through the end of the tube with the slit pointing toward a light source. Rotate the grating until a band of color appears on the inside of the tube. Tape the grating in place. Observe the bands of color produced by other light sources.

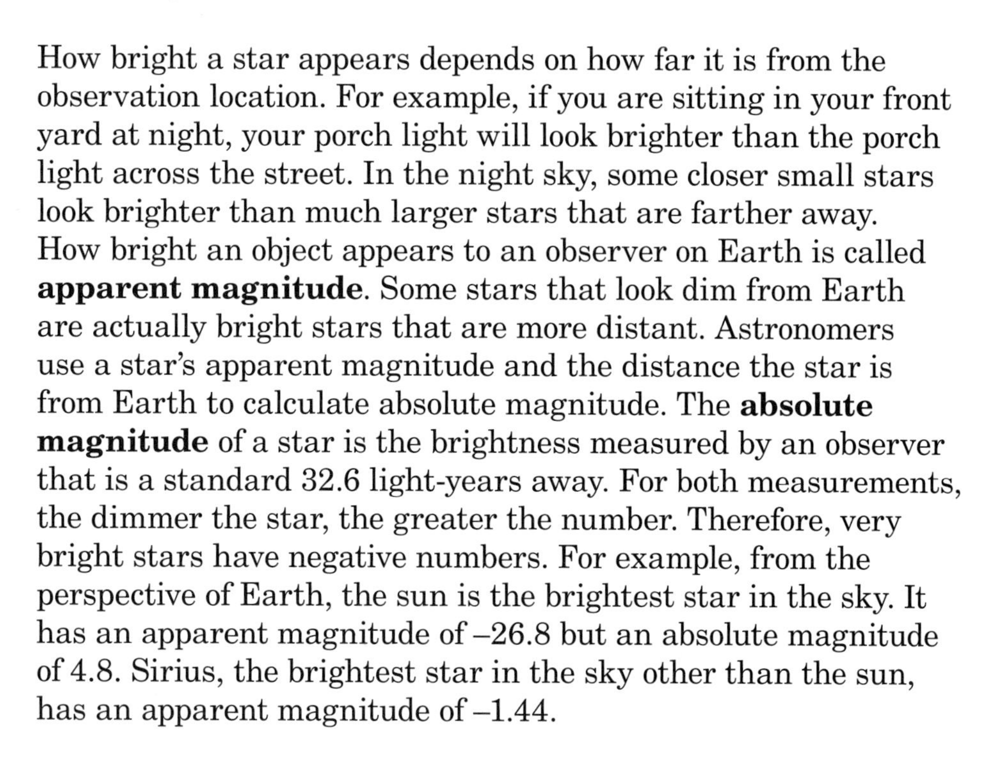

How bright a star appears depends on how far it is from the observation location. For example, if you are sitting in your front yard at night, your porch light will look brighter than the porch light across the street. In the night sky, some closer small stars look brighter than much larger stars that are farther away. How bright an object appears to an observer on Earth is called **apparent magnitude**. Some stars that look dim from Earth are actually bright stars that are more distant. Astronomers use a star's apparent magnitude and the distance the star is from Earth to calculate absolute magnitude. The **absolute magnitude** of a star is the brightness measured by an observer that is a standard 32.6 light-years away. For both measurements, the dimmer the star, the greater the number. Therefore, very bright stars have negative numbers. For example, from the perspective of Earth, the sun is the brightest star in the sky. It has an apparent magnitude of –26.8 but an absolute magnitude of 4.8. Sirius, the brightest star in the sky other than the sun, has an apparent magnitude of –1.44.

Determining a star's absolute magnitude requires knowing how far away the star is from Earth. Distances in the universe are much too great to be measured in kilometers, so astronomers created a new unit of measurement known as *a light-year*. A **light-year** is the distance that light travels in a vacuum in one

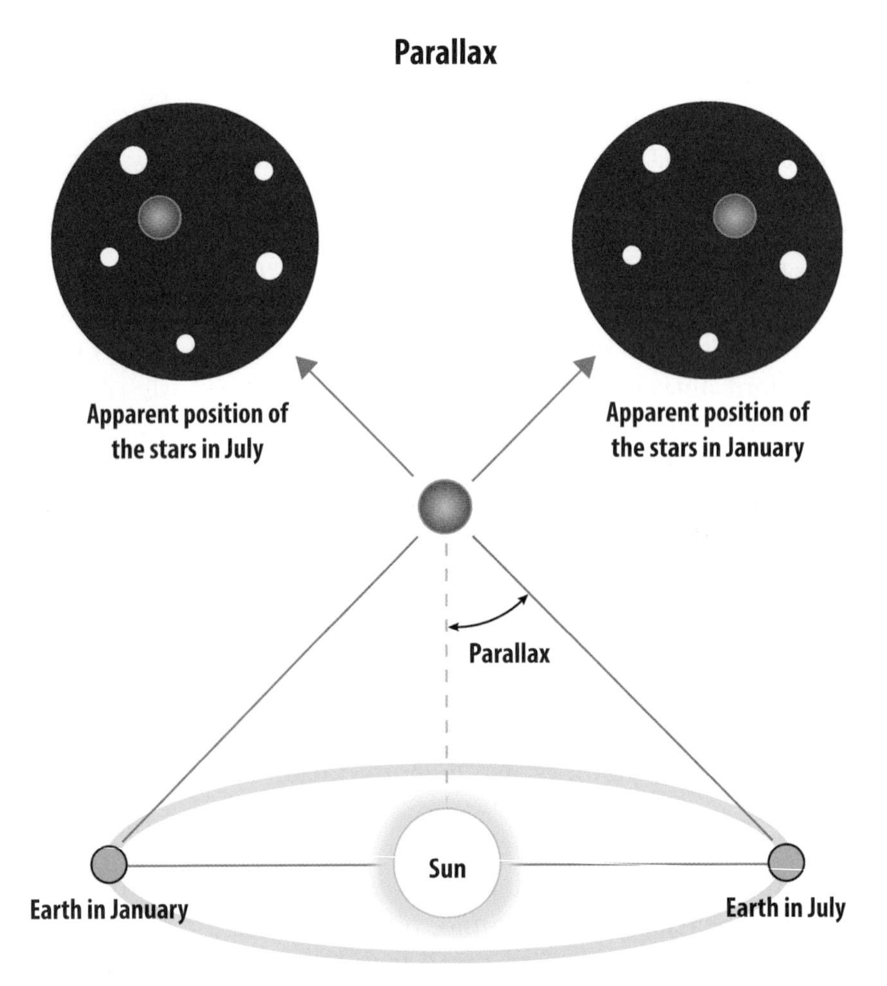

The locations of nearer stars seem to shift more than stars that are farther away. The shift can be measured to determine the distance to the nearer stars.

year, which is approximately 9.46 x 10^{12} km. Light, the fastest known thing in all of creation, travels about 300,000 km/sec. Light-years help astronomers avoid using large, cumbersome numbers. For example, Proxima Centauri, the closest star to Earth other than the sun, is more than 40 trillion km away, but astronomers refer to its distance as 4.25 light-years.

To determine the distance to a nearby star, astronomers measure its position in relation to other more distant stars. Six months later, when Earth is on the other side of the sun, they measure the star's relative position again. From Earth, it will look as though the star has moved. As the earth revolves around the sun, stars near it seem to move more than stars that are farther away. Astronomers then measure the star's apparent movement against the background of the distant stars. The apparent shift in an object's direction when viewed from two geographically distant locations is called the **parallax**. The different positions of a star as viewed from Earth and from the sun are called *the annual parallax*. Astronomers use the diameter of Earth's orbit, the angle of the parallax, and geometry to determine the distance from Earth to a star.

Because Earth rotates on its axis, different parts of the planet's surface face the sun. As a result, as Earth revolves, individuals see different stars in the sky at different times during the year. Earth's rotation makes the sun and most of the stars seem to move across the sky. The rest of the stars all seem to rotate around the North Star (Polaris), which is directly above Earth's North Pole. From the perspective of an observer on Earth, the North Star does not appear to move, which is why it has always been an important navigational aid. Each star actually does move in space, and over thousands of years, star patterns change shape. However, because the stars are so far away, this movement is not obvious.

LESSON REVIEW

1. Explain how a spectrum helps classify stars.
2. What type of spectrum shows all of the visible color?
3. Explain how emission lines form.
4. Why does starlight show absorption lines?
5. How have stars been classified?
6. Explain which is brighter: a star with an apparent magnitude of +5.3 or the sun, which has an apparent magnitude of –26.8.

Star trails

8.1.2 *Life Cycle of Stars*

OBJECTIVES

- Interpret H-R diagrams.
- Illustrate the life cycle of a star.

VOCABULARY

- **black hole** a massive celestial object with gravity so strong that not even light can escape
- **neutron star** an extremely small, dense star composed primarily of neutrons
- **pulsar** a spinning neutron star that gives off pulses of radiation at regular intervals
- **supernova** the violent explosion of a star

If you look at the stars night after night, individual stars do not seem to be any different from one another. However, stars do change, although it takes an exceptionally long time. Like other parts of God's creation, stars are born, then they mature and die. Individual stars go through this process in different ways. You may be wondering how astronomers discovered that stars have a life cycle.

One tool astronomers use is the Hertzsprung-Russell diagram (H-R diagram). The H-R diagram is a graph that plots the relationship between a star's spectrum and its absolute magnitude. It not only compares the brightness and temperature of stars but is useful for showing how stars change. In 1911, Danish astronomer Ejnar Hertzsprung developed a method of plotting the temperature and brightness of stars. Two years later, Henry Norris Russell developed a similar method. Their findings were combined into the H-R diagram.

The H-R diagram shows temperature along the x-axis and absolute magnitude (brightness) along the y-axis. Hot, blue stars are located at the left portion of the chart, and cool, red stars are located at the right portion of the chart. Bright stars are at the top of the chart and dim stars are at the bottom. A band of stars seems to stretch from the top left to the bottom right.

TRY THIS

Find the Main Sequence

For a group of students, record each student's height and foot length. Plot the data on a graph. Is there a pattern on the graph? How might the variables be related?

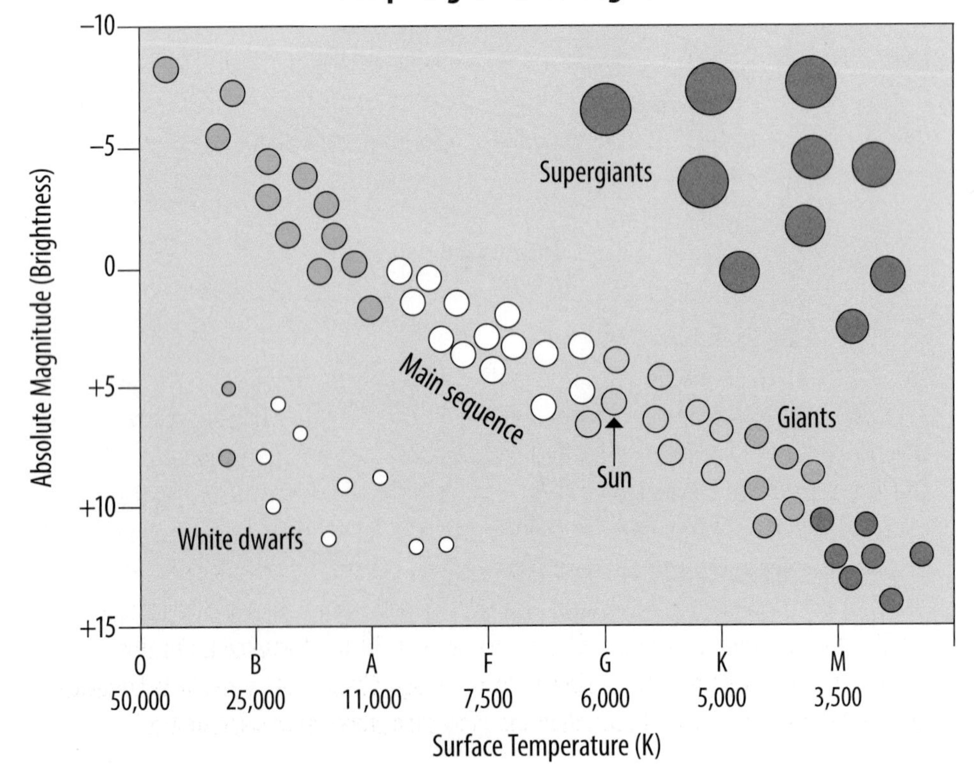

Stellar nursery in a nebula

This diagonal pattern of stars on the H-R diagram is called *the main sequence*. During most of a star's life, it is classified as a main-sequence star. As a star changes over time, it is moved across the H-R diagram. The life cycle of a star is depicted by the graph. Most stars, including the sun, fall into the main sequence. Although it seems bright from Earth, the sun is about 1 million times dimmer than the brightest stars.

Stars are born in nebulae—large clouds of interstellar material known as *stellar nurseries*. These raw materials begin to cluster together. The sphere of particles begins to contract from its own

BIOGRAPHY

Subrahmanyan Chandrasekhar

Chandrasekhar was an Indian-American astrophysicist who is best known for his work on the theoretical structure and evolution of stars and the later life cycle stages of massive stars. He attended Presidency College, the University of Madras, and Trinity College. In 1983, Chandrasekhar shared the Nobel Prize in physics with William Fowler for discovering that a star that exceeds 1.44 times the mass of the sun does not form a white dwarf but instead continues to collapse, explodes in a supernova event, and eventually becomes a neutron star. This discovery established what is known as *the Chandrasekhar limit*. He concluded that more massive stars continue to collapse and form black holes, which he attempted to describe mathematically. As a professor at the University of Chicago, Chandrasekhar conducted research regarding star energy transfer by radiation and convection processes on solar surfaces.

Red supergiant star cluster

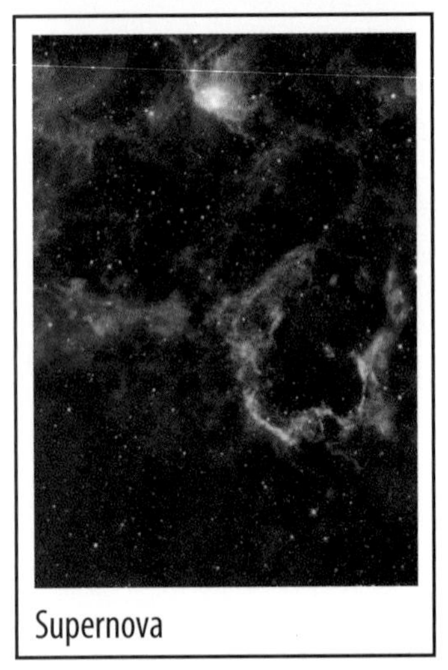
Supernova

gravity. It grows hotter as it becomes denser. When it is hot enough in the center (about 15 million °C), a nuclear reaction begins. As nuclear fusion begins to turn hydrogen into helium, a star is born.

Once a star's mass is stabilized, the force of gravity maintains the star's size. At this point, most stars would belong on the main sequence of the H-R diagram. This stage is the longest in a star's life cycle. A star's position on the main sequence during its prime depends almost entirely on its mass. Scientists estimate that a star with the mass of the sun stays at this main-sequence stage for about 10 billion years. Stars with less mass are located at the lower right of the main sequence, and more massive stars are found at the upper left.

As they age, most main-sequence stars move up and to the right on the H-R diagram to become giants or supergiants. A star at the end of its life cycle that expands and cools as it runs out of hydrogen is called *a red giant.* As the outer layers of such a star expand from its helium core, the star widens and becomes larger, cooler, and redder. At this point it begins to burn excess helium. Eventually, average-sized stars like the sun lose their outer layer of gases and eject materials, forming a planetary nebula. What remains is called *a white dwarf,* a small, hot, faint star at the end of its life. White dwarfs fall into the lower left corner of the H-R diagram because they are hot but dim.

Massive blue stars use their hydrogen much faster than cooler stars. They generate a lot more energy, which makes them very hot and causes them to appear blue. Their existence is short compared to the life span of other stars, however. When these massive stars age, they leave the main sequence in a very dramatic way compared to average stars. A blue star may collapse under its own weight and explode in a brilliant flash of light. Such a violent explosion is called a **supernova**. At this point, its absolute magnitude may reach a peak brightness that is a billion times greater than the sun. From the earth, it may look as though a bright new star has appeared in the sky.

What happens to a supernova? The leftover materials in the core of a supernova pack together to form a star with a diameter of about 20 km. This extremely small, dense star is composed primarily of neutrons, so it is called a **neutron star**. Imagine how dense such a small star must be to have a mass comparable to 1.35 suns compressed in such a small space! The material in a neutron star is so dense that on Earth a teaspoon of the star matter would weigh almost one billion metric tons.

A **pulsar** is a spinning neutron star that gives off pulses of radiation at regular intervals—picture something like the flashes of a lighthouse. Radio telescopes can detect these beams. Pulsars emit radio pulses and other radiation at regular intervals with a frequency of around 1,400 pulses per second.

If the leftover materials from a supernova are too massive to become a neutron star, they may collapse to form a **black hole**—a

Pulsar

Black hole creating X-ray flares

massive celestial object with gravity so strong that not even light can escape. To produce a black hole, a star needs to be at least three times as massive as the sun. Astronomers theorize that black holes are more than three solar masses squeezed into a ball that is only about 64 km across. Because black holes permanently trap light and other forms of energy and matter, they cannot be directly observed. Black holes are only detected indirectly, such as when they are orbited by a visible star or when dust or gas from a nearby star spirals into the black holes. In this case, the materials may emit X-rays, which astronomers can use to detect the existence of black holes.

LESSON REVIEW

1. What two factors are being compared in the H-R diagram?
2. In what portion of the H-R diagram will a star appear for the majority of its life?
3. If a star has a absolute magnitude of 0 and a surface temperature that is cooler than the sun's, where would it be located on the H-R diagram?
4. How is a star born?
5. How are white dwarfs created?
6. Why are black holes not visible?

When many people hear the term *star system*, they probably think it refers to constellations, but constellations are not really star systems. A constellation is a group of stars that forms a recognizable pattern. Individuals named the patterns they observed. The stars in constellations do not have any physical or gravitational relationship with each other. In fact, many of them are separated by great distances. Many of the constellations were recognized by ancient people who grouped stars together to form shapes of objects, animals, and people. They pictured a bear, dog, dragon, lion, and a winged horse. They saw a king, a queen, and a princess. People told stories of Orion (the great hunter) and Ursa Major (the bear). They also viewed objects such as a cup and a scale. Each culture and nation developed its own stories to account for the pictures seen in the sky, and these stories developed into mythology. Astronomers still use the Latin names of constellations.

In contrast, true star systems are groups of stars that influence each other gravitationally. Stars that form close to one another are bound to each other by mutual gravitational attraction. In other words, their individual gravity attracts them to each other, and they move as one body. Many stars are part of a **binary star system**—a pair of stars that orbit their common center of mass. Binary star systems are quite diverse. Some binary stars are extremely close to each other. Other pairs are separated by great distances, such as one-third of a light-year. Binary stars in close proximity may circle each other in a day. Those that are widely separated may orbit one another over perhaps even millions of years. Some binary star systems are orbited by planets.

OBJECTIVES

- Identify various types of star systems.
- Discuss basic features of different star systems.
- Describe how astronomers classify galaxies.

VOCABULARY

- **binary star system** a pair of stars that orbit their common center of mass
- **galaxy** large systems of stars and their solar systems, gas, and dust held together by gravity
- **galaxy cluster** a group of thousands of galaxies under the same gravitational influence
- **star cluster** groups of stars that have a common origin and are held together by mutual gravitational attraction

Binary star system

Sombrero Galaxy

Some stars are part of a triple or quadruple star system, but these systems are not as common as binary systems. Triple systems appear to be binary star systems that have trapped a single star in their orbit. Scientists believe quadruple systems are composed of two binary systems. Like binary star systems, the stars in these systems orbit a common center of mass. These types of multiple star systems are rather unstable. For example, if the three stars in a triple system orbit too closely, the more massive stars will push the smallest star out of its gravity range. The system would then become a binary system.

A large system of stars and its solar systems, gas, and dust that is held together by gravity is called a **galaxy**. God sustains a wide variety of galaxies in all shapes and sizes. Most galaxies are found in groups. Because galaxies are so enormous, astronomers prefer to measure them using large units called *parsecs* and *kiloparsecs*. A parsec (pc) is equal to 3.26 light-years and a kiloparsec (kpc), is equivalent to 3,260 light-years. The Milky Way galaxy is about 30 kiloparsecs across, but there are far larger galaxies. The larger galaxies contain over a trillion stars, whereas smaller galaxies may have only a few million stars. To estimate how many stars might be in a galaxy, astronomers observe its size, brightness, and mass.

Some scientists believe that there could be 100 billion galaxies spread throughout the heavens. These galaxies can be one of

Spiral galaxy

HISTORY

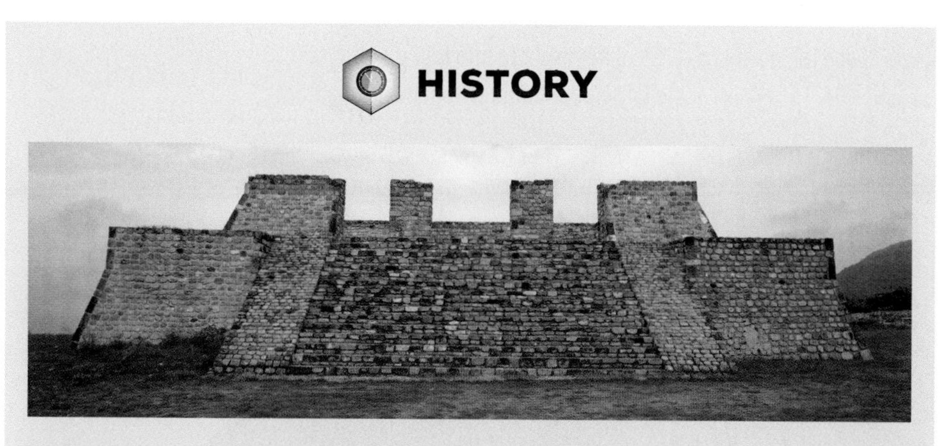

Xochicalco

Throughout history, many civilizations have marveled over the patterns of star alignments in the visible universe. The movement of constellations has been used to determine when to plant crops. Mariners also used constellations to navigate. Some groups of people even designed massive ritual structures patterned after star alignments. One such structure in central Mexico is known as *Xochicalco*. Built in the 8th century, this site was an important ceremonial center. It became a cultural link between the earlier Maya civilizations and the Aztecs. Much of the monument is decorated with images of rulers, priests, gods, and astronomers. In addition, calendar signs and a series of 21 calendar altars recorded the months and days of the ceremonial year. Caves located in the hillsides were used for ceremonies and served as underground observatories designed for tracking the sun's movement. Xochicalco was abandoned in the late 9th century.

three basic types: spiral, elliptical, or irregular. Most galaxies appear to be spiral galaxies, which contain lots of gas, dust, and young stars and have a central bulge. Revolving around the bulge are spiral arms that look blue because hot blue stars are found there. The central bulge is redder because the stars there are older and cooler. Although it is hard to tell from Earth's perspective, astronomers believe the Milky Way is a spiral galaxy. They estimate the galaxy's arms are 100,000 light-years across and contain about 100 billion stars. Most of the Milky Way's stars are in the central bulge. Since Earth's solar system is about 30,000 light-years away from the center of the Milky Way, the sun takes about 220,000,000 years to orbit around the galaxy's center.

Elliptical galaxies have very bright centers and very little gas or dust. Some appear elongated like a rugby football, but others look spherical. The apparent shape of an elliptical galaxy depends on a viewer's perspective. In other words, what appears to be a spherical galaxy may actually be the end of an elongated elliptical galaxy. Because these galaxies have little gas, they do not create new stars, so elliptical galaxies contain only old stars.

FYI

Constellations in the Northern Hemisphere

Astronomers divide the northern celestial hemisphere into four quadrants: NQ1, NQ2, NQ3, and NQ4. Thirty-six constellations are found within these quadrants.

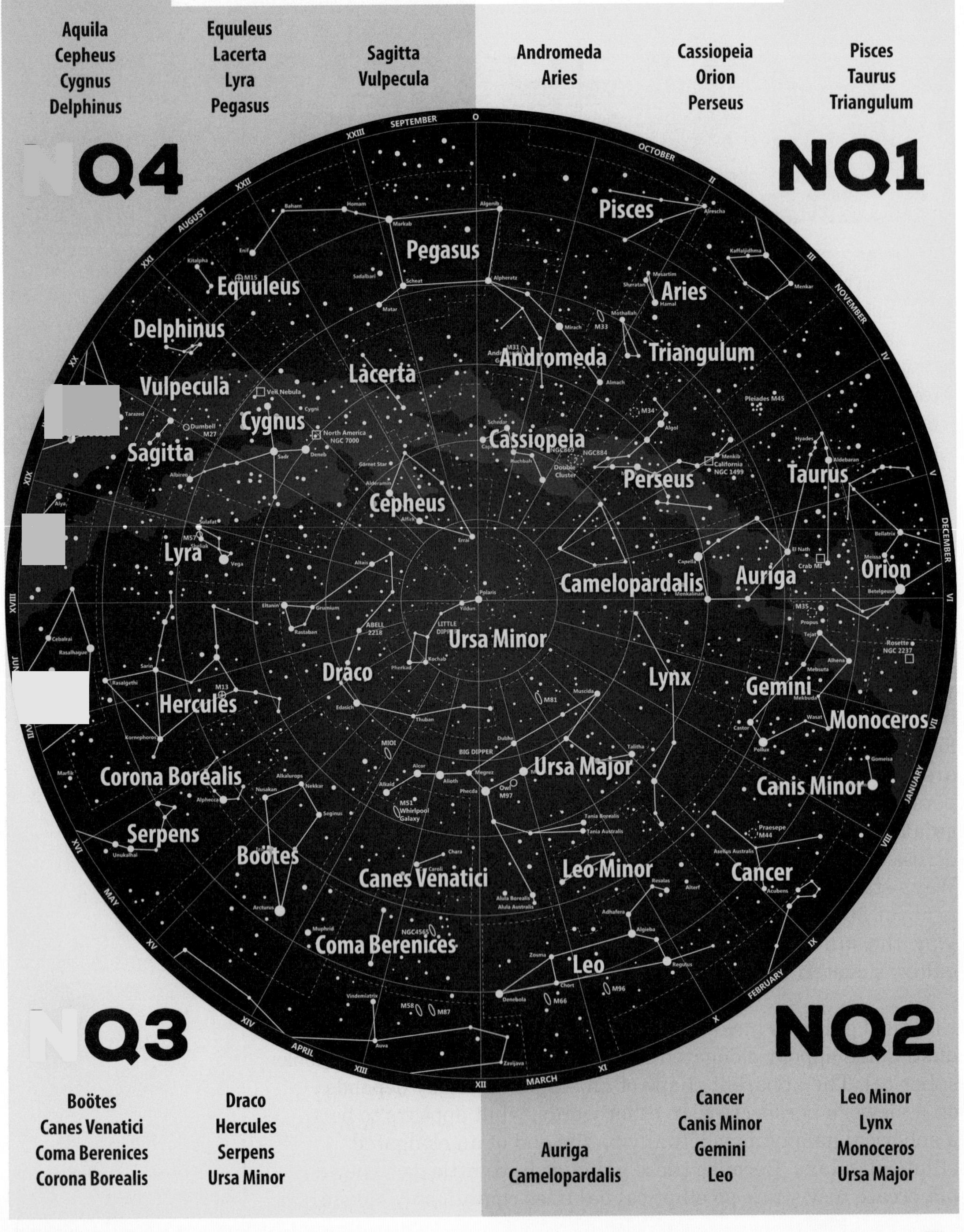

Irregular galaxy

Irregular galaxies have no definite shape and contain very little mass. Like spiral galaxies, some irregular galaxies have a lot of gas and young stars but they do not have arms. Other irregular galaxies have a generally distorted look. Scientists believe that these galaxies may have collided with others in the past.

Regardless of their shape, all galaxies are in constant motion. The Milky Way zooms through space at a speed of 230 kph. Galaxies tend to congregate and can move through space as a unit spanning hundreds of millions of light-years across.

The gas and dust that galaxies contain is called *interstellar matter*. This matter forms the nebulae that give birth to stars. There are two basic types of nebulae: dark and bright. Dark nebulae are very dense and cold. They block the light of the stars behind them. Bright nebulae emit or reflect light from nearby stars. Spiral and irregular galaxies generally contain nebulae, but elliptical galaxies do not.

Globular star cluster

Star clusters are groups of stars that have a common origin and are held together by mutual gravitational attraction. There are two types of star clusters: open and globular. Open clusters are groups of a few hundred young stars that are loosely held together by gravity. Open clusters are usually located in the bulge of a spiral galaxy. The Hyades in the Taurus constellation

Rosette nebula

An artist's rendering of the most distant quasar

is the nearest visible open cluster in the Northern Hemisphere; it is 150 light-years away. New open clusters contain young blue stars.

Globular clusters are dense, ball-shaped groups of older stars. The Milky Way galaxy is illuminated by more than 150 globular clusters. Most of these clusters are located at the center of the galaxy. Omega Centauri, visible in the Southern Hemisphere, is one of the largest globular clusters in the galaxy. This globular cluster stretches across a distance of 150 light-years.

Galaxies, although extremely large, are not the largest units in the universe. A **galaxy cluster** is a group of thousands of galaxies under the same gravitational influence. A galaxy cluster may contain tens of thousands of galaxies. The Local Group, the galaxy cluster that includes the Milky Way, contains more than 20 galaxies. Galaxy clusters are arranged into superclusters, which are groups of galaxy clusters. Superclusters contain tens of thousands of galaxies, often millions of light-years across.

Looking through space is like looking back in time. Astronomers view distant galaxies and other celestial objects to learn how galaxies form and change over time. For example, astronomers study quasars, some of the most distant observable objects. Scientists believe that when the strong gravity of a black hole begins compressing an active galaxy, the galaxy becomes an intense stream of light and radio waves known as *a quasar*. From Earth, quasars look like tiny points of light. They are extremely bright because they drown out the light of surrounding stars. In fact, quasars are so bright they can be observed from billions of light-years away even though they are small.

LESSON REVIEW

1. What is the difference between a star system and a constellation?
2. Describe the basic features of three types of star systems.
3. Explain the basic classifications of galaxies.
4. How many kilometers across is a galaxy that measures 20 kiloparsecs?
5. What is the difference between an open cluster and a globular cluster?

God is the Creator and Sustainer of the vast universe. The book of Genesis gives readers a glimpse into the complexity of God's creation, which can be appreciated even more deeply through astronomy. Likewise, many of the psalms marvel at the vastness of the universe. The Bible states that God spoke and brought creation into being. Some Christian scientists believe that when God spoke creation into being, it was formed much like it looks today. However, others believe that God created the universe through a longer process, possibly even over billions of years.

OBJECTIVES

- Summarize the predominant young-earth and old-earth explanations of how the universe was created.
- Analyze the evidence used to support the main models of how the universe was created.

VOCABULARY

- **Doppler effect** the apparent shift in frequency of waves emitted by a moving source

Scientists cannot do experiments on events in the past to perfectly prove the age of the universe. All the calculated ages for the universe rely on assumptions—young earth as well as old earth. Scientists who believe Earth and the universe are young point to the biblical account of Creation. According to the account in Genesis 1:1–19, God created Earth before He created the sun, moon, stars, and other planets, so nothing in the universe is older than planet Earth itself. If Earth is young, every other thing in the universe is younger still. Genesis 1:14–16 explains that God created the sun, moon, and stars individually and then placed them in the heavens. This order of creation directly contradicts the idea that these celestial bodies formed before Earth—or that they formed by a random interaction of dust and gas in the void of space.

Many astronomers and scientists assume the universe is ancient because of their measurements of celestial objects and events. By interpreting their findings, they theorize that the universe

The universe expansion

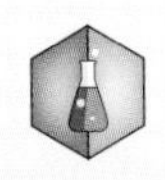

TRY THIS

Expanding Universe

With a marker, draw randomly placed dots on a deflated balloon. Slowly inflate the balloon and observe the position of the stars. What happens to the distances between the dots as the balloon expands? Is there a center from which all of the dots are moving or an edge toward which they are all moving?

is 13.82 billion years old. One scientific model is the Big Bang theory. According to this model, all the contents of the universe were held under tremendous pressure, density, and temperature until finally there was an enormous expansion of space. This event marked the beginning of energy, time, space, and matter. Physical events before the Big Bang are unknown, and scientists do not try to explain them. According to the model, after the Big Bang, gravity began affecting the matter that was expanding outward in all directions. The force of gravity began pulling matter into clumps. These clumps became galaxies, which continued to move outward into the universe and formed galaxy clusters.

In contrast to what you might visualize, objects in the universe are not flying out from one central point. Rather, all celestial objects are moving away from one another because the space between them is expanding. Picture the dough for a loaf of raisin bread: after the dough is mixed, the raisins are a certain distance apart. As the dough rises and expands, each raisin moves away from every other raisin. The universe is like the rising bread dough in that it is expanding in all directions. And like the raisins in the dough, every distant galaxy is moving away from all the other galaxies.

Scientists use the principles they observe in creation to support the Big Bang model. For example, astronomers have determined that most galaxies are moving away from each other and that the universe is expanding at a tremendous rate. How do they know this? To answer that, think of what happens when a fire truck speeds past. As it moves away from you, the pitch of the siren becomes lower because the sound wavelengths are longer. The apparent shift in the frequency of waves emitted by a moving source is called the **Doppler effect**. The Doppler effect applies to light waves as well as sound waves. If a star is moving away from Earth, its light waves will be slightly elongated, or stretched, as they reach Earth. Longer light waves occur on the red end of the light spectrum. So, the light of a star moving away from Earth shifts toward the red end of the spectrum. This color change is called *the redshift*. Because the light from all distant galaxies and quasars has shifted toward red, astronomers have concluded that the universe is still moving outward. It is not known if the universe will continue

The Doppler effect

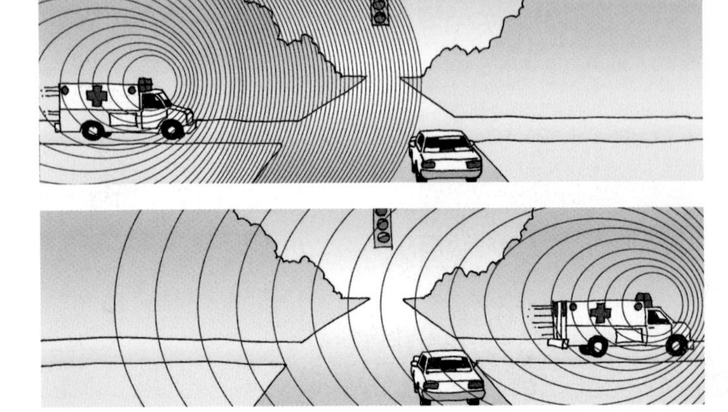

to expand or will eventually collapse in on itself, but current evidence suggests that it will continue to expand.

Another piece of evidence used to support the Big Bang model emerged in 1964 when two scientists using a low-noise antenna heard annoying static and tried unsuccessfully to get rid of it. The intensity of the static did not vary, and it came from every direction. The static was identified as cosmic microwave background radiation that was coming from every part of the universe. Many scientists believe this radiation is a product of the Big Bang because its temperature readings match what they estimate those of the Big Bang radiation would be. In addition, this type of radiation is found throughout space.

However, because scientists cannot do experiments on events in the past, the Big Bang model is not testable or repeatable through laboratory science. No scientific method can prove the age of the universe. Young-earth scientists point to evidence that the temperature of the universe is uniform and was never hotter than it is now, which contradicts the Big Bang model of a cataclysmic, hot beginning. According to physics, the creation of matter in the form of hydrogen and helium gas from the energy of the universe's expansion should have created an equal amount of antimatter. However, the universe contains primarily matter

The Wide Field Infrared Survey Telescope is scheduled to launch in 2020 to search for evidence of how the universe began.

with only tiny amounts of antimatter present. Spiral galaxies also indicate that the universe is younger than many supporters of the Big Bang believe. The centers of these galaxies rotate faster than the outer arms, which causes the spiral structure to tighten rather than unwind. Young-earth astronomers point out that if these most-common galaxies were billions of years old, they would no longer have a spiral shape—they would be compressed into balls or disks. Yet the heavens are filled with beautiful spiral galaxies. Other researchers point to the fact that if the universe was very old, there would be evidence of many supernovas. For example, the Large Magellanic Cloud, a nearby galaxy, would have evidence of about 340 supernovas if it was billions of years old, and it would have remnants of about 24 supernovas if the galaxy was about 7,000 years old. The actual number of supernova remnants found in the Large Magellanic Cloud is 29, which indicates the galaxy is only thousands of years old. Even scientists who do not believe in God have argued that something had to have sparked the instant of creation that is represented by the Big Bang. In fact, some atheistic scientists disagree with the theory because they feel the Big Bang model points to the need for a Creator rather than explaining how the universe appeared without one.

Spiral galaxy NGC 1232

Supernova remnant NGC 2060 in the Large Magellanic Cloud

Although much of the scientific community has accepted the Big Bang model as a workable explanation for the beginning of the universe, the model cannot answer many questions, such as the universe's exact age or the future expansion or collapse of the universe. Ecclesiastes 3:11 states, "no one can fathom what God has done from beginning to end." It is important to remember that models are tools created by people in an attempt to understand how the eternal God works in His creation.

LESSON REVIEW

1. Summarize the young-earth and old-earth explanations for how the universe was created.
2. What are two pieces of evidence used to support the Big Bang model?
3. What are two pieces of evidence that suggest the universe is young?
4. What conclusions can you draw about how the universe was created? Why?

8.2.1 *Rockets*

OBJECTIVES

- Summarize the history of the rocket.
- Explain how a rocket is propelled.

VOCABULARY

- **payload** the cargo or equipment carried by a spacecraft
- **propellant** a fuel used to produce the hot gases that power a rocket
- **rocket** a machine that uses escaping gas to move
- **thrust** the force that causes a rocket to accelerate

Have you ever dreamed of going to the moon, landing on Mars, or sailing past Jupiter? Throughout most of history, such achievements were possible only in dreams or science fiction. In the early 20th century, science fiction books that described fantastic trips to the moon and into space sparked the interest of many young people who later made important contributions to the field of space flight. But the key to exploring space was the **rocket**. A rocket is a machine that uses escaping gas to move. The first rockets were developed as weapons by the Chinese in the 13th century. For over 700 years, rockets were used for warfare. The concept of rocketry being used for space travel developed gradually.

Self-taught Russian teacher Konstantin Tsiolkovsky (1857–1935) enjoyed the science fiction writing of Jules Verne, who wrote about space flight in books such as *From the Earth to the Moon*. Tsiolkovsky developed the basic theory of rocket propulsion and suggested the use of liquid propellants. A propellant is a fuel used to produce the hot gases that power a rocket. He even calculated how fast a rocket would need to travel to escape Earth's atmosphere and determined how much fuel would be needed. But even though Tsiolkovsky explained how rockets work, he never built any himself.

Robert Goddard (1882–1945) of the United States is considered the father of modern rocketry and space flight. When he was a teenager, he read H. G. Wells's *War of the Worlds* and dreamed of making a device that could go to Mars. In 1914, while he was watching fireworks, he came up with the idea of launching a rocket. His first rocket went 12.5 m into the air. Goddard believed that rockets could travel in a vacuum even though most scientists at the time did not agree. In 1926, he launched the first rocket powered by a liquid propellant. Between 1930 and 1941, Goddard continued to build and test rockets of increasing complexity. Because at the time, rockets were used for weaponry, not space flight, Goddard assisted the U.S. military

Robert Goddard

during both world wars. Goddard's larger rockets reached altitudes over 2.4 km.

During World War II, Germany developed the V-2 rocket, the first long-range guided missile. The V-2, which was used in the bombardment of England, was designed by the rocket engineer Wernher von Braun. During the war, the German government built a center where von Braun and members of his team built and tested rockets as part of the war effort. At the end of the war, von Braun and his team surrendered to the United States, where they hoped to continue their rocket development for space travel rather than military use. The addition of Germany's best rocket scientists was a great benefit to rocket research in the United States in the 1950s.

After World War II, the Cold War began. The Cold War was an arms race between the United States and the Soviet Union (U.S.S.R.), the superpower that included Russia and 15 soviet socialist republics. One outgrowth of the political tension and arms buildup of the Cold War was what is called *the Space Race*. The United States and the U.S.S.R. both wanted to demonstrate their national strength by getting into space. In response to the launch of Sputnik in 1957 by the U.S.S.R., the United States formed the National Aeronautics and Space Administration (NASA) on July 29, 1958. NASA unified the separate teams that were working on rocket development in the U.S. The many accomplishments of NASA include a series of dependable rockets. Until recently, rockets were designed for single launches, although some components of the rockets for the U.S. space shuttle program were retrieved and used on subsequent missions. The entry of private companies into rocket design and production has sparked innovations that allow rockets to be landed back on Earth and reused. For example, on April 8, 2016, SpaceX successfully landed the first stage of a Falcon 9 rocket on a ship in the Atlantic Ocean.

The space shuttles used both liquid and solid propellants during launch.

The structure of a rocket is fairly simple. It includes a body tube, nose cone, and fins. Most of the body tube houses the propulsion system, which includes a fuel tank and an oxidizer tank. The nose cone contains the control module. The control module includes the rocket's guidance system and a recovery system designed to bring the rocket safely back to Earth. The **payload**, which is the cargo or equipment carried by the spacecraft, is also in the nose cone. The fins of the rocket are designed to provide stability during flight.

Rockets move by propulsion, meaning they are moved forward by a force. Propulsion moves spacecraft or jet planes by pushing something out behind them. For example, when you blow up a balloon and then release it, the air rushing out the open end of the balloon propels it to move. This response occurs according to Sir Isaac Newton's third law of motion, which states that every action has an equal and opposite reaction. In the case of a rocket, the action of the hot gases rushing out through the exit nozzle causes the reaction of the rocket moving in the other direction.

How can any action be large enough to propel a heavy rocket into space? The mass of the rocket, including the fuel that it carries, is much greater than the mass of the hot gases that stream out of the rocket. These hot gases are under so much pressure, however, that they exert a tremendous amount of force on all the interior rocket walls except the exit nozzle. Therefore, as the gases are directed out through the nozzle, the rocket is pushed upward.

TRY THIS

Bottle Rocket

Rockets are propelled by pressure created in the combustion chamber and directed out the back of the rocket. Create your own rocket using a 2 L bottle, water, and air. Read the package directions before using the water bottle launcher. Wear safety goggles and stand as far from the launcher as possible. Use the bicycle pump to build pressure inside the bottle, but be very careful not to overpressurize the system. Predict how high the rocket will go and how long it will stay aloft. What caused the water bottle rocket to fly into the air? How is the water bottle rocket similar to a space rocket? How is it different from a space rocket?

Modern **propellants** include liquefied gases, which are very powerful, and solid explosives, which are simpler and very reliable. In a typical liquid engine, hydrogen serves as the fuel and oxygen as the oxidizer; the fuel will not burn without oxygen. The hydrogen and oxygen are stored separately until they are released into a chamber where they ignite. Some liquefied gases burn on contact; others require an ignition system. The reaction of the two propellants produces the hot gas action needed to move the rocket. One advantage to liquid propellant engines is that they can be controlled to allow the engine to stop or restart, which is not possible with solid propellants. Liquefied hydrogen

gas was used by NASA, Russia, and the European Space Agency as the fuel in most rockets that launch spacecraft. However, because of its tremendous power, liquid oxygen has become the fuel of choice for SpaceX and other entities that launch satellites.

Solid propellants are usually a mixture of an explosive, such as nitroglycerin, with a binder. One common binder is nitrocellulose, which is cellulose that is treated with very flammable nitric acid. The binder solidifies the fuel. A typical solid propellant combination is nitroglycerin and nitrocellulose. Solid propellant mixtures are poured into a mold inside the rocket and allowed to solidify. Then, the mold is removed, which leaves a narrow tunnel through the center of the solid fuel. This long tunnel forms the combustion chamber of the solid rocket. All solid propellants require an ignition system. When the solid fuel in the combustion chamber is ignited, its surface burns at a predictable rate, which provides the thrust necessary for acceleration. Solid propellant motors are used in a variety of ways. For example, solid propellant rockets can be used as the final stage of a spacecraft launch or used to boost payloads such as weather satellites into higher orbits.

The force that causes a rocket to accelerate is called **thrust**. The thrust of a rocket must be sufficient to give the rocket what is called escape velocity, which is the speed and direction necessary for an object to break free of Earth's gravity. Otherwise, a rocket will fall back to Earth. The thrust of a rocket also must be great enough for it to reach what is called orbital velocity, which is the speed and direction needed for a rocket to orbit Earth.

FYI

Nuclear Propulsion
Researchers at NASA are testing the use of nuclear rocket engines to power rockets. Nuclear rocket engines generate more thrust and are twice as efficient as conventional chemical rocket engines. But, radiation is a real hazard. At the Marshall Space Flight Center in Huntsville, AL, scientists are using a simulator to perform realistic, but nonnuclear, testing. They can test how the nuclear engines will work without risking the hazard of using nuclear materials. NASA's nuclear rocket work may be key to landing human explorers on Mars. The Nuclear Cryogenic Propulsion system could transport people through space more efficiently than conventional spacecraft. It might also reduce the crew's exposure to harmful space radiation and carry heavy payloads.

SpaceX rocket in preparation for launch

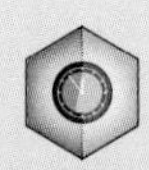

HISTORY

Early Rockets

Basic rocket technology is more than 800 years old. Throughout most of history, rockets were used for war. For example, around 1232 AD, the Chinese stuffed bamboo with a flammable powder to make "fire arrows." The Mongols produced their own rockets and used them in attacks against Japan and Baghdad in the 13th through 15th centuries. The Mongols also may have introduced their rockets to Europe. In the early 1800s, Englishman William Congreve designed rockets that could travel close to 3 km and carry explosive warheads that weighed up to 27 kg. The British used these "Congreve rockets" on the American soldiers at Fort McHenry in 1814. Francis Scott Key, who witnessed the battle, then penned the line "And the rockets' red glare, the bombs bursting in air" for what became the U.S. national anthem.

LESSON REVIEW

1. Who developed the theory of rocket propulsion and liquid propellants?
2. Who is the father of modern rocketry?
3. Why was NASA formed?
4. Rocket engine propulsion illustrates what law? What does that law state?
5. What is the force that propels a rocket?
6. How is thrust produced?

Rocket Parts

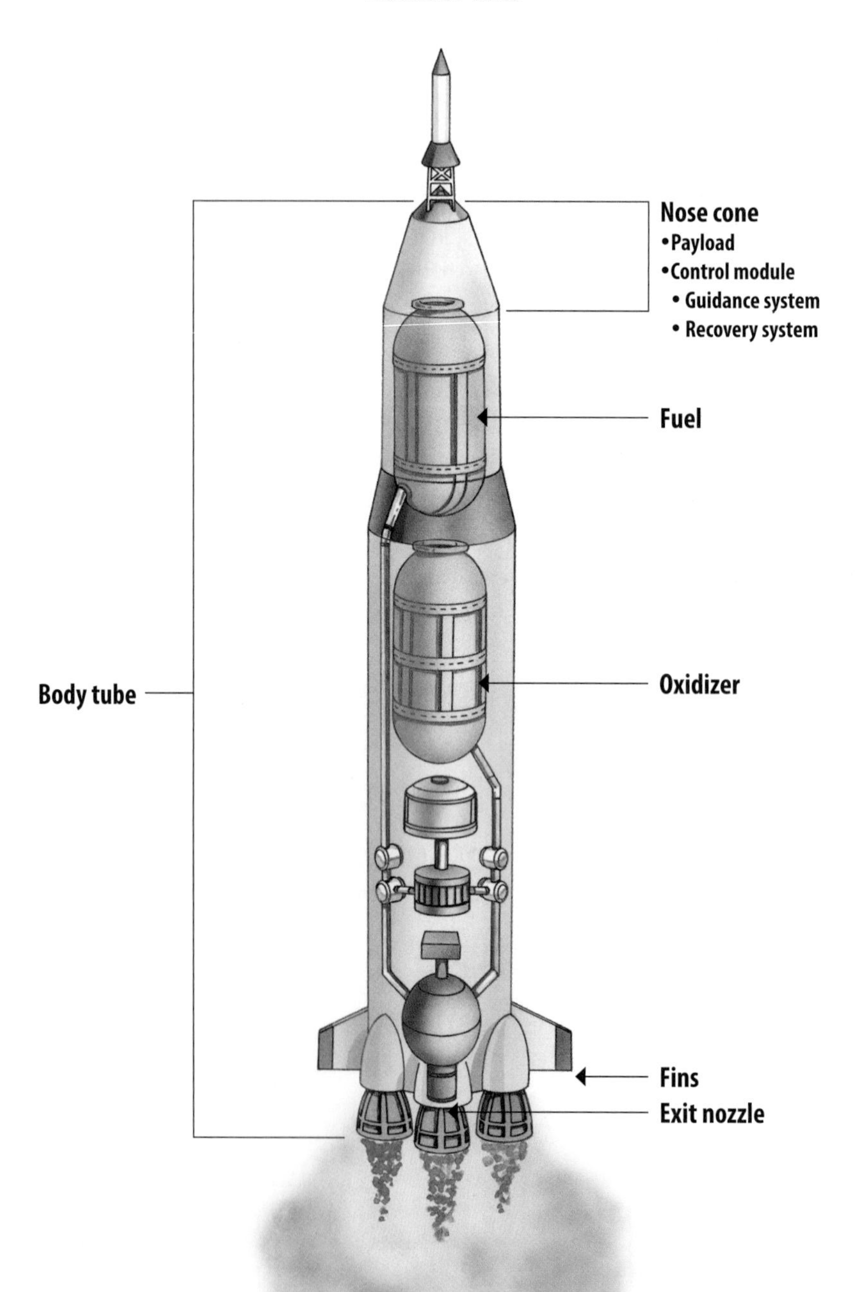

OBJECTIVES

- Describe how a space probe reaches its destination.
- Evaluate the benefits of using space probes.

VOCABULARY

- **space probe** an unmanned spacecraft designed to gather data

Why are rockets sent into space? One use of rockets is to launch space probes. **Space probes** are unmanned vehicles sent into space to gather information. Space probes have widened the understanding of the solar system. Rockets launch space probes with enough energy to achieve escape velocity and then to navigate among the planets.

Space probes are designed for different missions. Some may fly by or orbit a planet, and others may land instruments on a planetary surface. Because the planets are moving and because they are so far away, it may take years for a probe to reach its destination. Setting a probe on the correct course requires extremely precise calculations. However, by using radio commands and computers, the path of a space probe can be adjusted even after it has been launched. Radio-transmitted commands and computers provide midcourse corrections to a probe's trajectory. Instruments can channel data back to Earth via radio contact between a control station and the space probe. Space probes carry radio transmitters and receivers, magnetometers, and television cameras that are sensitive to infrared, visible, and ultraviolet light. Probes may also carry devices to detect micrometeorites, gamma rays, and solar wind.

Space probes have greatly increased scientists' knowledge of the solar system and the universe. Space probe missions have made discoveries that have enhanced the understanding of Earth as well. The United States and the former Soviet Union have launched the most space probes. Although many of these missions failed or were incomplete, many were also successes.

Galileo space probe

HISTORY

Astronomical Units

The distances in space are truly astronomical—so large that they are hard to imagine. Over the centuries, many scientists attempted to determine the distance between the sun and the earth. For example, Tycho Brahe estimated the distance at 8 million km, and Johannes Kepler's estimate was 24 million km. In 1672, Giovanni Cassini used the parallax method to determine the distance between the sun and the earth. By comparing the position of Mars in the sky from Paris and from French Guiana in South America, he calculated the distance to be 140 million km. Cassini's figure was very close to the number used today for the average distance to the sun, which is 149,597,871 km. This distance is referred to as *an astronomical unit* (*AU*). The AU is handy for measuring distances within the solar system, but going beyond it, the light-year is better.

For example, the United States' early Pioneer missions to the sun, moon, and gas giants did not meet their objective of close-up photographs of the moon, but they did gather data on the area between the earth and moon, including information on the Van Allen radiation belts, which are bands of high-energy radiation in the magnetosphere, where charged particles from the sun are trapped. On later missions, *Pioneer 11* became the first spacecraft to fly by Jupiter and to study Saturn.

Planetary probes enable scientists to learn about the other planets in the solar system. For example, NASA's Mariner missions confirmed that Mars had high temperatures and a carbon dioxide atmosphere. The missions also disclosed that the cratered surface of Mars had huge volcanoes and showed evidence of water. A later Mariner visit to Venus revealed the planet's heavy atmospheric pressure. And Mariner missions gathered data from Mercury that revealed the planet was more massive than previously thought.

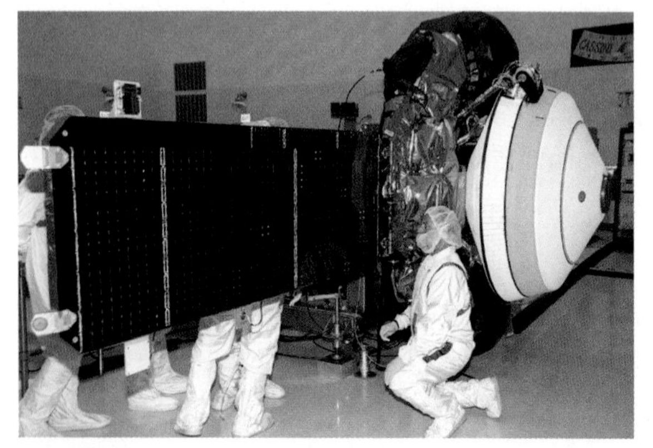

Technicians work on *Genesis*, which collected solar wind particles.

Probes are also used to study smaller orbiting bodies and other phenomenas in the solar system. The European planetary probe *Giotto* approached Halley's Comet and successfully flew by the comet Grigg-Skjellerup. Japanese probe missions have included *Sakigate*, which monitors the solar wind, interplanetary magnetic fields, and plasma waves, and *Hiten*, which orbited the moon.

Scientists use solar probes to monitor the sun. Solar probes gather information about how the

FYI

Space Probe Missions

Space Probe / Date	Detail
Luna 1 (U.S.S.R.) January 1959	The probe flew past the moon and was the first spacecraft to orbit the sun.
Pioneer 4 (U.S.A.) March 1959	The probe flew past the moon and went on to orbit the sun.
Mariner 4 (U.S.A.) November 1964	*Mariner 4* took the first close-up images of the Martian surface and revealed that Mars's atmosphere was very thin.
Pioneer 10 (U.S.A.) March 1972	The first probe to visit a gas giant, *Pioneer 10* sampled solar wind, photographed Jupiter, and traveled past Pluto.
Viking 1 and *Viking 2* (U.S.A.) August and September 1975	The Viking missions looked for signs of life on Mars, collected soil samples, and evaluated the planet's climate.
Voyager 1 and *Voyager 2* (U.S.A.) August and September 1977	*Voyager 1* detected Jupiter's rings. *Voyager 2* was the first spacecraft to fly by all four gas giants and is still searching for the edge of the solar wind's influence.
Giotto (Europe) July 1985	This probe flew by Halley's Comet, obtaining photographs of the nucleus and analyzing its content.
Galileo (U.S.A.) October 1989	In exploring Jupiter's moons, this probe revealed that Europa may have liquid water. *Galileo* took the first close-up pictures of an asteroid and sent back pictures of the comet Shoemaker-Levy 9 slamming into Jupiter.
Clementine (U.S.A.) January 1994	The probe mapped the composition of the moon's surface, discovered evidence of water at the moon's southern pole, and tested technology for national defense.
SOHO (NASA and ESA) December 1995	*SOHO* was launched to observe the processes that fuel the sun's corona and to study the sun's interior.
Mars Pathfinder (U.S.A.) December 1996	*Mars Pathfinder* deployed a rover (*Sojourner*), which collected data and recorded images of the surface of the planet.
Cassini-Huygens (International) October 1997	The first probes to orbit Saturn, these two probes have separate missions. The smaller probe, *Huygens*, was dropped onto Titan, one of Saturn's moons. In April 2017, *Cassini* will alter its orbit to pass inside Saturn's innermost ring.
Mars Odyssey (U.S.A.) April 2001	*Mars Odyssey* identified materials in the rocks and soil and determined the amount of water present on Mars. It is still in orbit and communicates with other space probes.
Deep Impact (U.S.A.) July 2005	The probe impacted Tempel 1 comet. The impact and the debris were analyzed to determine the comet's composition.
Curiosity (U.S.A.) November 2011	*Curiosity* landed on Mars to gather information about elements, climate, and water sources in preparation for a human mission to Mars planned for the 2030s.
Hayabusa 2 (Japan) December 2014	*Hayabusa* is scheduled to reach asteroid Ryugu in June 2018.

TRY THIS

Accuracy from a Distance
Space probes must travel long distances without a pilot on board. Scientists consider many variables when calculating a space probe's path. To gain understanding of the variables involved, toss a small ball into a wide-mouthed jar that is 1 m away. Move the jar another meter away and toss the ball into the jar again. How does the added distance affect your accuracy? Now have a partner hold the jar and orbit slowly around you at a distance of 2 m. Try to toss the ball into the jar. Have the partner move another meter away and orbit around you again. Toss the ball into the jar. How does the orbiting of the jar affect your accuracy? What does the ball represent? What does the jar represent? What do you think are some variables that scientists have to consider when plotting a course for a space probe?

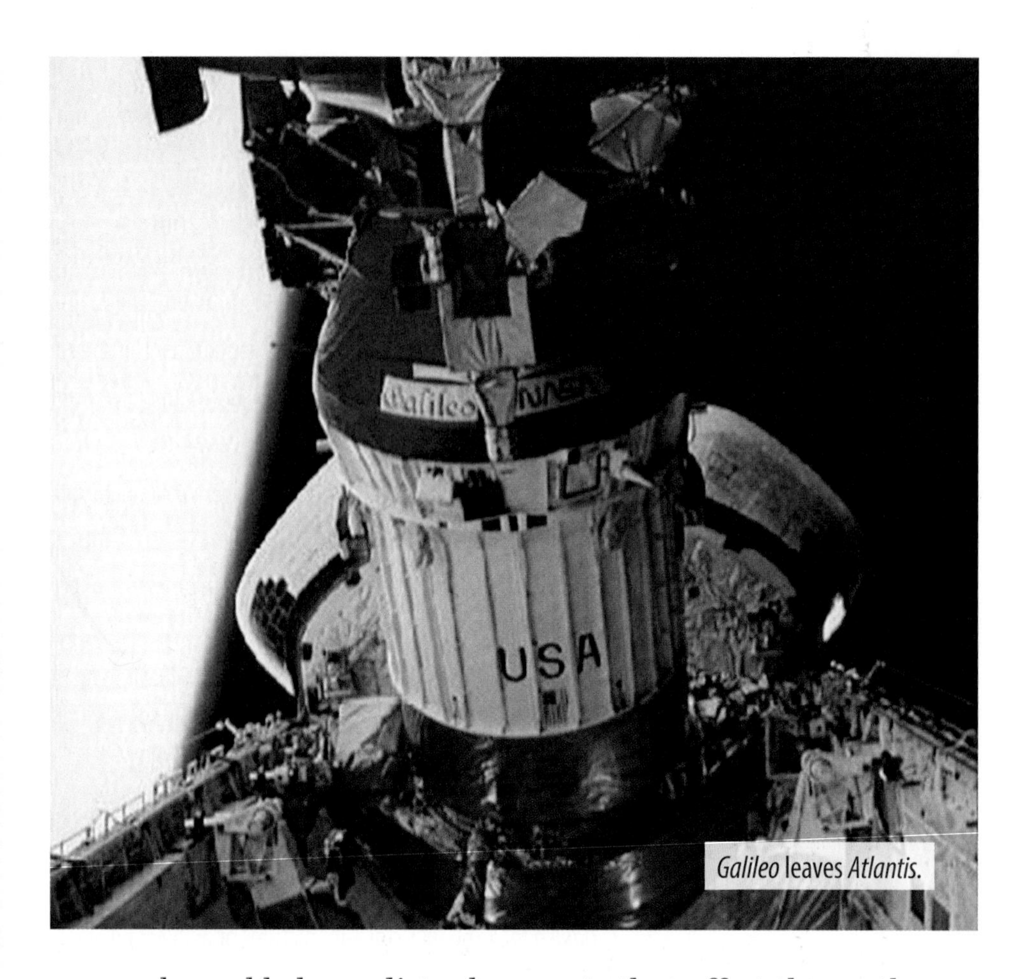

Galileo leaves *Atlantis.*

sun works and help predict solar events that affect the earth, such as sunspots or solar flares. Interplanetary space probes are designed for a more generalized study. Some are launched into space to gather information on whatever they encounter in the solar system. Such probes can keep relaying data to Earth for years. For example, *Pioneer 10* was designed to last six months but actually transmitted information for over 35 years. This space probe will continue to travel into deep space. Its last known trajectory indicates it is headed for Aldebaran, the fiery red star eye of the bull in the Taurus constellation. Aldebaran is about 68 light-years from Earth, which means *Pioneer 10* could reach it in 2 million years.

LESSON REVIEW

1. What is needed for a space probe to get into space?
2. Without a pilot, how do scientists direct a space probe to its destination?
3. Why is navigating in space difficult?
4. What did scientists learn about Mars, Venus, and Mercury from the Mariner missions?
5. What were the benefits of the Pioneer missions?
6. Which probe gathered information about comets?

In 1955, U.S. President Dwight D. Eisenhower announced that the United States would contribute to international space science by launching a **satellite**, which is a natural or artificial object that orbits a planet. Similar to space probes, satellites are designed to gather data. But unlike space probes, satellites and other spacecraft that orbit the earth usually do not need any navigation once they are in orbit.

The Soviet Union kicked off the Space Race on October 4, 1957, when it launched the first satellite, *Sputnik 1*. This satellite, which weighed only 84 kg and was only 58 cm in diameter, orbited the earth every 96 minutes, and sent information back until January 4, 1958. *Sputnik 1* burned up on reentry into Earth's atmosphere. You might think that the whole world celebrated the triumph of entering the frontier of space, but *Sputnik 1* sparked a fierce competition between the Soviet Union and the United States. The American public saw this Soviet success as a national security threat. If the Soviet Union had the ability to launch a satellite, it might also be able to launch missiles carrying nuclear weapons. As a result, the U.S. began funding its own satellite project and on January 31, 1958, *Explorer 1* was launched. This satellite carried instruments that measured cosmic rays and small dust particles and recorded the temperature of the upper atmosphere. *Explorer 1* also discovered the Van Allen radiation belts.

The idea of an artificial object orbiting Earth was startling in the 1950s. Today, however, satellites are very common. They are launched by governments and by private companies. But what keeps them in orbit? Satellites are placed in orbit high enough so the friction of Earth's atmosphere does not drag them down. At that height, the same laws that keep the moon in orbit also govern artificial satellites. The forward velocity of the satellite plus **inertia**, the tendency of a moving object to keep moving in a straight line, and Earth's gravity keep the satellites from plunging back to Earth or flying off into space. These three forces together cause an object to follow a circular path. This force is called *centripetal force*.

Satellites use four specific types of orbits: low Earth, medium Earth, geosynchronous/high Earth, and polar. Satellites placed into orbit 180–2,000 km above the earth are in low Earth orbit (LEO). These satellites travel very quickly; they move at about 27,000 kph. Their velocity has to be fast enough to overcome the force of Earth's gravity but slow enough to allow the satellite to stay in orbit. In higher orbits, such as medium and high

OBJECTIVES

- Explain how a satellite is able to orbit.
- Correlate types of satellites with specific orbits.
- Compare the types of orbits.
- Infer the benefits of satellites.

VOCABULARY

- **inertia** the tendency of a moving object to keep moving in a straight line unless another force acts on it
- **satellite** a natural or artificial object that orbits a larger astronomical body

FYI

Where No Dog Had Gone Before

In 1957, the Soviets launched *Sputnik 2*, less than a month after *Sputnik 1*. *Sputnik 2* was occupied by a dog named Laika, who was the first living being to orbit the earth. They sent her into orbit in a pressurized space cabin.

Earth orbits, satellites are farther from the earth, so they experience less gravitational pull and move more slowly. They also experience less friction. Medium Earth orbits allow satellites to work in groups to provide global wireless communication. Because the orbit is higher than a low Earth orbit, each satellite in a group can cover a larger area, which means fewer satellites are needed to do the work.

At 35,780 km above the earth, satellites can maintain an orbit speed that matches Earth's rotational speed. This type of orbit is called *a geosynchronous orbit*. In a geosynchronous/high Earth orbit, the satellite is always positioned in the same location above the earth and can observe an entire hemisphere. Satellites with a geosynchronous/high Earth orbit are positioned over the equator because the force of gravity is consistent at this latitude. In contrast, polar orbits allow a satellite to view nearly every part of Earth as it rotates. This type of orbit is useful for monitoring weather patterns or mapping the earth.

Earth's rotation and atmosphere affect satellites. Satellites are usually launched in the direction that Earth rotates (from west to east). By using Earth's rotation to boost the rocket, less rocket fuel is needed to place the satellite in orbit. However, launching satellites into a polar orbit requires more rocket power and more fuel. A nearly polar orbit moves perpendicular to the rotation of the earth; therefore, it cannot use the earth's rotational motion to propel it into orbit. Friction with Earth's atmosphere slows a satellite down, and the lower the orbit, the more friction it

Satellite Orbits

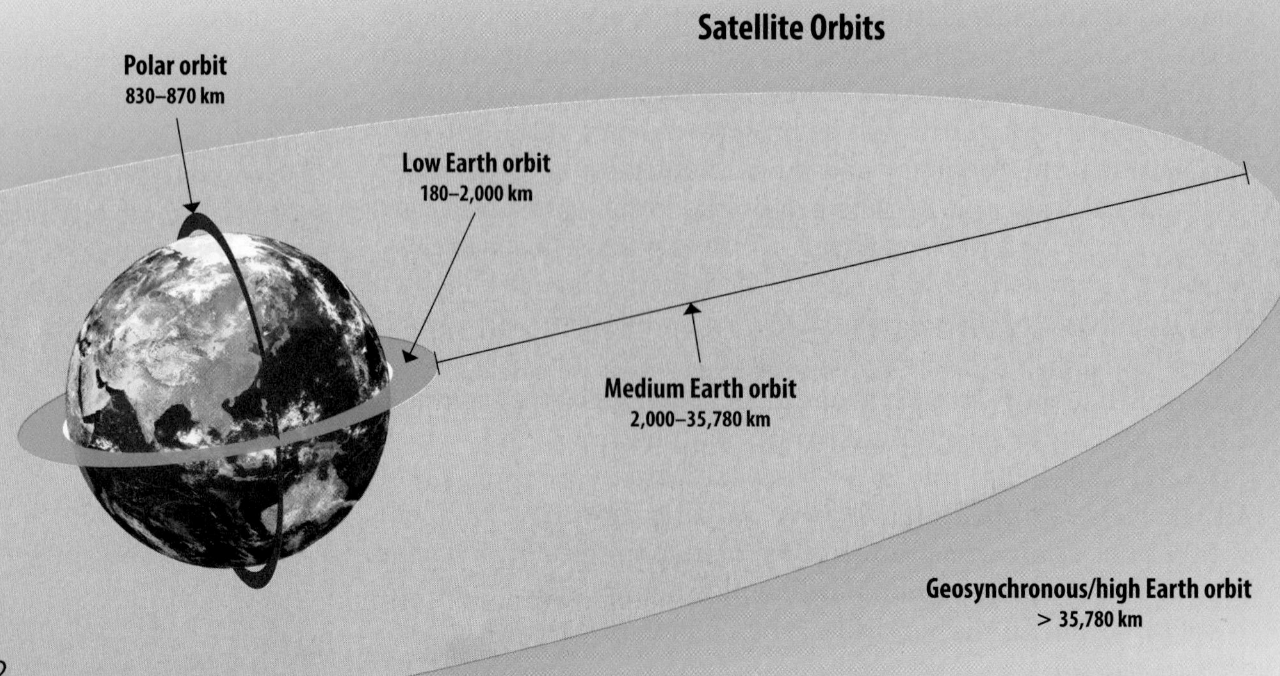

Nanosatellites

In 2010, NASA started the CubeSat Launch Initiative (CSLI). It provides an opportunity for educational institutions and nonprofit organizations to conduct low-cost research by sending nanosatellites on launches to the *International Space Station*. CubeSats are small spacecraft, averaging about 1,000–3,000 cm^3 and weighing approximately 1 kg/1000 cm^3. Since the beginning of the program, 46 CubeSats have launched. The *TJ3Sat* was the first built by a high school and the *STMSat-1* was the first built by an elementary school.

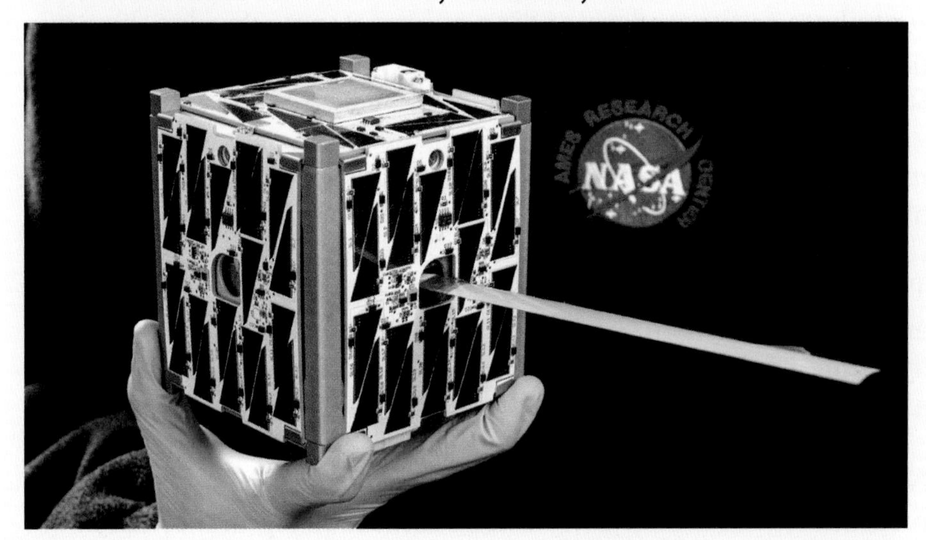

experiences. Eventually a satellite slows down so much that gravity pulls it back toward the earth. When this happens, friction with air molecules in the atmosphere causes most of the satellite to burn up in space.

Several different types of satellites orbit the earth, including satellites for communication, weather monitoring, navigation, and scientific discovery.

Communications Satellites. Communications satellites beam television programs, radio messages, telephone conversations, and other kinds of information all over the world. The satellite receives a signal from a transmitting station on Earth, and it beams the information to somewhere else on Earth, perhaps even on the other side of the world. Communications satellites are placed in a geosynchronous/high Earth orbit. NASA's first communications satellite, *Echo 1*, was launched in 1960. By 1962, TV signals could be sent from continent to continent. The first commercial communications satellite, *Intelsat 1*, could handle only 240 voice circuits or one television channel at a time.

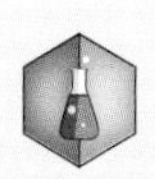

TRY THIS

Satellites in Orbit

A center-seeking force that causes an object to follow a circular path is called *centripetal force.* Satellites depend on centripetal force to maintain orbit. Sew one end of a ribbon to a tennis ball. Gently swing the ball to ensure it will stay attached in orbit. Reinforce with more stitches if necessary. Swing the tennis ball over your head, maintaining a constant speed. What exerts the centripetal force on the tennis ball? What would happen to the tennis ball if you continued to hold the ribbon, but stopped exerting force? Why? How is this system like a satellite orbiting the earth? How is it different?

Current satellites can handle tens of thousands of voice circuits or multiple TV channels. About 60% of all global communications pass via satellites. Telecommunications satellites are useful only when they rotate in a certain range. This range is becoming crowded with working satellites and space debris.

Weather Satellites. The United States' first weather satellite, *Tiros 1,* was launched in 1960. This satellite allowed meteorologists to see how Earth and its clouds look from above. Weather satellites, which orbit in an LEO or a polar orbit, contribute to the understanding of how storms develop, how wind patterns are created, and how ocean currents behave. Weather satellites are especially valuable in tracking hurricanes. They give information to improve predictions of hurricane tracks, intensities, and surges, giving people time to prepare. Data about clouds, humidity, and surface properties come from the polar-orbiting Operational Environmental Satellites. These satellites make nearly 14 orbits every day and provide environmental monitoring information on climate, ocean dynamics, volcanic eruptions, forest fires, search and rescue, and global vegetation.

Navigation Satellites. Navigation satellites can be found in medium Earth orbits. They send continuous signals to ships and airplanes so navigators can pinpoint their exact position. This helps them find their way even in a storm when other information may not be accurate. These satellites also send signals to the global positioning systems (GPS), a group of 32

Great Salt Lake, September 2011

satellites used to pinpoint exact locations on Earth. Handheld GPS receivers can identify a person's location within 15 m.

Scientific Satellites. Scientific satellites help scientists make new discoveries about the universe, such as evidence of distant stars and black holes. Satellites have also been helpful for scientific research in meteorology, astronomy, geophysics, and oceanography. From Earth, astronomers have a hard time seeing into space because Earth's atmosphere interferes with light coming from far away. To avoid this problem, satellites are sent outside the atmosphere to take pictures. The Landsat satellite program, started in 1972, has taken millions of images that used to track global and regional changes on Earth. *Landsat 8* was launched in 2013 and is currently providing data on glacier movement to help scientists understand how ice movement is changing globally. Images of the Great Salt Lake in Salt Lake City, Utah, have revealed that it is changing size. Such information would be difficult to obtain at ground level.

LESSON REVIEW

1. Explain how a satellite stays in orbit.
2. What can cause a satellite to fall back to Earth?
3. How is a polar orbit different from other orbits? Why does it take more fuel to place a satellite in a polar orbit than a geosynchronous orbit?
4. How is a high Earth orbit different from a low Earth orbit?
5. What are the benefits of navigation satellites?
6. In which orbit are communications satellites found?

Great Salt Lake, September 2016

8.2.4 *Working in Space*

OBJECTIVES

- Infer how science progresses through the work of previous scientists.
- Explain the benefits of space research and exploration.
- Identify the challenges of working in space.

VOCABULARY

- **space station** a satellite from which vehicles can be launched or scientific research can be conducted
- **spin-off** a by-product or fringe benefit derived from a previous product

The ambition of the space programs of both the Soviet Union and the United States was to put a human explorer into space. Both countries accomplished that goal in 1961. With each subsequent mission, the scientists from both countries' space programs gained knowledge that was needed for the next mission. Even through failures, information was gained that led to better technology and safer missions. What began in the 1950s Cold War as a competitive space race has become a cooperative endeavor that benefits people worldwide.

The first person to orbit Earth was Soviet cosmonaut Yuri Gagarin on April 12, 1961. On May 5, 1961, U.S. astronaut Alan Shepard was launched into space but not into orbit. This step was a major achievement for the U.S. space program, because many Americans were afraid that they were losing the Cold War to the Soviet Union. When President John F. Kennedy announced the goal of reaching the moon, the announcement inspired the nation. In February 1962, John Glenn was the first American to orbit Earth—an important step toward reaching the moon.

On July 20, 1969, *Apollo 11* took Neil Armstrong, Edwin "Buzz" Aldrin, and Michael Collins to the moon. Neil Armstrong became the first human to set foot on a place other than Earth. The nation and the world watched as he took the first steps and said, "One small step for [a] man. One giant leap for mankind." Although the main objective for *Apollo 11* was to fulfill President Kennedy's goal, it also had a scientific mission; it brought 22 kg of moon rocks back to Earth. Solar devices were also planted on the moon to monitor moonquakes and the solar wind.

Neil Armstrong

Next Stop, Mars

In the planning stages for the *ISS*, NASA had three goals: establish a human presence in space, foster international cooperation, and conduct research. These goals are still in place, but a new goal has been added—send people to Mars. Before sending people to Mars, research must be conducted on the effects of zero-gravity on humans and potential health risks of long flights. The *ISS* is a great place to test many of the conditions that people will face when traveling into deep space. The *Orion* spacecraft is also being tested in preparation for a mission to Mars. Scheduled to launch in 2018, it will send astronauts beyond the moon and is expected to be the best deep space proving ground yet. On both the *ISS* and the *Orion*, NASA will be testing transportation capabilities, working in space, and staying healthy. Will humans be able to explore deep space? So far only space probes have traveled to such depths.

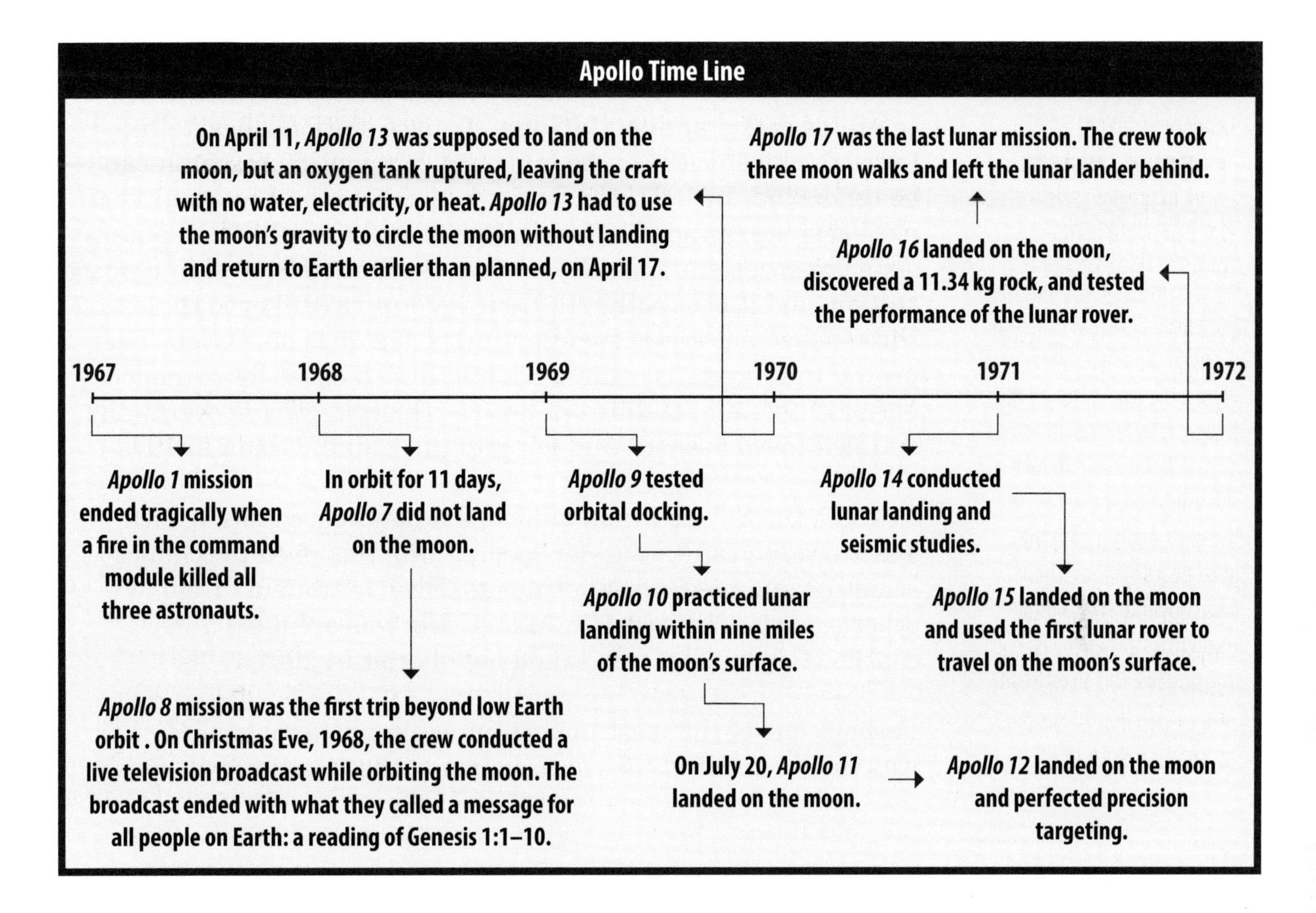

Apollo Time Line
On April 11, Apollo 13 was supposed to land on the moon, but an oxygen tank ruptured, leaving the craft with no water, electricity, or heat. Apollo 13 had to use the moon's gravity to circle the moon without landing and return to Earth earlier than planned, on April 17.
Apollo 17 was the last lunar mission. The crew took three moon walks and left the lunar lander behind.
Apollo 16 landed on the moon, discovered a 11.34 kg rock, and tested the performance of the lunar rover.
1967
1968
1969
1970
1971
1972
Apollo 1 mission ended tragically when a fire in the command module killed all three astronauts.
In orbit for 11 days, Apollo 7 did not land on the moon.
Apollo 9 tested orbital docking.
Apollo 14 conducted lunar landing and seismic studies.
Apollo 10 practiced lunar landing within nine miles of the moon's surface.
Apollo 15 landed on the moon and used the first lunar rover to travel on the moon's surface.
Apollo 8 mission was the first trip beyond low Earth orbit . On Christmas Eve, 1968, the crew conducted a live television broadcast while orbiting the moon. The broadcast ended with what they called a message for all people on Earth: a reading of Genesis 1:1–10.
On July 20, Apollo 11 landed on the moon.
Apollo 12 landed on the moon and perfected precision targeting.

In the early space missions, the spacecraft could only be used once, which was very expensive. Continuing to send people into space required developing a reusable system. In 1972, a space shuttle program was suggested as an economical way to get into space regularly. A space shuttle is a reusable vehicle that is launched like a rocket and lands like an airplane. The first space shuttle, *Columbia*, was launched on April 12, 1981. About two dozen successful missions followed; shuttle launches seemed commonplace until January 28, 1986, when *Challenger* exploded just after takeoff, killing all seven astronauts. In the aftermath of the disaster, no shuttles were launched until *Discovery* in 1988.

After 135 missions, including the loss of *Columbia* and her crew in 2003, the space shuttle program was shut down in 2011. However, NASA and other agencies continue to develop technology to make space travel more economical and practical. In addition, commercial companies are working to create rocket engines that would allow planes to reach orbit, release cargo, return to Earth, and land on an airstrip.

TRY THIS

Drinking in Space

Many common activities become difficult without the presence of gravity. Drinking is one of those activities. Place a glass of water on the floor and lie facedown across a chair. Bend down to take a sip, using your hands to tilt the glass and keeping the glass near the floor. Then bend down to take a drink through a straw. Why is drinking like this so difficult?

The space shuttle astronauts spent up to 19 days in space, but people have lived in space for longer periods on scientific satellites called **space stations**. A space station is a satellite from which vehicles can be launched or scientific research can be conducted. In 1971, the Soviet Union was the first country to place a space station into orbit. By 1982, the Soviets had put up six more space stations. *Skylab* was the United States' first space station, and it orbited Earth from 1973 to 1979. Three successive three-astronaut crews spent a total of 171 days on *Skylab*. They proved that humans could work and live in space for extended periods. Like all satellites in low Earth orbit, *Skylab* eventually spiraled toward Earth and fell into the Indian Ocean in 1979.

In 1986, the Soviet Union launched a new space station, *Mir*. The word *mir* is Russian for "peace." *Mir* was used to conduct scientific and medical experiments. Even astronauts from other countries visited *Mir*. In fact, *Mir* was occupied almost continuously until it was taken out of orbit in 2001.

Perhaps one of the most important accomplishments of *Mir* was that it inspired the construction of the *International Space*

BIOGRAPHY

Katherine Johnson

A brilliant mathematician, Katherine Johnson was born in West Virginia in 1918, a time in history where both her race and her gender made success in the sciences difficult. Because there was no high school for African-American students in her town, Katherine's parents sent her and her siblings to a high school 100 miles away. Katherine was a very advanced student who started high school at age 10. She graduated college at 18 with degrees in mathematics education and French. One of three students chosen to integrate the all-white graduate program at West Virginia University, Katherine left the graduate program when she married and began teaching in the public schools. In 1953, she became a "computer," one of a group of black women with math degrees who worked at the Langley Aeronautical Laboratory. Within weeks, she was assigned to work with the Flight Research Division. This group of engineers eventually was tasked with getting an American into space as part of NASA. Known for her accurate work, Katherine figured out the trajectory for Alan Shepard's flight and double-checked the new electronic computer's calculations for John Glenn's orbital flight as well. She was the first woman ever credited on a report in the Flight Research Division. Katherine worked on the Apollo program as well as the space shuttle. She retired from NASA in 1986. In 2015, she was awarded the Presidential Medal of Freedom, the highest civilian honor, by President Barack Obama.

Station (*ISS*). The United States, Canada, Russia, Japan, Brazil, and the participating countries of the European Space Agency (ESA) met in 1993 to plan this project. Construction of the *ISS* began in November 1998 with the launch of the Russian module *Zarya*. The building-block assembly was begun in December 1998 when *Zarya* and the American module *Unity* were successfully joined in space, creating a "true" orbiting space station.

The *ISS* was completed in 2011 and represents an unprecedented international cooperation. NASA provided lab modules, solar panels, supporting trusses, and living quarters. Canada's major contribution was the Mobile Servicing System, which keeps the station running. Russia's contributions included a service module, docking modules, life support and research modules, and transportation to and from the station. The ESA and Japan contributed transport vehicles and specialized laboratories. American commercial companies, including SpaceX and Orbital Sciences Corporation, have supplied transportation as well. A planned 2019 commercial addition to the *ISS* by Axiom Space will expand the station's research and make tourism possible.

Even on the *ISS*, living and working in space is challenging. Water and oxygen need to be supplied by the station. Food is generally dehydrated, although some fresh food is grown on the station. The temperature can be too hot or too cold. Astronauts are living in a very small space with people who are not family. It can be very overwhelming. Many astronauts experience loneliness. But the difficulties are not just emotional.

TRY THIS

Converting Sunlight

Spacecraft are fitted with solar panels designed to convert sunlight into energy. Remove the paper from two cans. Blacken the outside of one can with a flame and leave the other can shiny. Fill each can three-quarters full with cold water. Place a thermometer in each can, set the cans on a windowsill, and predict which can you think will absorb the most heat. Monitor the temperature change over the course of 15 minutes. Record the temperatures. Empty the cans and fill them three-quarters full with warm water. Record the starting temperature. Place them in a closet or drawer, make a prediction as to which can will maintain the most heat, and record the final temperature after 15 minutes. Which can absorbed the most heat? Which can maintained the most heat? How could engineers use this method to create energy for a spacecraft? What color do you think solar panels are? Why?

BIBLE CONNECTION

The Heavens Declare

Can you think of a good reason for space exploration? One answer can be found in the Psalm 19. The psalmist wrote, "The heavens declare the glory of God; the skies proclaim the work of His hands" (Psalm 19:1). The wonders uncovered by modern astronomy include a universe of unimaginable size and beauty. Estimates of the size of the universe suggest 200 billion galaxies with new research suggesting this number could be much larger. Each new scientific discovery should remind every person of the Creator's power and creativity. God has given humans the ability to discover the wonders of the universe, and there should be excitement and awe about these discoveries. Loving God includes learning about all parts of His creation.

In space, the lack of gravity makes everyday activities like eating, brushing your teeth, showering, or sleeping much more complicated. The lack of gravity significantly affects the human body, although most of the effects disappear when an astronaut returns to Earth. For example, the body's sense of balance is affected by weightlessness, which causes most space travelers to experience nausea, vomiting, and headaches until they adapt. When they return to Earth, their sense of balance takes a while to recover, so they may lose their balance and fall more. Even the circulatory system is affected by weightlessness. On Earth, blood and other body fluids settle in the lower part of the body and the heart stays strong by pumping against gravity. In space, people's body fluids move up in their bodies, which causes their faces to puff up and their sinuses to block. In fact, astronauts experience what is called *the space sniffles* throughout their time in space. Without gravity to pump against, astronauts' hearts do not work as hard, so they lose muscle mass and shrink. People working in space also lose muscle and bone mass throughout their bodies. The calcium from their bones moves to other parts of their bodies and can cause health issues such as kidney stones. Most astronauts spend several hours a day exercising, but even that amount of activity does not counteract the effects of weightlessness on their bodies. Astronauts are also exposed to radiation from space, which may lead to health problems.

The *ISS* and space exploration are controversial to some people who question the expense and effort required to build and

The first flower grown in *ISS*'s greenhouse facility

Mission Specialist Soichi Noguchi, Japanese astronaut, on *ISS*

maintain the space station. Some people claim that instead of putting effort into exploring space, solving problems on Earth should be the main priority. But the space program has brought great benefits to Earth. Information gathered by satellites can be used to make people better stewards of Earth or improve people's health. Weather warnings made possible by satellites have saved many lives, and information offered by navigation satellites makes travel easier and safer. Information gathered about Venus's greenhouse effect has helped scientists better understand how large quantities of gases could also affect Earth. The unique conditions of space, including weightlessness, temperature extremes, airlessness, and radiation, give scientists the opportunity to do experiments that would be impossible to conduct on Earth.

Perhaps some of the most valuable knowledge gained has been medical knowledge. Because people in space experience bone and muscle changes from weightlessness, the space program has helped scientists better understand osteoporosis and the muscle weakening that often comes with aging or illness. NASA technology has been applied to cancer treatments and has improved the treatment for diabetes. Space research on the body's balance system has led to a new understanding of nervous system disorders.

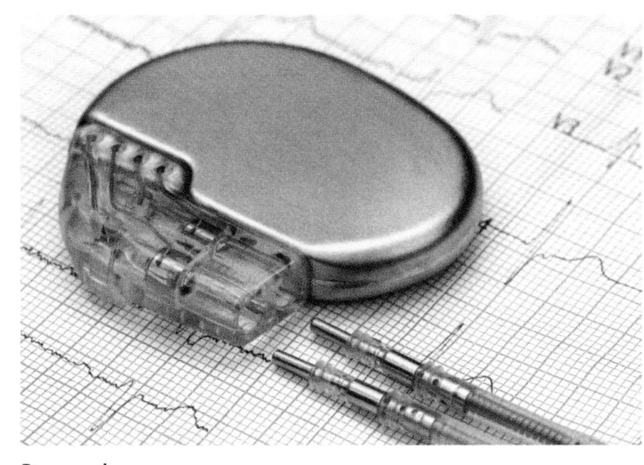
Pacemaker

FYI

Spin-Offs
To maximize the benefits of space technology, NASA's Technology Transfer Program makes its technology readily available to the nation. For example, NASA has developed a system to solve vibration issues experienced during a rocket launch. Companies are able to use this technology to test seismic effects on buildings and improve systems to dampen vibrations in bridges, ships, cars, and airplanes.

Some of the technologies created to prepare equipment and people to function in the harsh conditions of space have led to advances in certain materials, electronics, medicine, energy production, manufacturing, transportation, and even food. For example, what do blood pressure recorders, "invisible" braces, cordless power tools, freeze-dried foods, thermal clothing, pacemakers, smoke detectors, and scratch-resistant lenses have in common? They all use technology or materials first developed for the space program.

These products are all **spin-offs**, technologies resulting from research originally intended for use in space. For example, NASA invented scratch-resistant lens material to protect astronaut helmet visors. Heart pacemakers are similar to electronic monitoring systems that were first designed to operate satellites orbiting Earth. You may never travel in space, but you probably benefit from space research—and perhaps even take it for granted. The space program has helped people be better stewards of Earth, save lives, feed people, and enjoy the benefits of better communication. And those are just the benefits that are realized now. Scientists are already working on new possibilities, such as zero-gravity research, space manufacturing, and mining minerals and ores from asteroids.

ISS Expedition 50 crew includes ESA astronaut Thomas Pesquet, NASA astronaut Peggy Whitson, and Russian Cosmonaut Oleg Novitskiy, who left in November 2016.

It is impossible to see into the future and predict how useful space research will be. But it is possible to learn from the past. Each new step in scientific knowledge builds a bridge to exciting possibilities and teaches people more about God's world. Consider all the steps that led to what scientists know today. Many of these steps seemed useless at the time, but they contributed to new medicines, transportation, food production, technology, computers, manufacturing, and much more. As long as God gives people the ability to make new discoveries about His creation, people should be eager to make them!

LESSON REVIEW

1. List in order five space missions that led up to the completion of the *International Space Station*. How was each mission a step leading to the next mission?
2. Why was the space shuttle program started?
3. Why is it important to conduct research in the *ISS* before sending people to Mars?
4. How are space research and exploration beneficial?
5. What are three challenges of working in space?
6. Is God glorified through space exploration? Why?

aa lava that has a rough surface 3.3.3

abrasion the wearing down of rock surfaces by other rocks or sand particles 2.1.4

absolute magnitude the brightness of a star measured by an observer that is a standard 32.6 light-years away 8.1.1

abyssal plain a large nearly flat region beyond the continental margin 4.2.4

adhesion the force of attraction between different molecules 4.1.1

aeroplankton microscopic organisms that float in the atmosphere 5.1.1

aftershock a tremor that follows a large earthquake 3.2.5

air mass a large body of air with consistent temperature and humidity 5.2.7

algal bloom an explosive growth of algae caused by too many nutrients in the water 4.1.9

amplitude a wave's height or depth measured from the surrounding water level 4.2.2

anemometer an instrument used to measure wind speed 5.2.3

annular eclipse a solar eclipse during which the outer ring of the sun is visible around the moon 7.3.3

aperture an opening through which light passes 7.1.3

aphelion the point in a planet's orbit when it is farthest from the sun 7.2.1

apogee the point in the moon's orbit at which it is farthest from Earth 7.3.2

apparent magnitude the brightness of an object as observed from Earth 8.1.1

aquifer a permeable underground layer of rock 4.1.4

asteroid a rocky object in a variety of sizes that orbits the sun 7.1.5

asthenosphere the layer of the upper mantle composed of low-density rock material that is semiplastic 1.4.2

astronomical unit the average distance between Earth and the sun 7.2.1

astronomy study of physical things beyond the earth's atmosphere 1.1.1

atmosphere a mixture of gases that surrounds the earth 5.1.1

atmospheric pressure the pressure exerted by Earth's atmosphere at any given point 5.1.1

aurora a band of colored or white light in the atmosphere caused by charged particles from the sun interacting with Earth's upper atmosphere 7.1.6

barometer an instrument used to measure atmospheric pressure 5.2.2

bedrock the layer of solid rock beneath the soil 2.2.1

binary star system a pair of stars that orbit their common center of mass 8.1.3

biomass organic matter that contains stored energy and is used to produce fuel 6.1.7

black hole a massive celestial object with gravity so strong that not even light can escape 8.1.2

caldera a volcanic crater that is greater than 2 km in diameter and is formed by the collapse of surface rock into an empty magma chamber 3.3.4

carbon-14 dating the method used to determine the age of items of organic origin by measuring the radioactivity of their carbon 14 content 1.1.2

carbonation the process in which carbon dioxide from the atmosphere or soil dissolves in water to form carbonic acid 2.1.2

carbonization a process of converting organic material into carbon 2.2.5

CFCs synthetic compounds consisting of carbon, chlorine, and fluorine 5.1.4

channel the path that a stream follows 2.1.5

chemical weathering the breaking down of rocks by chemical processes 2.1.2

chromosphere the first layer of the sun's atmosphere 7.1.6

clastic rock a sedimentary rock made of rock particles and fragments deposited by water, wind, or ice 1.3.2

cleavage a mineral's tendency to split along definite flat surfaces 1.2.3

climate the pattern of weather an area has over a long period of time 5.3.1

climate change any long-term change in Earth's climate 5.3.3

cloud a visible collection of tiny water droplets or ice crystals in the atmosphere 5.2.5

coal a solid fossil fuel formed from decomposed plant remains 6.1.3

coalescence the process of coming together 5.2.6

cohesion the molecular attraction between particles of the same kind 4.1.1

comet a frozen chunk of ice, dust, and rock that orbits the sun 7.2.4

compressional stress the stress produced by two tectonic plates coming together 3.1.3

condensation the change of a substance from a gas to a liquid 4.1.2

conduction the transfer of heat from one substance to another substance through direct contact 5.2.1

contact metamorphism metamorphism that occurs when the heat of magma comes in contact with existing rocks 1.3.3

continental crust the crust on which the continents rest 1.4.3

continental drift the theory that the continents can move apart from each other and have done so in the past 3.1.1

continental glacier a glacier that covers a large area of land in a continuous sheet 4.1.3

continental margin the part of the earth's surface beneath the ocean that is made of continental crust 4.2.4

continental rise the base of the continental slope 4.2.4

continental shelf a broad relatively shallow underwater terrace that slopes outward from the shoreline 4.2.4

continental slope the steepest part of the continental incline located at the edge of the continental shelf 4.2.4

contour farming the plowing of furrows around a hill perpendicular to its slope to reduce erosion 6.1.6

contour line a line on a map that joins points of equal elevation 1.1.3

convection the transfer of heat that occurs in moving fluids, liquids or gases, caused by the circulation of currents from one region to another 5.2.1

convection current the circular movement of heated materials to a cooler area and cooled materials to a warmer area 1.4.2

convective zone the zone on the sun where convection currents bring energy to the sun's surface and take gas back into the sun 7.1.6

core the central portion of the earth 1.4.1

Coriolis effect the curving of moving objects from a straight path because of the Earth's rotation 4.2.2

corona the outer layer of the sun's atmosphere 7.1.6

cover crop the fast-growing vegetation planted on bare farmland to prevent erosion 6.1.6

crater a large circular indentation on a planet's surface 7.2.2

crest the highest point of a wave 4.2.2

crop rotation the successive planting of different crops to prevent erosion and to improve fertility 6.1.6

crust the thin hard outer layer of the earth 1.4.3

dead zone an area that has been depleted of oxygen by eutrophication 4.1.9

deflation hollow a soil depression scooped out by the wind 2.1.4

deformation a change in the shape or volume of rocks 3.1.3

density the mass per unit of volume of a substance 1.2.3

deposition the changing of a gas directly into a solid 5.2.6

desalination the process of removing salt from ocean water to obtain fresh water for drinking, irrigation, or industrial use 4.2.6

desertification the making of new deserts by degrading land that used to be healthy and productive 6.1.5

desiccation a type of fossilization where the organic material becomes dehydrated 2.2.5

divide a ridge or other elevated region that separates watersheds 4.1.5

Doppler effect the apparent shift in frequency of waves emitted by a moving source 8.1.4

drumlin a long tear-shaped mound of till 2.1.6

dwarf planet a spherical object that orbits the sun but is not large enough to move other objects from its orbit 7.1.5

dynamic metamorphism metamorphism that is produced by mechanical force 1.3.3

Earth science the study of the earth and the universe around it 1.1.1

earthflow the movement of wet soil down a slope 2.1.3

eclipse the casting of one celestial body's shadow on the surface of another celestial body 7.3.3

electromagnetic radiation a form of wave energy that has both electrical and magnetic properties 7.1.4

electromagnetic spectrum the entire wavelength range of electromagnetic radiation 7.1.4

ellipse a closed curve along which the sum of the distances between two fixed points is always the same 7.2.1

El Niño periodic changes in oceanic and atmospheric conditions in the Pacific Ocean that cause unusually warm surface water 5.3.3

environmental science the study of the relationship between organisms and the environment 1.1.1

epicenter the point on the earth's surface directly above an earthquake's focus 3.2.4

equinox a point in Earth's orbit at which the sun crosses the plane of Earth's equator, causing the hours of day and night to be nearly equal everywhere on Earth 7.3.4

erratic a piece of till that is not native to the place where it was deposited 2.1.6

eutrophication the process by which nitrate or phosphate compounds overenrich a body of water and deplete it of oxygen 4.1.9

evaporation the change of a substance from a liquid to a gas 4.1.2

extrusive rock an igneous rock formed when lava cools on the earth's surface 1.3.1

fault a fracture in the earth's crust along which rocks move 2.2.4

faulting the breaking of the earth's crust and the sliding of the blocks of crust along the break 3.1.3

felsic rock a light-colored lightweight igneous rock that is rich in silicon, aluminum, sodium, and potassium 1.3.1

fissure a tear in the crust caused by the friction of a fault 3.2.5

floodplain a flat area along a river formed by sediments deposited when a river overflows 2.1.5

fluorescence the ability of a mineral to glow and change color under ultraviolet light 1.2.4

focus the point inside the earth where an earthquake begins 3.2.4

fog a low-level cloud caused by condensation of warm water vapor as it passes over a cold area 5.2.5

folding the bending of rock layers due to stress in the earth's crust 3.1.3

foliated structure a rock structure with visible layers or bands aligned in planes 1.3.3

footwall the landmass below the fault 3.1.3

fossil the preserved remains or impression of an organism that lived in the past 2.2.5

fossil fuel a source of energy formed from the buried remains of dead plants and animals 6.1.3

full moon the phase when the entire near side of the moon is illuminated *7.3.2*

fracture a mineral's tendency to break along irregular lines; a break in the Earth's surface 1.2.3

friction the force that resists motion between two surfaces in contact with each other 7.2.4

front the boundary between two air masses 5.2.7

furrow a ditch in farmland 6.1.6

galaxy large systems of stars and their solar systems, gas, and dust held together by gravity 8.1.3

galaxy cluster a group of thousands of galaxies under the same gravitational influence 8.1.3

gas giant a larger gaseous planet of the outer solar system 7.1.5

geocentric centered on or around Earth 7.1.1

geologic column the order of rock layers 2.2.4

geology the study of the solid earth 1.1.1

geothermal energy the energy collected from heat trapped in the earth's crust 6.1.7

geyser a hot spring that periodically erupts 4.1.4

glacial drift the general term for any sediment deposited by a glacier 2.1.6

glacier a large mass of moving ice that forms on land and remains from year to year 2.1.6

greenhouse gas a portion of atmospheric gas molecules that deflect infrared radiation back to Earth's surface that was initially on a path to escape into space 5.3.3

groundwater all the water found underground 4.1.4

gully a narrow ditch cut in the earth by runoff 2.1.5

hanging wall the landmass above the fault 3.1.3

hardness a mineral's resistance to being scratched 1.2.3

heat the transfer of energy from one substance to another 5.2.1

heliocentric centered on or around the sun 7.1.1

horizon a layer in a soil profile 2.2.2

hot spot a place on the earth's surface that is directly above a column of rising magma 3.3.1

humidity the amount of water vapor in the air 5.2.6

humus the nutrient-rich organic material in soil 2.2.1

hydroelectric power electricity produced from the power of moving water 4.1.8, 5.1.7, 6.1.7

hydrolysis the breaking down of a substance by a chemical reaction with water 2.1.2

ice age a period of time when ice collects in high latitudes and moves toward lower latitudes 5.3.3

ice wedging the mechanical weathering process in which water in the cracks of rocks freezes and expands, widening the cracks 2.1.1

igneous rock rock formed from cooled and hardened magma 1.3.1

incineration the burning of solid waste materials 6.2.1

index fossil a fossil that is useful for dating and correlating the strata in which it is found 2.2.5

inertia the tendency of a moving object to keep moving in a straight line unless another force acts on it 8.2.3

inner core the solid center of the earth 1.4.1

interglacial period warm periods that occur between glacial periods when large ice sheets are absent 5.3.3

intrusion a large mass of igneous rock forced between or through layers of existing rock 2.2.4

intrusive rock an igneous rock formed when magma cools beneath the earth's surface 1.3.1

ion an atom with an electrical charge that has gained or lost one or more electrons 5.1.2

isobar a line that connects points of equal atmospheric pressure 5.2.9

isostasy the equilibrium in the earth's crust maintained by a flow of rock material in the asthenosphere 3.1.1

Kuiper belt the region of the solar system outside Neptune's orbit 7.2.3

landslide the rapid downhill movement of a large amount of rock and soil 2.1.3

latitude the distance in degrees north or south of the equator 1.1.3

lava the magma that has reached the earth's surface 1.3.1

law of superposition a law that states that layers found lower in the sedimentary rock formation are older than layers found closer to the top of the formation 2.2.4

leachate a solution formed when pollutants from sanitary landfills are dissolved in rainwater and seep into the groundwater 6.2.1

levee a structure built to prevent a river from overflowing 4.1.8

lightning the electric discharge of energy from storm clouds 5.2.8

light-year the distance light travels in a vacuum in one year, approximately 9.46 × 1012 km 8.1.1

liquefaction the process by which soil loses strength and acts as a liquid instead of a solid 3.2.5

lithification the process that transforms layers of rock fragments into sedimentary rock 1.3.2

lithosphere the outermost rigid layer of the earth, composed of the stiff upper layer of the mantle and the crust 1.4.2

lodestone a piece of magnetite that naturally acts as a magnet 1.2.4

longitude the distance in degrees east or west of the prime meridian 1.1.3

Love wave a fast surface wave that moves in a side-to-side pattern as it travels forward 3.2.4

lunar calendar a calendar based on the phases of the moon 7.1.2

lunar eclipse an event that occurs when Earth passes directly between the sun and the moon, causing Earth's shadow to block the sun's light from the moon 7.3.3

lunar regolith a loose layer of rock and dust on the surface of the moon 7.3.1

luster the way a mineral's surface reflects light 1.2.3

mafic rock the dark-colored, heavy igneous rock that is rich in iron, magnesium, and calcium 1.3.1

magma the melted rock beneath the earth's surface 1.3.1

magnetosphere the area around the earth that is affected by the earth's magnetic field 1.4.1

magnitude the strength of an earthquake 3.2.1

mantle the portion of the earth's interior extending from the bottom of the crust to the outer core 1.4.2

mare a flat, lowland plain on the moon's surface filled with hardened lava 7.3.1

mass wasting the downhill movement of rocks and soil caused by gravity 2.1.3

mature river a meandering river located at low elevations 4.1.6

mechanical weathering the breaking down of rocks by physical processes 2.1.1

metamorphic rock rock formed when the structure and mineral composition of existing rocks change because of heat, pressure, or chemical reactions 1.3.3

metamorphism the process of change in the structure and mineral composition of a rock 1.3.3

meteor a meteoroid that enters the earth's atmosphere and burns up 7.2.4

meteorite a meteoroid that enters Earth's atmosphere and strikes the ground 7.2.4

meteoroid a rock fragment from an asteroid or comet 7.2.4

meteorology the study of the atmosphere 1.1.1

microclimate unique climate conditions that exist over small areas of land within larger climate regions 5.3.2

mineral a naturally occurring, inorganic solid with a definite chemical composition and a crystalline structure 1.2.1

mineralogy the study of minerals 1.2.1

Moho the boundary between the crust and the mantle 1.4.2

moraine an accumulated deposit of till 2.1.6

mudflow the rapid, downhill movement of a large mass of mud and debris 2.1.3

natural gas a mixture of methane and other gases formed from decomposed marine organisms 6.1.3

natural resource any substance, organism, or energy form found in nature that can be used by living things 6.1.1

naturalism the belief that matter and energy are all that exist and that undirected natural processes formed the universe 1.1.2

neap tide a tide that occurs when the sun and the moon are at right angles to each other 4.2.3

nebula a vast, moving interstellar cloud of gas and dust 7.1.5

new moon the phase when the moon is directly between Earth and the sun 7.3.2

neutron star an extremely small, dense star composed primarily of neutrons 8.1.2

nonfoliated structure a rock structure with no visible layers or bands 1.3.3

nonrenewable resource a resource that cannot be replaced once it is used or can be replaced only over an extremely long period of time 6.1.1

nonsilicate mineral a mineral composed of elements or bonded groups of elements other than bonded silicon and oxygen 1.2.2

normal fault a fault in which the hanging wall slides down the footwall 3.2.3

nuclear energy the energy that comes from changes in the nuclei of atoms of radioactive elements 6.1.7

oceanic crust the crust beneath the oceans 1.4.3

oceanic ridge the mountain chains that form on the ocean floor where tectonic plates pull apart 3.1.2, 4.2.4

oceanography the study of the earth's oceans 1.1.1

old river a slow-moving, flat river 4.1.6

ore a naturally occurring mineral from which a useful metal or mineral is recovered 6.1.4

orogenesis the process of mountain formation 3.1.4

outer core the liquid layer of Earth's core that surrounds the inner core 1.4.1

oxbow lake a lake formed when a bend of a river is cut off from the main river 4.1.6

oxidation a chemical change in which a substance combines with oxygen 2.1.2

ozone a three-atom form of oxygen gas (O^3) that protects Earth from UV radiation 5.1.4

pahoehoe lava that has a smooth or billowy surface 3.3.3

parallax the apparent shift in an object's direction when viewed from two geographically distant locations 8.1.1

payload the cargo or equipment carried by the spacecraft 8.2.1

peat a substance made of partially decayed plant matter 6.1.3

penumbra an area of partially blocked light surrounding the complete shadow 7.3.3

perigee the point in the moon's orbit at which it is closest to Earth 7.3.2

perihelion the point in a planet's orbit when it is closest to the sun 7.2.1

petrifaction a process in which the organic portion of an organism is infiltrated or replaced with minerals 2.2.5

petroleum a liquid fossil fuel formed from microscopic plants, animals, and marine organisms 6.1.3

phase each different shape of the moon made visible by reflected sunlight 7.3.2

phosphorescence the ability of some fluorescent minerals to continue to glow after an ultraviolet light is no longer focused on them 1.2.4

photosphere the sun's surface, which radiates visible light 7.1.6

planet a spherical object that orbits the sun and has removed other objects from its orbit 7.1.5

plasma a super-heated gas composed of electrically charged particles 5.1.3

plate boundary the point at which one tectonic plate meets another 3.1.2

plateau a large area of flat-topped rock high above sea level 3.1.4

plug a structure of hardened magma that forms inside a vent 3.3.4

pluton a body of magma that has hardened underground 3.3.3

pore space the amount of space between soil particles 2.2.1

porosity a measure of the open space in rocks 4.1.4

prime meridian an imaginary line that divides the Earth into the Western Hemisphere and the Eastern Hemisphere 1.1.3

projection a system of lines drawn on a flat surface to represent curves 1.1.3

prominence a fiery burst of gas from the sun that rises thousands of kilometers into space 7.1.6

propellant a fuel used to produce the hot gases that power a rocket 8.2.1

pulsar a spinning neutron star that gives off pulses of radiation at regular intervals 8.1.2

pyroclast a solid volcanic material such as ash and rock that has been ejected during an eruption 3.3.3

P wave the fastest seismic wave, which travels through solids, liquids, and gases 1.4.1

quarry a location where rocks are removed from the ground 6.1.4

radiation the transfer of energy through space by electromagnetic waves 5.2.1

radiative zone the zone on the sun where energy from the sun's core moves toward the sun's surface 7.1.6

radioactivity the ability of an element to give off nuclear radiation as a result of a change in the atom's nucleus 1.2.4

Rayleigh wave a slower surface wave that moves in an elliptical pattern while it travels forward 3.2.4

reflecting telescope a telescope that uses a series of mirrors to magnify objects 7.1.3

refracting telescope a telescope that uses a series of lenses to magnify objects 7.1.3

regional metamorphism metamorphism that occurs when large regions of the earth's crust are affected by high temperatures and pressures 1.3.3

regolith a loose layer of rock and soil 2.1.3

rejuvenated river a river with an increased stream gradient and power to erode 4.1.6

renewable resource a resource that is constantly available or that can be replaced in a relatively short period of time through natural processes 6.1.1

reservoir a natural or artificial lake used to store and regulate water 4.1.8

reverse fault a fault in which the hanging wall climbs up the footwall 3.2.3

rift a deep crack that forms between two tectonic plates as they separate 3.3.2

rille a channel on the moon 7.3.1

rock cycle the process by which one rock type changes into another 1.3.4

rocket a machine that uses escaping gas to move 8.2.1

rock pedestal a mushroom-shaped rock formed by the erosion of the rock's base 2.1.4

runoff water from precipitation that flows over the land 2.1.5

salinity the amount of dissolved salt in a given quantity of liquid 4.2.1

satellite a natural or artificial object that orbits a larger astronomical body 8.2.3

seafloor spreading the process by which a new oceanic lithosphere is formed at a mid-ocean ridge as older materials are pulled away from the ridge 3.1.2

seamount an underwater volcanic mountain that rises at least 1,000 m above the abyssal plain 4.2.4

sedimentary rock a rock formed from sediments that have been compacted and cemented together 1.3.2

sediments particles of minerals, rock fragments, shells, leaves, and the remains of once-living things 1.3.2

seismic wave a wave of energy that travels through the earth 1.4.1

seismograph an instrument that measures and records seismic waves 3.2.4

shale a clastic rock composed of silt- and clay-sized particles in flat layers 1.3.2

shearing stress the stress produced by two tectonic plates sliding past each other horizontally 3.1.3

shelterbelt a barrier of trees or shrubs designed to protect crops from wind damage 5.2.10

silicate mineral a mineral formed by bonded silicon and oxygen atoms 1.2.2

sinkhole a hole in the ground that forms when an underground cave collapses 4.1.4

sludge the solid waste leftovers from sewage treatment 6.2.1

smog a dense, brownish haze formed when hydrocarbons and nitrogen oxides react in the presence of sunlight 6.2.2

soil creep the extremely slow, downhill slide of soil 2.1.3

soil profile a cross section of soil layers and bedrock in a particular region 2.2.2

solar calendar a calendar that uses the amount of time Earth takes to orbit the sun 7.1.2

solar eclipse an event that occurs when the moon passes directly between the sun and Earth, causing the moon's shadow to block the sun's light from a portion of Earth 7.3.3

solar energy the radiation from the sun that causes chemical reactions, generates electricity, and produces heat 6.1.7

solar wind the continuous flow of plasma from the sun 5.1.3

solstice one of the two days of the year in which the sun's most direct rays reach farthest north or farthest south 7.3.4

space probe an unmanned spacecraft designed to gather data 8.2.2

space station a satellite from which vehicles can be launched or scientific research can be conducted 8.2.4

spin-off a by-product or fringe benefit derived from a previous product 8.2.4

spring tide a tide that occurs when the sun, moon, and Earth are aligned 4.2.3

star cluster groups of stars that have a common origin and are held together by mutual gravitational attraction 8.1.3

stewardship the attentive management of something entrusted to one's care 6.2.4

streak the color of the powder left by a mineral when it is rubbed against a hard, rough surface 1.2.3

strip cropping the planting of alternating bands of crops and cover vegetation in a planned rotation that are of equal widths 6.1.6

subduction the process of one tectonic plate being pushed under another tectonic plate 3.1.2

subduction zone a place where one tectonic plate is pushed under another tectonic plate 3.3.2

sublimation the change of a substance from a solid to a gas without passing through the liquid state 4.1.2

submersible a small underwater vessel 4.2.5

subsoil soil that is rich in minerals that have drained from the topsoil 2.2.2

supernova a violent explosion of a star 8.1.2

surface tension the force that pulls molecules on the surface of a liquid together to form a layer 4.1.1

S wave the seismic wave that travels only through solids 1.4.1

tectonics the study of the movement and changes in the rocks that make up the earth's crust 3.1.1

telescope an instrument used to make distant objects appear closer 7.1.3

temperature the measure of energy in the molecules of a substance 5.2.1

tensional stress the stress produced by two tectonic plates moving apart 3.1.3

terrace farming the construction of steplike ridges that are built into the slope of the land 6.1.6

terrestrial planet a smaller, dense, rocky planet of the inner solar system 7.1.5

theism the belief that the universe was created purposefully by a supernatural being 1.1.2

thrust the force that causes a rocket to accelerate 8.2.1

thunder the sound that results from the rapid heating and expansion of air that accompanies lightning 5.2.8

tidal range the difference in water height between high and low tide 4.2.3

till unsorted rocks and sediments left behind when a glacier melts 2.1.6

tiltmeter an instrument that uses liquid to register changes in the earth 3.3.5

topography the surface features of a place or region 2.1.1, 3.1.5

topsoil rich soil formed from mineral fragments, air, water, and organic materials 2.2.2

trace fossil a fossil of a track, trail, burrow, or other trace of an organism 2.2.5

transpiration the loss of water by plants 4.1.2

trench a deep underwater valley 3.1.2, 4.2.4

tributary a stream or river that flows into a larger stream or river 4.1.5

trough the lowest point of a wave 4.2.2

tsunami a very large ocean wave caused by an underwater earthquake or volcanic eruption 3.2.5

umbra the dark, central portion of a shadow that completely blocks the sun's light 7.3.3

unconformity the eroded surface that lies between two groups of strata 2.2.4

UV ultraviolet radiation from the sun 5.1.4

valley glacier a long, narrow, U-shaped mass of ice that takes shape as ice moves down a mountain and through a valley area 4.1.3

varves light and dark layers of sediments deposited in a yearly cycle 1.1.2

virga a streak of precipitation that evaporates before reaching the ground 5.2.5

volcanic bomb a fragment of molten rock that is shot into the air by a volcano 3.3.3

volcano a vent in the earth's crust through which lava, steam, ashes, and gases are forced 3.3.1

waning moon the phase after the full moon and before the new moon, when its appearance is shrinking 7.3.2

water budget the relationship between the input and the output of all the water on Earth 4.1.2

water table the boundary between unsaturated and saturated ground 4.1.4

watershed an area of land that drains into a particular river system 3.1.4, 4.1.5

wavelength the distance between identical points on two back-to-back waves 4.2.2

waxing moon the phase after the new moon and before the full moon, when its appearance is growing 7.3.2

youthful river a fast-flowing, irregular river with a steep, V-shaped channel 4.1.6

zone of aeration the underground region where pore spaces contain both air and water 4.1.4

zone of saturation the underground region where pore spaces are saturated with groundwater 4.1.4

A

B

C

S

Credits

Unit 1

Chapter 1

William Whewell, **page 7**, Wellcome Library, London, CC-BY-4.0
varves, **page 9**, James St. John, CC-BY-2.0
landscape, **pages 10–11**, Sasha Sormann, CC-BY-ND 2.0
Chatham Islands map, **page 15**, Alexrk, CC-BY-SA 2.5
Mercator map, **pages 15–16**, Daniel R. Strebe, CC-BY-SA 3.0, August 15, 2011
tectonic map of Europe, **page 18**, Polyethylen and Woudloper
topographic map, **page 18**, NPS
bathymetric map, **page 19**, NGDC/NOAA/GLOBE/ Great Lakes Bathymetry/ Darekk2/CC-BY-SA 4.0
weather map, **page 19**, Department of Commerce/ NOAA Central Library Data Imaging Project
Hydra star chart, **page 19**, IAU and Sky & Telescope, CC BY 3.0
Crux star chart, **page 19**, IAU and Sky & Telescope, CC BY 3.0

Chapter 2

salt crystals, **page 20**, Mark Schellhase, CC-BY-SA-3.0
oyster pearl, **page 21**, Keith Pomakis, CC-BY-SA-2.5
New Jerusalem fresco, **page 24**, Warburg, CC-BY-SA-3.0
marble wall of Ruskeala, **page 25**, Aleksander Kaasik, CC-BY-SA-4.0
diamond with adamantine luster, **page 29**, Natasha Ptukhina, CC-BY-SA-3.0
turquoise, **page 29**, Mike Beauregard, CC-BY-2.0
malachite, **page 30**, Jonathan Zander, CC-BY-SA-3.0
streak plates, **page 31**, Ra'ike, CC-BY-SA-3.0
Friedrick Mohs, **page 32**, Joseph Kriehuber/Peter Geymayer
chrysotile serpentine, **page 33**, Raimond Spekking/CC-BY-SA-4.0
rutile quartz, **page 33**, unforth/CC-BY-SA-2.0
halite, **page 34**, Didier Descouens/CC-BY-SA-4.0
sylvite, **page 34**, Chris857, CC-BY-SA-3.0
lodestone, **page 35**, Teravolt/ Adam Munich/CC-BY-3.0
wernerite in daylight, **page 35**, H. Zell/CC-BY-SA-3.0
wernerite under ultraviolet light, **page 35**, H. Zell/ CC-BY-SA-3.0
Iceland Spar calcite, **page 36**, ArniEin/CC-BY-SA-3.0
zircon, **page 37**, Parent Géry, CC-BY-SA-3.0

Chapter 3

rhyolite, **page 39**, Ji-Elle, CC-BY-SA-3.0
gabbro, **page 40**, Mark A. Wilson, Department of Geology, The College of Wooster
mason jar soil, **page 42**, Judith Browning
White Hoodoos near Wahweap Creek, **page 44**, Mark Stacey/NOAA, CC-BY-2.0
West Texas oil pumpjack, **page 47**, Eric Kounce/ TexasRaiser
Mount Sodom salt cave, **page 47**, Mark A. Wilson, Department of Geology, The College of Wooster, CC-BY-SA-3.0
gneiss, **page 48**, Huhulenik, CC-BY-SA-3.0
pink quartzite, **page 48**, Amcyrus2012, CC-BY-SA-4.0
schist, **page 51**, Michael C. Rygel/CC-BY-SA 3.0
oil shale, **page 51**, Georgialh/CC-BY-SA 3.0
slate, **page 51**, Jonathan Zander/CC-BY-SA 3.0
igneous intrusion, **page 53**, Arlette1, CC-BY-SA-3.0

Chapter 4

Kola Peninsula drilling site, **page 54**, Andre Belozeroff, CC-BY-SA-3.0
aurora borealis, **page 57**, Nelly Volkovich
Mount Everest, **page 60**, Jone Jones, CC-BY-SA-3.0
Dead Sea, **page 61**, Mark A. Wilson, Department of Geology, The College of Wooster, CC-BY-SA-3.0

Unit 2

Chapter 1

broken rock, **page 65**, Till Niermann

exfoliated rock, **page 66**, Wing-Chi Poon, CC-BY-SA 2.5
plant roots, **page 66**, Diego Delso, delso.photo, CC-BY-SA 4.0
weathered rock erosion, **page 67**, Wilson44691/ Mark A. Wilson (Department of Geology, The College of Wooster)
chemical weathering, **page 70**, ThinkGeoEnergy, CC-BY-2.0
landslide, **page 71**, HerbyThyme, CC-BY-SA 4.0
El Salvador landslide, **page 74**, USGS
New Dell Creek channel draining, **page 74**, US Air Force/Master Sgt. Paul Gorman
dust storm, **page 77**, Library of Congress, Prints & Photographs Division, FSA/OWI Collection, LC-USF34-004072-E
water runoff, **page 80**, Forest and Kim Starr, CC BY 3.0
levee breach (cropped), **page 82**, Forest and Kim Starr, CC BY 3.0
Namibia floodplain, **page 82**, NASA Earth Observatory, EO-1 team
river delta, **page 83**, Justin Hall, CC-BY-2.0
alluvial fan, **page 83**, Mikenorton, CC-BY-SA 3.0
Himalaya valley, **page 84**, DanHobley, CC-BY-SA 3.0
tarn, **page 85**, G310ScottS, CC-BY-SA 3.0
drumlin, **page 85**, Boschfoto, CC-BY-SA 3.0
erratic, **page 85**, Coaxial at English Wikipedia, CC-BY-SA 3.0
kettle lake, **page 85**, Algkalv

Chapter 2

silt (cropped), **page 91**, Infrogmation, CC-BY-SA-3.0
agronomist, **page 95**, AusAID/Australian Department of Foreign Affairs and Trade, CC-BY-2.0
global variation in soil map, **page 97**, Ninjatacoshell, CC-BY-SA-3.0
biological soil crusts, **page 98**, Nihonjoe, CC-BY-SA-3.0
intrusive rock, **page 102**, Jonathan, s. kt
angular unconformity, **page 104**, Jimmy Thomas, CC-BY-SA-2.0
fossil jewel beetle, **page 106**, Torsten Wappler, Hessisches Landesmuseum Darmstadt, CC-BY-SA-3.0
ammonite mold and cast, **page 107**, Mike Viney, The Virtual Petrified Wood Museum, www.petrifiedwoodmuseum.org
baby mammoth, **page 109**, Thomas Quine, CC-BY-SA-2.0
paleontologist (modified), **page 110**, NPS

Unit 3

Chapter 1

Wegener world map, **page 114**, Joseph Hutchins Colton/ Geographicus Rare Antique Maps
Du Toit's continents, **page 115**, LennyWikidata, CC-BY-SA-3.0
oceanic spreading, **page 116**, Surachit/USGS
etching of James Hutton, **page 116**, CC-BY-4.0, Wellcome Library, London
Abraham Ortelius, **page 116**, Plantin-Moretus Museum
Principles of Geology, **page 116**, by Sir Charles Lyell, displayed at Northeastern Illinois University, courtesy of Nobel International University
Clarence Dutton, **page 116**, NOAA/Department of Commerce
Alfred Wegener, **page 117**, Picture: Alfred Wegener Institute
Oreo cookies, **page 118**, Evan-Amos
Harry Hammond Hess, **page 120**, Orren Jack Turner/Seeley G. Mudd Manuscript Library at Princeton University
Mid-Atlantic Ridge, **page 120**, NGDC/NOAA/ NCEI/US Department of Commerce
subduction, **page 120**, Booyabazooka

seafloor spreading, **page 121**, USGS
types of faults, **page 124**, Jesús Gómez Fernández & Gregors, CC-BY-SA-3.0
Hooke's law springs, **page 124**, Svjo, CC-BY-SA-3.0
folding rock, **page 125**, Patrick McGillycuddy

Chapter 2

Nepal earthquake, **page 130**, Hilmi Hacaloğlu
Mark Twain, **page 131**, A.F. Bradley, New York
San Andreas fault, **page 131**, Ian Kluft, CC-BY-SA-4.0
plate boundaries, **page 132**, USGS
San Francisco earthquake, **page 136**, Arnold Genthe/LOC
Hayward fault creep, **page 138**, Kai Schreiber/CC-BY-SA 2.0
seismograph, **page 141**, Daderot, CC0-1.0
Charles Richter, **page 142**,USGS
optical electromagnetic seismograph, **page 142**, Apple2000, CC-BY-SA-4.0
portable seismograph, **page 143**, Dieter Franke/Germany
sand boils, **page 144**, Timothy Musson, CC-BY-SA-2.0
tsunami damage, **page 145**, Lance Cpl. Garry Welch/US Marine Corps
base isolators, **page 146**, Mike Renlund, CC-BY-2.0

Chapter 3

Mount Etna, **page 149**, Mstysalv Chernov, CC-BY-SA-3.0
Teide volcano, **page 151**, NASA/JPL
Mid-Atlantic Ridge, **page 152**, Underlying data source: Müller, R.D., M. Sdrolias, C. Gaina, and W.R. Roest 2008. Age, spreading rates and spreading symmetry of the world's ocean crust, Geochem. Geophys. Geosyst., 9, Q04006, doi:10.1029/2007GC001743. image developer: Mr. Elliot Lim, CIRES & NOAA/NCEI, Boulder CO
Iceland Mid-Atlantic Ridge map, **page 153**, USGS
Ring of Fire, **page 154**, Eric Gaba/Sting/UCLA
pahoehoe, **page 155**, USGS/HVO
pumice, **page 155**, Robert DuHamel, CC-BY-SA-3.0
dike in Makhtesh Ramon, **page 156**, Stéphanie Gromann
volcanic ash, **page 157**, Austin Post/USGS
volcanic bomb, **page 157**, Mark A. Wilson, Department of Geology, The College of Wooster
Roque de Agando, **page 159**, Diego Delso, delso.photo, License CC-BY-SA-4.0
Parícutin, **page 160**, James Allan, 1985, Smithsonian Institution
Aniakchak, **page 161**, USGS
volcanic eruption (cropped), **page 161**, Dr. Wolfgang Beyer, CC-BY-SA-3.0,
David A. Johnson, **page 162**, USGS
ash-covered car, **page 162**, USGS
Spirit Lake, **page 163**, Stephan Schulz, CC-BY-SA-3.0
bulge on Mount Saint Helens **page 164**, USGS
volcanologist, **page 164**, USGS/HVO
Mount Saint Helens monitor installation, **page 165**, USGS
volcanic soil, **page 166**, Paxson Woelber, CC-BY-SA-4.0

Unit 4

Chapter 1

hydrogen bonding, **page 168**, Michal Maňas, Qwerter, CC-BY-SA-3.0
surface tension, **page 169**, Booyabazooka
meniscus, **page 170**, PRHaney, CC-BY-SA-3.0
Greenland ice thickness map (modified), **page 177**, Eric Gaba—Wikimedia Commons user: Sting (http://commons.wikimedia.org/wiki/User:Sting)
Guadalupe River Watershed map, **page 183**, Water Board Staff of the California state government.
Big Horn River tributaries, **page 184**, NASA

Congo-Nile Divide, **page 184**, Imagico and Aymatth2/CC-BY-SA 2.5
oxbow lake, **page 188**, Massimo Tava, CC-BY-3.0
Goosenecks State Park, **page 188**, Michael Rissi, CC-By-SA-3.0
beaver dam, **page 191**, Hugo.arg, CC-BY-SA-4.0
Kelimutu Crater Lake, **page 192**, Rosino, CC-BY-SA-2.0
levee break, **page 193**, US Army Corps of Engineers
Hetch Hetchy, **page 194**, Inklein, CC-BY-SA-3.0
hydroelectric power station, **page 195**, Dr. Bernd Gross
phytoplankton, **page 197**, USGS/NASA/Landsat 7, CC-BY-2.0

Chapter 2

hydrothermal vents, **page 201**, Pacific Ring of Fire 2004 Expedition. NOAA Office of Ocean Exploration; Dr. Bob Embley, NOAA PMEL, Chief Scientist
Portishead docks low tide, **page 208**, David Webb/ CC BY 3.0
Portishead docks high tide, **page 209**, David Webb/CC BY 3.0
River Winster tidal bore, **page 211**, ©Copyright Don Burgess and licensed for reuse under this Creative Commons License/CC-BY-SA 2.0
echo sounding, **page 216**, US Navy
ROV *Hercules*, **page 217**, Mountains in the Sea Research Team; the IFE crew; and NOAA/OAR/ OER
Delaware beach nourishment, **page 219**, US Army Corps of Engineers
manganese nodule, **page 221**, Koelle aka Walter Kölle/CC-BY-SA 3.0
OTEC, **page 222**, Bluerise BV aka Bkleute/CC-BY-SA 4.0

Unit 5

Chapter 1

Solar Max, **page 230**, NASA and Marshall Space Flight Center
Curiosity, **page 232**, NASA/ JPL-Caltech/MSSS
James Van Allen, **page 234**, NASA/JPL
filament eruption, **page 235**, NASA
ozone hole, **page 239**, NASA/Goddard Space Flight Center

Chapter 2

flowstone/dripstone, **page 246**, US National Park Service/NPS photo by Jason Walz
hurricane hunter plane, **page 267**, Michael Black/ NOAA

Chapter 3

Hawaii, **page 279**, Jacques Descloitres/NASA/MODIS Land Rapid Response Team/GSFC
convergence zone, **page 281**, NOAA-NASA GOES Project
world map of Köppen-Geiger climate classification, **page 281**, Dr. Markus Kottek and Dr. Franz Rubel, http://koeppen-geiger.vu-wien.ac.at/shifts.htm
volcanoes, **page 289**, USGS

Unit 6

Chapter 1

Mária Telkes, **page 316**, Photo of Dr. Mária Telkes courtesy of New York World-Telegram and the Sun Newspaper Photograph Collection, Prints and Photographs Division, Library of Congress, LC-USZ62-113268

Chapter 2

controlled burn, **page 331**, Chief Petty Officer John Masson, U.S. Coast Guard Atlantic Area

Unit 7

Chapter 1

Edwin Hubble, **page 343**, HUB 1042 (4), Edwin Powell Hubble Papers, The Huntington Library, San Marino, California
Spitzer space telescope, **page 352**, NASA/JPL-Caltech/R. Hurt (SSC)
GALEX, **page 353**, NASA/ JPL-Caltech
Chandra X-Ray Observatory, **page 354**, NASA

Swift satellite, **page 355**, NASA E/PO, Sonoma State University/Aurore Simmonnet

JWST data path, **page 355**, NASA/STScI

Thor's helmet nebula, **page 360**, ESO/B. Bailleul

Chapter 2

solar system moons, **page 378**, NASA

Chapter 3

Tycho crater, **page 385**, NASA/GSFC/Arizona State University

Edwin E. "Buzz" Aldrin, Jr., **page 390**, NASA

lunar eclipse, **page 395**, CC0 1.0 Universal/Jake Hills

Unit 8

Chapter 1

supernova, **page 408**, NASA/JPL-Caltech/ UCLA

black hole flare, **page 410**, NASA/JPL-Caltech

Sombrero Galaxy, **page 412**, NASA/JPL-Caltech

quasar rendering, **page 416**, ESO/M. Kornmesser

WFIRST telescope, **page 419**, NASA/GSFC/ Conceptual Image Lab

spiral galaxy NGC 1232, **page 420**, ESO

supernova remnant NGC 2060, **page 421**, ESO

Chapter 2

Robert H. Goddard, **page 422**, NASA Goddard Space Flight Center's Flickr Photostream, CC-BY-2.0

SpaceX rocket, **pages 424–425**, Michael Seeley/ We Report Space, CC-BY-2.0

Genesis solar arrays, **page 428**, NASA, Kennedy Space Center

Galileo, **page 430**, NASA

Great Salt Lake, **pages 434–435**, NASA/Joshua Stevens/US Geological Survey

Neil Armstrong, **page 436**, NASA

Katherine Johnson, **page 438**, NASA

SpaceX *Dragon*, **page 439**, NASA

space station flower, **page 440**, NASA

Soichi Noguchi, **page 441**, NASA

Expedition 50 crew, **page 442**, NASA/Bill Ingalls